October 2007

The Kokopelli Journals

For Nancy & Dennis,

You travelled through Utah as we were traveling through New Mexico, Arizona & Utah — lonely travelers immediately post 9/11....

I hope you will enjoy this layered journey of life as our story unfolds —

Blessings y milagros to you both —

Laura
Cockerille
Giannini

"In The Kokopelli Journals we join the Giannini/y's on an enchanting trip through the Land of Enchantment. Laura's Journal is very good reading."

Tony Hillerman,
author of the Navajo rez mystery series,
featuring Joe Leaphorn & Jim Chee

"The Kokopelli Journals captures the American Southwest's layered, colorful cultures, woven into a Wild West adventure akin to Thelma & Louise – with a wild pup in tow! A deeply moving and delightful story for any animal lover and embracer of life…"

Elaine Pinkerton, author of Santa Fe on Foot,
The Santa Fe Trail by Bicycle, and Beast of Bengal

"The Kokopelli Journals remind us that even on days of tragedy, like 9/11, life spurts along in its usual mixture of nobility and humiliation. I spent 9/11 sitting in Georgetown, on the Potomac River, watching the black smoke curl up from the Pentagon, after having evacuated a conference room opposite the White House. Laura and Peter Giannini/y spent the weeks immediately after 9/11 trying to escape the memories of past tragedies in the landscape of the American Southwest, dedicated to the trickster, Kokopelli. If lost dogs, the love of land, and the struggles that come with relationships can save the world, they will certainly need the deeper wisdom of the trickster. None of us find what we expect – but I expect you will enjoy this story."

Carl Pope, Executive Director,
The Sierra Club

"Laura's The Kokopelli Journals contains a certain multi-layered magic. This writing takes unexpected and rewarding turns through personal revelations, history, geology - all while following the rescue of Dingo/ Kokopelli, an abandoned stray of a desert pup. The magic here is in the telling… Laura's depth of feeling, and her outlaw passion for humanity, is a reminder that life has much to offer when our hearts are open and we allow ourselves to feel, to experience, and to savor…"

Barry R. Sisson President,
Cavalier Films, Inc.
Co-Financier of The Station Agent &
Executive Producer of Charlie's Party

The Kokopelli Journals

A Southwest (mis)adventure of discovery,
compassion, empowerment...
and mischief.

Written & illustrated by
Laura Cockerille Giannini

Wild West Woman Publications, LLC

ISBN 0-9767585-0-4

Library of Congress in-Publication and Cataloging Data

Giannini, Laura Cockerille
The Kokopelli Journals, adventure narrative nonfiction novel
1. American Southwest - adventure nonfiction
2. Four Corners, USA - narrative nonfiction
3. Animal stories
4. Southwest Indians (Navajo, Hopi, Apache, Pueblo) - history & lore
5. Travel post-September 11, 2001
6. Environmental
Library of Congress Number: 2005902868

Published by Wild West Woman Publications, LLC
P.O. Box 88
Barboursville, VA 22923
www.kokopellijournals.com

First Edition

The Kokopelli Journals is proudly 'made in America,' from inception to com-pletion. Printed on paper produced with chlorine-free bleach manufactured by Finch Paper, winners of Forest Stewardship Council Awards for the past twenty years. Text formatted by BlackBird Media in Harrisonburg, VA.

Drawings, illustrations, & one pathetic cartoon by Laura Cockerille Giannini.
Maps by Doug Jwanouskos, Niraj Patil, and the author/artist.
Jacket designed by Niraj Patil.

Publisher's Note: Although this book is based on actual events, some of the names have been changed to protect individuals. In some bookstores, this book may be categorized as 'Historical Fiction.'

Kokopelli

Kokopelli is the hunched-back flute-player of Indian legend, found especially around the Four Corners area, in Native American art. For centuries he has been painted and carved on sandstone canyon walls throughout the Southwest.

Kokopelli is considered to be the 'Mischief Maker of the West,' the trickster, the 'flute-playing music man,' with nary a care in the world. He is a symbol of fertility, (with his hunch back supposedly full of seeds), of music & mirth, and of celebration & fun. For years I have wanted to adopt a husky puppy from one of our local animal shelters, here in Virginia, and name him or her 'Kokopelli' after this mythological figure, because I love the American Southwest and all of the images it conjures.

But no, I could not find this pup out east. As fate would have it, I would need to find my puppy out west, waiting for me under a sagebrush, starving on an Indian Reservation with the spirit of Lakota – our recently deceased husky-wolf cross – found in her. This is the true tale of finding this wayward pup, 'losing' her, and then finding her again, on the wrong side of the law. It is a story of dedication, of faith in the unknown and a belief in that '6th' sense, as well as the power of love.

This sojourn through the Four Corners parallels the aftermath of September 11th, 2001, which was my husband's and my 25th Anniversary, and why we were going west, in the first place. We also were trying to 'change the channel' on the anniversaries of two murders in our lives that made autumn a difficult time to fathom, even before September 11th. This is a roller coaster ride of emotions and events, so buckle up your seatbelt, and I welcome you as you travel with us vicariously on this great sojourn through the land of American Indians, Conquistadors, Hispanics and Anglos – the haunting and seductive land on which they all have merged, called the American Southwest. Join us in 'Kokopelli's' spirit…

Enjoy!

Laura Cockerille Giannini

In Gratitude

The writing of The Kokopelli Journals has been an epic undertaking and, with anything this involved, key people have been instrumental in seeing it through. I have a number of people to thank along the path to completion, but those who have had a major influence in many of the decisions I have made in writing are Amy Lemley, Jeff Galbraith, Bob Podstepny, and Isabelle Ramsey, each an intelligent, insightful and forthright friend.

Amy, you were the first to open my eyes to the inside world of the book. You gave me excellent feedback as how to get a leg-up and a direction to travel. I thank you, and wish you all success in your own writing.

Jeff, your input in some of the early decisions, when writing about the murders came so freshly on the heels of September 11th, helped me define a difficult and extremely emotional path. You were astute in your observations, when I was mired in memories. Thank you for your feedback and gentle questionings.

Bob, I know you did not want me to self-publish the 1st round, but I will not apologize for listening to my heart. I will thank you, however, for your many suggestions throughout the writing of The Kokopelli Journals, and your playing Devil's Advocate throughout. Your honesty, integrity, and insights have helped shape this multi-dimensional story into a more cohesive whole. I greatly appreciate our friendship (and my honorary membership in the "William and Mary Alumni Association").

Isabelle, my fiery, feisty, outspoken dear friend — you had the guts to tackle an entire rough manuscript and help me to sculpt it more cleanly with your astute and clever insights. I thank you, as well, from the bottom of my heart, for your courage and witty honesty — and your wonderful throaty laugh. I am so pleased that you were overjoyed by "all the personal little things that brought the story to life," and for "all the spirituality."

I also thank my friend Elaine Ilsley, who generously shared her cabin in the remote reaches of Nelson County, when I was seeking a quiet place to write. You are a wise old soul and I love you. And while I'm thinking of 'quiet spaces,' my thanks to Rob Foster and the many fine folks at the Doubletree Hotel, in Charlottesville, where I spent many a night penning this story. Yes, it felt like home, only much more serene.

I am indebted to Jake Joseph and to young Dan Harper, for their impressive computer skills in saving the Kokopelli manuscript at various stages of work...If it weren't for you, well...

Appreciation, too, to geologists Gary L. Gianniny and Aaron Cross for your careful perusal of certain chapters for accuracy in details.

And I thank my brother John, and his good wife MaryAnn, for their belief and support in this endeavor, both financially, and in generous spirit. I pray we reach the stars and moon; there are so many things to do...

In fact, a thanks to all of my many friends, within the book and not – in the East, and now in the Southwest – for your support and love and laughter. Just by being yourselves, you helped make it happen. You know who you are.

And a note of thanks, while I'm at it, to the law in Arizona – speaking from firsthand experience – you were fair and by the book. I sincerely appreciate that.

And of course I thank Peter, my dear husband and loyal friend for 1) your stubbornness with little Dingo in the first place – otherwise, there would *be* no story, and 2) your undying patience and love for me through our lives together. I've been anything but easy to live with, in my own stubbornness, hot temper, and convictions – but then, you knew that early on. We've had a merry run for our money – and I promise you more of the same in our years ahead. So buckle your seatbelt, my friend. As you observe later in the story: "I may not live as long, but life certainly hasn't been boring..." I love you dearly. And, of course, there are our three most wonderful children, "Skye, Jared and Natalie," who had to put up with a busy and distracted mother in much of this time of writing. You, each in your unique ways, helped me see it through. I love you, but you know that.

I am asked repeatedly: "Who are my readers?" and I answer:
I picture my readers to be individuals not afraid to venture into the great wide world, seeking to explore and question and walk wide-eyed into nature, with mouths agape and hearts apounding. I imagine gentle people with a deep respect for all of life's creatures, celebrating the differences that bring such diversity to this world, and secure enough in themselves to tolerate differences in others.

I see them as strong and capable women, from all walks of life, and the men who enjoy the company of such women, and whose masculinity is not threatened by such strength, but instead celebrate this independence.

I see my audience as curious adventurers who welcome life and ideas, creativity and spirituality, with trusting eyes and open arms, ready and willing to embrace this beautiful world with a resounding "Yes!"

You, gentle souls, are the readers I envision, and it is my sincere hope that you enjoy these 'journals' – and our journey together – through this recapturing of our great midlife adventure. I welcome you into our world.

We look forward to a time when the power of love will replace the love of power. Then will our world know the blessings of peace.
William Gladstone

Introduction

Part I: Week One in the Four Corners

Part II: Week Two in the Four Corners

Part III: Return to Reality

Part IV: "Going Back In"

Part V: Wild West Woman in Action

Part VI: The Long Arm of the Law Comes East

Endnotes

Maps

A note from the author:

This story before you actually happened. I have tried to be as true as humanly possible in the retelling/living of it through these pages. Because of the sensitive nature of some of the events, I have changed some of the names to protect identities. You are free to guess whose names these are.

I have included some of the Southwest's rich and turbulent history – of course including that of the Native Americans – in the Four Corner area. If this does not interest you, I have designed the story fairly well that you can simply pass over this information and read on, uninterrupted by background details. A dream catcher will mark the beginning of such reading, as well as a boxed-in page.

This also goes along with environmental musings. I feel deeply about this great big beautiful earth on which we live, and am incensed at some of the regressive directions the federal government is taking us in recent years. I believe these issues are part of the time and place of the story; others don't. You are free to decide, which – after all – is still one of the beauties of this wonderful country (I think). If environmental ponderings do not interest you, again just read on. A feather and a boxed-in page will cue you in to these thoughts.

And finally, as <u>The Kokopelli Journals</u> offers a parallel reality of the times immediately post 9/11, I have included headlines literally from newspapers in and around our travels. I found them to be of tremendous interest, as issues evolved; you may not. If so, skip them and read on. Think of it all as interactive reading...

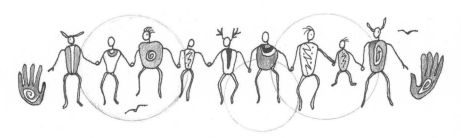

Circle of family/friends

Introduction

"*... life is like a thump-ripe melon —
so sweet and such a mess.*"
Greg Brown, from his beautiful
song, *"Rexroth's Daughter"*

ONE

The Adventure Began: La Hacienda

"No plans, no goals, just Future,
as brilliant & faceted as a diamond,
as wide & vast as the sky."
(My journal entry, early '80s)

Grass grew tall and luxuriant out of the back bumper of the battered old wagon housing saddles and a bale of hay or bag of grain. Inside the wagon a small mouse made his home. The young man and his father would enjoy a hearty laugh about 'the farmer next door,' and 'the need to mow the bumper,' as they strolled together past this car on their after-noon walks through the neighborhood.

Meanwhile, discordant musical renderings from a brass instrument in a high window down the way wafted through the night air as the older man and the younger woman made their way home. They would grin and grimace and hurry on inside.

Who knew then that the mobile female farmer and the noisy young trumpeter would meet, exchange stories, and laugh outrageously as they compared notes and came to find that *we* had been those eccentric neighbors…

Peter Gianniny and I met at La Hacienda, Charlottesville, Virgin-ia's, first Mexican Restaurant, in the spring of 1975. He was a waiter and I, a waitress, and although it wasn't love at first sight, we worked our way there through friendship. We met just after he had graduated from the University of Virginia with his Bachelors of Arts degree in German. Pete was preparing to hit the road for the summer with his cousin and several college friends for a tour of America, Canada and Mexico by bus. He was working hard to save money for this grand exploration.

Pete had lively warm chocolate brown eyes, framed under expressive arched brows. Just turned 22, he was a tall and rangy fellow with an exuberant head of wavy cinnamon hair that reached his shoulders. His jaw gently sloped to his ears and his face was clean-shaven. His nose was of medium size, just the right fit for his face, his cheekbones were high, and his lips were full of merriment and laughter. While I was attracted to his fun-loving, outgoing personality, his handsome face, broad shoulders, long legs and tapered waist didn't scare me away at all. Peter, however, was leaving to discover America, and I was concentrating on my art studies at the Virginia Art Institute, planning to become a full-time artist one day. The summer months passed on by.

In the fall Pete came back to work at La Hacienda. He was full of stories of his travels and on Cloud 9, amusing me by telling me how he planned to learn at *least* 8 languages before he died (with a name like his, I suggested that he start next with Italian) and that he wasn't sure where he was next headed. My relationship with Bill had ended – too much drink and too much temper after the drink for my tastes – so I had settled into my art classes and riding my horses, pastured outside of Charlottesville. I made a living waiting tables, and splurged with an occasional night on the town.

With a little time our friendship gradually turned to love. I knew this for sure the afternoon I took a carefully balanced tray full of dirty dishes and headed into the kitchen through the outgoing door – the one where you were *supposed* to come out with your tray loaded down with plates full of rich Mexican foods – which is exactly what Peter Gianniny was doing at the time. I remember the intense look in those eyes to this day: scolding, disciplining, and at the same time, tickled and amused. He simply said, as our eyes locked, a foot apart, "Laura, you *know* this is the wrong door." To which I replied, as I ducked under his tray, balancing my precarious load of empties, "But it works for me, Pete." And I gave him a smile big enough to melt his heart. Or so I hoped, because that look, under those wonderful arched brows that looked like birds in flight, had melted mine. And to this day Pete has been trying to have me walk the straight and narrow.

I had just turned 19 when Pete and I first met in the spring of '75. I was tall and slim, with legs strong from riding. My shoulders were broad, my arms a little too long, but toned from working with the horses and hoisting heavy trays. My chestnut hair was long and thick and I wore it parted in the middle, and often pulled back in a ponytail, in those hippy days of worn-out blue jeans and peasant tops. My eyes changed from hazel to green, depending upon the light and what I wore. My nose was too wide for my tastes, but unless you lived in Hollywood, what could you do? I told myself that Liv Ullmann also had a wider nose and full lips and here she was a beautiful Scandinavian actress starring in all of these Ingmar Bergman films and plays. I had a square, determined jaw and high cheekbones. Pete told me my lips were luscious and he loved my smile. But I was also having a terrible time with teenage acne, and was very self-conscious about this at the time. Pete said it never bothered him, as 'he saw through it to the beauty below.' He said that I was unlike anyone he had ever met. Alas, here was true love.

I was a strange mixture of shy and reserved/bold and impetuous, always finding myself in some sort of pickle from a quick temper or a spontaneous act. But I lived life full out and head on, the kind of living where one often learns the hard way. Pete told me he loved my independent spirit – nurtured by leaving home early and often from the age of 14 on, after my father's remarriage to the stepmother from hell. I left for good at 17 and never looked back. Pete loved my resourcefulness and impish ways, he said, and the way I championed principals and good causes – like helping raise funds for Greenpeace, through Cleveland Amory's *Fund for Animals*, to stop the bludgeoning of harp seal cubs. (This cause is now one of the many layers of painted murals on the Beta Bridge at UVA.)

Peter was just the opposite of me in many ways, and opposites do attract, and thus our romance. He was grounded and patient, with a natural born diplomacy about him. I was attracted to his keen intelligence, his zany Aquarian sense of humor, his innate kindness and his sense of fairness. He was daring and athletic, and we made a deal early on that he would teach me to speak German and I would teach him to ride. This got about as far as my learning *"Ich liebe dich"* and *"Scheisse,"* two indispensable words in a (one-sided) bilingual relationship. We stopped the riding lessons when he refused to allow me to adjust the stirrups on both sides so that his legs were balanced, insisting that he was hanging on just fine, thank you. The things we love about someone often, over time, might also become the things we come to hate – or to accept as unchangeable – and we carry on. Pete had many more redeeming qualities than drawbacks. That fall he moved in with me on Highland Avenue, in Charlottesville.

One wintery night in our home at Highland, before the cozy fireplace, Peter Gianniny got down on one knee in the ratty, worn-out, buttoned-up, tattered blue jeans I adored, wearing some nondescript tee shirt and his shaggy head of hair, asking, "Will you have me?" Instead I had a panic attack. The idea of marriage made me want to turn and run for cover. I had witnessed my parent's stormy marriage spanning 40 years of their lives, and then my father's volatile second marriage; they had been paltry role models for blossoming young love. Long-term commitment scared the hell out of me, and here was the man of my dreams asking me if "I would have him" – which, from all indications, kneeling on that knee meant, "Will you marry me?" I didn't know what was wrong with this picture, but it took Pete another several months to convince me that we could make our love last for the long haul, and so we finally set the date for the following fall. We looked at the calendar together, decided that Saturday, "September 11th, 1976" had a nice ring to it, and we were engaged. Although we still celebrate November 9th, the date Pete moved in, our families rejoiced that we planned to end our year of living in sin.

On this glorious fall day in September, Peter Gianniny, by now affectionately dubbed 'PeterWop,' and Laura Cockerille, lovingly dubbed 'LauraWop,' officially tied-the-knot. We were married in the great outdoors, meaning the 60-acre horse pasture that I leased for my horses in Shadwell (birthplace of Thomas Jefferson), which gave my future father-in-law an ulcer with worry that it would rain that day and if it did, *what* would we do with all the elderly guests? I simply had a gut feeling that it would not rain, and kept assuring Al that this would be a beautiful day. To this day, we laugh over that forecast. The day could not have been more perfect to tie that knot under what our friends jovially called the 'hanging tree,' a fine sycamore in the middle of this great open field, as the horses curiously looked on. Under this hanging tree our Minister, Jim McDonald, stood reciting our vows, all the while Pete's and my huge Borzoi/Malamute cross, Borgie, threatened to lift his leg on Jim's dark robes.

Our wedding budget was all of $400, provided by my mother, Eloise, who also made my long muslin dress and bandana, the essence of simplicity and innocence. She, Pete's mom, Jean, and several others made the floor-length pastel gingham bridesmaids dresses. My sister, Mary, was maid of honor. Pete and I baked a dozen wedding breads, loaves of banana nut, cranberry, blueberry, and spiced breads, and spelled out the word 'Love' on a breadboard that we made, covered with burlap, and adorned with wild flowers. And this was such an appropriate thing to do, as Pete and I married strictly for love, as we *certainly* had no money. We were head over heels, alive with optimism and hope for our future,

4

despite my trepidations nagging from my parent's past. His family was so warm and welcoming, so together and real, that I felt we really had a chance.

Pete's family, immediate and extended, knew we were on a minimalist budget for this outdoor wedding. They made dishes and beverages for the reception, made arrangements of flowers to adorn the tables, and the nosegays for the bridesmaids, as well. Our reception was within walking distance of my dear friend, Browning Largent. Her beautiful home was on a hill overlooking the wedding pasture. Browning and I went for a ride the morning Pete and I were to be betrothed, as it was too gorgeous a day *not* to ride. We rode the trails on her big red horses and breathed the clear cool air and I did not want to return, full of newborn butterflies about this commitment thing. Finally Browning was able to convince me to turn our mounts around, take a shower, and get beautiful: this was an important day, as my Prince awaited…

But that was then and this was fifteen years later. We had lived on Highland Avenue for five years, then moved to a cottage in Keswick for another five – where my horses and menagerie had joined us – and were now five years into our own mortgage on a mini-farm in Somerset, Virginia. Pete was now a manager at a plastics firm called Kendrick, traveling much of the time, and I had become an animal portrait artist, trying hard to keep up with commissions while raising our three young children, Skye, Jared and Natalie, on our busy little farm. Through the many twists and turns of life, called fate, we were on the verge of adding a troubled new face to our young family.

TWO

Lakota, Spirit Dog

"The soul would have no rainbow if the eyes had no tears."
Native American proverb

His eyes were a clear glacial blue – haunting, seductive eyes – full of pain and distrust in humanity. At a very young age they had seen, and his body had felt, great pain inflicted upon him by a human hand. They were fringed in black lashes, surrounded by kohl liner, both of which emphasized the pale blue of the eye that mirrored the tormented inner soul.

He must have been about six months of age when he came into our lives, truly a fine animal physically, and in wounded spirit. He had the markings of a pure Siberian husky, with the typical black mask and the perpetual 'smile' of the breed, which is one of the things I've always loved of this type. Like gray horses, when he was younger he was very dark, but as he aged these darks became lighter. His eyes, however, were the feature that caught one's attention immediately: one could look into their depths and see the soul of the wild.

I had been looking for a husky, or husky-cross, at the local shelters for several months, with no luck. A client of mine learned of my search and told me about a dog that had shown up, mysteriously, at a friend of hers. Being a small world, it turns out that this was a mutual friend and used to be Pete's and my neighbor from our days living in the heart of Keswick. David and his wife, Jo, raised Jack Russell Terriers at their kennel.

I called David to ask him about this animal. He said: "Laura, it's the strangest thing. One morning I went out to feed the dogs and there, in one of the kennels, was this odd-looking, half-grown pup. Looked like a wolf, or a wolf-cross, or something. The poor dog had a telephone cord wrapped around his neck. I tried to get near him, but he was scared to death – someone had been beating up on that pup, and badly. I just closed the kennel door and tried to figure out what to do with him. I didn't want to advertise that we had found him, because I didn't want the bastard that had done this to get another chance at him. Please tell me you'll come out and take a look at him. I'll loan you a portable kennel for a couple of weeks. Maybe you can salvage him." This is what David had said: "Salvage him." After some poor fool had savaged him. But I was willing to give it a shot.

Pete, the children and I drove over to Keswick, talking about the situation on the way. Normally, Pete would be extremely apprehensive about being a part of a responsibility such as this, but there was something about this poor, nervous, beaten-up pup that reached out to us both. I took one look at him and fell head-over-heels. Here was an absolutely beautiful black, gray and white Siberian husky that definitely looked as if he had been crossed with a wolf. Here was the animal I had been looking for. There was an electrical connection between the two of us that even David felt. I went into the kennel with him, speaking quietly, reaching out my hand for him to take my scent. He actually leaned over and touched me. David was thrilled, saying this was as close as he had let anyone get. I took it as a 'sign,' and looked happily at Pete, who nodded in agreement. We would give his "salvaging" a go and see what happened.

Somehow David managed to put the terrified creature in a wire carrier, which we put in the back of our truck, along with the portable kennel that David had loaned us. We drove home with this feral fellow who roamed the carrier with a wild and scared look in his eyes; I felt we had trapped a wolf. I quietly prayed to God that we would know what to do with him and would somehow be able to bring him back from that fear and lack of trust in humankind (isn't this often an oxymoron?) that had been beaten into him.

The first thing we did when he came to our home was to set up the kennel, between the house and the barn, where we would be able to see it from the deck. We put a doghouse in it, and then "Ruffian-Tuff-Stuff," our small and feisty older dog, in there for company. Ruffian was quite a character. Our best guess was that a dachshund had mixed with a beagle, and Lord only knows what else, to produce this original. She was about the size and almost the length of a dachshund, with bright intelligent brown eyes and a small pointed snout. Her profile looked for all the world like a seal. Her large triangular ears framed her face and had a mind all their own. I used to say they hung on 'curtain rods,' meaning that when she lifted these ears, they rose up to frame that inquisitive face in a most delightful way.

My young nephew, Sean, named her "Ruffian" after the famous and courageous thoroughbred filly – a legend in her own time. I had just painted a portrait of this horse and Sean was intrigued. Ruffian (the dog) had a glossy black coat, like her namesake, but unlike her, she looked put together with leftover parts. Hence, the face. Her front legs were crooked and bowed and her back long, ending in a funny little rear-end and a hound-dogs tail. Ruffian was a comedy in canine form. But what I remember most about this small dog was the great big heart that beat in her sturdy chest. She was all heart and love and determination: *full* of determination, just like her namesake, especially in her younger years. And so I added the suffix "Tuff-Stuff" to her name, after she had been with us awhile and we had come to appreciate her moxie.

Now Ruffian had years on her, graying heavily throughout her face. She had become something of the matron of the animals on our mini-farm. We put her in the kennel and released our new arrival to be there with her, hoping she would have a calming and motherly influence on him. When we closed the door to this makeshift pen, she looked at me in disgust and disbelief that I would do this to her – trap her inside this, this *thing* with this wild, unruly pup running around like a madman? Had we gone *nuts??!!* I assured her that she had a very important job to do, and that I would be visiting them often. Ruffian just glared at me and disappeared into her doghouse.

The time had now come to name this feral spirit dog. I wanted something that touched upon his untamed nature and might capture his essence. I thought of 'Sinatra' because of his musical voice and those very blue eyes. But the name needed a quality from the wild.

I had been terribly impressed with Kevin Costner's film, *Dances with Wolves*, watching it, mesmerized, many times. Winning 7 Academy Awards, the movie took America by storm. It centered around the Sioux Indians, living in the North and South Dakotas. The Sioux call themselves "Lakota," meaning "The People." It is directly from *Dances with Wolves* that I borrowed the name Lakota for this new dog that entered our lives in January of '91. He must have approved, for he responded immediately to this name.

When Lakota came to be with us, it was a relatively mild winter. I had lots of time to go down and visit them. When I entered the kennel Lakota would go to the far corner, cringing down with his head tucked low and his tail tucked deeply under his legs, sure I had come in there to beat him again. It just broke my heart to see this behavior. I prayed to God that whoever had done this to this poor dog did not have other animals in their 'care' or – God have mercy – children.

My job here was to replace Lakota's memories of humans as a source of fear and pain with kindness and trust, instead. *Hmmm...* I had my work cut out. This pitiful canine that lay shaking before me had quite a lot of baggage to overcome. So, like any good woman wanting to find a way to her loved one's heart, I started with food. I would go in and greet Ruffian, giving her big hugs and loves, hoping that Lakota would be mentally osmosing this, and then I would go to him, talking quietly, reassuring him that he would never be beaten again. I would kneel down beside him, gently, gently touching him, feeling his body jump away from my touch as if my hand were fire. I would offer him tidbits, morsels of meat or dog biscuits, that at first he ignored. Ever so gradually he would take it from me and then drop it, refusing to eat until I was gone. Many times a day I would go inside that kennel and do the same thing over again, ingraining it in this poor, beaten beast that those days of abuse were over, promising him he would never be hurt again. Often I would tell him this through clinched teeth and tears, seeing how deeply this intelligent, sensitive animal had been hurt.

A strange thing happened after several days of this repetition. One day I went out to feed and love the two, and Lakota did not go to the fence, as far away as he could get. No, he moved away from me, around the doghouse, this spirit-dog, refusing to let me near or to be touched, at all. Like a wolf, he glided around the pen, his head hung low, watching me carefully. It seemed as if he wanted me to touch him, but he couldn't yet trust it. So I just talked and watched this neurotic sort of behavior, not really knowing what to do next. It was Ruffian who figured that out. She had had enough of captivity, and decided to fly the coup. She dug a hole big enough for the two of them, and together they escaped from their Alcatraz.

Okay, now they were free. I knew that Ruffian would hang around the yard – this was home. But had Lakota bonded with her, or us, enough to take that cue? Was he calling this home? There lay the question of the hour. I would go out, praying that he hadn't run off. I'd call his name and he would come running, which delighted me, but then he would stay just out of reach. Lakota would bound around the yard, more comfortable and relaxed than I had ever seen him, but he could not, yet, trust a touch. I had to reassure myself that we had made headway; he was here, not wandering away, as huskies are wont to do, and he responded to his name. These were considerable accomplishments, under the circumstances. Two pieces that fit in an unsolved puzzle...

And so the winter days ticked on by. Lakota stayed in the yard with Ruffian. He was now a peripheral member of the family, orbiting around our farm like a wayward moon. I would take our young children for walks, calling the dogs to join us. Ruffian stayed close by and Lakota would bound joyously through the woods, in his element. Per chance he would let me get close enough that my hand might touch his back or tail, he'd jump aside as if scalded, but then he would come near again. He so badly wanted this contact, but when it happened he just didn't know what to do with it. Gradually, almost imperceptibly, a transition was taking place. On these walks he started to gravitate closer to us, just out of range, but looking for accidental brushes of my hand. He had started to trust me not to hurt him and my heart just sang. Progress was made in baby steps, but this was another huge piece of the Lakota puzzle, and one of the most important.

Lakota joined our family when our children were all very young. Skye was six, Jared four, and Natalie had just turned two. Friends and family were extremely concerned when we brought this beaten wolf-like animal to our farm – afraid, that with his own history of abuse – that he would turn on one of the children, at any provocation, and maul them. They thought that the kindest, or safest, thing to do was to have him euthanized, before anything could happen. I found the irony of this thought disturbing: here Lakota had been beaten badly by some fool, and so Lakota should be sentenced to death.

The thought of possible danger to the children hadn't escaped Pete or me, but there was something about Lakota that we trusted implicitly. The dog had a gentleness of spirit about him that he and I both felt strongly. Indeed, Pete always felt that whoever had beaten him had done so intentionally, trying to make him vicious so that he might be a guard dog, or protect a drug ring, or some such. But Lakota did not have meanness in him – instead, they had simply been close to breaking his spirit. It was a gut feeling in us that trusted him not to harm our children, and we never once had cause to regret taking this chance. Of course we were careful, but it all resolved itself.

It was Natalie, in fact – our two-year-old – who was instrumental in turning the boy around. I think he gravitated towards her innocence, her total trust in him. Before we knew what had happened, the two of them had buddied-up, and were strolling around the yard, her hand casually draped over his body, as they explored the wonders of nature. He would lie close to her, protectively. Natalie would toddle over, put her arms around his neck, give him big hugs, and he was loving every minute. We were watching the memories of abuse slowly turn for this gentle canine, another puzzle piece firmly in place, working toward the whole.

Soon after this I went to the yard one day, bent down and made playful overtures with Lakota. Immediately, he reverted to his cowering, defensive posture – he had no idea what I was doing. I fell to my knees, speaking gently to him, then mischievously jumped towards him. At first he looked confused, shocked. I laughed at the expressions on his face and, still on my knees, made a playful gesture towards him again. This time he jumped aside, rather timidly, mind you, but he didn't cower. I laughed again and told him he was a good boy. He liked that. I did it again. He jumped aside and then he bowed down, starting to return the play. This was another milestone in our relationship. This dog had never played with a person, perhaps not even with another dog (I had never seen it). He was about ten months old now, and was just learning to let go and laugh. I choked, between laughter and tears, and continued making a fool of myself in our front yard teaching this adolescent dog a game. When I went outside from then on Lakota would come bounding up, like the puppy he was, bouncing and bowing before me, inviting me to play with him. I bloody well felt like Helen Keller, working one of her miracles.

Lakota was a handsome, well-bred fellow and I regretted having him neutered so soon. I would love to have had him sire one litter of pups, keep one or two, and have had a chance to 'start over with him' with no history of abuse. But I believe strongly in spaying and neutering, so I took him to the vet shortly after he came to us. I thought it would also help curb his wandering nature, and this it did. Some one, at one point, had probably paid a lot of money for him and then thrown it down the drain with abuse. Their loss was most definitely our gain.

Lakota was probably the most intelligent dog – and we have had many – to share life with us, but he also was the hardest to "train." He learned what he darned well pleased. If it suited him to do what I asked at that time, why he would certainly consider it. If not, tough. I just kept trying, but always gave credit to the wolf in him for his independence. This one had a mind all his own. There was always a wolf-like presence about him, a grace and hint of the wild, something that would never be fully domesticated. To the day of his death, ten years later, he stayed a little aloof, a little reserved, and always remained shy around strangers.

But this dog was such a gift to us, a fine gentleman who shared our full lives and enriched each one, simply by his existence.

And so this wolf-dog and I bonded over those winter months when he first came to be with us, and as spring came along he, and the flowers, bloomed. As the world emerged from winter's grasp renewed, full of hope and promise, so did Lakota.

Walks with us were Lakota's favorite things in the world. He astounded me by staying in the yard, but he waited. He had favorite places around the yard, one of which was a Japanese arborvitae, a viridian-colored, spiral-leafed evergreen that my mother and I had bought on a sojourn to New Market, Virginia, where she is now buried. We had planted it outside the front walkway. The shrub was supposed to have stayed small, but had favored the location and had ballooned. Lakota loved lying beneath its shade, looking for all the world of a wolf in deep woods. We would put cedar chips at the base and he would nest in them, waiting. When I came outside, he would initiate play and then look for cues of our going out for a stroll. If we did, he became delirious, bounding around and making his strange wolf sounds.

Huskies don't bark, they howl and make all sorts of throaty vocal sounds. When a husky tries to bark, it's downright embarrassing. Lakota and I had a repertoire of communication, all sorts of growls and howls and throaty purrs. In fact, when I'd bury my head in that thick fur coat of his, he would emit this very low, guttural sound that might sound threatening to some folks. But it was a sound of contentment, tantamount to a purr in a cat. Outsiders might think we were nuts, my connection with this dog, and the range of sounds we shared to communicate. Let them wonder; this was love.

On these walks Lakota came to assign himself to walking behind me, and to the right, as if I had trained him to heel. He would reach up and touch my hand with his cool moist nose, to reaffirm his presence, or he would take my fingertips ever-so-gently in his teeth, a kiss. We walked the lands over and around our farm like this for all those good years, Lakota, my canine shadow, always there. First thing I'd do upon coming outside was to call his name. If I were working in the garden, he would be close by. Out with the horses, there he was. Nested in a chair, reading something, and there was Lakota, lying close to my feet. When we came home from a trip to town, be it night or day, he would be waiting under the golden corkscrew willow, at the top of the drive, or down by the Colorado Blue Spruce, at the bottom of the driveway. For a decade we were an extension of each other.

There was a quiet and unfathomable understanding between us, this once-abused wolf-dog and myself. He brought out the latent Indian maiden that lay dormant in the soul of this east-coast mother and wife. I am a woman who will walk with wolves and this one called to that untamed and restless side of my own spirit, the side that questions and yearns and wonders what else is out there…

One of the hardest things in the world in sharing our lives with the animals we love is knowing, in the great scheme of existence, that likely we will live much longer than they. When one joins us in the "Walk of Life," as Mark Knopfler would say, we know that with the tremendous joy they will bring to us, how they enrich our days, that, ultimately, there will also be tremendous sorrow in their passing. This is inevitable. Kahlil Gibran, from his writings in *The Prophet*, faces death beautifully. I do not. I have seen far too much death and dying in my lifetime to accept it gracefully and without question.

Lakota died suddenly on July 24th, 2001, at about ten and a half years old. Apparently he had a stroke that crippled his rear end and left him dazed and disoriented until his death shortly afterwards. I was distraught with grief, stumbling around in a fog throughout the day. As Pete had left on a business trip that morning, I called our compassionate friend and builder, John Bice – who raises Labrador Retrievers with his wife, Peg – to come and help bury him.

While waiting for John on that sweltering summer afternoon, I had begun digging his grave beneath the arborvitae, in front of our walkway. I dug through the sweat and tears, overcome by pain. "Lakota's nesting place" had become his resting place. We had a quiet ceremony for this gentle spirit that had graced our lives for all of those fine years, many in which we had raised our children. Skye, Jared and Natalie joined us in prayers and tears over his grave, and little Natalie decorated the fresh load of cedar chips atop his grave with an array of flowers, just picked from the garden. Lakota had long been her guardian angel, and now it was her turn to be his.

Lakota died on a Tuesday morning. Pete was to be in Chicago until Thursday night. I went through the motions of taking care of the farm, the children, all the details of our lives, but I was numb, in shock and disbelief over Lakota's absence, his sudden death.

I would go outside and call Lakota, momentarily forgetting his loss, and then have his absence crash down upon me, jolting me back to reality. Or I would see the arborvitae in front, the ground covered in fresh cedar, knowing that Lakota now lay beneath — at rest, I would tell myself — and fall apart again. God, it hurt. There was a huge void in my life.

So I looked up the numbers of all the area animal shelters, asking them if they had any husky or husky-cross puppies, or mature dogs. Only one did, at our local shelter; this animal was a cross between a German shepherd and a husky, they thought. And so the Thursday that Pete was to come home, I told Natalie we were going on a surprise outing, gathered Jared from work at the winery, and collected Skye from the coffee shop where she worked. We drove through a sudden, outrageous thunderstorm, to the animal shelter.

The wonderful ladies that volunteer there brought Trey out for us to see. He was four years old, a mature dog, and good-sized, probably around 85 pounds. I could definitely see the shepherd — and the husky — immediately. His breeding looked to be Malamute, a larger breed than the Siberian. Trey was primarily brown, with shades of black throughout his heavy coat; he had cream-colored legs, chest and chin; his eyes were a beautiful golden-brown. The things I noticed about Trey immediately, however, were not these features, but the fact that the boy had an under-bite, causing his lower teeth to protrude, with one lower wayward tooth sticking straight up, altogether. He also had a crooked nose. This combination gave this large and gentle dog a real dufus-expression that was downright comical. I fell in love with him on the spot. But realizing the emotional state I was in, and the fact that this was clearly a rebound situation, I had come with a list of questions.

I asked if he had been around kids before. Oh yes, his original home had had children. Had he been around other dogs, cats, horses? Yes, the first home actually had all of these. He loved cats, was fascinated by them. He had gone out on rides with his former owner (this was an exceptional plus, as I wouldn't have to worry about this large fellow chasing our horses). As far as dogs, though, this is why he was here. His prior owners had had a Jack Russell Terrier, an older male, and the two dogs would team up, chase down and kill animals in the woods. The owners would not tolerate this, and so, with the Jack Russell being older, had decided to put Trey up for adoption. The staff at the shelter called the owners, asked if they minded if I called them, and when they said "no," I called them straightaway. This is how I found so much about him, and how the kiddos and I came to bring him home.

God was with us that night in adopting Trey. I asked the right questions, but his adoption was a knee-jerk reaction to Lakota's death, I'll be the first to admit. There was something about his soulful, imploring eyes, some promise in them that if *only* we would bring him home with us – out of that awful, noisy, crowded place – why, he'd not let us down. He would be a good boy, he told us, as he wagged his whole huge being. He'd do *any*thing we'd say, just please, *please* take him home. I looked at his silly, goofy-looking face, into those pleading eyes, and asked myself who else would take him home? He had been in this shelter since January; here it was late July – they wouldn't be able to keep him much longer. Was he to be euthanized simply because he was not a perfect specimen of a dog? He was neutered, so his fine traits wouldn't be passed on, and he was to be a family dog, in any case. Frankly, I loved his mug – it was full of personality – and I loved his whole demeanor; there was just something so gentle, yet protective about this big fellow.

The ladies there had grown quite fond of him, which is why I think he hadn't yet been put to sleep. I had discussed the possibility of adoption with Pete the night before, so he wouldn't be completely in shock upon homecoming that night. I discussed Trey with the children and we signed the papers. And so we led our newest family member out into the pouring rain, whereupon he trustingly hopped into the back seat with Jared and Natalie, as if he'd been doing this his whole life, and home he came.

We dried Trey off and let him come inside, at first, to acclimate and see the house. Heather and Emma, our indoor cats, of course were terrified by the big, enthusiastic lug, but they quickly sensed that he meant no harm. It actually surprised me how quickly they accepted him. As Lakota aged we had installed fencing around our backyard and had started keeping him in there so he wouldn't wander into the road and be hit by a car he might not hear. We now put Trey in this fenced-in area and gave him shelter, a leaf of hay for bedding, and settled him in. As if standing by the promise he had made, Trey never barked or whined that night, nor did he scratch at the doors. He just settled in and appointed himself guardian of our home.

Pete came in late, travel-weary. I had told him earlier, by phone, that we had a new acquisition, and had told him all about Trey. Pete was tremendous in understanding the need to fill the void that Lakota had left. Not, of course, to replace him – this would have been an impossibility – but to have another large, sweet dog be a part of the farm. Trey, too, won Pete's heart from the get-go, with his good manners, his innate gentleness, the careful way in which he played with the children, and the loyalty and protection he showed. We have not for a moment been sorry that we adopted this large, funny-faced fellow from the shelter. But we sure did laugh when, out in the yard one day, Trey discovered the dove cage and went immediately into a rigid 'point.' We had a bonus of bird-dog in this crazy, mixed-up mutt!

The children grew up surrounded by these wonderful animals, inside and outside our home. From them they learned to care for others and to share unconditional love that poured out from the hearts of our critters into the hearts of our kids. Our children did not have mountains of monetary riches as they grew into young adults, but far better than this, they had the love of their parents and extended family and of their animal comrades, and a vast open countryside for their curiosity to explore. Lucky and wealthy, indeed, were they.

All would have continued along just rosily, had all been good in this world. But life is complicated and there lurk evil forces we do not understand, as we were soon to find out.

THREE

The Fall of Autumn

"There is no sorrow that cannot be borne if told in a story."
Isak Dinesen

I have come to know death intimately many times through that transition of loved ones to the unknown. I have known death, the result of the natural progression of aging, and of young lives ended abruptly, where I have fought the reality of that passing to the core of my soul. But the hardest deaths that I have ever faced are those of loved ones whose lives were deliberately erased by another's hand. Such death leaves a hole in the heart the size of forever, and at times it feels like it is taking forever to come to terms with these losses.

How does one face the death of a loved one – especially someone violently murdered – and still go on living? What is life? What is death? Is it but the flip side of life, as sleep is to awake? For questions of this magnitude I go to the poets and seek their wisdom that transcends the ages and gives me strength and guidance to carry on.

The Lebanese poet, Kahlil Gibran, writes from *The Prophet* of Death:

"You would know the secret of death.
But how shall you find it unless you seek it in the heart of life?
The owl whose night-bound eyes are blind
unto the day cannot unveil the mystery of light.
If you would indeed behold the spirit of death,
open your heart wide unto the body of life.

For life and death are one,
even as the river and the sea are one.
In the depth of your hopes and desires lies your silent knowledge of the beyond;
And like seeds dreaming beneath the snow your heart dreams of spring.
Trust the dreams, for in them is hidden the gate to eternity…

… For what is it to die but to stand naked in the wind
and to melt in the sun?
And what is to cease breathing but to free the breath from its restless tides,
that it may rise and expand and seek God unencumbered?

Only when you drink from the river of silence shall you indeed sing.
And when you have reached the mountain top, then you shall begin to climb.
And when the earth shall claim your limbs, then shall you truly dance."

Permission granted by the Gibran National Committee, P.O. Box 116-5375, Beirut, Lebanon. Phone & Fax (+961-1) 396916; E-mail: k.gibran @ cyberia.net.lb

George
March 17th, 1944 – September 27th, 1997

If Lakota's eyes as a pup were the bluest and most haunted eyes that I had ever seen, George's hazel eyes were the most kind. Our friend George was tall and solidly built, with soft brown hair and a short style that made him seem boyish. I don't know who cut them, but his bangs were always cut at an angle across his forehead – long on one side, sweeping straight across to short on the other. It just looked goofy, but it was George. Gold wire-rimmed glasses framed his warm hazel eyes, and he usually wore a little smile, but his voice was what I really don't want to forget. His words were soft, melodious, and carried a laugh in them. A photograph can keep the physical memory alive; the voice must remain etched in one's memory by continual replay, lest one forget…

I remember vividly two phone conversations that especially stand out. One was shortly before his murder, when we were talking about a gold ring that he was making of a dolphin 'swimming' in a circle. I found later that that might have been a ring Pete was talking to George about making for me, but I hadn't a clue then. We were discussing where he was to put a small diamond, and he said the blowhole would be the most obvious, but he couldn't bring himself to do that. "Laura," he said, in his wonderful musical voice, "that's where the dolphin *breathes*. I just can't cover up the blow-hole." I laughed with him and agreed, suggesting that he make the diamond smaller and use it for the eye. That's what he decided to do.

The second conversation that I remember was actually much earlier. I was simply overwhelmed by three young children and the constant struggle of keeping my patience when I was overwrought and exhausted and Pete's business travels with Kendrick seemed unending. I had lost my temper with them on too many occasions and felt like a horrible mother, as hard as I was trying to keep it all together. He let me confide to him these terrible, deep secrets of my ineptness and then said to me very seriously: "Stop it, Laura. Stop doing this to yourself. You're tired, and strung-out, and you're human. You love those kids, and it shows. You are one of the most caring and loving mothers I have ever seen, and those children know you love them. They are very lucky to have you." I treasure that talk, those words, the support and that voice. It was a sparkling oasis in a long hot desert of self-doubt, in those early years of motherhood.

Another thing about George that I remember distinctly was that he did not dress to impress. He dressed to be comfortable. His very favorite outfit in all the world, and which all the world identified George, was a faded pair of blue jeans and a white cotton tee shirt. No slogans, no advertisements, no colors. Stark white. And some brown leather belt, perhaps adorned with an Indian-designed buckle, perhaps not. To finish his attire he wore moccasins or sneakers. When he had occasion to dress up he wore a brightly colored Hawaiian shirt with dark slacks and black shoes. I don't think he owned a single necktie or a suit. I'd certainly never seen him in one.

Pete and I had known this good man almost twenty years. George and I started our studios in the mid-'70s, he, with his intricate jewelry, custom designed and inspired by nature. I, with my custom animal portraits and limited-edition print of *"The Belmont Stretch – 1978,"* the last Triple Crown win, to date, of Affirmed and Alydar, nose to nose, in the backstretch at Belmont Park. My print of this race was spanking new and I was selling it at the Greenwood Arts & Crafts Fair in the fall of that year in Greenwood, Virginia, where I grew up. George was in a booth beside me with his table of jewelry.

George lived in a simple white house on Leonard Street in the Belmont area of Charlottesville. The house had neat blue shutters with flowerboxes under the windows. His grass was always neat and trim; the flowers always bloomed. This home could have been Anywhere USA, tidy and cared-for. Like George, a simple man with a kind and unlined face belying his half a century of living, the house did not stand out as anything special. But oh, if one looked inside! Behind the exterior of both the house and the man lay treasures that one would never fathom from a quick glimpse of the surface. No, inside his home and his mind lay riches collected from years of curiosity about the world around him. He used to tell me that what he made in his jewelry-trade he would invest in his collections and it showed. His home was a museum of artifacts found from around the world, especially from the Far East, a land that fascinated and captivated him.

George loved the Orient and the Orient loved George. One walked through the front door, past his home-security system, into another world. Huge, hand-carved and ornate Japanese chairs sat in his living room, the wood deep and dark, like the secrets of the Emperors. Intricate silk tapestries hung from his walls and lush oriental rugs adorned the floors of this simple ranch-style house. Buddha's, fat and full, sat laughing on end tables. A fiery-looking jade dragon pranced haughtily along the mantle. Incense burners sat beside lotus plates. I kidded him that his doorbell should be a resonant gong. It was strange standing amidst these treasures in this small house; I felt out-of-place, like listening to Antonio Vivaldi played by the London Symphonic Orchestra in a gymnasium of the local high school. At least the walls might be painted Mandarin red, but no, they were as white as George's tee shirts. He and his home were a study in contrasts.

Another vivid memory is that of George's magnificent collection of Samurai swords, those of the warrior aristocracy of Japan, each in their hand-carved sheaths. He knew the bloody history behind every one, and the battles in which the Samurai had been killed.

Walking downstairs to his studio one left the Orient and walked into a veritable Natural History Museum. Here was his collection of stones from around the world, and his books on all subjects that might rival a library's. He would impress visitors, friends and strangers alike, with his knowledge and enthusiasm for the – often opposing – world of nature and man. George was a walking encyclopedia, with a persuasive voice and dry, intelligent sense of humor – once one got past his shyness. Behind those gold-rimmed glasses and his boyish face there lay volumes of knowledge of the world around us, soaked up by the insatiable curiosity of his mind: the mind of a scientist or an inventor – open to the world, watching it unfold to him its secrets in wonder, always a child in awe.

This is another of the things I loved about George – that quicksilver mind in the man who lived his life with the joy of a child. My father had been a research chemist and had had a similar mind, and the same child-like curiosity, but Dad had lived his life in his own esoteric thoughts, drifting above those around him. Although George's thoughts were light-years beyond most, he connected with others. Indeed he loved people in his shy, quiet, unassuming and introverted way, and he loved to share what he had acquired and learned.

And here was his studio, where he made his jewelry and smithed his gold. He had cabinets and storage bins around the room, housing supplies of all nature to create the necklaces and bracelets and rings. A large safe sat to the side, to hold more valuable stones and the cash he kept on hand. Sometimes his designs were amazingly elaborate and sometimes deceptively simple. Always they were created meticulously and with love. This was the world of George.

Our friendship with George had always been low-key. We just knew him. We would always know him. He was a soft-spoken fixture in our lives and a part of our family. One evening, several years before his death, Pete and I asked George, after he had joined us for dinner, if he might consider being a godfather to our son, Jared, about 5-years-old at the time. He had no children and he was such a Renaissance-kind of guy he would be a tremendous role model for a child. We suggested that he sleep on it. George leaned back in his chair, thought a moment, and then smiled and said, "I don't have to sleep on this. I'm honored that you would ask; I would be proud to be Jared's godfather." From that moment on, George took his 'role' as godfather to heart. With no children of his own, and having just been 'given' one, he was there for any occasion to share Jared's growing up: baseball games, birthday parties, piano recitals, general fun and frolic… If it meant something to Jared, it meant something to George. He adored the boy.

In July of 1996 we had floated the James River in Scottsville, Virginia, together on a lazy Sunday afternoon on huge old Mack truck inner tubes. Our bodies lay sprawled backwards across the mass of black rubber, like spiders that had been splatted by Garfield's fly swatter. The hot summer sun beat down upon us from above but the water still had a chill from mountain-fed streams. George, bedecked in the wetsuit that he used for diving expeditions, could have cared less. It was his first time tubing (imagine – a first for George!) and he was like a child high with a new discovery. We planned to make this a date for each summer thereon, knowing then that we had all the time in the world…

Another day earlier that spring, or perhaps the next, with Jared in the height of his Little League baseball experience, George joined us at the county ballpark. He found a place in the shade of a big old sycamore and parked his beloved car. What can I say about George's car? I want to call it a Dodge Dynasty, but don't know if this is correct. It was a large white sedan, the kind with a squared-off front-end and trunk, rounded headlights and a black vinyl top. If I can't remember the make or model I can remember that George loved that car, keeping it immaculate, inside and out. It always looked freshly washed and waxed, the dark – probably leather – interior shone richly with care. This car was his pride and joy. That spring afternoon, in a game of toss on the sidelines between Skye and a friend of hers, an uncaught ball landed squarely on the hood of this car with a walloping **'Thump!'** leaving a nice, neat dent. We all heard the thud. Pete, George, and I turned around on the bleachers to see the ball rolling off the hood, down to the ground, damage done and Skye and her friend's guilty, hound-dog looks. Gulp. "Oh, George, I'm so sorry," I blurted, looking for words better than that.

He simply looked at me and said, "That's okay, Laura. That's what insurance is for." Cool as a cucumber, his reaction and his answer. The next time we saw George and that beautiful car of his, no-one would have been able to tell it had tangled with a wayward ball in some little back-country ballpark – not a trace of a dent was in sight.

George joined us for Jared's 11th birthday in March of 1997, bringing the girls both special coins for the each of them, as well as a bodacious snake ring he had made just for Jared. We all got busy in the spring/ summer of '97 and didn't float the James in mid-summer. Because of a prolonged drought the river was low anyway. He later joined us in the summer at "Tivoli," a beautiful plantation bed & breakfast in Somerset, for Jared's piano recital. He was with us in body that day, dressed up in one of his festive Hawaiian shirts and dark pants, his car freshly washed, but his mind was elsewhere – George had met and fallen in love with a lady in his T'ai Chi class. Although he was very hush-hush about it for some reason, after his death we found from his fiancée, Connie, that they were to have been married by Christmas. After the recital, George joined Pete and me for dinner with Skye, Jared and Natalie at the Pizza Hut in the town of Orange and whooped it up, my trying to discipline the children with table manners, and Pete and George both behaving like little kids. I gave up with the manner-thing; it was futile. We said our goodbyes after dinner, tentatively set a date to tube the James River later that summer or early fall, and George drove off in his shiny white sedan.

It was August of '97. Who knew then that this was to be the last time we would ever see George, our dear, beloved, and understated friend, alive. In the midst of busy lives, it is human nature to consider it a given that there will always be another time. How little do we know…

On Saturday night, September 27th of 1997, George was shot in cold blood in the back of his head and robbed by two spineless thieves who planned to take all that he had worked for, for all of those years, to London to start a jewelry business. These were two people that George knew and trusted. He let them into his home, past his state-of-the-art security system, into his studio and there Dorian Lester and his vamp side-kick pointed a Glock 9mm point-blank at the back of this dear man's skull, as he knelt down beside his safe to show them two spectacular diamonds. The trigger was pulled. I know, I know – *"Guns don't kill people. People do."* And this one most certainly killed George with but a single bullet. All his dreams, his visions, his hopes of a future with Connie, all this compassionate man knew and loved, gone, in that squeeze of a trigger. This man, our friend of almost twenty years, low-key gentle George, with the heart of a child and the depths of an ocean, was dead. By another man's hand. It just could not be.

It rained that Sunday, starting sometime in the night. Precious, desperately needed, life giving rain, the first we'd seen in months. It began the night George was killed. Heaven wept.

Pete and Natalie walked up the driveway to get the Sunday paper. They stood beside the mailboxes and Peter glanced over the headlines. There at the top of the front page was a simple line that said, **Jeweler killed on Leonard Street.** Pete screamed, *"No! It can't be!"* And little Natalie looked up at her dad: "What, Daddy, what?!" He looked down at her innocent face, composed himself, and brought the paper in. And then he read the story. Pete came into the bedroom that morning, a cup of fresh coffee for me in hand, and put it beside the bedside table. I looked at him sleepily, wanting to cuddle, commenting on how wonderful the rain sounded outside. He was acting oddly; he had a strained look on his face and the paper tucked under his arm. Peter changed from the navy and orange UVA polo shirt he'd been wearing into a black flannel shirt. Strange. And then he looked down at me in such a way that I jumped out of bed, asking, "What *is* it, Pete? Why are you acting like this – like someone has died, or something."

He looked at me, all the sadness of the world in those expressive brown eyes, and said, "Laura, I just don't know how to tell you this…. There are just no words. But someone did die…" Peter paused, not knowing how to continue, and then he summoned the words, "George was shot and killed last night in an apparent robbery." And he dropped the paper on the bed, pulled me into his arms, and held me against his chest. *"NO!"* I screamed against him. *"No, it* can't *be!* What do you mean George is *dead?* What do you mean *killed?!"* He was crying; I was crying, held tightly against him, both of us trying to make any sense of anything. Pete told me what he had read. There was very little known at that time, just that his fiancée had found him when he hadn't shown up at her house for dinner, lying in a pool of blood beside the safe in his studio. The police were looking for suspects. No one knew much… We just sat there on the edge of the bed for the longest time, holding each other numbly, tears streaming down our faces, lost in the shock of a tidal wave that had just washed away the world, as we knew it.

My mother had been visiting us for a week from her home in Lexington, Virginia. We were to take her back that day. The three of us stood in the living room, preparing to go. I remember fragments – the deep, sad look on her face – that wise, lined face that had seen so many heartaches over so much life in her 81 years. She wanted to comfort us, I could see this in her eyes. She had met George and had liked him very much. She knew we were just blown apart emotionally by the news. But she was silent and melancholy; she knew not what to say. None of us did. I remember gripping a chair, not able to stop the tears from falling down my face, or keep my body from shuddering violently, the emotions colliding inside me, ricocheting off one another. Madness – it *couldn't* be happening, not again! This was just an awful nightmare; soon I would thrash myself awake, find Pete, lie in his arms, and hear him tell me everything was okay. Yes, it was just a nightmare. But no, Peter was pacing around the floor, gathering things up to go, looking dazed and in shock. His body language and the dead look in his eyes told me that, indeed, it had. We were living this nightmare, the three of us, in our different ways.

I have no way of sharing with you, my unknown reader – unless you have experienced this agony yourself – what this does to the psyche of those that live on, in having someone you love ripped savagely away in an instant of unspeakable, premeditated greed. There is no justification, or ever any clear understanding, to help one come to terms with a death such as this. A life – and George lived his life fully and richly, giving so much of himself to others – is ripped apart by another's hands. Friends and families of the victim are just shattered in grief. Time helps. Friends and family console one another, share stories, cry rivers of tears, but the pain looms on and a hole in the heart remains. So the end of September haunts us for that reason. As now September 11th will now haunt so many.

And it haunts us for another reason from long ago, and I will tell you why, because it, too, is an integral part of this story. Although I will not go into great detail here, as it is an unhealed wound for two families, still, even though the horror occurred over thirty years ago.

October 1st, 1969. This was the age of Vietnam; of hippies; long hair with daisy chains; necks adorned with multiple strings of beads; fringe jackets, leather thongs (sandals), and bell-bottomed jeans with holes chewed out of them; marijuana and LSD; peace signs were everywhere. It was the era of Woodstock, Free Love, tattoos and the Black Panthers. Elvis was now solidly considered "The King" of Rock n' Roll. Jimi Hendrix, Janice Joplin, and Jim Morrison – all bigger than life – yet all would be downed by drugs overdoses. And, like Coca-Cola, Rock 'n Roll had not yet earned its 'Classic' title. Life was lived – and people died – in neon color. John F. Kennedy and his brother, Bobby, had both been assassinated; Civil Rights was in its infancy and had just claimed Martin Luther King, Jr. Simon and Garfunkel sang *Scarborough Fair*. The Beatles and Marilyn (aka 'Norma Jeane') Monroe were on their way to immortality. This era changed the tide of history, bringing youth – with its energy, idealism and outrage – front and center. This day changed our families forevermore.

Mary and Galen

If Mary's eyes could have foreseen the devastation that would shatter her world as she knew it, she would never have returned to the 'safety' of her home on this fateful day.

My older sister, Mary – freshly turned twenty-seven – was a mother of two young sons. She was tall and slim, with stylish short dark hair, a quick wit and a happy smile to share with all. She and her husband, Simon, and their sons lived in a quiet suburb outside of Charlottesville, Virginia. She had gone to town on this fine October morn, to the grocery store and the library, and returned home to fix the boys some lunch before their naps. My father had joined this nascent family, on his way to a chemical convention at Dupont, in North Carolina. They had had a glass of wine after lunch, and Dad left for his trip. Mary then changed to a housecoat, for comfort, and sat down to read stories to the boys from the new library books before she put her two-year-old, Sean, to bed in his room.

There was a knock on the door. Thinking it was Dad, famous for forgetting something, she answered it. It was not our father, but a neighbor from down the road, someone she only knew vaguely, nodding "hello," as she gardened and he walked past. The man asked her for a drink of water. Here, the details are vague to me, as I was only 13 when this happened, but it was a simple enough request. She went into her kitchen for the water; when she returned the man was in her living room. He asked her if she'd like to have sex with him. She refused and asked him to leave immediately. He became angry and demanded sex, attacking her viciously. Mary, at this point, thank God, doesn't remember much of what happened. She vaguely remembers that her 4-year-old son, Galen, tried to fight the man off of her before she lost consciousness. Mercifully, Mary remembers just bits and pieces of the attack.

Sherman Jones brutally raped, beat, and stabbed my sister repeatedly with a butcher knife in the living room of her quiet suburban home, while tiny little Galen tried to pull this monster off of his mother. Galen died on his bed, with his blood-soaked blue blanket clutched to him, a knife in his heart. His brother, Sean, was asleep in his crib in another room, which is very likely what saved him. If this man had known about Sean we're fairly sure that he, too, would have been killed. Likely, in his rage, the man never saw Sean at all.

Sherman Jones then cut the telephone cord as he left, sure that my sister was dead and there would be no witness to his violent attack. Little did he know the stock from which my family came, the survivors we are. Her sister-in-law, Anna, who lived next door and had been trying to call, found Mary. They were on a party line and the phone was acting strangely, so she came over to check on things. Through the screen door Anna saw Mary lying there in a pool of blood. I guess she must have rushed to a neighbor's house to call the rescue squad, but it was Anna who found the devastation, took control, and it was Anna who, ultimately, saved Mary's life.

Sherman Jones, this black man – who had bet earlier while drinking with his poker cronies that "he could have sex with that woman" – went into a killing rage. Whether he snapped with memories from Vietnam, whether they were racially motivated, or if the alcohol fueled a deadly combination of a mix of emotions, no one knows. Something in him caved and he became a monster, intent on destroying their lives. Our families came to find, after the attacks, that he had had a history of violence since he was a child and now that he was a man, it had escalated. He was known to abuse his wife and children. He had been dishonorably discharged in Vietnam, and had turned to drugs. His family was at odds as to what to do with him. When this happened, they – a good, quiet family living in the area – were horrified. Appalled. But it wasn't the family that did this, nor raised the monster, just as in the bin Laden family. The black sheep here walks alone.

I still don't know who it was that called my sister, Elizabeth, with whom I had been living at the time. But I remember the call, the instant distress on her face, the "No! It *can't* be! It's not *true!*" The horror, the agony. I kept asking her, "What is it? What has *happened?*" But I was a child, and I was ignored. I only heard fragments from that time. It wasn't until much later in my life, when I was grown and had children of my own, that the magnitude of what had happened to my sister and her husband and their sons, and our two families, was fully understood. My daughter Natalie is the age now that I was then – such a child, with a child's grasp of life, I cannot imagine her beginning to comprehend the brutality of that day.

I do remember being at the University of Virginia Hospital that night, with part of our family there, and some still coming in. We painfully waited to see if Mary would somehow survive the attack. My mother was flying up from Ft. Lauderdale, Florida, where she lived. Our father was returning from his business trip to North Carolina. My older brother, Charles, was there, as was my other brother, John, who had immediately driven from Virginia Commonwealth University, in Richmond, where he was going to college – as if he'd just willed himself to appear. I was an adolescent kid on the sidelines watching the adults in my life succumb to untold agony, shock, and disbelief. I watched John walk into the huge curtains in the waiting room around the floor-length windows, sobbing, clutching the curtains, his hands locked on them. I thought he would pull them down around him to block out the world. This was my twenty-year-old brother, seven years older than me, an adult, my idol, who never cried. He had always been fun loving and on top of things. Not now. He was an emotional wreck. Both of my brothers were enraged and talked about forming a posse to find this man and lynch him outright. Indeed, half the sleepy little town of Ivy, blacks and whites alike, were ready for vigilante justice. *"Point us to the bastard, we'll see that he never does this despicable act again!"*

27

But Mary lived to identify her attacker. The first thing she asked when she came out of the operations to save her was whether Galen had made it – she had to know. Then she managed to tell the detectives who had done it. They found Sherman Jones at work late that night at the restaurant where he waited tables. He was picked up and taken to jail by the police before anyone else could touch him. Charlottesville was in an uproar and the case was handled quickly.

Mary and her husband, Simon, faced the trial, the grueling photographic evidence, the brutal testimonies, and Galen's blood-soaked blankie. The murderer's court-appointed defense attorney tried to say that our *father* had done this to his daughter and grandson, as his fingerprints were on a glass of wine at the house; no other prints could be found; and, besides, Dr. Cockerille could not remember what he was wearing that day. *Un*believable. The prosecuting attorney decided to separate Galen's murder with Mary's vicious rape and attack. Should the jury decide, for any reason whatsoever, to give the man a light sentence, or – God forbid – let him go, then they would try her case separately. Not to worry. Sherman Jones was sentenced to Capital Punishment in record time and sat there smiling at my sister, as the verdict was read.

How does one possibly go about starting a life of normalcy after a death of their child? Especially one killed so savagely, and out of nowhere? As Nicholas Evans writes from *The Loop*, his follow-up to *The Horse Whisperer*, *"…the loss of a child is an abyss from which few families return. Some claw their way again toward the light, perhaps finding a narrow ledge where, in time, memory can shed its skin of pain. Others dwell in darkness forever."*

Mary and Simon numbly made it through the trial, limping along, but blown apart. Mary turned to the church, her friends and family, and a psychiatrist, who told her she must put Galen's photograph out, to face the reality of his death, not hide from it in her subconscious. Simon turned inward, and to the bottle, lost in a great dark chasm of despair from which he never truly emerged. He had lost his first-born son, his namesake, (Simon Galen) to this unspeakable act. Why go on?

But they did go on. The three of them moved to another house in Crozet. The marriage limped along for four more years; Sean became six. His father just could not participate in his life; perhaps because his first-born was dead, perhaps he felt he dared not let himself love this son, like he had the last. God only knows. But Sean grew up adoring his father and his father just could not respond. He was an empty shell of himself. So more dominos fall, in an echoing wave of destruction, after a tidal wave of violence gone before.

The U.S. Supreme Court abolished Capital Punishment in June of 1972. In the upcoming years each state had to decide whether or not they would allow the death penalty. Virginia held a resentencing hearing for this case in 1974. Why they could not simply commute the sentence to life in prison I, our families, nor God himself, will ever know. In this hearing all the evidence, long kept on file, was reinstated. Mary and Simon were expected to go through this torturous ordeal all over again, to rip away the emotional scar tissue that had just begun to cover those deep and fragile wounds. It was too much for this etiolated marriage to survive this agony again. Sherman Jones was sentenced to life in prison. The marriage ended.

Mary and Sean moved to the coastal Carolinas, to a beach house that she and Simon had jointly owned. Simon kept the new house in Virginia. Their lives, once again, began again. Life goes on. One must also, or just succumb to being lifeless, and Mary had fought way too hard a comeback to be lifeless. She continued to see a physiatrist, when able, and she became ensconced in an Episcopal Church in her community, pouring her heart and soul into trying to understand how this could have ever happened. She valiantly raised Sean on her own. He was told that he had had a brother when he was young, as a counselor had recommended. Over the years, as he could understand more, he was gradually told what had happened to his brother.

Years later, when he was a restless teen, Sean plunged into an abyss of survivor's guilt, trying to fathom the depths of this news. Shunned by his father, raised by his mother as best she could on her own, but now feeling lost and alone with his heartaches, he became suicidal. A counselor intervened and became close to this floundering young man, reaching out to him as a father might. He reached deeply into Sean's tormented soul, laid a gentle healing hand upon him, and calmed the turmoil of churning emotions. Sean was brought back from the brink of despair and has grown into a compassionate and gentle young man now, wise and worn beyond his years. He, like his mother, has sought solace in the church. He lives quietly, simply and without malice, in the foothills of the Blue Ridge Mountains, in Virginia. In a tender reversal of roles, Sean helped his aged and ailing father, as they tended to their interrupted relationship from years gone before; the rejected son became the attentive father. As I was writing this book, Simon died quietly with his family at his side. He is now laid to rest, I pray in peace, beside his firstborn son.

Mary continues to live close to the beach and has found family, solace, and continuing comfort in her church. Mary has faced the devil, himself, and not only survived the encounter, but has emerged a whole person again, with a resilient spirit, through her faith in God. She spent thirty-plus years of her life searching her soul after losing her young son to this horrendous attack — yet she refused to surrender her life, or give up hope in the beauty of life. Mary has since trained to become a massage therapist and has a thriving practice of her own, now helping others through their own pain.

So we drove through the precious rains to Lexington, that Sunday after George's murder, to return my mother to her home. The soft gray mist swirling around us, surreal, and the sussurant sound of the tires swishing along the pavement, surreal. My tears were endless, and sorrow that was more so, mingling with the tears from the sky, surreal. I didn't know that day where George's murder ended and Galen's began; they blended and swirled inside my head — fragments from each intertwining and I wanted to implode, like Edvard Munch's painting, *The Scream*, and hide, or find a switch to stop my mind from thinking at all. Distant mountains and middle ground trees were a wash of muted Monet watercolor shapes, drifting by in slow motion. We were driving through a dream, physically there — but detached and looking down at ourselves — with Pete intently watching the road, his face at times in rugged profile, jaw clinched and hands tightly on the wheel, his thoughts churning inside that quiet, now tearless, head. Somewhere in there he was processing this bitter, unfathomable news. His emotions were reined-in with a heavy hand. Occasionally he would reach over, take my hand, and just silently hold it.

My mother sat behind us, a mere ghost of herself, not knowing what to say or do to comfort either of us, or how either of us might lessen her distress. I remember her face and her snowy hair glowing like a halo. The multitude of heartaches she had seen in all her years resurfaced and reflected in her quiet, knowing eyes, pools that mirrored devastating losses of her own. I'm sure October 1st came raging back to her on this day, too. For her, this was a daughter who had been raped and savaged, and a grandson killed in cold blood. The rain was so apt, so poetic. Tears washed the heavens and grief poured from the skies over us all, sent to cleanse the blood away, clean the wounds. But rain could not penetrate the path to our hearts and wash away the devastating memories. No, these memories of Mary and Galen, this bitter grief of yesteryear, were ripped wide-open again by George's senseless and brutal slaying. We would not awake from this nightmare for some time.

"My heart is sore-pained within me,
And the terrors of death have fallen upon me,
Fearfulness and trembling have come upon me,
And horror hath overwhelmed me,
And I said 'Oh, that I had wings like a dove,
for then I would fly away, and be at rest.' "

From "Wings like a Dove," author unknown***

And so, dear reader, autumn – as beautiful and clear as the months are – is a dying time for me. The falling leaves quietly remind me of these lives that once were vibrant – and still should be so – except for the hatred or greed of a lost and angry soul.

And now, four years after George's murder, in the fall of 2001, Pete and I were readying to celebrate a major anniversary. Our sparkling toast of 25 years of marriage should have been just cause to bring out the Dom Perignon. Twenty-five years, in my family, is just cause to light up the world, for divorce runs rampant. My father and mother were married for 35 years – Richard Burton/Liz Taylor kind of love and war years. They were two brilliantly talented individuals who unfortunately mixed like oil and water. They had 7 children over the course of this volatile marriage, insisting on "staying together for the sake of the children." Finally, after 35 years of excitement, they separated for 5 more years, limping along, finally petering out, and then quietly divorced, an anti-climax to all the volatility. Many of my siblings have been married and divorced, some more than once. Only my brother, John, and I have managed to stay the thick and thin for this long-haul commitment.

So, you see, this quarter of a century landmark was to be exemplary. And then Osama bin Laden and his legion of hate mongers poured blood all over this profound day. His unspeakable attacks on the Twin Towers and the Pentagon, and all of the innocent people sacrificed on those four ill-fated flights, ripped open all the old wounds, and the blood intermingled again, in a quagmire of raw emotion that just won't heal.

I keep the myriad emotions of the September 11th attack on America in a glass box high on a shelf in the corner of my mind, away from the everyday clutter. It remains separate. If I want to examine it, I bring it down, handled ever so carefully, so the box won't shatter and shred my emotions even more than the deaths of autumn have already done. These autumnal deaths were so personal, and took such a toll on my psyche, pushing me close to the edge of that fine thin line bordering on sanity. I've learned how to cope with these extreme emotions and that is to use that clear sheet of glass – look, examine, question – but don't go in there and feel a thing. Not yet.

And so, like my sister tucked in her home – oblivious to impending danger as she settled to read her young sons' naptime stories – and, like George – leading two people he trusted into the sanctity of his studio – America thought her homeland safe and untouchable, enclosed by her sheltered and secured shores. In a heartbeat these sanctuaries were entered, violated, and destroyed. In a heartbeat these lives – and all the lives of those that loved the people injured or who had died – were irrevocably shattered and forevermore changed.

We had all lost our innocence.

"O, this is the poison of deep grief; it springs all from [her father's] death –
and now behold!
O Gertrude, Gertrude,
When sorrows come, they come not single spies,
But in battalions…"

The King, in *Hamlet*, speaking of Ophelia to the Queen, William Shakespeare

*Names have been changed to protect the family.
Galen: "Little Bright One "
Sean: "God is Gracious"

Part 1
Week 1 in the Four Corners

*"We have not inherited the earth
from our ancestors;
We have borrowed it
from our children."*
Chief Seattle – 1854

FOUR

The Adventure Begins

"All the flowers of tomorrow
are in the seeds of yesterday."
Italian Proverb

And so, in the midst of our plans to travel, the ghosts of our murdered loved ones from autumns past still came a haunting and here we were now, faced with the September 11th attack on America slamming us in the face. Would we ring our hands in anguish and say, *"Enough is enough. We'll play it safe and stay at home...?"* Or would we continue with our plans – to go west and overlap the dates of the anniversaries of the two murders – and still carry on with our lives, despite this apocalypse on America, and *could* we do this, with our country in deep mourning?

Peter's dear parents, Jean and Allan, were eager to step-in and help us realize this trip of our dreams. They were excited for the chance to have so much one-on-one time with their grandchildren, which they had never had before – not to this extent, by any means. We had thought of it as a great opportunity for the kids to get to know their loving and steadfast grandparents much better, as well. And, to provide a mid-trip break for all, Mary kindly agreed to leave her massage practice in North Carolina and drive up Friday, to stay through the weekend, to return on Monday, October 1st, obviously a very hard date for her to face.

The answers came in stages, in several days of discussions between the two of us, and then discussions with Peter's folks and Mary, despite the turmoil in the news. They were all game to continue our plan – indeed, they encouraged us to go – knowing how much this trip meant and how many months of planning it had entailed. They would keep our children safe. So Pete and I rallied and decided to carry on. We would face the future and make it ours, hold our heads high with an American heart, and go on.

Before our trip headlines from *The Daily Progress*, Charlottesville's hometown paper, on September 9th read: **Avoiding the sins of the father: Bush tries to connect on economic issues. FBI should have no role in appointment of judges. Downturn turnaround: several signs suggest recession is averted. We really don't want truth in politics: Most Americans are quite content with fibs and even outright whoppers, so long as their demands are met or they think their demands are met…** (This was a headline by Ellen Goodman, syndicated columnist of *The Boston Globe*.)

Three days later, on September 12th, after the world had turned inside out, headlines in *The Daily Progress* read: **THE UNTHINKABLE: World Trade Center collapses, Pentagon hit in terrorist attacks. World watches in horror as terror unfolds in U.S.: Foreign leaders condemn attacks against America. Residents donate blood amid medical emergency. FAA closes all American airports for the first time in history.**

Sept. 12th headliners from *The Freelance Star*, a newspaper in Fredericksburg, VA, read: **TERROR'S TOLL: A grim task of recovery in New York — trade center death's to be in thousands. Americans Unite: Patriotism is mixed with anger/ Firefighter's helping out in New York. Pentagon: Amid recovery efforts, strong emotions surface at disaster scene. Attack used as support for missile defense. Supreme Court denies request to halt minute of silence law. Area pair flew, died together; married flight attendants** [Kenneth and Jennifer Lewis, from Culpeper, VA] **were in Pentagon crash. Probe identifies hijackers, finds ties to bin Laden. Fighting 'asymetric warfare' requires down-and-dirty intelligence.**

Thursday, September 13th, *The Daily Progress* headliners: **Nation mourns loss of thousands; massive probe identifies hijackers. Rescue efforts virtually futile amid rubble. White House targeted. Events canceled as world joins U.S. in mourning:** *"Irrespective of the conflict with America it is a human duty to show sympathy with the American people, and be with them at these horrifying and awesome events which are bound to awaken human conscience." – Libyan leader Moammer Gadhafi*

NATO allies pledge support for U.S. Military: Terrorist attack on U.S. from abroad would be considered an assault on entire alliance. *The Freelance Star*, September 13th, 2001: **Attack's ripple effect spread: Spike in gas prices has customers fuming/ Traveler's finding it's a long, long journey home. Star, Stripes flying out of area stores: Residents snap up banners in show of solidarity. For stock**

investors and brokers, a waiting, worrying game.

These stories continued, as we prepared to leave.

Sunday, September 16th, 2001, *The Daily Progress*: **Bush Prepares nation for war: Pakistan promises support. Miss America show will go on as planned. Bin Laden wishes to rid Islam of Israeli, American 'infidels.' Terrorism suspects quietly made plans in U.S. towns. How do you protect children from side effects of great evil?**

Monday, September 17th, 2001, *The Daily Progress*: **Washington caught unprepared for terrorist attack at Pentagon. Bio terrorist assault could be far worse. Keep a stiff upper lip; go shopping. Indian store owner killed, Lebanese-American, Afghanis targeted...** "**Mesa, AZ** – *An Indian-immigrant gas station owner was shot to death and a Lebanese-American clerk was targeted by gunfire at another gas station, police said Sunday... Police were investigating the possibility that the crimes were motivated by Tuesday's terrorist attacks in New York and Washington...Around the country, several apparent backlash attacks and threats have been reported against people of Middle Eastern and Southeast Asian descent...*"

Tuesday, September 18th, 2001, *The Daily Progress*: **Markets reopen with record drop. Suspect wanted 'dead or alive,' President says. Boston** [Logan International] **airport opens with tighter security. Reagan airport's future uncertain. Taliban leader** [Mullah Mohammed Omar] **to let Islamic clerics decide future of bin Laden.**

Wednesday, September 19th, *The Daily Progress*: **Taliban promises long war if attacked** – **Afghan clerics will decide bin Laden's extradition today. New war can't be won with old methods. Pressure to reopen Reagan International Airport mounts. Boeing planning major lay-offs. French leader** [President Jaques Chirac] **vows to combat terrorist.** And more good news, the same day: *The [Charlottesville] Observer*: **West Nile Virus found in** [Albemarle] **county.**

And in the midst of all of this angst, loss, and national sorrow, the 'esteemed' Right Wing Reverends' Pat Robertson and Jerry Falwell issued the following statement on national broadcast, in an article entitled: **God allowed us to get 'what we deserve,' Robertson, Falwell say:** *"We have imagined ourselves invulnerable and have been consumed by the pursuit of... health, wealth, material pleasures and sexuality,"* wrote Robertson in a 4-page statement issued Thursday [Sept. 13th] by his Christian Broadcasting Network." I cannot altogether disagree with that, as a blanket statement as to what is happening in America. But they go *way* overboard to fanaticism, themselves, when they continue: *"Terrorism,"* he said, *"is happening* *because God Almighty is lifting his protection from us."* Jerry Falwell, Baptist Minister and chancellor of Liberty University in Lynchburg, Virginia, said that night on Robertson's program, "The 700 Club:" *"I really believe that the pagans and the abortionists and the feminists and the gays and the lesbians who are actively trying to make that an alternative lifestyle, the ACLU, People for the American Way – all of them who have tried to secularize America – I point the finger in their face and say, 'You helped this happen'."* Pat Robertson agreed. *"I totally concur."* God please save us all from the religious zealots and fanatics, overseas and at home: those that truly believe that their way is the only way, and the rest of us be left to burn in hellfire and damnation. What a way to polarize an entire country.

NON SEQUITUR © 2001 by Wiley Miller. Dist. By UNIVERSAL PRESS SYNDICATE. Reprinted with permission. All rights reserved.

Every great vacation has a thrill and a promise that hangs sweetly in the air, like honey-suckle afloat on a summer breeze. This was no different. After all, so much of the excitement in such a trip is the actual planning and anticipation. Just ask Pete, who painstakingly made up an itinerary, with a day-by-day blow of where we would be, and for how long, then change it again. He must have made ten of these itineraries in the months before we left. This is how he plans and packs. I call the post office, stop by the bank, arrange umpteen lists of child-, animal-, and plant-care, and – *fin*ally – pack.

So much of what transpired on this anniversary trip, once we were able to 'let go'and leave, fell into place like a jigsaw puzzle, one piece added at a time, in an unintentional, yet preordained, place. It was all as if it were exactly meant to be. A part of this letting go, leaving-it-all-behind-us attitude, was simply freeing the way for the serendipitous to be allowed to happen. One had to open oneself up to the new experience on a daily basis. Have our plans, yes, but – like a good red wine – let them breathe, as well. Throughout the trip, as I tend to do (just ask my husband) I looked for the 'signs' and stayed tuned into them. Call it the 'Indian' in me. They were subtle, but they were there.

September 6th – September 22nd had originally been planned as the two weeks when we would travel. Yet somehow those dates hadn't 'felt' right. We would be too rushed to properly prepare our trip; the children hadn't been in school long enough to establish a routine; we'd be out west, amongst these incredible wonderments, on the dark side of the moon; and – perhaps, most importantly – later dates in travel would overlap the anniversaries of the two murders and help ease the heart-break and angst of this time of year. Listen up to that little voice, change the dates, be flexible. So weeks before our travel, we had decided to cel-ebrate our actual anniversary here at home with the kiddos. Dates were changed to *leave* on September 22nd and return on October 6th. Who then could have realized how prophetic this was to become.

We had booked our flights around theses new dates, rearranging our travels to various destinations literally by the light of the moon. The first week, as the moon grew more robust, we would visit the 'cities' of Santa Fe and Taos and then drive on to Bluff, Utah, as we left civilization for the Wild Blue Yonder. The second week we planned to see the Grand Canyon by day, and hike down into it at night by the light of the full moon, watching the world as she does, with her omnipotent golden eye. Later that week, with the remnants of la Luna, we would trek 250 miles on to the magical Canyon de Chelly, in Chinle, Arizona.

So PeterWop – our endearments endured – and I packed and re-packed, made our lists and changed them again. We were like little kids off to Disney World. We trailered Tequila and Aristo, two of our herd, to our good friends, Frank and Sandy's, to graze on their pasture for a month. Hopefully the grass would grow in our fields – if it rained. Virginia, the summer of 2001, was beginning to look like the deserts we planned to visit. SunUp and Holly, our inseparable pair, went to Barbo-ursville Vineyards, literally horse-heaven, offering huge fields of open pasture, with stands of old trees and streams running throughout. There was so much land, unused by the vineyard for grapes, thus so much grass, even the incessant drought, and the cattle grazing upon the green-ery, did not overwhelm the abundance. Here they would graze in the shadow of Governor Barbour's ruins – the site of outdoor Shakespear-ean Theatre – amidst succulent foods and luscious wines, each August. Our dear friends, Patty and Luca, who manage the Winery, rolled out the red carpet for us and for them for our anniversary. With the horses away, much of the daily ritual was lessened for the caretakers at home.

But there would still be plenty to do.

Jean and Al had come out that evening to help, and to be with the kiddos in the morning. Pete and I got our portable lives all packed up, ready to leave our little farm and loved ones for two weeks of 'unencumberment.' Pete tells me that I pack too much. He's right, of course, but I plan for contingencies, emergencies, and opportunities. Thrilled to be on the threshold of our dream trip, we stayed up late Friday, the 21st, tightening loose ends, too excited to sleep much, knowing we would need to be up at the crack of dawn, anyway. Our flight was to leave about 6:15 AM from Charlottesville and – with tightened airport regulations – we'd need to be there over an hour early (ugh) for checking in, our bags rummaged through for incendiary devices, weapons, nail clippers, sharp objects, and the like, our bodies frisked and scanned. Grin and bear it, we said; the end would be well worth the means.

Saturday, September 22nd

Pete and I left in the wee, dark hour before dawn, to make it to the Charlottesville-Albemarle airport in plenty of time for the bag and body check. We patiently waited for our over-stuffed luggage and whatnot to be riffled through and then we loaded and were on our way west, to the Four Corners, USA. We would travel to Charlotte, North Carolina and then on through Dallas/ Fort Worth, Texas, where we would change flights from US Airways to American Airlines, for the last leg into Albuquerque. Because of this change in flights we had the luxury of, once again, going through all the newly stringent airline searches. A strange mix of exhaustion and excitement hung about us. We tried to rest in flight, but apprehension and anticipation kept us wired. We weren't worried about in-flight terrorists now; it was just hard to be going so far away from our children and the farm. This madness had redefined the world.

Once we left Charlotte, our flight carried a number of young military recruits headed to Dallas/Fort Worth, and probably Fort Hood. I sat beside Pete, my joy running through a gamut of other emotions as I watched these strapping young men board, all in the prime of their lives, each head freshly shorn, each youthful, unlined face a mask covering the emotional turmoil they must be feeling inside, with America having been so recently and violently compromised. *Were these fellows headed to missions most likely in Afghanistan now, once their training was complete, to face only God knows what?* My throat contracted and I fought back stupid tears. *They* sat rigid and proud, not letting a smidgeon of sentiment slip through the mask. *I kept thinking of my teenage son, Jared, tall and slim as spaghetti, only fifteen years old. In a few years, he would be these young men's ages. Would the draft be reenacted? Would he, too, be asked to go fight the great unknown, in some foreign land, because their beliefs so acutely clashed with our own? I thought of my nephew, Will, on the USS Peterson, headed to the Mediterranean Sea. Too young to legally drink a beer, yet he would lay down his life for his country and this war.*

What lay ahead for the United States of America, for the world, in light of this new terrorism on our own shores? Would we be watching our young men and now women, grow up, once again, to become the first line of defense in preserving these very freedoms we hold so near and dear to our hearts? These freedoms so many of us so recently took for granted in our softened civilization. But thanks to earlier generations of other once-young people, such as these fellows were now, our democracy, our Constitution, our unique place in all of the world, was secured. My mind questioned, and thoughts of our anniversary escape were replaced with these intense ponderings. I had been reading the current issue of *Newsweek* during this flight, which went into great detail about what was known at the time of Osama bin Laden and his terrorist network, now front and center in all of our minds. *Our worlds had collided – his and ours. Early warnings had been there, hints of intense hatred of the American people, of our way of life. Starting with his fury at the USA in audaciously placing military centers in Saudi Arabia, at Mecca and Medina, sacred Muslim Holy sites, during the first Bush administration in the Gulf War in the early '90s. In 1998 it was found that he was behind the bombing of the American Embassy in Africa. In October of 2000, he and his fanatical thugs were responsible for the suicide bombing of the USS Cole in Yemen. Yes, this intense loathing of America, all the freedoms – and, in the terrorist minds, the wanton opulence and decadence – we stand for had simmered for years in a cauldron of vile stew, which had finally boiled over, and spilt its putrid contents of hatred upon our continent.*

As we left the plane, I was blindsided by a mix of intense feelings for these brave young people – young adults entering the prime and promise of their lives, willing to lay down their futures for our great country – as they shipped off to this ungodly war. The heartache of what might await them, my worry for Will, and the onslaught of feelings since the attacks, and at this time of year, overcame me. I stumbled between these proud young men, with Pete's arm held protectively around me, knowing how deeply my emotions will dive, and the rawness poured out of my body in naked sobs of a child as we entered the tarmac and the beginning of our great adventure.

Looking back, writing this now, I am so torn. A part of me, like so many Americans, is trusting and, like a child, wants to believe in honor and integrity, all the best in people, live ours lives in good will, helping those in need, or who are hurting. It is our culture, what we have teethed on, for Christ's sake! I continually ask how a culture of such unrestrained hatred can be cultivated in a network of people and in the name of Islam, which – when not distorted, as these men have done – is said to be a peaceful religion.

Looking back over history, the books are filled with the hate and unrest of poisonous, brilliant, maniacal minds and the multitudes of men who will follow such a leader. Look at Adolph Hitler, the unadulterated evil that fell in his wake, and that of his own "Axis powers," and the war the world fought to bring it to an end. Ironically, because of the infinite unrest between the Jewish and the Palestinian people, and of the building hatred of the Arab world, in general, against the Israelis and the Americans, over lands 'given' the Israelites in 1948, after World War ll ended, I now wonder if we aren't there, on the brink of such a war, once again – only this one to be fought with technology and weapons almost beyond comprehension.

DILBERT, © 2002, by Scott Adams. Distributed by UNITED MEDIA. Reprinted with permission. All rights reserved.

Stop, I am depressing myself. This story is not about this, at all. It is just the darkness that hangs like a pending storm over our beautiful Indian summer days. It is the Indian summer that is to be the focus here. Not the storm. It is of the light, the sweet charity of life, of the 'signs' we followed that led our vacation down our very own Yellow Brick Road of wonderment and wizardry. The storm clouds hung above and around us throughout the trip, but Pete and I created our own magic, a blanket impervious to the elements of events that on this trip we had no power to change.

FIVE

The Turquoise Trail

"Logic will get you from A to B. Imagination will take you everywhere."
Albert Einstein

Pete and I arrived at the Albuquerque International Airport (Sunport), adjacent to the Kirtland Air Force Base, about noon (2:15 EST). Early. Half the day, and all the night, awaited – 'twas wonderful. Stepping through this tarmac, emotions were altogether different. Indeed, the excitement and anticipation had returned. Here we were, once again, walking through this captivating Southwest airport, full of the culture of the inhabitants of this intoxicating land.

A bronze statue of an Indian brave – stretching high to capture an eagle in flight – called "Dream of Flight," by Lincoln Fox, a Plains Indian artist, is one of my favorites. In a statement regarding the statue he said, *"I have been interested in the theme of flight since '63. It is the spirit of man, as represented in art. It is universal in scope... There is a part of man that longs for something, a hollow deep within that must be filled. We search for truth in every direction. We attempt to stuff that emptiness with various addictions. But ultimately, there is but one thing that will fit and fill this void, making us complete. That thing is the reuniting of the created with the creator. Man's search and struggles in his pursuit of truth provides an endless array of subjects for my art."*

Sunport is full of murals, statues, and glass cases of revolving displays by a variety of artists, many Native Americans, some from Santa Fe. Of course, Pete – like many – must attempt to walk by, invisible blinders strapped to his face, else he would have to look, and thus 'waste time'... No, he must claim our luggage, so that we can leave the airport, so that we may locate our rental car, so that we may hit the road, and – *finally* – begin our journey to discover the Turquoise Trail, the 'High Road' to Santa Fe, instead of taking Interstate 25. To him, this is the point our trip is born. To me, we're already staring at it.

Funny, the way men and women work through their differences. Or maybe this isn't really a gender thing, at all. I have also known men (granted, with a strong connection to their 'feminine side') who will stop and gander, breathe it all in, with the best of them. And I have known women (plugged into that machismo 'get it done now' mode) who march right on through life. Always on time. All missions accomplished. And totally unplugged to the pulse of the fragile here and now.

Funny, too, how each trip takes on its own character that sets it apart from another. Sometimes this is as simple as traveling to the same locations, but during a different season, as we were doing now. Last year, kids in tow, we toured the Four Corners states in mid-to-late June. This year, just Pete and me, it was late September to early October – the fall. Yes, this gave it a distinctively different flavor for one, as it was no longer tourist season (thank God). But three other elements set this vacation apart in what becomes fixed in the long-term memory. The first, and most obvious, was that we traveled so soon after the suicide hijackings. Patriotism was breathed in and breathed out; flags were proudly flown, and they were everywhere, and they were at half-mast, through the first week of our trip. Updates on the news and in the headlines abounded.

The second vivid memory was that we were lucky enough to see "The Trail of the Painted Ponies." Some brilliant individual had a brainstorm to provide artists throughout New Mexico with a full-sized prototype of a quarter horse and give them creative rein to decorate them however they pleased. The results were spectacular! Most of them were as bold and colorful as the land they represented, but some were subdued and more introspective. Several were in the airport, along with a brochure describing the event and where to locate these works of equine art elsewhere in one's travels.

What a coup to be out west just now! This was the beginning of the serendipity that enchanted our world, almost to the end of our two-week stretch. Which brings us to this, the third vivid memory: Serendipity, defined as "the gift of finding valuable or agreeable things not sought

44

for." Another word, that we would come to know only after this journey was complete, was 'kismet.' The word was later suggested to me by Tony Perros, my dear friend, and my very dear cousin, Paulette's, husband. Tony told me it was straight out of *The Arabian Nights*, and it meant that events fell into place exactly as they should, in a predestined sequence – just as the events came to unfold themselves in this, our great adventure. Kismet is described simply as "Fate," in Webster's 7th Collegiate Dictionary.

And so Pete and I managed somehow, despite our different traveling styles, to make it through Sunport together, collect our considerable luggage and arrive at National Rental Car, to choose our wheels. Because Pete travels so frequently, Corporate America smiles sweetly upon him: he is a member of the "Emerald Isle," and so there are additional perks. I get added-on as a second driver for nada, which is no big deal as I barely saw the backside of the steering wheel the entire trip. (Another man-thing, but fine with me, as I become the navigator and ever-ready photographer.) Another perk is that we could choose freely among the impressive collection of vehicles. Our wants were simple: a good CD player for the selection we had brought; ample trunk space to hide and hold our beloved belongings, and a combination of good gas mileage and comfortable front seats for the endless hours we'd be facing ahead on desert roads, especially in Arizona. Who knew then the extra miles we would see... We chose a gray Camry sedan that met these needs nicely. Once decided, all luggage transferred, I put the CD case and laser cleaner in the glove box, pulled out an Eric Clapton mix I had burned, and we were on our way.

"Legend has it that in these brutal Southwest deserts, turquoise was formed by the tears of Indians grateful for rain falling from Father Sky to mingle with Mother Earth.
It is said that these tears became "the stone of the sky and water."

Last year, in our "Family Circle" version of touring the Southwest, we took I-25 north, straight up from Albuquerque to Santa Fe. We had never heard of the Turquoise Trail at this point and wish we had, because it is so much more interesting a way to that destination. I picked up a brochure somewhere towards the end of that trip, and so suggested to Pete that we give it a go to begin this one. It is a little difficult to find – look for NM 14, off of I-40 – the Sandia Crest National Scenic Byway, they call it (NM 536) – on the east side of the Sandia Mountains. If one has the time, it is worth the effort. One starts through Cedar Crest, where Pete and I took a little jaunt up the mountain to Sandia Crest, (elevation 10,678 feet) in the Cibola National Forest. Sandia Peak Ski Area offers a year 'round recreational resort and the world's longest aerial tramway. Here, we witnessed a group preparing for an early fall wedding with breathtaking mountain scenery as their backdrop. Because of the intimacy of the occasion we did not linger. Instead we drove leisurely back down from whence we had come, savoring the shimmering golden aspen leaves flirting with the breezes and the deep green evergreens and listening to Clapton's version of "Swing Low, Sweet Chariot," with his gorgeous gospel backup. We reminisced about our own wedding, back in September of '76, in that horse pasture under our 'hanging tree,' surrounded by family and friends, on a perfect fall day, much like this one.

There is nothing spectacular about the Turquoise Trail, unless you are awed by incredible views of backcountry New Mexico, and love funky little towns, or ghost towns that were quite something in their mining hey-day, but need a bit of imagination today to bring that reality back. A bumper sticker I appreciate reads: **"REALITY IS FOR PEOPLE WHO LACK IMAGINATION."** If you don't lack that, and do enjoy exploration, then discover this winding route to Santa Fe. Some of these old mining towns barely exist at all, anymore. I couldn't even find San Pedro on the map, but it used to be one of the most lively and is/was located barely a mile past NM 10, outside of Golden, at the base of the San Pedro Mountains. In 1832, however, this almost non-existent ghost town was cause of quite the commotion, when here the Spanish found copper and gold. This was 'placer gold' – nuggets and dust found in sand and streambeds – the type of gold that started the gold rush of 1849.

'Golden, New Mexico' is what I remember. We were there, and then we weren't. What I saw of it was the remains of an ancient Spanish church atop a hill, which we stopped to photograph. *'This was built in the 1830s, and later restored by Fray Angelico Chavez, the noted poet-priest. It's hard to believe, but in the early 1900's some 3,000 people lived here. The town had a newspaper, a bank and even a stock exchange...*

"Golden has a lonely aspect, the town is almost lost in the overwhelming vastness of the New Mexico landscape. Far off to the northwest broods the long, blue ridge of the Jemez range. Almost lost in the haze in the distant west is the round dome of Cabezón Peak. To the southwest is the towering bulk of the Sandia Mountains. Ten miles north of Golden the road tops at the head of a long draw. Far away lie the majestic Sangre de Cristos. The view is tremendous. Soon you see evidence of old mining. Tunnels area visible among the nons to the east..."*

I remember entering Madrid, New Mexico. I just loved this crazy, funky, artsy little town – so *very* different from magnificent, continental Madrid, Spain. Pete and I found a shady place to park and walked hand-in-hand along the main area that also happens to be the highway through town. Houses, shops, boutiques, restaurants, and the old Santa Fe locomotive No. 874, are all within a stone's throw. It's considered a ghost town, and I suppose it certainly is for ore once mined here, but it has certainly come to life in color and crafts and quilts! Pete and I found a place for pizza, right out of the '60s, including bottled "Rt. 66" root beer out of an ice box. The pizza was cooked to order in an old brick oven and was delicious. We ate inside, where the day was cooled by lazy ceiling fans and dark hardwood floors. We were warned not to drink the water – which Madrid barely has, and what it does have has the rotten egg smell of hydrogen sulfide, not at all appealing. There was a delightful patio outside, as well, very tempting – but the inside was so camp, we couldn't resist. Pete and I are both old hippies; we felt right at home.

We didn't go in, but one can also check out the "Old Coal Miner's Museum," offering mining and railroad history, artifacts and lore, as well as actually see below-ground coal seams. This museum even shoots the old-time photographs – that beautiful sepia-toned imagery – to give the model that Wild West look.

Between the water from a well drilled in 1984, and the current drought in the Southwest, I'm betting that water might be on Madrid's 'wish-list' more now than gold or copper, itself. But *"coal, not gold, was Madrid's bonanza. This is one of the few places where bituminous (soft) and anthracite (hard) coal are both found. The hard coal deposits are believed to be the only ones west of the Mississippi River. Legend has it that General Stephen Watts Kearny supplied his army from the coal seams here. And at one time, it is said, ox teams hauled hard coal from here to St. Louis.*

"In the 1880s, a Santa Fe railway subsidiary opened mines in Madrid. By 1899, when Colorado Fuel and Iron Company leased the mines, 3,000 persons lived here. The property was later sold to Albuquerque and Cerrillos Coal Company. The late Oscar Huber, who went to work for the company in 1910, later acquired control. The town is now owned by his heirs.

"In its early years, Madrid shipped a million tons of coal annually. But coal demand slackened in the '30s and production slackened. Many miners moved away. In 1934, the population dipped to 1,300. World War II brought a temporary end to the decline. The town shipped 20,000 tons of coal to Las Alamos, where the first A-bombs were built.

"War's end and the rapid conversion of industry and railroads to other fuels

spelled Madrid's doom. Production dwindled… Gone like the rest of Madrid's glory are its famed Christmas decorations. The lightened displays drew nation-wide notice, and its streets were choked with traffic from all over the state. Turned on in Madrid for the last time in 1941, they have now been bought by the Gallup Jaycees, and will be displayed there."

They've since returned! I read in our Turquoise Trail brochure that *"in December, the spirit of yesteryear lives on with Holiday Open House and the lighting of the town."*

Yeah, well, for being a defunct ghost town, Pete and I thought Madrid to be full of the living and the doing. It's an artsy little offshoot of Santa Fe… We drove along this offbeat winding route, listening to Clapton's "Let it Grow," laughing and enjoying ourselves immensely. One of those perfect moments lived in the here and now.

Continuing north on the Turquoise Trail, one drives through Cerrillos, which means "Little Hills," in Spanish. *The town exudes a pleasant feeling of a quiet Hispanic village. In fact, if there's one thing that separates Cerrillos from Madrid, it's the continuity of a long history of Hispanic families who still live in the small enclave. That, and the fact that Cerrillos has water.*

"Before the prospectors of the late 1800s, there was turquoise, discovered more than 2,000 years ago in a mountain the Indians called Chalchihuitl. When the Spanish invaded, they used the Indians as slave labor to help excavate the blue stone at the Mina del Tiro, or the Mine of the Shaft. It was during a major excavation of Chalchihuitl that the entire west face of the mountain caved in, entombing the Indian laborers.

"There are still stories of restless death and the men who were never recovered. Others talk of the undiscovered riches still in the earth. The old Indian lodes were rediscovered in 1879, setting off a boom that enticed miners from throughout the country. Gold was discovered in nearby hills. The Mina del Tiro yielded silver ore. The Cash Entry Mine produced silver, copper and gold…. But it wasn't the romance of gold or silver that gave the area its real worth. It was the gritty reality of coal first discovered in nearby Waldo, about three miles west of Cerrillos. The railroad set up a spur from Waldo to Madrid in 1891, touching off another succession of boom years.

*"Although Cerrillos had water, it didn't have the highway and that made all the difference. The Turquoise Trail bypasses the town of about 200, which probably accounts for its ability to retain a sense of quiet…"**

So there you have it, some of the history of these quaint old Ghost Towns that so haunt the Old West. The yesterday and the today. Continuing on NM 14, the drive continues to be scenic backcountry New Mexico, dense thickets of chaparral open to passing vistas looking over distant mountains, and then more cozy enclosed scrub-pine areas, entrances to ranches, and eventually – before reaching Santa Fe – one is warned not to pick up hitchhikers, as the New Mexico State Penitentiary sits here, ominously. Surrounded by rolls of razor wire and lookouts for escapees, it gives one Stephen King kind of chills down their spine. Not far in the future, as fate would have it, I would pass this prison again, feeling altogether differently about its inmates and how they might have 'gotten there.' I would come to realize it might be easier than one might think…

*This information is based on *New Mexico Magazine – Ghost Town Issue* – from the Feb.1998 issue, and an article on Madrid entitled "A Highway Haunted by History," written by Ralph Looney.
**This information is from the same issue, in an article called "Jewels of the Turquoise Trail, Madrid and Cerrillos Experience Shining Resurrection," written by Denise Kusel. Reprinted with permission.

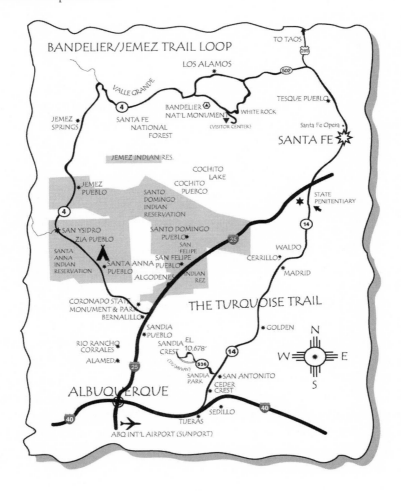

SIX

Santa Fe, Evening Out

*"There are many kinds of fruit that grow on the tree of life,
but none so sweet as friendship."* Anonymous

Cynthia

Pete and I were to rendezvous with our friend, Cynthia. We had met her the year before at the Dairy Queen in Chama, New Mexico, when we stopped with a car full of parched kids. She had been standing to the side, there in the restaurant, after she had put in her order. I walked over and spoke to her as she was wearing leather chaps, which meant – to me – horses. I asked her if she rode and she had said, "Not what you think," pointing to her Harley Davidson, parked outside. I had to grin. We started talking, sharing a little of our lives, and ended up trading addresses, as I had just had Lasik surgery done on my eyes, and she was interested in this vision-correcting operation. Before leaving the Grand Canyon, that trip, I had dropped her a post-card telling her how much I'd enjoyed meeting her. When we arrived home, there in our mail awaited a postcard from Cindy, telling me the same thing. We started writing. The letters became lengthier and then we'd call one another, having so much to share. Before I knew it, Cynthia had set me up with an e-mail account on Hotmail to bring our correspondence into the 21st Century. I called her "Motorcycle Mama;" she called me "Wild West Woman." Our friendship blossomed – by snail mail, by e-mail, cards and the telephone – which is hilarious as we had only met in person, for about twenty minutes, there in Chama.

And so here we were, more than a year later, about to see Cynthia again. She planned to come down to Santa Fe to meet us at our hotel with her husband, David, and their three children. We would have quite the time that first night in! But when we arrived at the Comfort Inn about 4 PM, checked in and went to our suite, we found she had ridden her bike down from Maxwell, where they live, solo. For our anniversary she had waiting for us a bottle of Santa Fe Vineyards White Zinfandel, a bouquet of flowers, and a card with a note saying she had had to come alone. That was okay – we were happy to see her and the three of us would hit the town that night. We looked her up, exchanged big hugs, and thanked her for her thoughtfulness. How she'd managed to haul all those gifts to the hotel, especially the flowers, on "Smiley," her motor-cycle, I don't know, but we sure did appreciate it. Pete and I decided to take her to dinner somewhere in the Plaza.

Cynthia is about 5'4" and jokes with us about her height. I am 5'8"; Pete is 6' even, so we hover a little above her, but amongst friends, who cares? It makes for some good-natured ribbing. Cindy is slim, petite, pretty and a little boyish, with her short, chic hairstyle. She has a soft, slightly accented voice, is very pleasant and has an unassuming way about her. She knows this area well, as she was born in the tiny Arizona town of Ganado, directly south of Chinle but many miles away, even as the crow flies. Cindy has lived and taught on reservations, has been a missionary in churches to aid the Indians, and was a lively tour-guide for us that night.

As we headed to our Camry for our evening visit, we paused for a moment entranced by the late afternoon sky. Clouds whorled and danced in diaphanous wisps through the fading turquoise of day. Mauves and apricots swirled through these mists, painting for us a visual welcome to Santa Fe. Just south of the hotel and the restaurant next to us, The Horseman's Café, a *huge* American flag – at half-mast, in memory of the lives lost or irretrievably impacted by the hijack attacks just eleven days prior – snapped proudly in the winds against this magnificent canvas. I felt a catch of emotion in my throat watching the red, white and blue against that Maxfield Parrish palette and stood there a moment to simply absorb the mixed bag of intense feelings that temporarily overwhelmed me. How can there be such beauty in this world and, at the same time, so much hatred?

We loaded up and headed down Cerrillos Road to make our way to the Paseo de Peralta, down Palace Avenue, and parked in front of the beautiful St. Francis Cathedral. We would take a leisurely stroll through the Plaza and enjoy a little magical mystery touring through this eclectic area, taking in the array of festive and/or whimsical Southwest window displays, as we walked. Dinner would find us when all were ready, which was soon enough, as we were all pretty hungry and additionally enticed by the luscious smells wafting through the air.

There were *so many* potential places to eat... the aromatic scents and alluring decors made choosing difficult, but we finally settled on The Coyote Café, with a balcony called the Rooftop Cantina high above the streets, overlooking the activities below. We could eat and still not miss the action. The Coyote Café is quite the happening nightspot. It is adorned with howling, seated caricatures of the bandana-wearing canines and metal Mariachi skeletons playing in a band hang on a huge wall overlooking the inside dining area. Large tropical plants grace the Mexican tiled floors and the whole atmosphere feels welcoming and lighthearted.

We sat at the bar overlooking the shops and restaurants below, starting the evening with Margaritas for the ladies, and Pete's inevitable beer. Before dinner arrived we were moved to a table close to the bar and could watch the comings and goings from the kitchen, bringing lucky patrons all sorts of delectable salads, varieties of Southwest cuisine, and American plates, for the less adventurous. Cynthia, Pete and I shared stories and we had a fine old time. We had plenty of questions about her life growing up in Arizona, her time in New Mexico, and of the area, in general. But as the evening passed, exhaustion and "altitude sickness" set in. This happens to some not yet accustomed to the high thin air; it's important to acclimate slowly and drink plenty of fluids – water, *not* alcohol. I developed a killer headache, after the one drink. Cindy, long acclimated to the high mountainous altitudes, enjoyed a second Margarita and Pete had a second beer, unharmed by the altitude or fatigue.

Bless her heart, after dinner Cindy was ready to party. On New Mexico time and fueled by two large Margarita's, the night was young for her. No children, no worries, our girl wanted to *play!* She wanted to find a band and dance the night away! But Pete and I – two hours ahead on the East coast clock, jet-lagged, and pooped in general – had to regretfully rein her in. My head was ready to explode with one of those headaches that made the jolting action of simply walking a misery. We were light years apart in our plans for the remainder of the evening. What a fine way to start these carefree days and our reunion with our charming friend, but c'est la vie. Poor kid.

Back at the hotel Cynthia gravitated to the hot tub while Pete and I called it a night. So much for our 'romantic first-night away' – I swallowed a couple of heavy-duty aspirin, drank lots of water, and opted-out of anything more. All I wanted to do was lay my head on a cool, soft pillow, find a position where it didn't pound, and not move a muscle. Pete, too, was exhausted by then and glad simply to sleep. And sleep we did. Deeply, quietly, laced-together there in the dim foreign room, we did not peep until morn.

The next morning brought relief, with solid sleep and another megadose of aspirin to start the day. By the time we met up with Cindy, who was already up and raring to go (does the girl run on Energizers?) we were good to go, ourselves.

Time to find Art and say hello.

Art

We met Art last summer at this hotel with our family in tow, which is a big reason we were back at the Comfort Inn. He is responsible for the breakfast bar during the week, and takes great pride in its quality and appearance. I complimented him on this fact last June. He then came to our table, with maps and tid-bits of information about Santa Fe, Taos, and New Mexican history and lore at his fingertips, all of which was extremely helpful in having our first experience as touristos in these parts be flavored by a local.

Art is an older gentleman, gray and slight, a little bow-legged and kind of shy. I fell in love with him at first sight; he exudes kindness. A pilot in World War II, he shared photographs of his days in the service, during the first trip and more on this trip, as well. Art's dark eyes, under heavy graying brows, twinkle with intelligence, humor, and promised mischief. He called himself a 'Coyote' (someone half-Mexican); the other half was Irish. Art often spoke of his wife, Carole, throughout our original visit, and again on our anniversary trip. Pete and I kidded one another about Carole's existence at all. Did she, really, or was she like the fabled 'Mrs. Columbo' – always referred to, but never seen? I let Cindy in on our speculation, for when she met Art that morning, the verdict was still out.

Sunday, September 23rd

That Sunday morning, our first full day in Santa Fe, Art pooh-poohed breakfast at the hotel, insisting that he take us all out to The Pantry, a local breakfast and lunch restaurant with huge servings of indigenous food. He introduced us to the concept of asking for both red and green chilies with our eggs. "When you ask for both in these parts," he explained, "we call it Christmas." I asked impishly, "Why not Feliz Navidad?" and winked at him. Art just cocked an eyebrow at me and admonished with a smile, "Behave yourself; I'm teaching you something."

After our lively and entertaining breakfast at The Pantry, snapping photographs of one another during and after eating, we returned to the hotel. Cindy needed to pack up to go. As she had ridden 'Smiley' for the visit, she was all dressed in her motorcycle leathers, her big space helmet, and had rain gear close at hand. She found a place to pack the Virginia peanut tin we had given her. All ready to take off now, Cynthia looked small but totally competent there in her black leather jacket astride the big Harley. With hugs and promises of staying in touch while on the road, Cindy was on her way back to her own three children, all younger than ours, her husband and her home, 140 miles away in Maxwell, New Mexico, close to Eagle's Nest and Cimarron. This was Cindy's reality.

After this Pete and I were on our own and no longer pressed for time and exhausted. The afternoon ahead was wide open with whatever we wanted to do. Hey, hey. No difficulties deciding here.... bring on the hot tub and a quiet, spacious suite bedecked with flowers and wine... We knew what to do. The headache was long gone, we had rested-up, and now it was time to play. Twenty-five years of togetherness had made practice about perfect.

Later. Somewhat hungry and ready to roam around Santa Fe in the evening, we decided to go on back to The Plaza to enjoy again the festive window displays and a cup of java at Starbucks. I understand that they have begun selling 'Fair Trade Certified' coffee – that which guarantees the small coffee farmers in Third World Countries a set price-per-pound, regardless what the volatile coffee market is doing. This simple ability to count on how much they – the farmer, the grower and harvester of the bean – will make has made a tremendous impact on their own ability to feed their families, keep their farm, buy a donkey or two to carry the load to market… to live in dignity, proud of their daily efforts. In this country, and across the world, we of many resources take for granted that – of course – the farmer is paid for his hard days work. How little we know and how much we take for granted. These men made $2-$3 *a day* – less than Americans pay for a single small latte or cappuccino, with barely a blink of an eye, at any given Starbucks.

The beauty is that Fair Trade Certified is also often organically- and shade-grown, as well, which is a win-win for all involved, but you have to ask for it. (As I've written this book and checked out multiple coffee houses, I've found that it is usually the smaller, more socially conscious and individually owned outlets that are the ones most committed to carrying a larger selection of these beans.) As the TransFair USA Fair Trade slogan goes, *"Change the world one cup at a time."* * Or one bar of chocolate at a time...

This Fair-Trade concept is now being expanded to the production of the cocoa bean, which produces chocolate. "'Cocoa is easily produced in harmony with nature when the cacao trees are planted under the canopy of the rain forest, not in the open fields typical of the full-sun plantations,' says Sabrina Vigilante, marketing coordinator for the Rainforest Alliance's sustainable agriculture program. 'Sustainable cocoa farming is the next best thing to a rain-forest preserve...' ** Working with natives of the rain forests, they are being taught to plant and harvest this bean in the shade of the great forests, rather than burning them down to plant in the open. Again, it is a win-win: the forest continues to flourish, and the birds, which act as natural insect predators, keep their habitat. The cocoa bean thrives, and the natives are able to make a living off their lands, without destroying them. The chocolate from such production is specially marked as organic or with a Rainforest Alliance label. Paul Newman, actor and humanitarian extraordinaire, along with his family, have become involved in these Fair Trade programs; Newman's Own Organics is responsible for seeing that such chocolate has gone main-stream in the grocery store. His daughter, Nell, shares her father's global philanthropic vision. Over a decade ago she started the organic branch of the family company. To date, this family has given over $127 million to environmental and social causes.

So yes, Starbucks now offers the fair-trade beans by the pound, and yes, they had one type of caffeinated fresh-brew here, but none offered in decaf, which I must drink. Pete, with a cup of Fair Trade in hand, and I, with a decaf skinny latte, lucked into a copy of *The Washington Post* that we found lying around and caught up with current events.

Headlines read: **FBI knew flight schools had been infiltrated. Investigators identify 4 to 5 groups linked to bin Laden operating in U.S.:** *No connection found between 'cell' members & 19 hijackers, officials say.* **Borderless network of terror:** *Bin Laden directs a global crusade.* **The week that redefined the Bush presidency. Sleepless nights, shattered psyches:** *Anxious attack survivors, country, struggle to cope.* **Shoppers are tentative and few:** *Not in buying mood, consumers focus on necessities.* **Plane with Saudi pilot evacuated at Dulles.**

Sobered, Pete and I continued reading: **Germans probe likely links between profits and terrorists. Early Flights, late-night lines at BWI** [Baltimore-Washington International] : *Confusion over check-in times has passengers sitting, waiting in silent airports.* **The view from the ground; Amtrak:** *The boost that began Sept. 11 may not be temporary: Ridership jumped at least 71% after attacks.* **First U.S. Planes land in Uzbek Air Base. Beware of con artists exploiting tragedy. Time to rebalance, not retreat;** *Crisis is a reminder to look at 401(k) choices, but some may be over reactive.* And finally, **How did spending become our Patriotic Duty?**

Pete and I continued to read, digesting the news and the changes in the whole fabric of our great country, amidst the graphic and terrible photos of the devastation of the Twin Towers. Then we quietly put the paper aside for other eyes. We had had our fill.

After our coffees, we strolled the Plaza for a while to think of things other than all this grim news. We soon choose a romantic outdoor patio called The Shed, where we had dined one evening with the kiddos last June, when the world was still innocent. It had been a cozy atmospheric place to eat then, and proved the same more than a year later. The Shed is set back under the walkway from Palace Avenue, beckoning the traveler and locals, alike, as the setting is just beautiful. Tables were placed throughout the patio, and trailing vines such as bougainvillea and wisteria wove their way up supporting pillars along the perimeter of the outdoor 'room.' Tiny white lights danced amongst the greenery and candlelight on the tabletops combined to enchant the evening. Here it would be easy to leave the reality of that other world behind us for now.

Spanish guitar music strummed in from some unseen source, creating the perfect fanciful evening for our first night alone. We dined on appetizers and red table wine, still not too hungry from the huge brunch we had shared with Art and Cindy. Space and time converged to create a luminous and leisurely supper, surrounded by this natural setting. Life was about perfect then, as this Sunday evening became a snapshot in memory, etched softly in that shimmering courtyard.

Afterwards, we continued strolling through the Plaza, arms linked and in no hurry to get anywhere, taking in more of the endlessly imaginative window and shop displays. We meandered through the old downtown on this beautiful fall night, passing the San Miguel Mission, one of the oldest mission churches in America, and The Loretto Chapel, which was built by Jean Baptiste Lamy, on the Old Santa Fe Trail. This historic small church was built for the Sisters of Loretto in the mid-1800s and contains the 'miraculous staircase,' a circular stairway constructed with no nails, or other visible means to support the curvature of stairwell leading from floor to loft. Legend has it that a stranger came to town with a sturdy donkey in tow, laden with unidentified wood, with which the stranger built the stairway. The man finished and disappeared, with no expectation for compensation. It is speculated that it might have been Christ, himself, in mortal form.

Santa Fe was originally named in 1609 by Don Pedro de Peralta, the newly appointed governor, "La Villa Real de Santa Fé de San Francisco de Asis" (translated: the Royal City of the Holy Faith of St. Francis of Assisi). Thank God someone had the presence of mind to abbreviate the fair city's name. From the Loretto Chapel, with the fat and ripening moon rising above the skyline, we strolled past The Palace of the Governors, built in1610. The Palace of the Governors holds the distinction of being the country's oldest public building – in America's oldest capital city. It houses a permanent collection of artifacts from Santa Fe's history, a Museum of Fine Arts, a Museum of Indian Art and Culture, and a Museum of International Folk Art. It was the original seat of Spanish government in the state.

After our late evening sojourn through downtown Santa Fe, Pete and I headed on back to our hotel to languish a bit more in the pool area. When traveling, we find hotels that offer indoor and/or outdoor pool facilities. I take a kickboard with us, stored deep in the suitcase, for water exercises. I have old riding injuries in my neck and shoulders from my days of 'breaking' horses. (Actually, I used more of a 'Whisperer's' approach, but the horses did not always reciprocate...) If these old aches and pains aren't moved on a regular basis, I stiffen up like a case of upper body lockjaw. So the pools are most welcome, especially on such a long trip, for a good cardiovascular and muscle-stretching stint, which I've devised with a mixture of water calisthenics, aerobics and yoga movements. I come out of the water feeling like a million soggy dollars. Pete may or may not do laps, or join me in the water workout, but we both usually end up in the hot tub.

So here we unwound before we returned to continue where we left off earlier with our wine and flowers and dark quiet room, now lit by candles we had brought from home. We were starting to relax into our vacation now. And this, aside from all the updates in the news, was a perfectly grand first full day of our two-week celebration of love, as we remembered a quote from 'Anonymous:' "Anyone who thinks the way to a man's heart is through his stomach must have flunked anatomy." I liked Anonymous.

*Frances Moore Lappé and her daughter, Anna Lappé, wrote a book called *Hope's Edge*, which offers much more information on how the Fair Trade concept began. She remarks that 'coffee is the second most valuable commodity in the world,' coming only behind the god-almighty crude oil, for which powerful nations will go to war (the latter are my thoughts; I am also thinking that potable water may soon run second on this list – perhaps even first in the arid Southwest). Ms. Lappé talks of shifting economic and environmental paradigms in our rapidly changing world.

** Info on Fair Trade chocolate is shared from an article in the February 2003 issue of *Country Living* magazine called "The Sweetest Chocolate."

As with any grassroots movement, the individual consumer has to be involved. And so, my dear enlightened readers, please let that be you.

SEVEN

Jemez Trail Loop/Bandelier

"You have noticed that everything an Indian does is in a circle, and that is because
the power of the world always works in circles, and everything tries to be round...
The sky is round, and I have heard the earth is round like a ball, and so are all
the stars. The wind, in its greatest power, whirls. Birds make their nests in circles,
for theirs is the same religion as ours... even the seasons form a great circle in their
changing, and always come back again to where they were. The life of a man is a
circle from childhood to childhood, and so it is in everything where power moves."
Black Elk, Oglala Sioux holy man (1863-1950)

Monday morning, September 24th

Whenever Pete and I travel and plan to be away for any length of time
we either take a cooler with us or buy one on the road. This simple acquisition saves us a boatload of money in lunches, especially when we
have the kids in tow, and gives us the freedom to eat whenever hunger
strikes, with no need to be around civilization. The cooler pays for itself
tenfold – and gives us a small refrigerator, to boot. Believe me, in the
middle of an endless dusty desert road, one might be tempted to sell a
piece of their soul for an ice cube. Therefore, this little traveling icebox
might keep one spiritually untainted.

Peanut butter – or I should say Skippy's "Super Chunk" – is a mainstay in our mobile pantry. Add to this thick slices of a rich wheat bread
(the heartier, more multi-grained stuff, the better) and any rich fruit jelly
or jam and a cup of cold milk, and you're looking at a stick-to-your-ribs
mouth-watering lunch that borders on country gourmet. An apple for
dessert, to clean the peanut butter off one's teeth, tops the meal. Life
just doesn't get better than being perched on the edge of a butte or cliff,
overlooking some awesome sunset, your loved one(s) beside you, and a
pb&j in hand.

So Monday morning PeterWop and I went shopping for our cooler, a thermos, basic foodstuffs, beer and wine, and we were set to roam awhile, like a week or two, with but the basics replenished, as needed. This day we planned to head out on the Jemez Mountain Trail, northwest of Santa Fe, find Los Alamos and the White Rock Overlook, then take in Bandelier National Monument, home of some of the ancient cliff dwellers that are found throughout this area. From here we would continue on NM 4, on through the Santa Fe National Forest, and into the Valle Grande, then down past Jemez Springs (hoping to stop for a dip in the warm waters), and on to the Jemez Pueblo, where the Jemez tribe live. From here we would complete the loop, pass the San Ysidro and Zia Pueblos, travel on down to Bernalillo, hit I-25 and then head north to Santa Fe again, in the late afternoon or early evening.

Since the Los Alamos National Laboratory's Bradbury Science Museum is closed on Mondays, we passed this chance to see exhibits on the development of the first atomic bomb. This museum also offers displays on modern nuclear weapons and computers, as well as solar, geothermal, fusion and fission energy sources. *It would have been interesting to see,* I thought, *especially in light of the current insanity rampant in the Middle East, with talk of potential use of nuclear explosive devices.... But no, we, our civilized societies that have developed these weapons of mass extermination, would never again use such weapons on one another. This reminds me of another bumper sticker that I sure wish was true*: **"IT WILL BE A GREAT DAY WHEN OUR SCHOOLS GET ALL THE MONEY THEY NEED AND THE AIR FORCE HAS TO HOLD A BAKE SALE TO BUY A BOMBER."** *Sure, and in a perfect world.*

Pete and I wove our way through the residential area that houses those that work at Los Alamos to locate White Rock Overlook – literally in their backyard. We left the car to walk the short trail to partake in this amazing 360° panorama of the New Mexican vistas surrounding us, viewing the Rio Grande meandering far below, an infinite watery serpent writhing slowly south. We properly 'oohed and aahed,' taking the mandatory tourist shots and generally enjoying ourselves before we left to wind our way back through the Los Alamos subdivision to find our way back to NM 4, and continue on to Bandelier.

*See map, page 49.

BANDELIER NATIONAL MONUMENT

Bandelier National Monument, established in 1916 and covering 32,737 acres, is home to prehistoric Pueblo ruins that date back to 1200-1500 A.D. It was named after Adolph F.A. Bandelier, a self-taught anthropologist/historian, who explored over a hundred ruins in Mexico, Arizona and New Mexico in the late 1800s. His experience with the Cochiti Pueblo Indians, who lived in this area, prompted him to write a book about these gentle people, called *The Delight Makers.*

Bandelier is a large area with a road that winds through the old Indian enclave, offering shady parking sites and a visitor center. Pete and I happened on a tour guided by a tiny slip of a ranger named Alyse, who was very knowledgeable and sprinkled her talk with anecdotes and humor. She led us into Frijoles Canyon, showing us the "Big Kiva" and the "Tyounyi Pueblo" (pronounced 't-yun-i'). The kivas were sites dug into the earth or rock where one would climb down inside for holy functions: sacred ceremonial 'rooms' for religious celebrations and ceremonies. Mesa Verde, in southwest Colorado, is full of these Anasazi cliff dwellings and a large number of kivas may be seen there.

After the tour Alyse left us to explore on our own the talus houses, or cliff dwellings, built into the base of the towering "tuff" stone cliffs. Tuff rock, despite its name, is soft ash rock remnants from the lava flows of millions of years ago. Basalt, another rock found in this region, is shiny, black, and extremely hard; the ancients used it for early tools as its strength was forged in extremes of heat, created by the hardened lava flow.

As we climbed up into the base of these sheer cliffs, and if we looked carefully, we could see pictographs (the painted images) and petroglyphs (the carved images) rendered by these aboriginal artists centuries ago, depicted high above us on the faces of the vertical stone walls. Some of these images were at such impossible heights I wondered if some of the artists might not have had wings. There were overhangs here and there, and in one cool deep shaded area the Wop and I were delighted to find a tiny stream of water running underneath these stones, close to the path. As the day was intensely hot and the sun shone relentlessly, Pete and I stayed underneath this spot of Eden a bit to calm our pounding hearts

and cool our sweating brows. We were both still acclimating to these altitudes; the climb up into Frijoles Canyon – wait a minute… one climbs
down into a canyon – this must be Tsankawi Mesa? But then *that's* the top
of the flattened areas… wher*ever* we were in Bandelier was hot as hell,
spectacular to behold, and gave one a tremendous respect for the fortitude of these cliff dwellers to literally carve out a life in this area.

One of the main reasons the Indians chose Bandelier, ranger Alyse
had explained to us, was the fact that a strong body of water, the life-
blood of the west, ran through the bottomland. Water in these lands
allowed hope to spring eternal. The ancients could grow crops, thus
literally put down roots. They could raise livestock and they, themselves,
would not die of thirst. So for centuries they lived and farmed this area
and prospered. They need not be nomadic to exist.

Also in this area are three distinct types of trees. The piñon, found
throughout the Southwest, is New Mexico's state tree, providing nuts
that are high in fat and nutritious but as tedious to eat as the hickory nut,
found in the east. The piñon trees are wiry and sturdy, able to withstand
the harsh sun, winds, and droughts of this wild country, and so, like the
old pioneers that settled the west, and the fortitudinous Indians before
them, they survived. Junipers, another tough tree also able to endure the
harsh arid climate, are everywhere. The Indians ate their berries and used
their wood for building, as well as firewood – and cleverly even 'shaved'
the bark for an early brand of diaper! The third main tree growing tall
and abundant here is the Ponderosa pine, which provided the only truly
straight wood available to the Pueblo people. Ponderosas were the long
lengths of lumber used in the kivas, as uprights and horizontals over

which they laid thatched roofing.

After our exploration of Bandelier, Pete and I were ready to call a break, find a shady spot, and have a picnic lunch. We found a table under a leafy tree not identified by Alyse, and laid out our smorgasbord of pb&j, fruits, cookies and iced tea. The beer would have to wait until we were out of the park. Pete sat with his back to a trail leading up and over a ridge beyond; we noticed **"Do not feed the bears"** signs posted around the picnic area, and had seen warnings at the visitor's center. Seems that these big fellas could be a mite pesky in these parts... So I set up my camera, ready to shoot, with two objectives in mind. The first was to get the photo of the bear, as he or she or they ambled up over the ridge behind Pete; the second was to whip it around and get a photo of Pete's expression when I told him about our luncheon visitors. But alas, we enjoyed a leisurely meal, biding our time, and there was no sign of bear at all, thus no photographs to share with our friends: *"Do you remember when we saw that huge bear coming up behind you, Pete? Do you remember how you ran?! I didn't even have time to get the shot, and my camera was ready... (because I ran, too)."* Alas, none of that. So we packed up all our goodies, reloaded the car with all our picnic and hiking paraphernalia, and called it a day at Bandelier. Time to hit the loop again.

As we drove, Pete and I saw the damage from the huge fire in this area that started about a month after we returned from our June 2000 trip. Some unthinking ranger, practicing "fire prevention with a controlled burn" – in a severe drought on a windy day – started the blaze that devoured 43,000 acres of New Mexico. The resulting inferno claimed over 200 homes around Los Alamos and seriously threatened the nuclear facility, itself. We now witnessed the blackened ruins where forest had stood fifteen months prior. This road seems to have stopped the wildfire from jumping across to other areas of the park. In many places we have seen Ponderosa pines burned out at the bottom, but boughs of green atop the trees attest to life still within. Bright optimistic new growth sprouts below the great survivors; nature remains ever resilient.

The left side of the road was charred remains of what had been; the right mirrored the forest of yesteryear. Driving through this wilderness area of the Jemez Forest was a sobering experience, bringing back memories of news of the huge devastation known as "Wildfires of 2000," throughout the western states of New Mexico, Arizona, Colorado, Utah, Idaho, Nevada and Washington State. At that time, these were the worst fires of almost a century, burning over 1.3 million acres. One of Pete's brother's, Bob, was a firefighter and was called to duty from Ohio to give aid to the over-burdened leagues out west. His wife, Karen, went with him to help in dispatch service. The two were gone for months.

Millions of collective acres of western lands, parts of National Parks and recreational areas were lost. Many homes were burned and many lives were sacrificed by the brave souls that put themselves on the front-lines of these titanic fires. I thought of Nevada Barr's mystery, *Firestorm*, based on a wildfire in California, and of the sheer guts and training it would take to face this hell head-on. I thought of the burning hell inside the Twin Towers and the Pentagon. I thought of human bravery and the elasticity of the human soul, and felt humbled. *What we can bear and still move on...*

Even as I wrote this story, two huge forest fires in Arizona converged on Sunday, June 23rd, 2002, to create an explosive 500-square-mile wild-fire that prompted the evacuation of the small towns of Linden, Pine-dale, and Clay Springs. Heber-Overgaard, a community 35 miles west of Show Low, was overrun that Saturday. Over 300 homes were lost and over 15 businesses burned in the fire's wake. This inferno, in the dense pine forest bordering Arizona's White Mountains, burned over 330,000 acres, and firefighters struggled to save Show Low, which sits roughly 125 miles northeast of Phoenix. The drought and winds wrecked havoc on progress. I don't know how much of the Fort Apache Reservation disappeared in flames. (Show Low, a town of almost 8,000 people, is at an altitude of 6,000 feet. Many Phoenix area residents own summer homes here to escape the desert heat. Its economy hinges on tourism, recreation and – perhaps, no longer – forest products. Show Low was named when two old pioneers in the 1800s decided the town wasn't 'big enough for the two of 'em,' so the old coots played out a card game, deciding that "If you can show low, you win" – and you stay, I'll move on... I wonder just how many of these colorful western towns got their names in such a fashion.)

The fires the summer of 2002 topped the destruction of even those of 2000, burning over 2.3 million acres. They were so bad in three of the Four Corner states that an Associated Press cartoon out of *The Al-buquerque Journal* showed incendiary devices, naming them "Flarizona," "New Matchico," and "Charcolorado." Wildfires in Colorado burned into the suburbs of Denver, in one controversial fire that a seasoned U.S. Forest Service employee started. Called the Hayman Fire, it is said to be the worst wildfire Colorado had ever seen. It destroyed a sprawling area southwest of this capital city. Another fire burned into the northern realms of Durango, burning more than 70,000 acres in southern Colorado. This is hitting too close to home: Pete's younger brother, Gary, and his family live there… God Bless them all and send precious rain. Sounds like these states need a monsoon-type of downpour to drench the scorched, western lands – hold the lightning, please. I'm sure rain-drenched Texas would share.

We continue to drive along NM 4, where there are now living trees on both sides of the road, through the Jemez Forest, and suddenly, to the right, the world unveils a huge expanse of open land. The Grande Valle. *Un*believable! We've just entered Jemez National Park and we are seeing the forests change their types. Aspen have turned bright yellow and blaze in the afternoon sun against what look like blue spruces. Dense rock masses abut up amidst the trees, a study in texture and form. We see streams running through the meadows below us. And where there is water, there are people. Homesteads are scattered now on either side of these verdant fields. Cattle and horses, their fat bellies glistening in the late-day sun, graze these open meadows between tall stands of trees, as streams meander lazily through this pastoral paradise. I've come to find that the Grand Valle is home to one of the world's largest calderas – the collapsed crater of a volcano that is 3 million-years-old.

I am humbled by the landscape that surrounds us. I am drunk on the elevation, all of the sun today and the fresh open air. I want to lay my head back and snooze a bit, all this – and no booze – although we do have the Coronas and lime slices awaiting us in the cooler. Maybe we'll have these at Jemez Springs, taking in those warm baths? I am thinking: *It's been a strange sort of celebration. Pete and I have been planning this trip for so long, since we returned, in fact, from our Four Corners adventure last June, with all the family along. We nixed our original plans to celebrate our 25th in Europe: Spain, then travel by train over the Pyrenees Mountains (Basque region) into France. We'd visit southern France a few days, then head on into Italy. Two weeks of exploring Europe together with Pete 'hosting' France and Italy, as he had been there. I would 'host' Spain, as I had been there. But we weren't comfortable leaving the kiddos for that long – and having the Atlantic Ocean between us. Who knew. Intrigued so by the Southwest, we had changed our plans to stay in the United States, never having a clue that terrorists were planning their savage attack on American soil, as we planned our anniversary. On our –what was to have been – special day, we watched the world turn inside out, as the jets, full of explosive fuel, flew into one target after the next. We watched the World Trade Center's towers be hit, and then collapse, a tomb to those inside. My sister, Elizabeth, had called that day; she was in the University of*

65

Virginia hospital with a gastrointestinal problem. She had forgotten it was our anniversary. She told me to turn on the TV. She and I watched in horror, with the rest of America, as bin Laden's vicious plan unfolded before our eyes. We watched the firefighters, the police and EMT's run into this nightmare and then we watched the Towers collapse around these courageous souls. It could not be happening – it had to be some violent video sequence. But no, it was real. Too real to be digested; the carnage left Americans in shock, which is exactly what the bastards wanted – and for it to all be televised. These men that had come to the States to live among us, go to our flight schools, eat our food, sweat beside us in our gyms. They shaved their precious hair, read terrorist manuals on how to 'blend' into our country, and they counted down the days until September 11th, when they would board those four doomed airplanes and martyr their lives to Allah, and those umpteen damned virgins. Yes, and with their own sickened view of women. The raving, stinking bastards!

I read in Parade *magazine, much later, that Robert Redford – a man I admire for his gumption to stand up to the government about the environment and for his principles, in general – was supposed to have been on United Flight 93 – the one that crashed in the fields in Pennsylvania. Redford had finished his business in D.C. a day early, and so left for Los Angeles on September 10th. He said afterwards, "There but for the grace of God…" I am sure that if he had of been on that jet, he also would have been one of the saints that sacrificed the last minutes of their lives to thwart the killers from their destination, which, I've come to understand, was either the White House or The Capital, with Congress in full session.*

Our day of celebrating 25 years of marriage – the joy, the anticipation, and all our plans – all fell and settled with the ashes of the remnants of the damage. Somehow feeling joy was sacrosanct amongst the tremendous pain of humans touched so many miles away. I have lived on after loved ones were murdered; this was simply murder on a massive scale. I know intimately the onslaught of feelings one encounters with the aftermath, once the initial shock wears off. My heart just bled for the victims and their families. From one day to another, in which we – they – glimpsed unadulterated hell on earth, our faith in being 'safe,' 'secure,' 'isolated from world tensions' had been doused. We are so innocent. Suddenly an invisible, insidious enemy lurks amongst us, like a cancer amongst healthy cells. Our innocent and trusting core had been shaken to its depths – welcome to the way in which much of the rest of the world lives. Ironically, this assault on America has served to unite much of the "rest of the world" in our court. Few want the cancer of the al'Qaida infecting their nation. Countries – large and powerful and small and remote – united with the USA, providing support, covert information, landing bases for military operations, etc. Even Castro's Cuba has offered condolences and support!

Perhaps bin Laden and his al'Qaida network momentarily brought America to her knees in overwhelming grief and sorrow, disbelief and pain. With the exception of Pearl Harbor and the Oklahoma City bombings, Americans had never lived this madness so personally. But what bin Laden could not foresee, in his twisted mind, was the blanket of unification and patriotism that had lain dormant since World War II. He awoke a sleeping giant.

Americans, young and old, of every nationality, creed and color, those that had remembered this great country in wars before, and the untested, untried, innocent youth – the babes that had known only this nation in peace, and war in textbooks – united. Out of the ashes of September 11th, like the Phoenix, patriotism was reborn, burning fiercely in our collective souls. From multitudes of nationalities within a nation, the definition of what it is to be an American came to life. We cried the same tears of grief. Strangers cared for strangers and became friends. We shared our blood to heal the physical wounds; our monies to rebuild; our talents to raise those monies; our sweat to clear the mountains of ruin. We united as a nation, as we have not done before, and this helped us to heal.

Indeed, millions of people around the world, watching aghast – Americans and not – united to help us rebuild and to fight the tyranny of this ungodly act. Mary told me, for example, that she had read that Holland sent us a half-million spring flowering bulbs to plant throughout New York City – a reminder of Hope…

"Are you napping?" Pete asked me, as I'd had my eyes closed there beside him, head laid back, lost in these thoughts. I had missed all of this gorgeous scenery flashing by us.

I started, shaken out of these heated reflections. "No, I'm sorry – I just started thinking of how we had planned to go to Europe for our 25th, originally. And suddenly there I was, back to the day *of* our anniversary."

"I think about that, too, Ra, how can you not? But remember that we're here now, and there's nothing that we can do about that. Let's enjoy our trip, okay?" He laid a hand gently on my leg and smiled over at me. I took his hand in mine.

"No. There isn't a thing in the world that we can do, but I started thinking of 'our' day, Pete, and one thought led to another. It's all the things in the headlines, all over CNN, our conversations with strangers – it's everywhere. It's in the flags we're seeing in our travels, all at half-mast. How can we *not* think about it, when 'it' impacted so *many* people's lives?...," I fought to keep my furious tears at bay.

He said nothing, just squeezed my hand. I know his thoughts run deep, but he has a tendency not to verbalize them too much. We were coming into Jemez Springs now – time to get back to the here and now, as Pete had suggested.

We left the Grand Valle and headed to Jemez Springs, looking for some sort of pullover with the appropriate signs for the baths. Pete remembered soaking in these springs some 26 years before, when he toured the United States, Mexico, and British Colombia, by special bus pass with Greyhound ('Graydog' in Canada). He traveled with a couple of college buddies from UVA, Tom and Monroe, his cousin, Tuffy, and his German 'brother,' Jochen, from 'his high school year as an exchange student. That was the summer of '75, *his* magical mystery touring, just before he and I moved in and lived together in 'our year of sin.'

He would tell me of these carefree travels throughout the west; I would visualize one of our own. And here we were. Only he couldn't find those hot springs again for the life of him, even with the prospect of lucking out on another 'off-day,' meaning it was okay to skinny-dip. (Evidently they switched so that every-other-day one needed to wear a bathing suit; on the off-days, one didn't. If you got mixed-up, you got arrested. Anyhoo, this was how he'd described it way-back-when, and the single young buck had lucked-out on a skinny-dipping day more than a quarter-century ago.)

We couldn't find the springs. However, we did find a scenic spot, looking out over the Jemez River Canyon. Pete and I cracked open our Coronas, squeezed the limes, and toasted to our glorious day of exploration. From there, with the sun falling lower in the sky and goldening things up, we headed south, down NM 4 to the Jemez Pueblo, one of the many in what is called the 'Pueblo Society' in the northwestern quadrant of New Mexico. Each Pueblo has a sovereign government, run by its particular tribal leadership, each with its own religious ceremonies and dances that trace back over the centuries.

A common denominator amongst them all is what, in our privileged American culture, would be considered material poverty: abject, utter poverty (think Third World) rampant throughout these Indian nations. We have notoriously given the Native American (the indigenous – endemic, native, inherited, the ones that were here first) the poorest areas in our great and diverse land – to contain them on their reservations. But when it is realized the Indians are sitting on something of value – i.e.: natural gas, oil, coal, uranium, ores of gold, copper, or silver – rights to the land are demanded, to drain it dry of anything of commercial value, and then they may 'have' it again. It is not important that their sacred ceremonial or burial sites might be exactly where the corporations want to dig for these commercial riches. And God forbid the natives should receive the profit and better their impoverished situation; they are left with the poisoned remains.

I think of Isak Dinesen's book, *Africa*, in which her father, Wilhelm, commented about the American government's 'handling' of the Indians in the late 1800s, in order to take the land. *"They sometimes find it necessary to decimate [them] with the help of soldiers, though liquor, smallpox, venereal disease and other maladies usually do the trick, in concert with the extermination of their vital necessity – game... In a short time they sell their land to the government in exchange for a Reservation, a miserable little tract which they cannot leave without permission of an agent. Here, for a few years, they lead an abominable existence until... the whites get tired of having these wretched beggars in their backyard and send them further west..."*

It saddened me to drive through the Jemez Pueblo and see the small crowded homes clustered together on the dusty arid earth that grew so very little and offered so few ways in which to make a living. Native children played with balls and sticks and their small thin dogs in between rusted jalopies and beat-up old trucks and torn-down old fences. A few tired cottonwoods offered shade, but by far most of these battered homes lay in the full wrath of the blazing sun. It would be hard to find laughter and hope in a setting as this, but yet – like children of poverty throughout the world – there was still gay laughter that rang through the still high air, as they played with their balls and sticks and small thin dogs.

Children need so little to see joy in the moment, to invent the impromptu game. For them, this bone-tired, dried-up world was a magical kingdom – I smiled. I am on the 'bleeding heart' mailing list of most every charity in America, known through the country as a sap for good cause. But I made a mental note to rethink the requests that came in from the variety of Native American charities. Monies for basic needs: food, blankets, shelter, heating fuel for frigid winters, etc., was always in demand and greatly appreciated. I would return home and respond to more of those incoming requests.

We drove through the Jemez Reservation and on down to San Ysidro, where we picked up NM 44, past Coronado State Monument and Park. Coronado showcases partially reconstructed ruins of Kuaua, a Tiwa Indian Village and the ancient polychrome murals of animal and human forms it displays in a restored kiva. In the years 1300 – 1600 A.D. highly decorated polychrome pottery and mural painting flourished.

We continued on to Bernalillo, which is essentially a Spanish and Indian farming community and a point of livestock shipping northwest of

Sandia Peak. As Albuquerque expands northward, Bernalillo grows, as well. Northwest of Bernalillo are the Zia and Santa Ana Pueblos and the Spanish-American village of San Ysidro. The Zia sun symbol, borrowed for use on the New Mexican state flag, is a sacred Zia design representing the magical symbolic four: four seasons; four times of day; four ages of a person's life; and the four directions of the compass.

Santa Ana is one of the oldest missions in the U.S. It is closed to tourists, but Santa Ana is believed to have been erected by Fray Juan de Rosas, who accompanied Juan de Oñate on his expedition to New Mexico in 1598.

From Bernalillo, after a pit stop and a cup of fresh coffee to hit the highway, Pete and I headed north on I-25, a direct shot back to Santa Fe. I don't even remember what we did, or where we went, for dinner that night. I do remember being tired from our busy day of discovery, hitting the pool for exercise and the hot tub for relaxation, and calling it an early night for once. Using the 800# we had set up for communication with

 the kids, we called home at a halfway decent hour, to catch-up on our 'real life' with Jean and Al and each of our teens, allowing us a pang of nostalgia for our loved ones – each a gift – and our busy little farm. We truly have so much for which to be thankful.

EIGHT

Last Daze, Santa Fe

"To the dull mind all nature is leaden. To the illuminated mind the whole world burns & sparkles with light." Ralph Waldo Emerson, journal entry, 1831

Tuesday, September 25th

Today Pete and I stayed in Santa Fe. We abducted Art after his breakfast shift and took him to lunch at Castro's, a quaint and often jam-packed spot he had introduced us to the year prior, off of Rodeo Road. It offers native New Mexican fare, and plenty of it; each plate could easily feed two. The restaurant was housed in a simple building that came to life inside, with brightly colored decorations freshly out of Mexico, piñatas and bright blankets hung around the room and simple wooden tables and chairs awaited the throngs that came to enjoy the food. Locals abounded, and all knew Art, which made Pete and me feel part of la familia. We took our time over the meal, visiting and laughing.

Art had given us an array of goodies that morning: new brochures, pamphlets, a New Mexican cookbook for the kids, and a poster – indicative of Art's mischievous sense of humor – reading: **Lost Dog: 3 legs, blind in left eye, missing right ear, tail broken, recently castrated. Answers to the name "Lucky."** None of us knew it then, but part of the kismet of this particular trip was unfolding before our eyes... Pete and I laughed and added this to our collection of information to be packed along with us.

After our lunch Art suggested we go to Jackalope, a colossal tourist magnet, offering gifts and riches from throughout the world. They house a CD collection of Indian music – American Indian, or Hindu – if it is done well, it is here. There is a large collection of Native American, as well as South American, work. I even found a copy of *How The West Was Lost*, by Peter Kater, with R. Carlos Nakai, a haunting and seductive sound-track I'd had and lost years ago, and had had no luck in replacing, as I was told it was "out of print." But aha! It was here – and the sequel, as well! There was Latino music, and Reggae, Spanish guitar, and Boogey-Woogie Jazz piano…

Jackalope was a warehouse for color, texture, and form. Plays of light and shadows danced over the displays of brightly colored blankets and strings of baubles and beads. Chili ristras, of all shapes and sizes, hung on wooden ports beside skulls of antelope, buffalo, deer and goat – the primal red afire against the bleached bone masses. While Pete roamed around Jackalope, I spent an hour and three rolls of color film in bliss, shooting these festive southwestern compositions, with intentions of future paintings. Creativity spiced my blood and set it aflame like picante sauce; I was in heaven! I promised myself, next trip, I would return with unlimited film – both color and black & white – and a fresh eye, giving the artist free rein. I would come alone and on Navajo time, none of the men-folk in my life knitting their eyebrows and gazing meaningfully at their damned timepieces. Or I would come with another free-spirited artistic soul, like Beverly – a dear artist-friend at home – and we would feed each other's creative passion, lost in this form and fabric and textural paradise from around the world.

On top of the high terra cotta colored roof of Jackalope sat one of the Painted Ponies in a most imaginative space-alien-looking design. I laughed aloud and pointed up to Pete. "Look, Wop, they've made *that* pony into a horsefly!" He looked up and joined me in my laughter. Sure enough, the artist had painted the overall body metallic red-brown, added huge silver iridescent eyes, and had made large diaphanous wings that sprouted from his back. Then he or she had removed the original legs and added six jointed appendages that ended up in hooves. The result was a beautifully rendered but wacky creation shimmering against the blue western sky – my kind of tongue and cheek humor.

After our considerable time rambling through Jackalope (in all fairness, Pete was pretty patient) he and I headed for the Plaza. He wanted to take in the Sangre de Cristos, to photograph the aspens in blazing contrast to the evergreens, going up to the ski resort. I wanted unfettered quality-time on Canyon Road, off of Paseo de Peralta, the art district in Santa Fe. Once an old Indian trail, later to become part of the

Santa Fe Trail, it now houses some of the most beautiful art in the world, showcased in an array of eclectic galleries started literally decades ago by 'Bohemian artists and eccentrics looking for the cheapest place to live in the city.' Who knew then that these early beginnings would mushroom into an enchanting array of studios, shops, eateries, and places of worship, as colorful as the history throughout the town.

Pete would have enjoyed a stroll with me down Canyon Road, stopping to peep into a gallery now and then. But I've overdosed him too many times, getting sucked into the vortex of the creative moment, wanting to savor every detail and osmos it to my core. For me, Canyon Road was a visual orgasm. For Pete it was simply foreplay, and so he opted to go his way and spend the afternoon in own his brand of creativity.

Kahlil Gibran would have been proud of us, for we were each strong in our love for one another, yet reveled in our independence, like the pillars of which he writes in his verse on 'Love,' in *The Prophet*. In any case, we avoided a fight. And this much togetherness required some space, so off we went on our different paths – Pete, of course, taking the car for his photography sojourn, and me hoofing it with my good sneakers, my trusty backpack, and love of a long walk. We would meet up later at Starbucks for more Fair Trade coffee.

Camera firmly around my neck, like a huge and clunky ornament, I walked entranced, stopping here, stopping there, to frame a photo and capture a fragment of that place in time. One of the many curiosities I noticed in June of 2000 in Santa Fe was the wonderful and beguiling way fences and gates were used in "The City Different." No one settled for a picket fence – God forbid! – no, there were adobe walls of varying heights and colors; ornamental, in-laid cast-iron palisades; thatched fencing interwoven with whatever indigenous plants were on hand. Stone walls, some imprinted with shells *(From what seashore did these spring forth? I wondered, as the shells in these parts had long ago turned to sand...)* Gates were as ornate and as individual as the fencing, decorative, as well as functional. I laughed at the many bizarre and imaginative ways in which one could block-off an entry to – or invite one into – one's home.

So I enjoyed the fences and gates, the gardens and trees, and the people who watered these color-loaded patchworks of plants. I wandered into some of the galleries and talked with the owners or curators, managers or artists. I savored the art: paintings that were small and detailed, or huge and abstract, and exploding in color and form. There were, of course, a multitude of Southwestern landscapes and cowboy paintings. And beside them were florals and still-lifes. There were striking portraits of the noble redskin, rendered by tremendously talented members of that particular tribe. There were oils, acrylics, watercolors, and drawings. Gorgeously rendered bronzes – for which the Southwest is so noted – abounded, rich and coppery-toned, of animals and Indians, children and dancers. Artwork was literally from around the globe. Anything went. I visually orgasmed my way to heaven a hundred times over that day.

In the course of my afternoon on Canyon Road, I passed El Zaguan, a beautiful hacienda extraordinaire, offering a fine example of 19th Century architecture and housing a Victorian garden that sets the standard for Santa Fe. A man after my own heart stood behind a canvas, painting an oil of the scenery before him, a modern-day Monet. I took several candid shots of this artist lost in the essence of creativity on this joyous day.

On the way back I passed the Olive Rush Studio, which was originally an old Spanish farmhouse, turned into a gallery by Olive Rush. She was a well-known New Mexican artist with a wonderful claim to fame of turning over some of her commissioned murals to native talent, thus opening the door for Native Americans in the 1800s to express their talents and share their elaborate history and rituals. Olive Rush willed her studio to the Society of Friends that still meet there to this day.

By the time Pete and I met-up for our joe, I had but one shot left – to take a close-up of the antiqued bricks in the soft and worn Southwest colors on the walls of Starbucks that I thought were absolutely perfect for this area. Pete, too, was out of film, but was bursting with fresh air and a sense of accomplishment with his own afternoon. Although somewhat overcast, the sun had broken through often enough for him to get several (he expected) spectacular shots of the Sangre de Cristos, as he'd climbed up to the ski resort. He sat in the armchair, black Fair Trade coffee steaming beside him, his long denim-clad legs sprawled out in front of him, crossed at the ankles. PeterWop looked like a modern-day version of the Marlboro Man, sans smoke. He wore an Aztec-patterned sports shirt that I'd given him years ago for his birthday or Father's Day, which befitted the colorful heritage of the town, and he looked happy. The man had a couple days growth of beard on his jaw, threatening to blend with his salt & peppered mustache and goatee, his face was tanned lightly and life danced in his chocolate eyes. He, too, had had a fine time exploring the world solo. We shared our adventures, as we sipped the good java, the both of us pleasantly beat.

We found a copy of the *Albuquerque Journal*, dated the day before, on September 24th, and read it awhile. Headlines read: **U.S. Plans to Prove its Case: White House will publish evidence against bin Laden. Prayers & Patriotism: Crowds and clergy of many faiths in Yankee Stadium to honor those missing after the attack. Pavarotti wows pit crowd with song: Concert dedicated to the attack victims. El Niño may bring state wet winter. Low arsenic standard cries out for more study. Afghani speaks in Taos: Journalist says country-men victimized by war, Taliban. 'West Wing' mirrors attacks in new episode. NYC** [Fire Caption Patrick Brown, in Ladder Company 3, inspired the book, *Holding Fire* by Elissa Wald.] **firefighter who in-spired a novel is lost: Hero 'died doing what he lived to do.'** *"Paddy Brown, who helped inspire Wald's novel, is one of the 343 firefighters missing at the World Trade Center. He and 11 other members of Ladder Company 3 were last seen running up a stairway, headed for the fire above…"* **Under Suspicion: Lib-erty could suffer as we search for the enemies within. Faith fights terror's image: Muslims say peaceful religion is often misinter-preted.** And then, some relative good news, **'Tribute' telethon pulls in $100M…** *"Friday's* [September 21st] *star-studded benefit for victims of the Sept. 11 terrorist attacks, seen by an average audience of 59 million viewers, has raised more than $100 million for relief efforts…"*

"Isn't that great, Pete?" I asked, showing him this story. He put down the paper he'd been reading and took this article.

"Wish we hadn't been so busy packing that night that we couldn't catch this. I imagine it was very heartfelt, Ra. I'm glad they were able to raise so much money – that's really pretty amazing, considering the time they had to put it together."

"I know – but there were a lot of people that wanted to help and didn't know what to do. This is how they could contribute; I'm sure everyone that participated simply rearranged their priorities and said 'yes' to this effort. That's what America is all about."

"These last three weeks have been a huge testament to what American is all about." Pete responded, as he laid the article back on the table.

We continued to read the *Albuquerque Journal* for a while longer, absorbing all the news we could until we were saturated with 9/11 and related events. There was absolutely nothing we could do from here, except continue to be tourists and travel America, patriotically spending our money to help boost the sagging economy. Signs were draped on numerous hotels and restaurants, thanking Americans for doing just that – for traveling and continuing to strive for a semblance of normalcy – in this time of madness and uncertainty. All Pete and I were doing was trying to celebrate a day extraordinarily special to us that had had nothing to do with this apocalypse. But yet we couldn't be ostriches and bury our heads, as if nothing had happened. Through our trip we walked a fine line teetering between joy and profound sadness. At any given time we might be leaning in one direction or the other.

PeterWop and I finally left Starbuck's and found a place close by for a light dinner, at The Blue Corn Café & Brewery on Water Street, where they served 'New Mexican pub fare.' We had a couple of inventive and tasty salads, washed down by cold dark ales, shared more of our day, and then called it a night. We decided to take a stroll through the Plaza Mercado, 'Santa Fe's International Marketplace,' an enclosed, multi-layered shopping Mecca, on the way to our car. We passed several more of the lively Painted Ponies inside the enclosed mall.

Here we found Eclectica, a fascinating shop teaming with handmade items from around the world. We found some beautiful, hand-painted platters from Mexico and decided to have one sent home, as a Christmas gift for Jean and Al. Spreading them carefully on the wooden floor to eye the different designs, we chose one with predominant brilliant yellow sunflowers, as Jean favored this hue. It had a cobalt background with touches of bright greens and reds. We asked our amiable host to ship it to Virginia. Added to the package was a primitive 'Circle of friends,' also from Mexico, to later adorn our dining table. I found a handmade angel made of layers of cloth and shellac, choosing it for Mary for Christmas – a guardian angel for her home. We had this wrapped separately to take with us; it would too likely be crushed or lost in with the larger and heavier items. Quite happy with our selections, and knowing Pete's parents would be thrilled with the plate, we left this small shop and headed back to our hotel to pack up our growing collection of luggage. In the morning we would be headed on to Taos by way of the winding and ages-old High Road, leading us out of Santa Fe, higher and deeper into the mountainous regions of New Mexico.

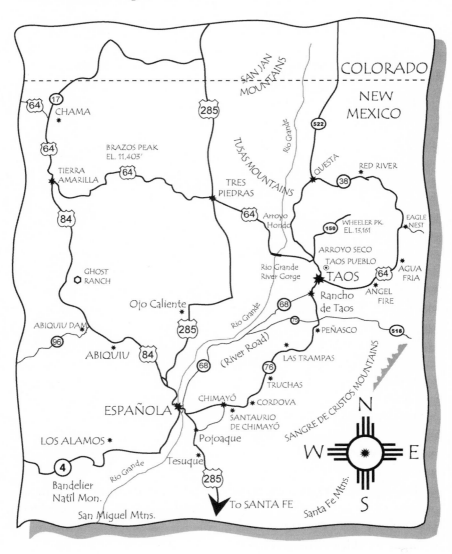

NINE

High Road to Taos

"Cosmic upheaval is not so moving as a little child pondering the death of a sparrow in the corner of a barn." Thomas Savage

Wednesday, September 26th

We headed north on 285, passing the entrance to the Santa Fe Opera, which I've heard is world-class, and we must surely experience on the next trip. A little later we passed 'Camel Rock,' a funny sandstone formation that does look for all the world like a prone camel, laying there chewing its cud in the warmth of the western sun. I would have to get a postcard for this one – it came and went before I was ready to shoot. We headed on through the Tesuque Indian Reservation and glittery signs that promised good luck in gambling. Pete and I grinned at each other. Sure, and there goes the rest of our trip! At the Pojoaque intersection, in the midst of the rez, we headed northeast on NM 76, the beginning of 'The High Road' to Taos. This turn took us almost to Española, known affectionately as "The Low Rider Capital of the World." Española, situated in the northern Rio Grande Valley, lies between the Jemez Mountains and the Truchas Peaks. It was founded in 1598 by the Spanish, as the first capital of New Mexico. Española is considered to be the central point for visiting the eight northern pueblos.

On another trip we would have to head north on NM 84, on up to Abiquiu and the Ghost Ranch. This was Georgia O'Keefe's turf – where she had lived and painted for many years at the end of her life. Apparently she spent her summer months at Ghost Ranch and the winter months in Abiquiu, in a house she had purchased in 1945 and spent the next few years restoring. Her adobe home and studio in Abiquiu looked out over the Chama river valley, where she would spend endless hours painting the Southwest skulls and turquoise skies, for which she became so famous. For the next twenty-five years or so, she continued painting and traveling the world. In 1973, as her vision deteriorated, a young potter named Juan Hamilton encouraged O'Keefe to continue painting and taught her to work in clay. They maintained a symbiotic friendship throughout the rest of her years, when she finally moved to Santa Fe in 1984 and in with Juan Hamilton's family, where she lived for the last two years of her life. Georgia O'Keefe died in Santa Fe on March 6th, 1986, at 98 years of age. Her ashes were scattered at Pedernal, the flat-topped mountain south of Ghost Ranch. My fantasies, when our East-coast life gets to be overwhelming, are of coming West to paint: finding a small place, a good dog, an acclimated, responsive horse, and a studio a la O'Keefe-style. Open my eyes and heart to this wonderment, as Georgia did, and as have so many other artists – inspired by the haunting, mystical "Land of Enchantment," as this state so aptly calls itself. One day...

We were turning off onto 76 now. Immediately to our right was a roadside stand with Hispanics selling assorted produce and chili ristras. "Pete! We've gotta' stop and shoot this – it's such a postcard!" He groaned and pulled over; it had begun: the blood charging through excited veins, heart pumping madly, eyes opened wide in wonder. For him, it'd be a long trip. For this man who liked to buckle his seatbelt and put the miles behind him, and this woman, who watched the world ever-changing, stories to tell from ages past, so vivid and alive before us, begging to be captured on film, to be remembered for our years to come. We traveled together, but our goals on the road were light-years apart.

Pete gave me a well-practiced "Be quick" look, and I smiled him a thank you, hopped out and got my shot from a distance, so as not to disturb the fellows, and waved them a thanks, too. We were on our way up the winding back roads that would lead us to old civilizations: Chimayó, Córdova, Truchas, Las Trampas, Peñasco – small towns with big, colorful pasts – like the Turquoise Trail. What we see today is but the scratchings on the surface that all of the families and their ancestors have lived in decades of life on the edge of the Sangre de Cristo (Blood of Christ) Mountains.

I tried to behave as we drove along the mountainous twisting road, looking for our turns to lead us into the Santuario de Chimayó. Here and there on treacherous turns or beside a tree an arrangement of silk or plastic flowers sprang from the ground in memory of someone lost in a car accident. Throughout New Mexico we have seen these commemorations. Often the shrines are in the shape of a cross, and some have placards with the loved ones name engraved. A final means of being in contact, of saying goodbye – closure. Respect and remembrance. Later, in Utah and Arizona, we saw none of these bright memorials. I am suspecting it has to do with the Catholic influence of the Hispanic culture so alive throughout this state. In Virginia, however, I'm seeing more and more of these markers remembering those killed on the highways, and we have quite the mix of cultures. One shrine in particular is especially poignant, as I know the story and see the crosses on each trip to town.

A local man lost his wife and two small granddaughters in such a car accident. They were headed south into Charlottesville, down the infamous 29 corridor, when a young and inexperienced driver overreacted to an insect entering her opened window. She lost control of her vehicle and ended up ramming this family's car, causing them to careen through the median into oncoming traffic. None but the young driver survived. She now lives with the haunting aftermath of this tragedy. The deceased woman's husband, in desperate grief, at first put up three white crosses in the median, with the name and age of his wife and granddaughters: Lois, 49; Renae, 10; and Cheyanne, 4. He painstakingly decorates the areas around the crosses, where his family died, according to the season. Easter finds lilies and pastel eggs; July 4th, the hillside is decorated with red, white and blue silk flowers and small flags. There are mums and asters in the fall, with ghosts and goblins for Halloween. At Christmas drivers passing by see red and white silk poinsettias, there under the stark white crosses. It is a bittersweet heartbreak to pass this ever-changing dedication to this man's loved one's and his tremendous, unfathomable loss.

A year after the crosses stood tall and proud at the place of the wreck, with the revolving holiday displays beneath, the Virginia Department of Transportation asked him to move the crosses across the road, on a hill in front of a church. It seemed they distracted some drivers. He did. So now when we pass, we see the three white crosses of this man's beloved family, and we continue to see the ever-so-carefully kept seasonal decorations on the tragic median. He has now planted three dogwoods in this area where the crosses once stood. Many times as we pass I remind our young teenage drivers of the importance of defensive driving, and I say a silent prayer for this man, who so loved his family that he – even years after their deaths – continues to pay tribute to his loved ones by caring for this site where their lives were ended in but the blink of an eye.

We followed the back roads and the signs directing us to "El Santuario de Chimayó" (the shrine of Chimayó) built in 1816 by Don Bernado Abeyta. It is a rustic little church that blends into the land as it sits at the base of a small mountain rising high above it. Built of wood and stucco, the entrance is found through a gated courtyard, a large sand-colored adobe wall surrounds this courtyard and stately conical cedars grow within the confines. The entry wall to this Kingdom of God rises in an archway to frame over ancient wooden doors, opened to us now.

Inside the courtyard floor was – surprisingly – soapstone or slate and in the center was an adobe headstone, engraved with four names: Francisco C. & Abenicia D. Chavez were engraved in granite inlaid in the upper part. Underneath, also engraved in granite inlaid in the adobe, were the names George D. & Frances M. Chavez. I thought they must be the founders, the original Fathers, and their spouses, of this beautiful, historic church. A wooden cross, adorned with white flowers, crowned this memorial. Pete and I took photos of one another inside the doorway of this entry, in the dappled shade, the gravestone and the quaint little church behind us.

Inside El Santuario de Chimayó one steps back through history. Nothing in this house of worship looks young. To our left an aged priest sat in his office, busy over papers, his black robes enshrouded him, his white collar stark against his creased, tanned face. As we entered, we noticed a table to the right was laden with prayer candles – the large ones had colorful designs of Jesus as a grown man; some had Mary and the infant Jesus on them. Smaller ones, in front, were red and blue; all were lit in memory of a loved one, an altar.

The inner church before us had small wooden benches on either side that led one's eye down the stone floor to the central altar – an old reredo, or Spanish paintings depicting religious stories on wooden panels. This intricate reredo, with its gilded paints and ornate carvings, claimed the wall at the back of the Santuario. Underneath a long narrow table stretched the length of the room, more candles burning atop. A large carving of Christ on the cross hung in the center of this reredo.

Soft light came from several large, square windows at the sides of the church, rising high above stark, whitewashed adobe walls. Huge pine beams supported the ceiling. Several people, black shrouds over their heads, knelt in the front pews in prayer. Pete and I became hushed, quiet, in reverence of the spiritual abundance in this tiny and ancient sanctuary.

We went back to the office to ask the old priest about the 'healing dirt,' of which Art had told us. He said yes, of course, we were welcome to have some, but first we must say a prayer of thanks. He led us to the front of the church where we, the tourists, the gringos from far away, knelt to pray with the locals. Humbled, I knelt there beside Pete, studied the altar a moment and then looked at Christ, with his head lain to one side in pain, the crown of thorns cutting into his scalp, and the blood of his life so vividly running down his face, his arms, his chest. Rosary beads were wrapped around his neck and flowed down the front of his body, in front of the loin cloth, and fell in a pool at his feet to mingle in this blood.

I thought of Christ's tremendous suffering for mankind, and wondered how much 'mankind' had actually learned over the years. I thought of the infinite brutal wars fought in the name of religion over the centuries, over the world, and thought of the infinite and continued oceans of bloodshed and pain.

I closed my eyes and bent my head down, in prayer for our family, and gave thanks for our many blessings. I thanked Jean and Allan and Mary for helping us make this trip happen. I said a prayer for Mary and Simon, for Galen and Sean, and for George and Connie, that they all find quiet and peace with the awful turn of events in their lives. And I prayed again for the thousands whose lives had so irrefutably been altered on September 11th. I prayed so intently that Pete said "Ahem," beside me, and nudged me with his elbow. The priest was waiting. I swiped the damned tears from my eyes and whispered: "Did you say 'Ahem,' or 'Amen,' because in here it's 'Amen,' you know… I'm ready, are you?" Pete smiled at my trying to pull myself together and get poised and graceful as I stumbled out of the pew. I pulled the plastic Ziploc baggie that Art had given us just for this purpose out of my hiking shorts, and followed the men – the Man of God, and my good man – into a small chamber in the back of the church. It was simplicity, itself.

Surrounded by adobe walls, brick-colored below and cream above, lay a bed of firmly packed golden dirt. In the center lay a large, cylindrical hole. The old priest, who looked as if he might have been the original founder, himself, and who we came to know as Father Roca, gave us a trowel to use to dig this 'tierra Bendita' (holy dirt) out of the 'posito' (little well). Art had told us that people came from all over the world to partake in this tierra Bendita. So I put a couple of trowel scoops into the baggie, closed my eyes in quick thanks, and rose up. Father Roca told us that each time this posito was refilled, he blessed it anew.

On a wall beside this chamber was a pastel of the head of Christ looking into the sky in anguish, the green Crown of Thorns leaving a bloody trail down his gaunt face. Beside this moving portrait, a hand-written placard was tacked to the wall. It read:

"I am blind, traveled many miles to find a place I love, in its silence and peace. I left this site.... a poem. If you are a stranger, If you are weary from the struggles in life, whether you have a handicap, whether you have a broken heart, follow the long mountain road, find a home in Chimaya. It's a small Spanish town settled many years ago by people with a friendly hand, their culture still lives today. They will tell stories about miracles in the land. Since 1813 Santuario is the key to all good. A church built as graceful as a flower swaying in a summer breeze, nested in a valley protected by wild berry trees. In the dusty roads of Chimayo little children with brown faces smile, Majestic mountaintops rule over the virgin land. When the day is done, the sun falls asleep without regret, Sleeping in the twinkle of a starry, stary night. It's that old country feeling in Chimayo I can't forget. In all the places in the world I have been This must be Heaven..."
G. Mendosa, Las Cruces

Santuario de Chimayo
Laura Cockerille Glaccum © '04

I took a photograph of this homage to Chimayó and the face of Jesus, distraught, beside it, with Father Roca's permission. We thanked him again and walked hand in hand up the aisle of the ancient little church in the New Mexican highlands and back out to the light of day. The magical dirt sat inside the plastic bag in my pocket and again I gave a little prayer of thanks for it, hoping – indeed – that it healed. I would bury some in our garden with a prayer of forgiveness for the men who had killed Galen and George and hurt Mary, Simon and Sean so much, on so many levels, bringing such pain and anguish to our families. *Bless them, Lord, for they know not what they do.* I would bury more with a prayer for September 11th, for the living and the dead; may God hold them all tenderly. I would give some to Beverly, to plant in her garden, as her father was so sick with cancer. I would give some to Emily and Shalom, Judy, Pam and Laney, and to other friends I knew, going through cancer or divorce, changes and pain in their lives… I hoped I had enough. I turned around and looked again at this tranquil old church so far removed from the hustle and bustle of east-coast life. I thought of a poem by ee cummings that he might well have written for this very Santuario:

i am a little church(no great cathedral)
far from the splendor and squalor of hurrying cities
—i do not worry if briefer days grow briefest,
i am not sorry when sun and rain make april

my life is the life of the reaper and the sower;
my prayers are prayers of earth's own clumsily striving
(finding and losing and laughing and crying)children
whose any sadness or joy is my grief or my gladness

around me surges a miracle of unceasing
birth and glory and death and resurrection:
over my sleeping self float flaming symbols
of hope,and i wake to a perfect patience of mountains

i am a little church(far from the frantic
world with its rapture and anguish)at peace with nature
—i do not worry if longer nights grow longest;
i am not sorry when silence becomes singing

winter by spring,i lift my diminutive spire to merciful Him Whose only now is forever: standing erect in the deathless truth of His presence (welcoming humbly His light and proudly His darkness)

Pete and I decided to keep the car parked where it was, in the shade of an old tree, and walk over to the place of the sprawling adobe wall and chili ristras. We wandered across the parking lots, past the buff-colored Vigil Store, circa 1948, with the words *"Santos, Wood Carvings, Popsicles"* painted in black block letters beside the entrance under the overhang. On the wall closest to the church, beside the entrance window, was the Virgin Mary painted in a bright pink gown, at prayer, a golden halo radiating from her entire body. Red roses arched over her head and lay at her feet. The sun shone on this colorful depiction, kissing her sweetly. A table stood beside the door, covered in brightly striped cloth, and a paper American flag was taped inside the window above.

Across the street three adobe arches rose over the entrance to a courtyard. Wagon wheels, cut in half and inlaid in the outer arches, caught filtered sunlight from a large tree inside the courtyard, its branches draped generously to share its cool, welcoming shade with visitors. Several depictions of Jesus were either painted directly on, or hung in paintings from, this adobe wall. My favorite was a large sign painted on wood of Jesus in a red robe looking languidly at us, a halo – dimmed by the suns rays over time – faded behind him. His lips were pursed, as if to speak, his eyelids half closed. Across the robe, in white script, ran the words *"Chimayó Holy Chile."* Beside this entrance sign two large red chili ristras, in the shape of crosses, hung from beneath the teal-colored support beam underneath the adobe arches, beside Jesus. In large red letters on a white sign, hand-painted above Christ's head, read *"Restaurant."*

Pete and I ducked under the ristras, many of the cross design, others of the typical cylindrical shapes, in different sizes and some in the shape of hearts or circular wreaths. The bold reds ablaze against the periwinkle sky were a sight to behold. Shadows danced a game of hide and seek, as the ristras swayed in the breezes. Pete and I shot photos of one another, our bodies framed by these festive ristras, and it was here that Pete's camera decided to go nuts. Apparently this was too much spice for it to handle. He had just put in a roll of fresh film; the camera shot about three photos and then took it upon itself to rewind the whole roll.

"Wait a minute!" he exclaimed, "That's a *brand new* roll of film!"

"How fresh is your battery?" I asked.

"Fresh enough. I just replaced it after the shoot Monday afternoon in the mountains, outside Santa Fe. It should be just fine. I'll try another roll of film." He slipped one out of his pocket, put the semi-used one in the canister, and reloaded. "Okay, stand over by the ristras again, Laura, and we'll see." He shot a couple more and these did fine. But two more photos into this roll and it rewound the new film again. "Well, *damn*. It's never done this before. It *would* have to wait until we're on vacation." He looked exasperated. I would certainly be, with most of the trip still ahead of us.

"I'll share my camera with you, Pete, don't worry about it. And maybe we can find a place to get a few disposables; they won't be great pictures, but they'll be better than nothing at all."

Inside the courtyard more ristras hung from every available hook. Long strings of garlic nodes, a pale parchment against the garnet ristras, hung. Atop a rough-hewn wooden cabinet rested the carved bust of a heavily mustached Hispanic man, a cigar in his lips and his hat broken in half. A pale conic bread oven laid claim to the opposing corner, a shadow play from the tree above moved beautifully across the hearth that spread like an apron in front. Soot inside the oven, stained from many a fire, told the story of its use.

Pete and I walked around the soapstone floor looking at the colorful sites and feeling very much like gringos new to the area. Underneath a metal awning, underneath the huge tree and behind a table laden with what looked like pistachio nuts, stood a man in a dark tee shirt. He was speaking energetically to an older couple, the woman in a dark brown outfit, drawn into the conversation, the man in a diamond-designed sports shirt stood with his hands stuffed down into his trousers, determined not to become involved, if he could help it. I watched with amusement. With all the endless enthusiasm of a used-car salesman, this fellow was peddling his wares. He was good. I strolled over to see what he was selling.

The guy had an expressive tanned face with a severely receding hairline that served the better to frame his intense dark eyes. His hands stayed in constant motion. I wondered if the Hispanics up here intermixed with Italians, or what, because these animated hands bespoke Italian heritage. The couple moved off, as the older man took his wife's arm and shook his head "no," meaningfully.

I walked over, looking at his table full of pistachios and bags of red and green powders and asked, "So, what are you selling?" Pete joined me, now curious, himself. The man began his spiel once again, becoming livelier as he talked. I looked at Pete and grinned. We exchanged smiles, the both of us getting a charge over his busy appendages.

"I only have the finest pistachios and chili powder in all of New Mexico!" he boasted. "You must try some!"

"Pistachios are grown here?" I marveled.

"You're not from around here, I see – of course they are. The finest pistachios in the world are grown at the Eagle Ranch, down in Alamogordo, not at all far from right here in Chimayó. Here, you must try this," and he waved his hand in a flourish, as he cracked open two pistachios and handed Pete and me each a large nut, instructing: "Now, you must first chew the nut, and hold it on the backs of your tongue, but do not swallow."

"Okay…" I thought, *"now what?"*

"Okay, now, I give you a 'chaser' of chili pepper, just a pinch, to mix in your mouth with the pistachio. Here, like this" – and he made a swishing motion with his mouth. He then poured a little of the red chili powder handily into the very same pistachio shells he'd just cracked open and handed them to us. "As they say, 'down the hatch,' but you must mix it first before you swallow."

We did as we were told, granted a bit dubiously, I have to say. I never in a million years would have mated a pistachio taste with chili pepper – but we opened up, poured the powder trustingly onto our tongues, 'swished,' watching each other all the while, a twinkle in our eyes, as we did. *Tourists.*

Damn! It was **good***!* I gave a surprised little laugh, *who woulda' thunk it?!* Our friend stood back, watching us with a big smile, hands on his hips and shaking his head, "Yes, yes, I *knew* you were going to like it! See, what did I tell you? Now you must try the green chili." Ever so adroitly he popped open two more pistachios, gave them to us to 'chew, not swallow,' then dipped the shells into the second chili powder.

"Okay, now, 'down the hatch!' " Evidently, this was a favorite phrase of his. We popped the powder into our mouths, mixed it well with the chewed-up nuts and swallowed. It was a different, smoky kind of taste – distinctly different from the first, but delicious, nonetheless.

"Now, which do you like better?" He first eyed me, then Pete, from behind a questioning eyebrow, hands back on his hips.

"I'm not sure," Pete said. "They're both good – surprisingly so, but the tastes are so different."

"I agree," I agreed. "My sentiments exactly. I guess we'll just have to try again." He gave me a quick smile.

"This is fine. You may try all you like, and then you may buy some to take back to your home, and to your friends. Share with them this unique New Mexican taste."

'Handy-hands' cracked open more nuts and handed them to us, then dipped the shells into the red chili powder. Another couple came along beside us with questioning looks. He reprogrammed himself and started anew, as energetic as before.

Pete and I bought a baggie of each of the chili powders, as well as a good-sized bag of the "World's Finest" pistachios; the salesman gave us a brochure on Eagle Ranch. With the zest in which he sold their nuts, they were probably relatives, or he received a fine profit from the deal. Nonetheless, Pete and I both love pistachios and we would enjoy them well en route. Perhaps even dipped into chili powders… We'd have to figure out the wine to go along with the pistachio/chili 'swish.' That would be fun… We also made a scrumptious homemade chili back home, and this chili powder would be just the ticket, added to it. We thanked him, as much for his showmanship as for the epicurean delights, and laughed our way to the car. This area was historic *and* colorful, with all it offered. I've since read that Chimayó, and the other small town towns along the High Road, are noted for their abundance of fine potters, weavers and wood carvers that make their homes and galleries in this area. I had photographed Chimayó hi and low, to well-remember our hour here. We looked at our watches. Gulp. I mean, *couple* of hours, how time does fly…Time to seriously hit the road.

We threaded our way back to NM 76, careful not to get lost on these winding back roads, and headed northeast again, past the tiny area of Córdova, and on into Truchas. I was trying so hard to be good, biting my lip as the scenery flashed by, a perfect photo opportunity missed here – and there – and, *oh, look! A painting!!* But I realized we had spent much more time in Chimayó than we had expected, and we had a good many more miles to go before we'd locate the Sagebrush Inn, awaiting us in Taos. Pete had been a good sport; it was now time for me to compromise. The Wop patted my knee, knowing my agony, and said: "You're doing good there, kid."

I looked over at him and warned: "Wait 'til we get to Truchas. I'll make up for being so good now." We had driven this high road last year with the children, but had gotten to the Santuario de Chimayó too late to see the church, or much else. But I remembered Truchas, a small Hispanic village built high and overlooking the endless line of the Sangre de Cristo Mountains. Just before entering the village there lay a graveyard, with multitudes of white crosses shining in the late sun. A dazzling array of artificial flowers decorated the graves; the panorama sprawled across the hilltop to the background of constant mountains, snow-capped in the distance, low-lying clouds mingling with the peaks. It took my breath away. I took several photographs, planning to overlay them in the album, as I'd 'lightened up' and not brought a wide-angle lens for this trip.

Pete and I drove on into Truchas where, as one enters, a sharp draw of breath at the spectacular mountainous beauty escapes. The road wraps along the top of the ridge and the mountains unfurl themselves away from the viewer – a rugged ocean with no end in sight. **"Tru-chas"** greeted us on a large brass sign, set in relief against the Sangre de Cristos. Pete drove slowly along here as I shot photographs of the old homes, a small church and a bakery, all blending into the environs, draped in vines and flowers, some surrounded by low stone or adobe walls. Curious faces watched us drive by. We waved. *More touristos passing through,* they thought, *what is it you want to see?...*

We found our turn, barely marked, at a high wall full of colorful graffiti, and wound our way past Truchas, headed to Las Trampas, passing more roadside crosses draped in flowers of memories, along these hazardous mountain roads. I imagined this area would be wicked in the winters here, high and snow-slickened. But the scenery would be astounding, often a trade-off for taking that risk.

Las Trampas was another small village with homes built close to the road, or set back up dirt roads that wound out of sight. A couple of beautiful old barns, beautiful in their simplicity and strength, rose from the ground, as if they had been borne to that location. Over a small and simple roadside home a flag saluted us. Even here – in the high reaches of New Mexico, so far away from busy civilization – there waved Old Glory. She was flying above this small home on the outskirts of nowhere, at half-mast, in respect for the dead of the huge cities on the shores of the east coast, thousands of miles away. Distance and proximity meant nothing; hearts still united in human suffering, and this was their quiet tribute. Each flag that I saw, fluttering midway up its flagpole, brought a fresh jolt of pain, a reminder of what still seemed so utterly surreal.

"The keeper of the flame"

TEN

Cowboy Movie Making

"In the midst of winter, I finally learned that there was in me an invincible summer." Camus

Pete and I drove past the small town of Talpa, on NM 518, on north to pick up NM 68, a straight shot into Taos. By now it was late afternoon. So much for a couple of hours on the 'high road' – our leisurely photographic sojourn had taken us 4 hours, or better, to make a 1¾-hour drive. How the natives would laugh! We had doubled the time – but oh, how we had enjoyed it! But now we wanted to find our hotel and choose a room before dark. We would be in Taos, according to PeterWop's industrious itinerary, for two nights – long enough to get comfortable. Pat, from the Comfort Inn in Santa Fe, had recommended the Sagebrush Inn, telling us of the 'old section,' in the back, facing the mountains. He had said these were spacious rooms with an 'Old-World' quality and they all included kiva fireplaces. Pete and I were intrigued. We arrived in Taos at dusk and soon found the Inn, on the outskirts of town.

The Sagebrush Inn was an expansive golden adobe structure with a flattop roof. Vigas – the beams running the length of the building to support the floors and protruding beyond the adobe outer walls by a few feet – were seen on both levels. The resulting protrusions threw decorative shadows on the structure below. A yellow New Mexico state flag, ablaze with the red Zia Pueblo sun symbol, flew proudly in the breezes, at full height. Beside this was the American flag, once again at half-mast, as if kneeling in prayer. A huge banner was draped over the entrance, seen all through the areas we've been staying, thanking Americans for traveling. Lights were already on, illuminating the building from the shrubbery below. The Sagebrush Inn was, indeed, very inviting.

We went into the office and asked for Louise, owner of the Inn, as Pat had suggested. Louise was a tall woman in her late 40s, with straight shoulder-length dark hair and blue eyes. She was friendly and direct, with a professional, no-nonsense manner about her. Pete and I requested to see a couple of rooms for our double-night stay. She gave us keys to a standard room, located in the main building overlooking the pool, and one for the suites in the back – the ones Pat had recommended.

Pete and I walked through the Cantina, a dark saloon-type bar with authentic cowboys parked on barstools, beers in hand and Stetsons on their heads, blue jeans, western shirts, dusty ole' boots – this was all real. Some smiled and tipped their hats as we passed. I felt we had turned the clock back a hundred years. In my lavender sleeveless top and hiking shorts, I felt out of place walking through their domain. Finely woven old Navajo rugs hung from the walls, and an array of original western cowboy artwork and paintings by Native Americans graced the rooms. A wooden dance floor lay open before a bandstand, and a large cream-colored adobe fireplace sat in the middle of the far wall.

We left the dark Cantina and entered an area of walkways that led to Spanish-looking buildings on either side and on to a long low complex in the back. The enclosure formed a courtyard, in the center of which lay a good-sized heated pool and patio, protected by wrought-iron fencing. Graceful, mature elms and locusts threw evening shadows over the scene. Soft lights glowed low against the first floor rooms and lights from the ceilings of the upper rooms shone softly down. Flood lighting was directed upwards into the canopies of trees. The iridescent pool shimmered in the middle, inviting us to swim. The effect was enchanting.

Peter and I located the door to the standard room on the second level, overlooking the pool. He tried the key. No dice. He turned it upside down and tried again. Still, no dice. I put down my backpack and tried every-which-way. Nothing worked, including a shoulder to the door. It wouldn't budge. I looked at Pete and said simply: "It's a sign."

He shifted his arched eyebrows and gave me 'that look.' "Now don't start that. The door's jammed, that's all. Let's try the back room."

And so we hiked on back under the trees, down the walkway under the portals, and found our room number. This key fit just fine, the door swung open, and we entered a foyer covered in warm, earthy Mexican tiles. To the right was a full bath, also tiled. In front of us a large room offered a king-sized bed and a huge dark credenza sat against the wall with a mirror above it and a TV on top. Beyond this two couches covered in an Aztec-design material formed an "L" around a spacious square coffee table. An array of magazines and brochures of the area lay atop. The ceiling was pine; huge golden lacquered Ponderosa pine beams ran horizontally down the length of the room. Beyond the couches a creamy corner adobe kiva-style fireplace, in-laid with hand-painted Mexican tiles around the arched fire screen, beckoned. A gigantic armoire engulfed the wall opposite the fireplace, carved in the same dark and ornate design to match the credenza. Louise told us later that this furniture was hand-carved in Mexico. Upon closer inspection (i.e. we opened it up and pulled it down) we found this 'armoire' to be a queen-sized Murphy bed, perfect to nest in before the crackling fire, like primitive man- and woman-kind.

Beyond this was a double-window and a back door. Like Alice, I had to find out what was on the other side. So, while Peter padded around the carpeted interior, I peaked out the back. A small patio, with two wrought-iron chairs and a dainty table, awaited a glass of wine to toast the end of a 'long day's journey into night.' It was perfect. In the distance the last leg of the Sangre de Cristos loomed afar, as if reticent to see us go.

I peeped back inside, feeling giddy and decadent. This room was almost double the rate of the standard room, but hell, *that* door wouldn't even open, and this one welcomed us…

Surely, it was a sign – and this *was* our 25th – why not splurge a bit? "Let's take it, Pete. Not even look back. Two nights here would be *wonderful!*"

"You won't gripe about the rate later, will you?" he asked.

"Nope. I promise I won't. And the Comfort Inn was so reasonable, we'll almost be within our 'daily' budget. Come on – we only live once, and all that. Let's take it!"

"Okay," he grinned. "I was hoping you'd say that. I *love* it! Let's go let Louise know and we'll bring the car around and unpack."

PeterWop and I checked in and unloaded our luggage, including the vase of flowers from Cindy. I had freshened them up with wildflowers found en route, tossing out the faded ones as we left Santa Fe. It looked gorgeous – a combination of Ginger and Marianne – city and country. The large magenta spider mum was still the focal point, frosted cream carnations, eucalyptus, Baby's Breath, and sprays of purple statice remained from Cynthia's original bouquet. I had added a couple of sunflowers and some asters I'd found roadside. The results were a festive and happy mix of color that we placed alongside our bottle of Merlot, in front of the mirror. We were home for a while.

"Let's eat," Pete said, "I'm famished. Maybe Michael's Kitchen is still open – remember that from last year? If we hurry, we just might make it."

"Alright. I'll hop into some jeans and a warmer top, and be right out." Dear Art had suggested Michael's Kitchen to us last trip – he had said it was a great place to take the family. He was right, as usual. The food was good, it was reasonable, and had something on the menu for any taste. Much like Castro's, it offered a variety of Southwest and Mexican fare, but plenty of American standards, too. And it included an in-house bakery where the aroma, alone, could make one salivate like Pavlov's dog.

We slid in just before they closed at 8:30, ordered a couple of easy Southwest plates, a couple of cerveza's, and discussed our day. From there, we tried to call home on Pete's cell phone, but had a spotty connection. We'd found it very hard to get a good signal from these parts. But we checked-in, letting them know we had arrived in Taos. All on the home front was well and kids were settling into school just fine, so we made that call short, promising a longer conversation the next evening. On our way out, we stopped by the bakery to pick up an apple fritter and a pecan sticky bun to share the next morning; what a hardship. And then we headed on back to our little patio, under the stars.

The Cowboy Movie Out Back...
Cowboy wisdom: *"Never smack a man who's chewin' tobacco."*
Texas Bix Bender

The ripening moon was rising over yon mountains and the sky was filling with stars; it was beautiful and clear that night. I had noticed earlier, when peeking out the back door, an old homestead-looking cabin with a corral behind it. Off to the right a school bus was parked, and beside it, a tepee squatted on the ground. I loved the eccentricity of the West – anything went. I thought for a moment that my Bohemian brother, Chuck, would be right at home in that school bus/tepee combo, set against the mountainous backdrop. He had fixed up an old school bus, himself. He'd added all the features of home in miniature, including a midget pot-bellied woodstove and chimney. He had storage nooks and crannies, shelves for his many books, and even a workshop built in the rear. Imagination was his limit and he was never short on that gift. He could build or refurbish just about anything, from guns to sailboats. Chuck's bus was a mother lode of invention and talent; he would be perfectly comfortable here.

Tonight, in front of the old homestead a horse trailer sat. A saddled bay quarter horse was tied to the outside and a dark-haired woman stood beside him. Beyond that lights were set up at the cabin and several cowboy-types were milling around. One scraggly-looking character kept riding a brown & white pinto pony in and out of the fencing, halfway over to the school bus, then neck-reined his mount and rode back into the corral. Back and forth, back and forth, it made no sense, unless maybe he was trying out the horse to buy it; even then, he would want to make sure she knew more than circle. I couldn't stand it. There was a horse within reach and I missed all our critters – I needed an animal fix. *And* there was a mystery to be solved.

"Pete, I'm going to mosey on over there and check out that horse. Maybe talk with the lady and find out what's going on."

"I figured you'd say that, Laura; I was just wondering when." He opted to stay and finish his wine and kickback for a bit, settling down into his chair. "Enjoy," he smiled and raised his glass, as I walked away.

So I sauntered on over to meet the lady, my wine still in hand. She had a full mane of dark wavy hair, was stout and sure of herself, there in her blue jeans and tee shirt. She reminded me of my very Italian sister-in-law, MaryAnn, John's wife. I liked her instantly. She was friendly and open to my curiosity. I stroked the bay's silky muzzle and introduced myself, telling her it was so wonderful to be close to a horse again and how I missed our four, back in Virginia. She told me her name was Geri Brown, and her husband was over there with the rest of the crew. I asked her what in the world were they doing? She told me they were making this grade-B Western that they intended to call *The Line Shack*, about a couple of old cowpokes getting together after many years, riding the fence lines, and reminiscing. The scene they kept shooting was one of them riding into the homestead after dark. I could see it now. All the elaborate lighting, and the black & white 'cut' sign. There were four or five men milling around the camera crew, a real mix of masculinity and ages, and most of them wore a cowboy hat, jeans and some sort of western shirt. *They must have come from the Cantina*, I thought.

At this point, realizing that I didn't plan to join him anytime soon, Pete ambled over and joined us. I introduced him to Geri and Chama, the bay gelding. I shared our story with Geri of meeting Cindy in Chama last year, and that the name had a special meaning to me. Geri suggested that we meet the movie crew and assured us we wouldn't be bothering them. So, leaving the horse, we all walked over to the set and got a birds-eye view of the goings on.

The cowboy on the pinto was an older gentleman, with long silver-blond hair flowing from under his black Stetson, and a face that promised a bonafide character. He wore chaps over his jeans and old beat-up leather riding gloves. He'd ride up to the door, swing off his horse and head to the cabin door, with a bow-legged swagger.

"Cut!" they'd say — "we *still* ain't got the lighting right, Johnny." And Johnny would swing back up, rein his pony around and ride back through the corral entrance, muttering something under his breath that I couldn't quite hear.

We were introduced to the group, told them where we were from, where we were headed, and why we were out west. I looked around the group at these rugged faces, full of lines and sun and stories, and knew these boys had seen some legitimate living in their time. I kept thinking we were in the company of the likes of Buffalo Bill Cody (Johnny Lewis, on the horse) Wild Bill Hickok, and Hopalong Cassidy, of old-time lore. And more in the present, the likes of Willie Nelson, Waylon Jennings, Kris Kristofferson and Johnny Cash. This was just too much fun; I was grinning from ear to ear, listening in on the banter between these fellows, all obviously good buddies, and their willingness to share themselves with us newcomers. One tall fellow with long black hair and equally dark eyes, named Andersen Kee, was a full-blooded Navajo – I found this out by inquiring of his ornate turquoise-studded belt buckle and the bolo he wore. He had made these, himself; he was a painter, as well; he and his cousin, over in Chinle, would get together to paint and show together. I was fascinated. Later he showed me more of his work inside the cabin – beautiful, intricate bolos, silver-laced boots, and elaborate belt buckles. I was truly impressed.

Rocky Sullivan, Geri's husband, was one of the younger fellows, about Andersen's age. He had brown hair that curled up around the nape of his neck, under his beige hat. His sturdy, tanned face hadn't yet seen all the creases and laugh-lines his older buddies had etched deeply into their faces. Rocky was telling us that he and Johnny ran a hot-air ballooning company, there in Taos. I perked up and asked him questions, Pete joining me now, asking about weather conditions for flying, how often they went up, where they flew, and about the Albuquerque Ballooning Festival that would start next weekend.

Another fellow joined us, a pleasant older man from the film crew with a full head of silvery-brown hair, held back in a little ponytail. He had a beard and moustache, as well. *Was this a cowboy symbol of virility or something, or did it just mean they needed less sunscreen? (Not that there was proof that they used it, judging from their laugh lines.)* His name was Russell; he was quieter than the others, and easy to talk to. Russell said that he used to be a producer/director in Hollywood and had come to Taos, trying to retire. "We could see where *that* got him," he joked.

A second lady joined the group, appearing from somewhere behind us. She was in her 30's, I guessed, slim, with shoulder-length dark blond hair and a shy smile. Her name was Dawn. I wasn't clear if she was married to, or dating, one of the fella's here, or if she, too, was just 'one of the boys.' She was obviously comfortable with the gang.

Another man came around to talk to us, a taller, heavier-set fellow, with a 2-3 day beard on his rugged face. He had on a buff-colored shirt and jeans, with maybe one of Andersen's belt buckles; he was introduced as Noel MacDonald: "ex-artist, ex-movie star, ex-saddle maker, etc., and he was now writer/producer/director of *The Line Shack*."

They continued trying to film Johnny riding in and dismounting, but finally got fed up. The lighting just wasn't right, and nothing they could do would change that. They'd have to do this tomorrow evening and get an earlier start. So Johnny rode on over to us, hopped off his horse a last time, and offered up his hand. His black hat contrasted with his silvery hair, which draped down over his shoulders, longer than Dawn's.

"You all been enjoying the show?" Johnny's cowboy drawl, with the laugh in his voice and the twinkle in his merry blue eyes, made him even more of a character. He had high cheekbones with leathery tanned skin that blended into a graying beard and mustache. Johnny was one slim and wiry dude; he must have had 0% body fat – perhaps he was in the minus range. He wore a denim shirt with pearl buttons and a bolo that Andersen had made (I asked).

"Well, we sure are here at the right time – it's made our night." I laughed at him. "If you ever do get this movie made, we certainly want a copy."

Johnny chuckled and said, "Honey, I sure hope we *make* it to the movie stage. We're tryin' real hard." Noel grinned over at him and gave him a wink.

We milled around in the crowd, visiting with the crew a while longer, finishing our wine and enjoying talking with these salt-of-the earth residents, as the night grew later. Soon we'd be needing to go on back to our room and let these folks get on with their night. But we joked and listened to stories as the time drifted by. We'd have missed all this, if we'd accepted the room in the middle. Funny those little crossroads in life that make all the difference in the world...

One thing led to another and we were back on the ballooning topic. Johnny looked at Pete and me and asked: "What are you two doing tomorrow? I mean early in the morning? Rocky's taking a balloon up over the Rio Grande River Gorge and I've already sold the basket. I could give you a real good deal."

The Wop and I looked at each other. "How early are you talkin', Johnny?" (I am *not* known for being a 'morning person' – 'night owl' is *much* more apt.)

"*Early*, honey, I'm talking about meeting my truck at your hotel just before 6 AM."

Gulp. That *was* early. That would mean we'd need to be up by 5 AM. *Ugh. But heh – what an experience!! I was feeling more strongly about that room waiting for us, so that we'd have wine on our little patio, meet this medley of good people... it was all leading to this once-in-a-lifetime ballooning experience out west... Hmm... Kismet.*

"Johnny, just how much is 'a real good deal'?" Pete asked, hesitantly. He knew these rides weren't cheap. But the getting-up part didn't faze him. The man could get up at the crack of dawn and sing in the shower.

"Well, let me see... you gotta' credit card? I promise you, I'll see to it that you can afford it. And hey, it includes a full champagne brunch, afterwards. Did I mention that?"

Pete looked at me. I looked at Pete. This was getting better all the time. We could see the hesitancy in each other's faces, but our eyes were dancing, all the same. "Do you think you could get up that early?" he finally asked.

"Just watch me, Wop! Okay, Johnny, we'll meet you out front at the crack of dawn. Whatta' we wear up in a hot-air balloon?"

He grinned over to Rocky and again to us. "Dress warmly, but in layers, so you can pull 'em off when the day heats up. We'll have coffee and donuts up there, waiting for you, and we'll introduce you to your basket-mates. They're here from the grand state of New York, out in your neck of the woods. Welcome aboard! Rocky here will pick y'all up. Don't oversleep now, Laura." Johnny added with a grin and a wink at me.

We laughed, shook hands and said our goodnights to all the crew. I stopped by and thanked Geri, who had returned to the trailer to settle Chama down. She was getting ready to load both horses, take them home, and tuck 'em in for the night.

Pete and I returned to our room, poured more wine to enjoy a nightcap on our deck – and this time to actually *sit*. The night had darkened, the gorgeous golden moon had risen higher in the sky, sharing her delicate light with us. It must have been around 11 PM by now. "Well, that's exciting, PeterWop – it's kind of the last thing we were thinking about, but it sure is fitting with the Balloon Festival, and all. See, I told you this room was a 'sign.' We were meant to be here…" and I gave him a little wink and a nudge.

"Yeah, yeah. I hear you." He looked over at me. Smiled. And he lifted his glass in a toast. "I don't know what we're getting ourselves into, but it sounds like quite an adventure. Wait 'til I tell my folks." *I quietly wished my parents were alive to share this trip with, especially my mother—how she would have loved this grand adventure!*

We sipped for a while in silence, just watching the night, the distant mountains, and that crazy teepee/school bus abode. "Pete, what day is this? I mean, the actual date?"

He thought a minute. "Let's see. Yesterday was Wednesday, no – wait a minute, *today* is Wednesday – we left Santa Fe this morning. Boy, it seems like *days* ago!… That makes today the 25th… no, the 26th." He looked at his watch in the dim light. "Just barely."

"Then that means tomorrow is the 27th. That'll be the fourth anniversary of George's murder. I wonder if he ever went up in a hot-air balloon? Let's take him up there with us, Pete – celebrate his spirit. He'd have loved that, and especially out here…"

Pete looked over and smiled again, and agreed that this would be a good idea – deal with the anniversary of something we could not change in a positive way. We clinked our wine glasses and he said, "Let's go build us a fire. See if that fireplace actually works."

ELEVEN

Hot-Air Ballooning Over Taos

"I would rather be a superb meteor, every atom of me in magnificent glow, than a sleepy and permanent planet." Jack London

The fireplace worked just great, using the small piñon log bundle the Inn had provided. It threw shimmering shadows around the room and over the pulled-down Murphy queen. We opted to use the king bed to only rest our suitcases on, while there. Light danced around the room and reflected off the large pine beams. The candles we'd brought with us reflected soft light from the mirror, beside the bouquet. It was all very romantic.

We had a wonderful night of passion and closeness, snuggling in, watching the embers glow from the kiva, and the teasing moon glow from up high outside the window of our bed. I suggested we just stay up all night, waiting for 90-minute intervals, and talking in-between... that way it wouldn't be so hard to wake up in the morning – we'd already *be* up... Pete gave me one of his looks and said, "Get real – let's get a *little* rest... it'll be another long day"... and I just said "Heh, heh..." and dove under the covers to goose him. I wanted to play, not sleep.

Not until it was time to get up, anyway. And then I was like the embers in the fireplace, all gray and used up. I pulled the covers over my head and snuggled down, comfy, ready to hunker in and chase down a few more zzz's. Not Pete. Somehow that man can rise and shine with a big ole' smile on his face. It's disgusting. He came padding over the carpet with a hot cup of decaf in one hand, his high-test in the other. "Razza, it's 5:30, you have just enough time to pop up and pull-on some clothes.

Remember, we're supposed to meet Rocky about quarter of 6:00 there, in front of the hotel. We don't want to hold the man up."

I groaned and rolled out from under paradise. It was *chilly*, and a long ways to the bathroom. I missed my morning stretches to get the old kinks out. *Ugh. This ballooning experience had better be good. I was sacrificing here.*

We had laid out our clothes the night before, thinking of high-altitude chill, and added warm layers, as Johnny had suggested. I had loaded my camera with fresh film, and had a camera bag with plenty of back-ups. Pete now had several of the Kodak one-time uses on hand, which we'd found in a drugstore on the way home from dinner. They would replace his funky and failed 'better' camera.

I chose not to drink much of the coffee, as all my life I've had an over-active bladder that had a mind of its own. Detrol is a joke – it looks good on the commercials, but may as well be a sugar pill, for the help it gives me. Whenever we travel, the first thing I learn is where the bathrooms are. Pete is wonderful about stops en route – finding strategic, discreet places to pull over for his country-girl wife. But I figured there wouldn't be much hope for discretion, or anything else, a thousand feet in the air, floating high over New Mexico, for an undetermined amount of time, in a crowded over-sized laundry basket full of strangers. ("Uh, excuse me, Rocky – I have to pee – would you please land this thing for just a minute?...")

Sure enough, as soon as the Wop and I reached the entrance of our adobe hotel, a long-bed, full-sized, white king-cab Ford 3500 monster truck pulled up with "CHAMPAGNE BALLOON FLIGHTS" written in red block lettering arched across the two doors on the side of the truck. In a circular logo brightly painted behind this, in front of the rear wheels and one of the gas tank covers, was "Pueblo Balloon Company, Taos, NM," wrapped around a colorful balloon over top mountains. Over the rear wheels was written, also in red block lettering, "FLY THE GORGE." If any one had any question at all, after this splash of advertising, what this truck was about, the huge straw-colored basket in the bed of the pick-up confirmed the notion these guys were *balloonists*.

Rocky sat at the wheel, a welcoming smile on his face. He waved for us to load behind him, so Pete and I climbed on in. Russell was seated beside Rocky. Both men gave us a hearty, "Good morning!" Neither of them looked the least bit sleepy. *They must have gone on home and straight to sleep. Hmm. There might be something to be said for that.*

The morning was still pretty dark as we drove down the Paseo del

Pueblo Sur, passing the tourist center on the right, sleepy shopping plazas, and – just before reaching the Taos Plaza – we passed The Rose of Taos, on the left. This was a small adobe building with vigas reaching out above the sea green window and door trim. Low-key lighting reflected in the windows, showing off the long southwest skirts and vests. During the day this boutique was adorned with these bold outfits outside, as they hung freely in the breezes in front of the store, tempting one to stop and browse. Pete and I had never slowed down to do this, but I surely wanted to.

We passed the Plaza, saw the sign for Pueblo Drums, and across the street, the World Cup Coffee Shop. Even they slept at this hour. Under the awning of this isle of stores was another painted pony, this one predominantly in turquoise blues, the mountains of this area painted on its side and a model of a small girl laid resting on the horse, her arms hugging its neck in love. They reminded me of Natalie and Holly and I smiled at the thought of the two. A bit later we passed the signs for the Taos Pueblo, pointing northeast, just before we swung across and picked up the Paseo del Pueblo Norte, ironically taking us in the opposite direction, towards the Taos Municipal Airport and the Rio Grande River Gorge, headed in the direction of Tres Piedras and Chama.

Rocky was explaining what to expect when we got there and that we would soon meet our basketmates. I was certainly curious, wondering if the terrorist attacks had affected us so deeply, how they would have affected this couple, who lived in New York and very likely knew individuals who had worked in the Twin Towers. Rocky stopped briefly at a gas station on the left to pick up two Hispanic men who greeted Rocky and Russell with "Buenos díos, amigos!" and hopped into the back of the Ford. I noticed everyone was wearing a heavy, lined windbreaker jacket to chase the morning's chill.

Once we turned to head northwest on NM 64 the land started to change, to become more barren and rugged, although I could still barely see anything past the headlights. Early dawn lay a filmy blanket of varying gray tones over the world, but I remembered this country from last year, as much – or as little – as I could see it now. This was a godforsaken world outside of Taos. We drove a ways, talking about our various lives. Rocky was telling us he was originally from Ireland and that, before his name was Americanized, his family was known as "O'Sullivant," but over the years the first and last letters of the name had been lost. Pete and I were talking about the interchanging of the 'y' and 'i' in Giannini/y – and how his grandfather's name had lost the 'i' in World War I. We shared with them how Pete still, like his family, used the 'y' at the end of his name, but that I used the 'i,' with my version of Giannini, as there was no 'y' in Italian. I always kidded Pete that he spelled his name wrong. We all laughed, adding that the banks, and his folks, just loved this flourish, and that when we had to spell it together, we simply dotted the 'ÿ' in compromise. One of the many in a marriage… Russell just listened and laughed, but I never did learn his last name, or what might have become of it over the years. *Maybe he was afraid that I'd try to change it…*

The gray tones of the world were lightening as we continued to drive up NM 64, when we finally took a right and headed straight into – what looked like to me – a road to nowhere. "Do you always have to come this far out of Taos to launch this thing?" I asked Rocky, leaning forward, so he could hear me.

He laughed, "Well, if you want to fly over the gorge we do. We can fly much closer in and around Taos, but the prevailing winds have to be just so…" he paused, and added: "and of course you don't want to tangle with any electric lines. The beauty of Taos is that most of 'em are buried, except along the highway, which makes this an *excellent* place to fly."

Good point. Guess there was no remote control up there, and no neck-reining that enormous mass of captured air, to glide around structures or telephone poles, or high-headed trees. One would have to be paying a goodly amount of attention up there and planning way ahead, I would think, to keep that balloon floating along where you – not the currents – wanted to go… *Hmm, this might be a bit more complicated than I had initially envisioned. I'd have a lot of questions ahead for this man, our pilot, who would ultimately be responsible for our making it back to the kiddos we were raising.* "Do you carry a lot of insurance?"

Rocky laughed aloud, following my drift, and said "Well, no more than a parachutist would, or Evil Knievel," he added, nudging Russ. Russell turned around, grinned and winked.

"How's *your* insurance, these days?" Russ couldn't help asking. He and Rocky were almost giggling up front. Pete was sitting there grinning, too, watching us all and, for once, with little to say.

My attention refocused on some kind of crazy residential structures we were passing – some sort of partial-looking housing, half-in and half-out of the ground. The morning light was now a pale ghost illuminating the quiet still world we traversed. The sun hadn't yet risen, but she was close. The fellows in the back were sitting up on the edge of the bed now, bumping along and speaking animatedly, probably in Spanish, and pointing at something off in the distance.

"Okay, guys — what in the world are *those* crazy-looking houses?" I asked, ready for anything.

They looked at each other, deciding who would take this one. Russell decided it was his turn to play. "Well, you see, Laura, these fancy-pants easterners moved out here, with a bunch of money in their pockets, and decided to build themselves some homes. This is an 'east-coast subdivision'." He and Rocky were rolling up front. I had to laugh, too, at their humor. Pete looked out at the houses and said, "Looks like they ran out of money."

"Yup." Rocky said, dryly. "That's why there's only half of 'em built. The other half, the part that's in the ground, is unfinished. It's like a big prairie dog hole in there." Russ, who'd been trying to contain his laughter, spit out the coffee he'd just sipped.

I laughed with the nuts driving us out to this unknown destination. "Yeah, and I guess these people are evolving into some alien-type of critter who only comes out at night, wearing mining helmets — cause that's what they use down in their homes, right?" I could play their silly game. "Okay, now for real, what the hell are they? We don't build things like that out east. We have a lot of trees, so we build geodesic domes and Colonial-style homes. Things like that."

They exchanged a look, wondering if they were ready to stop the game. Then Rocky looked in his rearview mirror, his eyes twinkling in fun, and said to us, "Okay, I'll be straight with you. They're called 'earth ships' – really. They're houses built by people who want to be totally 'off the grid,' meaning they don't use modern technology at all, like we know it. See those solar panels on top? They collect the sun's heat and store it and use it for electricity. Of course, there's plenty of sun out here. And they're built into the ground like that because the ground temperature, below the frost line, is always in the mid-50s, so they don't use heat or AC, even out here."

"Well, what about water? How do they get that way out here, in the desert? Do the panels also liquefy energy?" Now I wanted to play again.

"Yup. They wring out the 'ole rays until they yell 'uncle' and turn 'em to water," Rocky said. "Actually, they collect rain water and store it. They're really very independent people who are, literally, off the grid. You have some big state or national tragedy, like September 11th, that takes out lights and water, and these folks move right along. If they don't have a TV or radio, or buy a newspaper, they wouldn't even know it. There are 30 or 40 homes out here in this area, and they're all self-contained."

I was impressed. The old western pioneering spirit certainly hadn't died. I thought again of my brother, Chuck, in his Montanan-independent-type way, and how he could live in one of these Spartan desert homes just fine. Or maybe Sean, Mary's son – if he could pull himself away from the mountains – would get into this bare-bones kind of lifestyle. But as far as water went I was thinking they were sure optimistic; rain was scarce out here. I was betting they'd truck some of that in, or go out in the early mornings, like about now, with a straw, sucking up dew off the sparse vegetation. This was sounding – and looking – like some futuristic movie, maybe a dry cousin to Costner's Waterworld, *or a spin-off of* Planet of the Apes. *They could call it* Survival of the Thirstiest, *or something. But I was good, and kept these thoughts to myself.* "Well, okay, I have another question for you." This one was usually on my mind, with the stupid incontinence problem. "What do they do for bathrooms in there? Or do they just answer Mother Nature's call out *in* Mother Nature?"

The cowboys looked at each other. "Well, I guess they've got bathrooms inside them, just like any other home," Russ said. "But there *is* the flushing problem. Maybe they use chemicals, like buses and airlines do. I don't know, guess we haven't given that one too much thought." He looked back, stumped, and shrugged his shoulders. "Oh well."

"Oh well. I'm sure they've got that covered, being a basic need and all. Or maybe in their alien-evolution they've worked it out so that they no longer have body functions."

"Yeah. That must be the answer." Rocky agreed, glad to be off the hook.

Pete could see my wheels still turning and decided to change the subject. "What mountains are those?" Off in the distance they glowed now, in overlapping layers of pearlescent mimosa and lilac tones. The sun, a brilliant neon spec, peaked up through the eastern folds.

"Off to the right are the Sangre de Cristos – if you look real hard due east, when we pull in to get the balloon ready, you'll see Wheeler's Peak – that's the highest mountain peak in all of New Mexico, you know, at over 13,000 feet. West now, those are the San Juan's, off in the distance."

"Good grief, Rocky – the Sangre de Cristos just don't end! I thought we were seeing the last of them out behind our hotel," I said.

"Those are the San Juans you're seeing, out behind the Sagebrush. No, the Sangre de Cristos actually go on up into Colorado, on past Fort Garland and the Great Sand Dunes Monument, where they eventually turn into the Rocky Mountains. They're impressive, aren't they?"

"Yeah, they are. They're a beautiful chain of mountains, alright..."

Pete's voice trailed off as we slowed down to join another truck already waiting for us in the wide open, rolling landscape. This was also a big white king-cab, this one a dually, with Verizon Wireless written across it in black and red lettering. A good combination for ballooning.

Johnny was standing there with a big grin on his face, waving at us, his black Stetson right in place, and – looking out of place for a cowboy – was a teal-colored jacket, lined in bright purple. Under this he wore a muted-olive green flannel-looking shirt. He wore dusty ole' boots and his faded jeans were held up on his non-existent hips with a belt and a big ole' silver engraved buckle, probably one of Andersen's. Johnny, or some early-morning Susie-homemaker, had set up a small, portable, metal table with a swayback dip in it, offering a plate of donuts and a large thermos of coffee and Styrofoam cups. All this rested on a checkered red and white tablecloth, looking very festive, indeed, in the soft early morning light.

Pete walked over and gave Johnny a hearty handshake, asking, "That coffee sure looks good, do you mind if I have a cup?"

"Help yourself there, Pete! Help yourself! That's to make sure everybody's eyes are opened to take in this incredible scenery we're about to show you. How 'bout you, Laura, you want a cup, too?"

"No thanks, Johnny, not now. I'm holding out for that champagne later on." I smiled at him, looking around.

All the boys were busy with their jobs of laying out the balloon in a long ribbon of color out behind our truck. It was huge, laying there all deflated and dejected, like a rainbow that had lost its arch and fallen to the ground to rest. These guys seemed to know what they were doing, each working on a specific task, deft hands busily doing their jobs.

Okay, question time. "Johnny, what is it the balloon is made of? It's *huge*. It must be tremendously strong."

"That's for sure, honey. Ours is made of Dacron polyester, special-ordered. Some balloonists use nylon, but this can be heated hotter."

"Heated hotter?" Pete walked over with his steaming coffee. I stole a tiny sip.

"That means when we turn the burners on we can use more juice, and the material can handle it just fine."

"Oh, okay. That makes sense." They were now attaching long wire-like ropes to the basket. "What's that you use then, if not ropes. They look like some kind of cable, or something." I asked.

"Yup, they're cables made of Kevlar – some of the strongest material known to man – it's what they use in bullet-proof vests. They're virtually indestructible."

"Oh, so if we're shot at by some sniper or terrorist, we'll just duck and hope they miss the fabric – but the bullets will just zing right off the cable lines," I teased.

Johnny laughed; Rocky had joined us. "Yeah, but we only get shot at about every blue moon. What we really need to watch out for are those low-flying military jets they have around here. They're hell on a balloon." Rocky winked at Johnny. He was at it again.

I heard a big **'Whoosh!'** and looked around, startled. "That's an inflator fan," explained Johnny, with a smile at my greenhorn reaction. "It's like a mini airplane prop and it blows the inside of the balloon full of air, as you can see 'em doin' now." Sure enough the balloon, still on its side, was becoming engorged with air, filling up, slowly coming to life before us. I saw stripes of color rising up from the ground – brown, with sporadic white stars around the top, then a purplish/blue, followed by a brick-colored stripe, then several of orange tones, leading into a large band of bright yellow, then a band of dusty olive, followed by teal, and a large band of brown anchored the colors, at the bottom. As the balloon filled, I could see an image of the caramel-colored Taos Indian Pueblo on the side of the filling form, windows, doors and vigas all in a darker tone. It was gigantic, rising from the ground like a multi-colored loaf of party bread, with which the cook had gotten carried away with the yeast.

The basket was laid-out on its side, too, the Kevlar cables all connected now, and supports rose out of the basket, a tobacco brown network of upraised arms, attached to the woven straw-colored container. "What's the basket made of?" I asked.

Johnny said, "Wicker," like it was obvious.

"Just wicker?" I repeated.

"Yup. Heavy-duty wicker, that's all. She weighs almost 200 pounds dry weight, 300 when's she full."

"When she's full?" Pete asked. "You mean with fuel, right? What do you use?"

"Propane. Pure propane. When she's full, like she is now, we call it 'wet weight;' we use about 120 pounds of propane to fill 'er up."

"Wow!" That's almost what I weighed. "How much does the balloon, itself, weigh?"

"Y'all sure ask a lot of questions," Johnny laughed, but I could tell that he was enjoying himself. So far he could answer them all – I found this to be a relief. "The fabric, alone, weighs some 350 pounds. That's

1.9 ounce to the yard, but y'all have to do the math there," he drawled, "I keep forgettin'."

I looked back at the balloon, lying on its side still, curved with air. Russell and one of the Hispanic fellows, in a red jacket and baggy brown pants that sagged dangerously down over his hips, were holding up the cables, keeping them from tangling with the lower ones, I guess, as the air continued to fill the mass. A couple was heading in our direction. They had been out walking around the area, exploring. They joined us, coffees in hand. "Hey Pete, Laura, these are the New Yorkers I was telling you about. Fred, Betty, these folks here are from Virginia. They're out here on their anniversary. They'll be your basket mates, along with Rocky, as your faithful, experienced pilot."

"If you said he had a good nose on him, I'd swear you were talking about a bloodhound." Pete said of Johnny's comment.

We laughed. Fred and Betty were maybe ten years older than us, all wrapped up in their warm jackets, looking around curiously, as the balloon expanded. They said they'd never been hot air ballooning, either.

They both had pleasant faces. There was something familiar about the couple that I couldn't quite put my finger on. Fred was a tall and solid man with broad shoulders, a barrel chest and a tapered waist. He looked more like a farmer than someone who lived in a large city. His profile reminded me of our proud nation's eagle, with his strong nose. His silver hair receded from his broad tanned forehead and his expression was alert and focused. He held dark glasses and a white ball cap with a black brim. A heavy black and green jacket over a denim shirt and jeans kept him warm. Betty was diminutive next to Fred — my height but smaller boned, with narrow shoulders and a slim, fit build. She had short styled auburn hair; her oval face was animated, with a curious and interested gaze. She radiated friendliness; they seemed to be too warm and informal to be New Yorkers. She held a tan fedora and wore a heavy taupe windbreaker. They looked like seasoned travelers, comfortable with new experiences, and curious about the world. I liked them immediately.

"Hello, I'm Fredrick, but call me Fred — and this is Bette — with an 'e,' like Bette Davis." Fred explained, in greeting, in a deep voice. We all exchanged handshakes.

"So, you're from New York?" I asked, "The city?"

"Right outside the city, but we both work there." They could sense the next question. "And yes, Bette was working in the city on September 11th. She saw the Towers fall."

A somber silence befell the group. The heart fell from our good-natured joking with a thud. Suddenly we weren't travelers from different states, standing here with these capable cowboy balloonists – we were all just Americans, caught up in the wake of a horrible tragedy that touched each of us differently, but profoundly, nonetheless.

I tried to change the subject. "Johnny tells us you're newlyweds. We're out here for our anniversary, too, you know. We thought about staying home, but decided we'd worked too hard on the trip not to come. Besides, we didn't want the terrorist mentality to think they could dictate our lives, keep us at home, shuddering in the closet, and all..."

"I know exactly how you feel." Bette finished, emphatically. "We thought about changing our plans and staying at home, too. But we said 'to hell with them!' We're not going to let them ruin our celebration, our joy, of a very special event!" She looked up at Fred and took his hand.

Fredrick smiled down at her, wrapped his large arm around her shoulders, and squeezed. "That's right. We're here to celebrate. We left that all behind us for the time being."

Out of the blue we heard what sounded like a pistol shot. With all this talk of snipers and terrorists, a couple of us ducked reflexively. Johnny piped up in his cowboy twang: "It's one of them Arab terrorists! Run for cover!" Somehow, the way he said it, no one could take offense and we laughed, a little self-consciously.

"Naw, y'all, it's just the burner they turned on to heat the air inside. That's what makes 'er rise and fills 'er up. See?" And he pointed to the colossal balloon growing before us, a giant towering above us all, getting to her knees first, as she struggled to stand. More 'pistol shots' – or blasts of hot air – filled the still morning quiet, and soon she was ready to be sailing away.

"Alright now, did y'all sign your releases and make your potty stops? You'll need to do both before we load you inside the basket."

Good idea. Pete and I headed out in different directions to try to find privacy in a dip or arroyo, down behind a sagebrush or one of the scattered scrub pines. Fred and Bette said they'd taken care of business already, and headed over to sign the releases.

Pete and I came back, signed our papers, my kidding Johnny, "You mean, this could be *danger*ous?"

"Naw," he said. "It's a piece of cake. Really. We have flawless safety records, we're all FAA certified, and most times, we know what we're doing. We keep the stunt flying to ourselves." He grinned over at his buddy and added, "Don't we, Rocky?" Rocky smiled absently, his mind on something else at the moment. Time to load. "Okay, Rocky, preflight 'em. They're all yours."

"Preflight?" We looked at each other. *Did he mean this was our chance to change our minds?*

"What that means," Rocky said, "is here's the point I tell you what to do inside this 'hyar little basket, where'll you'll be standing, and what you can – and can't – hold onto."

And he proceeded to do just that, after we climbed inside the sturdy container and were assigned our places. Now it was getting real. The morning sun enveloped us, throwing gentle shadows around the sagebrush and a long one under the balloon. In my mind I could hear Joni Mitchell singing "Chelsea Morning" to serenade us, as Johnny said: "Hand me your disposable, Pete, and I'll take your shot, then throw it back up to you!" Pete quickly grabbed his camera and threw it down to Johnny, who stepped back as we arose and clicked, then came running over to toss it back into PeterWop's waiting hands. I got a shot of Johnny, hair billowing out from under his hat, which he then took off his head and started waving at us, a big ole' smile on his face: "Y'all have a good time, now! I wanna' hear *all* about it!" And his voice faded away as the balloon drifted out over the stark sage-covered land rapidly diminishing in size below us.

And then Cat Stevens sang "Morning Has Broken" as gentle winds caressed our faces. Pete and I looked at each other, smiled, and I nestled into his chest, covered by his rust-colored windbreaker, looking out over the vast western landscape surrounding us. *Okay, George, you're going up here with us, too, buddy; I hope you enjoy this ride, like you did the river tubing… I know you loved the Southwest…*

"There's so much sagebrush down there, Rocky." I commented, absentmindedly.

"Yeah. But that's not the way it used to be. The land here used to be knee-high in buffalo and prairie grasses – a real grazing bounty of a place. But when the Spaniards came out of Mexico several hundred years ago, they brought their cattle and sheep with them. The theory goes that the seed of the first sagebrush was on the wool of the sheep. Eventually, over time, too many animals overgrazed the lands and the sage plant started taking over. In fact, it's said it releases a toxin in the soil that poisons other plants. It gets any of the rains and just thrives here now, but basically it's useless. The livestock doesn't eat it and now the land is worthless for grazing. From Texas on into Canada there's a wide area of land known as the 'sage belt,' and that's about all that grows in that range."

"That's an intriguing story, Rocky. One of those outsider plants coming in and crowding out indigenous species. Kudzu has done that in the east." I responded. "If I remember it right, it was brought in from China in the late 1800s. In the 1930s the U.S. Department of Agriculture decided to use it for erosion control and distributed 85 million seedlings in the South. *Big* mistake." I looked down at all the sagebrush below. "It thrived, lush and hungry, overgrowing native species of plants, crowding them out with its deep, viridian-colored foliage and vining habits that can claim up to *2* feet of space a *day*." I shared with Rocky and the crew. *Maybe it was kudzu that had covered Sleeping Beauty's castle and not briars, at all.* I thought, bemused. *Maybe the storytellers hadn't gotten their facts straight.*

"Yeah, I've heard of that kudzu out east. Hungry stuff!" Rocky responded.

"I've heard recently on NPR about a carp, native to China and Siberia, that had been brought to the United States in the early '90s to clean fish farms of algae, but they escaped when the fish farm flooded. It is now on its way, via a waterway connection, to the Great Lakes. There are two species, the 'silver carp' and the 'big-head carp,' – if I remember – that grow to be 5-6 feet long, and can weigh up to 100 pounds. With no true stomach, they are voracious, needing to eat constantly – food, and pretty much anything will do – goes in one end, and straight on through. Officials are pulling their hair out, trying to figure out how to stop them before they reach the Great Lakes and devour everything in their path." We continued with our stories of takeovers by alien species.

Bette now joined our discussion. "I also was listening to NPR, Laura. It talked about an Asian oyster now threatening native species of the Chesapeake Bay – they're bigger, meaner, and hungrier than the native batch. They're bullies, all of them!" She laughed.

"Right, Bette. And now in the news, there's a voracious Chinese 'predatory northern snakehead fish' in a pond in Maryland that can grow to more than 3 feet long, eating everything in sight. They can even crawl short distances on land! These things will take over a body of water, and it's left officials in a quandary. Last I heard, they've resorted to poisoning them – but how can they be exclusive? Doesn't this mean the whole 9-acre pond? *Geesh!* What is it about these far-eastern species that make them have to take over their environment? The Chinese are laughing – saying they're delectable food fish. So it's all in the perspective… But then, China has a lot of people to feed…" Now we were all shaking our heads or laughing at these strange stories of sci-fi creatures usurping the country. "Give us a little time and we won't have to worry about terrorists." I added.

Now Fred joined in. "But we've done it ourselves, too. Now scientists have created a bioengineered salmon that was 'designed' to grow bigger, faster, and stronger than native species. They're spawned in fisheries now, but biologists are extremely concerned about their escaping into the ocean and intermixing with wild species, interbreeding and wrecking havoc with the native stock. Did you know that bioengineers are also designing grasses for golf courses – with built-in pesticides?"

"Yeah," Rocky said, "like the bioengineered corn. Sure and with its 'built-in pesticide' it kills off predatory bugs that eat it – but it kills off the Monarch butterfly, too. Monarchs were found dead by the hundreds in their migratory tracks, on the fringes of these corn-fields..." Rocky's voice hardened. "This bioengineered corn was found to be responsible for the kill. It was grown and harvested with little or no thought to environmental concerns – or long-term human health. Man had created a food source that repelled its natural enemies, which they thought was grand. But then the corn, meant only as feed corn for livestock, had gotten mixed in with the human food chain." He paused. "Do any of you remember that huge recall of corn products, like taco shells and cornmeal last year?" Most of us did. "All sorts of corn products had to be taken off the shelves with this mix-up. That must have been hell for Mexican restaurants!" Rocky continued: "If it kills the rootworm, other corn pests and butterflies, what are the effects – short **or** long-term – on the animals that eat this stuff?"

Fred continued the thought, "And those of us that *eat* the animals that eat this fodder? Now science is linking the correlation that routinely lacing the feed with antibiotics of cattle, hogs and poultry, on what they call 'concentrated animal feeding operations,' has lowered the resistance in humans to so many of the antibiotics available to us now."

I rejoined the conversation, as this was a pet peeve of mine. "Yeah, antibiotic use on 'factory farms' – and overuse of antibiotic prescriptions by doctors for years, *and* not following the prescribed dosages by patients – have all wrecked havoc on the 'miracle drug' of the 20th Century. We have a wonderful tendency to create a monster of mayhem in our zealous approach to possibilities in the pursuit of perfection. In any case, all of it sure makes for interesting topics in the state and national news. Much of it reads like the stuff of Stephen King's daydreams."

"Heh," Rocky chimed back in, "I like that 'creating a monster of mayhem in our zealous approach to the pursuit of perfection' thing. Do you think you can say that three times real quick?" He laughed, a twinkle in his eyes.

"Only if I write it down – and no, I'd trip all over my tongue." I slipped paper out of my backpack and jotted the thought down, while it was fresh in my mind. *Whew. This had been some heavy talking for our floating around up in space, lighter than air...*

I leaned over the rim and looked down at the ground, now far below our drifting air-borne chariot. The land dipped and rolled, covered in pale sage and stunted evergreens. The morning cast a wash of golden light over the world below us, gilding the ground as we swept along. The shadow of the balloon had now reached the edge of the gorge and was ready to be swallowed by its heavy brethren, laying in wait inside the canyon walls.

The conversation changed again. "How is it that the ride doesn't feel bumpy?" Bette asked Rocky, who had now taken off his heavy jacket and wore a white, buttoned-down, long-sleeved shirt with the circular Pueblo Balloon logo on his right chest pocket. Stitched in blue above the pocket on his left side was "Rocky. PILOT." His dark brown cowboy hat threw shadows over his face as he answered: "It's the wind, Bette. We're drifting along with the wind currents. Keeps the ride smooth as silk." And sure enough, it did. There was no feeling of queasiness or bumping along, as one might on a boat. However, if one had a problem with heights, this was not the place to be. Bette was beginning to look a little apprehensive, as we sailed over the edge of rim-rock at the gorge and started to descend down into the gulch a bit.

"Are you okay, Bette?" I asked her.

"Sure. I'm just a little nervous – it's a long ways down. I'll be fine." She smiled at me and moved closer to Fred, who was intensely watching the walls of the gorge around us. He put his hand reassuringly on her shoulder.

Rocky's eyes twinkled a moment and he said, "I'll need to be leaning over the edges every now and then to spit. Please excuse me, my mama taught me better than that, but it has nothing to do with manners, and everything to do with locating just which way the wind is going..." and with that he leaned over the edge of the basket and patooied away. We watched the sputum fly through the air. "Just what I thought," he added. "I'll be doing a lot of that – it's the surest way we know to get a quick answer." We laughed. *Long as we didn't have to do it. I thought of the scene in Titanic, when Leonardo di Caprio was teaching the very proper Kate Winslet the finer points of hocking a lugie over the side of the great ship. Life is a hoot.*

Rocky's hands were covered in heavy leather gloves. He reached up to give the balloon a stoke of air and we heard the great **"Whoosh!"** as the flame roared into the cavity above our heads. "Gotta' do that, too, periodically." He smiled and then his eyes roamed the gorge around us. "We'll see just how far down into the gorge we can go to today. Last week Johnny was flying and the winds were so calm, he just about sat on the river down there."

"Why do you fly so early in the morning? Is this a better time of day, for some reason?" Pete asked.

"Yup. The air is more stable in the morning and the winds aren't so strong as later in the day. The flying's more predictable." We floated further down into the gorge, watching the winding sliver of silvered water weave along the bottom. The rugged stoney cliffs bookended us on both sides, still deep in shadow; the sun hadn't yet risen high enough to shed her light in these depths, thus giving the gorge a deep and ominous look. Somewhere behind us we heard a raptor screech, as it flew up and out of the canyon.

"We won't be able to get down quite as low as Johnny did – winds just aren't as calm today. But we can get in here pretty low." Rocky steered us down and between the walls. Bette looked more at ease now, closer to the ground.

We drifted along, moving above the river. I was intently watching for wildlife in and around the rocky outcrops, but we saw nothing but quiet deep shadows on the various sized rock slopes. Pete and I snapped some photos of the surroundings and of each other. After a while, Rocky asked: "Everyone ready to head back up?" With a unified nod of 'yes,' he **"Whooshed"** the balloon with heated air and we began our gradual ascent out of the gorge. In the distance we could see the huge bridge that spanned the east and west sides of the gorge.

"How high will we be going up today?" Pete asked our pilot.

Rocky turned to Pete, "Oh, about 1,000 feet up, I guess. We'll be flying about an hour."

"How do you know where we'll land, Rocky? Do you plan it ahead, or radio in to Johnny and the boys?" I asked.

"No, actually they'll be watching out for us, as we're pretty much at the mercy of the currents up here. We call 'em our 'chase vehicles,' and we do keep radio contact, but they keep visuals, as well. They'll follow us along and, towards the end of the flight, we'll radio in the exact recovery area. Of course," he winked, "we could just stay air-borne as long as the fuel'll hold out, and we can see if we can make it to the Arizona border and surprise 'ole Johnny…."

We all laughed. *I bet that* would *'surprise 'ole Johnny' – and us. We'd* all *be getting more than we'd bargained for! And our champagne brunch would turn into a dinner. But then we'd just have to come back for the Camry, and lose all that head start on tomorrow.*

"Maybe we'd just better stay the course. Can I fly this thing a little, Rocky?"

He glanced over at me and grinned. "Sure and in a little while. Maybe as we're coming down, I'll give you the controls. That okay, Pete? You want to give it a go, too? Fred? Bette?"

They nodded no, and Pete just grinned and said, "We'll see." And he took a picture of Rocky, with his tawny gloved hand at the helm, as he added another roar of air to the great balloon. Then Pete leaned down to look up, "Rocky, will you do that again? I want to get a photo." Rocky obliged, the dragon's breath of flame roared up inside the Ruebenesque rainbow, and we rose a little higher. Pete now had his black ball cap turned around backwards, the rim out of his way, as he shot his photos. The years melt away when he does this – a young kid, looking for fun or trouble.

"Hey, let's get some shots of each other!" Bette suggested. "This would be an opportune time, with the mountains off in the background. It would be lovely."

So we took turns posing and shooting and trading cameras, so we'd all end up with memories of the trip when we headed back to our various realities. I even got a close-up of the marble plaque inside the basket, reading: **"The Maggie Ann: Custom Designed For Pueblo Balloon Company by 'Pilot' Margaret Harmon."**

Rocky leaned over and spit again to get his wind reading. Pete joined him this time, getting in on the fun, and together they watched the sputum float on down, out of sight.

I thought of how absurd it would be for anyone below to be standing there, looking up at this beautiful balloon soaring above them, their hand cupped over their eyes to block the sun, when – suddenly – **SPLAT!** *– they get nailed on their forehead with this liquid bullet of directional patooey. Of course, this person would more likely think the assault be that of a bird, for who in the world, other than now-experienced balloonists, such as ourselves (ha, ha), would ever think this be the device used to judge the winsome wind.*

So the boys were boys and I entertained my Larson-like images, as we sailed up and over the Rio Grande River Gorge and bridge, down far below us; the Rio Grande no longer looked so 'Grande' from this height. As with anything in life, it was all just a matter of perspective. Bette was starting to get that queasy look again and she huddled into Fred, who drew a protective arm around her, assuring her, with his quiet presence, that she'd be just fine. Moving back the rim of my safari hat, I discreetly shot the two of them in this loving embrace and promised myself I'd send them a copy. There was such sweetness in this gesture.

Off to the right in the distance, carved out of the infinite miles of desert and sagebrush, was a large rectangular pit, a swath of pale sand amidst the soft sea of sage and golds. "What's that, over there?" I asked Rocky, and pointed.

"Oh, that's a gravel pit they're working. Looks real interesting when we fly in closer."

The huge shadow of our balloon sailed over the relief of earth below, leading us to the pit. I took photographs as we came in, fascinated by the shadows and plays of light under our craft. Mack trucks that would normally dwarf a large man now looked like midget matchbox toys lined up against a child's sandbox of mounds and creations. We watched as what appeared as tiny specs, smaller than ants, must have been people moving around on the ground that seemed miles beneath us. I'm sure this made Bette feel better. I sneaked a peak; her eyes were closed, for the time.

In the other direction the sun now lit the Rio Grande Gorge, bringing to life the heavily rocked surfaces, in sandstone and peachy tones. The river was now a beautiful peridot green, snaking her way through the great chasm. The Sangre de Cristo Mountains were veiled by distance, to the point of disappearing. There was such a wonderful calm here. Such peace. *George, are you here? I can almost feel your presence…*

We cleared the gravel sandbox, watching shadows from the backlit trucks reaching long and low before them. The balloon headed off into the desert, as if going to nowhere, like the feeling we'd experienced this morning, heading in to meet our flight.

Our shadow paralleled us, teasing us, attached, but not. We would reach out our arms and wave to it. Sometimes we could see the shadow wave in reply. And then, *way* down below, the lands from whence we had come rolled away from us, looking like another planet, covered in soft lavender gray shadows and endless sand hills. Dirt roads cut ribbons in switchback patterns and disappeared behind knolls or distance. It was a lonesome world down there.

As we sailed towards the end of our flight, moving in closer to the ground as Rocky fueled the rainbow less and less frequently, Bette visibly relaxed. We saw a compact homestead off in the distance, and the first fencing – it looked like barbed wire – that we had noticed in the all of this vast spaciousness. A small clapboard house, utilitarian outbuildings, corrals, old cars and such, came into view as we flew in closer, and then on by. Outside one of the corrals opened onto nothing but sand – here, sagebrush did not even grow. The only thing visible were holes punched intermittently throughout this barren 'pasture,' pale sand heaped up around them. "Are those prairie dog colonies?" I asked Rocky, thinking there was nothing else they could be.

"Yup. They're all over the place out here, Laura. Sure wreck havoc on the livestock, but then I guess they learn pretty quickly to steer clear of 'em." I didn't see any livestock down there to be wrecked havoc upon. Maybe the holes had claimed all the poor beasts, already, broken their legs, and now they were just sun-bleached skeletons. But I didn't see any bones down there, either. Oh well.

"May I fly now, Rocky? We seem to be pretty close to the ground now."

"Surely. I'll show you what to do." He pulled his burly leather glove off his right hand; I put it on. It gobbled my hand right up. He instructed me when to pull, and I heaved down hard, ducking a little when the flame roared above me in response. "Good work!" he said – "Again!" I repeated the pulls at his command and soon fell into a rhythm of when it was needed. This was just too cool. I'd nod at him the question and he'd nod back 'yes,' – or 'no,' and we flew along over the parched earth that reminded me of some of the scenes we had all been seeing of Afghanistan. Off yonder we could see the chase trucks and Rocky radioed contact with Johnny, saying, "All's calm up here. Laura's flying us in." We laughed. Yeah, for all of ten minutes.

We were chasing our shadow along the ground, as it echoed our descending flight. Now the great floating beast below us answered all waves and – unlike Peter Pan's free-spirited sprightly shadow – this one kept up with us, loaming larger as we floated down out of the sky. Rocky took over the controls and I quickly switched gears to photograph this phantom at play.

"Okay, crew, we're gonna' be landing real soon. It could get a mite bumpy, so here's whatcha' do. I'm going to tell you where to hold, and you hold on tight when I say to – and brace your legs, but keep some flex to the knee." Rocky instructed us.

Down on the ground now, in easy sight, Johnny, Russ, and the boys were racing over in our direction. "Bring her on down, Rocky!" Johnny was yelling.

"Naw, I think I'll fly right on back up. What's he *think* I'm gonna' do?"

Rocky mumbled, the latter more to himself than any of us. "Okay, hold on *tight* now!"

The balloon landed with a walloping **'Thump!'** and swayed a bit – we hung on tightly, as Rocky had said, taking the swaying in our knees and watching one another's face with relief. As if we were in the center of a football scrimmage, men and hands surrounded us, all steadying the basket, human anchors holding us to the ground. I had a momentary vision of the balloon deciding she wanted more air-time and lifting off again of her own accord, leaving their bodies dangling and fussin' and cowboy cussin,' but the image soon passed. She held steady to the ground, saving this surprise for another day. *But Oh! How grand it had been! George, I hoped you got as much of a kick out of this as we did!* I grinned over at Pete, who was smiling from ear to ear, happy and excited. Bette looked relieved to be aground; Fred had a quiet look of satisfaction about him. Rocky was busy with all the undoing and in helping us get out of the basket safely. All in all, I'd say it was a pretty awesome experience for each of us greenhorns. On top of all our memories, we would have photographs to take home, something to share with family and friends and grandkids down the road.

"Okay, fellas, I've gotta' dumb question for you." Pete piped up, holding firmly to the uprights outside the basket, helping the other men, and looking high up into the balloon. "Now that you've filled her with all this hot air, what do you do with it?"

"Easy, Pete," said Johnny. "We stand here the rest of the day holding her down, hoping that military jet'll fly on thru,' *then* we can call it a day, and go on home. Oh, and I was just jokin' about that brunch." Johnny Blue-Eyes winked at the boys. "Y'all ain't doin' nothin' the rest of the afternoon, are you?"

"Naw. We didn't have anything planned this trip." Fred joined in the fun.

"You see that valve way up top in the balloon?" Rocky pointed high inside – "That's a release valve. We'll pull that open – like this," and he did – "and all that hot air just goes up and out the top. Thus, once again we prove a law of physics." He did and immediately the balloon started loosing buoyancy. We all watched her slowly deflate and, as she did, the men guided her back over the ground, a reverse of the mornings work, as the giant fell to her knees. Our rainbow lay resting again, stretched over terra firma. The basket lay on its side, and once again Russ and the boys held the Kevlar riggings up high to prevent their tangling with lower lines.

"While these fellows pack her all up, who wants a cold drink?" Rocky asked. A man was hauling a cooler over our way.

"I'd like a Heineken about now." Pete said instantly. "But I'd settle with any old cold beer."

"I'd like a Heineken, too." Added Fred. "Hey, but like Pete there, I'm not fussy."

"I want a Long Island Iced Tea." Bette said firmly, "to celebrate a safe landing." She smiled her warm smile and looked very happy to be on the ground.

"Sorry y'all. If wishes were horses, and all. I'd like a cold brew about now, too, but what I was offering was more along these lines…" Rocky opened the cooler to show us a variety of soft drinks.

"Shucks," I said. "I was hoping you meant gin & tonics, or spiked lemonade, or some such." I winked at Rocky, and accepted a Sprite, thankful to be on the ground and able to drink *any*thing, knowing bathrooms were now back on the menu.

All of us had a cold drink in hand. We sipped and watched the end of the hoopla, taking the last photographs of one another telling stories and jokes, and the men all working on the balloon pack-up. Then we began to pull off our layers of clothing, as the hot morning sun rose high in the now familiar sky.

TWELVE

Champagne Balloon Brunch

"Timing has a lot to do with the outcome of a raindance."
Texas Bix Bender

As we drove with Rocky and Russell over the back-country of northern New Mexico roads towards our brunch destination, Rocky braked the truck quickly, exclaiming, "Hey, did y'all see *that?!* They're not common out here, but occasionally we see one."

"See what? What are you talking about, Rocky?" Pete asked, the both of us leaning over the seat, looking around the road ahead of us, all big gringo-curious eyes.

"The tarantula! It was a *big* one! It's mating season, and those big boys are combing the desert now, looking for females."

"You're pulling our leg there, Buddy," I said, dubious." You're just playing with us."

"No way, Laura. Really. It was a tarantula and they're out here." Hurt that I didn't believe him, he turned to Russell for confirmation: " Right, Russ?" Russell nodded in agreement, adding:

"They're out here, alright, and they do get crazy at mating season, running all over the place for miles and miles, looking for a honey. They forget to eat, to sleep. Poor lonesome fellas."

"I used to do that," laughed Pete. "Glad those days are over." We all laughed with him.

I could just picture the huge, shaggy black spiders scurrying around the desert, hunting up a female. If they depended on sighting one, they were shit out'a luck for, as big as they are, they still lay low to the empty reaches of ground out here. I then had an image of a tarantula running around, standing on two of it's eight legs, on tippy-toes, another of his hairy legs shading his eyes, as he scanned the horizon looking for the ladies, leaning first one way, then another. And then I had another image of a tarantula skeleton — all worn down to nothing but vertebra and an afro of dense black hair, frozen in mid-motion and petrified by the intense sun. It had starved for love. Poor dude. What it needed was the equivalent of a duck-caller, only in spider-lingo. This way, it could rest under a sagebrush in one spot, tooting away on this whistle, alerting females to his love pad.

While sitting there, going into Larson-mode again, I noticed the flea-bitten windshield on this nice truck. "Rocky, okay, I believe you about the tarantula, but now tell me what did-in your windshield? Looks like somebody used it for bb practice."

They laughed up front. "Yup. Out here it don't take no time at all for a windshield to look like that — all the gravel pieces on these open roads being flung up at you, and all. All serious cowboy trucks that goes any-wheres, look like that."

"I bet Novus could retire out here. Looks like y'all could play con-nect-the-dots and come up with constellations and critters, and all kinds of concoctions, when you're driving along and get bored. My son, Jared, used to play a game when he was a preteen, where he'd target one bird-poop on the windshield, and eye it all the way into town, watching the perspective change around it, as we drove, or something. Honestly, I never could figure out just what the point of the 'game' was — but it kept him busy."

"We'll just have to keep the bird-poop game in mind," joked Russ. "We do have god-awful long drives out here, between ballooning events. But I personally like the connect-the-dots. Kind of like a Rorschach test, or something."

"Yup." I said. "You all could dig deep into each other's minds, learn all kinds of kinky secrets, with your windshield spatterings." I laughed, and looked over at Pete, wondering why he wasn't in the thick of these conversations.

The Wop was leaning back, his head against the seat and his ball cap pulled down shading his eyes, resting, with his windbreaker over his lap, but he was listening to our banter and smiling. "I don't need to say any-thing. You all are doing just fine." And then we pulled into a parking lot in front of a large low brown building with a huge sign atop, reading: "OVERLAND SHEEP COMPANY."

"*This* is where we're having brunch?" I asked.

"Yup. You like mutton?" Rocky pulled around to the back parking lot of the building, found a shady spot under a large old tree, beside Johnny's Verizon truck. Bette and Fred were already standing in the lot, looking around, Bette talking animatedly and pointing at something in the back. Johnny was telling us we were to follow him 'round to the other side, to the 'Ranch Café.' We did. Our group passed a pond that could be in any setting out east, surrounded by ferns and greenery, with lily pads in bloom floating in it, like an Oriental screen print. Goldfish lazily swam beneath the water. This must have been what Bette had been talking about. It was very pretty and very refreshing out in these hot open spaces. We turned the corner and there under a porch, under a long overhang, were outdoor tables and chairs – a western veranda. A stretch of lawn lay out in front with several mature locusts and elms throwing welcome shade, and a line of mountains afar.

"Okay, are those the Sangre de Cristos or the San Juans?" asked Pete, his direction uncharacteristically thrown off.

"The Sangre de Cristos," Johnny answered, "we're facing east."

"Oh. Okay. They look pretty much the same, from a distance." Pete conceded.

A pleasant older waitress came outside. "Hey, boys, how're y'all doin' today? How was the flight?" She smiled at us. Her bottle-induced flaming red hair fell in soft waves around her pale, lined face. She looked as if she had lived a long life in a short time. But in the echoes of living, in these lines, there was still a softness, an acceptance, a coming to terms with her life. She looked as if she could now quietly handle about anything that came her way.

"Hey, Thelma, you lovely lady, you." Johnny greeted her. "Rocky says it was all smooth sailing!"

"Yes, it was beautiful," Bette agreed. "It was such a lovely day to fly."

"Good. Good. Can I bring y'all coffee?" We ordered, a couple of us settled on decaf, and Bette asked for hot tea.

"Okay, order anything you want on the menu. Food's all good. And it's on us," said our generous host.

These were cowboy/man-sized meals, full of beans and potatoes, meat and salsa. All sounded scrumptious; I hadn't thought about it much, but daggone, it was time to eat…

I looked at my watch – it was after 11AM – we'd been up for almost six hours with no sustenance at all – no *wonder* we were famished!

We placed our orders after Thelma brought the drinks out. I asked for a 'breakfast burrito,' with eggs and cheese, green chilies and potatoes in a flour tortilla, with bacon on the side. And juice. That'd be the ticket. Pete got an omelet with ham, cheese and chilies, toast and juice. He'd developed an appetite, too, with the high-altitude fresh air… We all ordered sizeable meals; everyone was hungry.

We settled back with our coffees, Bette's tea, and the juices that Thelma brought us, talking and visiting, asking Johnny and Rocky, Russ and Andersen, about the upcoming Kodak Albuquerque Balloon Festival the following weekend.

"Y'all going to be around next weekend?" Johnny asked. "We'll be there, for sure – wouldn't miss it! You could come see us. We have buddies coming in from all over the place."

"Because of flight schedules, we need to leave first thing Saturday morning, the 6th. Damn. Flights were *all* booked on Sunday, and Pete has to be at work on Monday. We hated having to leave at the beginning of a weekend, but it couldn't be helped."

Bette and Fred said they were leaving on the 4th, to return to New York. They, too, were flying in and out of Albuquerque, but to and from LaGuardia.

"That's too bad," Rocky said. "We'd love to have you visit us. Saturday's when it all starts, and it's really something to behold. Balloons from all over the world."

"It sure is something," Johnny continued. "Maybe you can watch a little of it before your flight leaves, or from your plane?" *Well, double damn,* I thought. *Here this balloon festival is a once-a-year, world-renowned event, and we were flying OUT when the balloons were going UP!* Ugh.

"You know something funny," Johnny added, "the security at the event will be incredible, like nothing we've ever seen before. All the balloonists will be screened and frisked for bombs and explosives and the like. Sure, like we're going to self-destruct over Albuquerque."

"I guess everybody's gun-shy," Fred intoned "– so to speak. Everyone's spooked. At least they didn't cancel the event."

Everyone agreed that was a good thing. The topic was changed to how truckers were being monitored heavily now, screened and questioned, their loads all checked carefully. Drivers were eyeballing each other, watching for any potential terrorist threats. And we all were getting stories of how people running crop-duster businesses were being approached by those of mid-eastern origins with questions on flights, and trying to arrange questionable flights to theoretically use the planes to spread biological or chemical sprays over heavily populated areas. For now, crop-dusters were grounded. It was all too bizarre to fathom. The world, as we knew it, had gone nuts.

I had to change the subject and get on to something brighter for a while. "Hey, Johnny, I notice those big monsters you're driving are all Fords. You're partial?"

"Yeah." He laughed. "They've been real good trucks."

"Uh huh." Andersen spoke. "Well, I remember the time —"

"Not *that*, Andersen!" Johnny squeaked —

"Uh huh," Andersen insisted. "The time in Chinle, when we had that fancy-pants Ford truck of yours down there in the bottomlands." He turned to us easterners, explaining: "You see, the bottom of Canyon de Chelly – down in there, some 15-17 miles in – is covered in deep sands, and when these get wet, you find pockets of quicksand. Well, it was one of those times… we were all down there – Rocky, Johnny, Russell, Noel and me – driving around, and it started to rain. To *pour*. And Johnny's truck started sinking in deeper. And deeper…" The guys were all laughing now, reminiscing,

"Yeah, and Johnny was yelling, '*Help!* I'm going to lose my truck'!" Rocky cut in —

"And we had my truck down in there," Andersen continued, "the one they always ribbed me about, my little ½ ton Chevy." He paused for effect, his dark eyes dancing with fun, "Hey, Russ, Rocky – *Johnny* – just *how'd* you get out of that predicament you were in?" He tilted his head, cupped his hand over his ear, and grinned, listening up for the answer.

"Alright. Al*right!* Uncle – this time. I'll be damned if that itty bitty little Chev-ro-*leh* didn't heave and haw and eventually get us out of that man-eating —"

"Truck-eating," Russ corrected.

"Okay, *truck-eating*, quicksand." Johnny looked exasperated.

We all roared at the conversation, picturing the cowboys and Indians, down at the bottom of the winding canyons, watching Johnny's truck disappear, whooping and hollering at each other, pulling out ropes and jumping around, thinking fast on their feet, as Johnny's Ford sank deeper and deeper with big ole' **'Glurb! Glurb!'** sounds. What a colorful picture *that* was! What a tale that would have been for the insurance company… *You lost your truck* where?

"Hell, that quicksand's been known to swallow the likes of *dump* trucks," Russ reminisced. "They just plain disappeared, never to be seen again."

"Until they show up down yonder in *China*," drawled Johnny. "That's where *my* truck was headed!" We were belly laughing at these characters by now.

"We got Johnny's truck pulled out. It was no longer white; it was all covered in mud up to the top of the tires, and above — what a mess. It was *all* beat to hell, and Andersen's little truck was beat-up, in hauling Johnny's out of that mess. But, I'll tell ya'," Rocky winked a big one at Johnny, who sat there looking sheepish, "Andy's Chevy won this one, hands down."

"Wait'll *next* time," Johnny murmured, refusing to concede, his arms stubbornly crossed over his chest, while he leaned way back in his chair.

Thelma bringing out our grub saved his pride. She placed huge platters of food before us — a feast after famine. I eyed my delicious-looking breakfast burrito and said simply: "There's a doggy-bag." Patient Thelma smiled down, "You just tell me when, honey."

Everyone dug in, all of us hungry. The food was great, the company even better. Rocky had opened a bottle of champagne to much fanfare and poured out a glass for each of us, but skipped one for himself.

"You not thirsty, Rocky?" I asked.

"Naw. I'm allergic to the stuff." He drawled... "Used to like it *too* much."

"Oh, okay." Enough said.

"Hey, you boys might know something about this article I read recently about a strange humming sound driving residents nuts in a place called Kokomo, Indiana. They call it 'the Kokomo hum' — it's like a diesel truck constantly idling off in the distance." I remembered this tid-bit from one of my umpteen readings somewhere.

"Yeah. I heard something about that — and years ago, the early 1900s, I think it was — they had something like that going on here, in Taos." Johnny commented.

"Right. The article talked about Taos. This mysterious noise residents kept hearing at the turn of the century — nobody know where it came from, but it sounded like a diesel engine idling off in the distance — not that they had those then. Wouldn't let up. If I remember correctly, it caused sleeplessness and dizziness — all sorts of weird symptoms."

"Yup. And then it just died out. Nobody ever figured out what caused it. I'd forgotten about that, Laura. Maybe it was an alien spaceship coming up out of Roswell." Johnny laughed and slapped Russell on the back, mimicking eerie twilight-zone sounds.

"Maybe so. There are all sorts of strange, unexplained things in the world." Fred said.

"Laura, *where* do you read all this stuff?" asked Pete, eyeing me quizzically, over a sip of champagne.

"Oh, a little here, a little there. I subscribe to a gazillion magazines, as you know. Just wish I could keep track… Wish I had one of those 'photographic minds' — *heh*, and *then* I wouldn't be needing my camera!" I kidded him, and prodded his knee. Pete grinned and took another sip. I enjoyed more of the filling burrito, washing it down with coffee.

We discussed the ballooning and where the boys had traveled with it. Johnny was telling us that Hollywood was making a movie about his life — a full-length feature film, as a biography, of sorts. "What will it be called?" Bette asked, with interest.

"For now, they're using "Pueblo Ballooning" as the working title. They're not sure yet. Hollywood's thinking of using Sam Elliot to play my part. He's a colorful cowboy character."

"Why not just use you, Johnny?" I asked.

"They're afraid he'll cause too much trouble," Russ leaned over and jabbed Johnny in the arm.

Johnny feigned his feelings being hurt. "I wouldn't." he said.

We laughed. "We'll keep an eye out for it, Johnny. Good for you." Pete said, between bites.

We talked some more about the movie, and Johnny's illustrious life, as we ate. Thelma came out to bring more coffee and hot water for Bette's tea. Rocky was working away on uncorking a second bottle of champagne. It popped loudly, fizzing over his hand as he asked: "Who's ready for a refill?"

"You ready for that doggy-bag, honey?" Thelma asked me, reaching for my plate. How 'bout you, hon?" She asked Bette. Bette declined the offer with a shake of her head and a "No thank you."

I answered her, "Sure am. We've got a cooler with us, and I'm sure there'll be some poor dog on the rez who'll need this more than I do."

"Ah, so it'll be a *real* doggy-bag, then!" Fred asked, looking amused.

"Yup." (I was beginning to like that word. Out East we use 'Yep.') "Have you ever been to the rez?" I asked them, glancing over at Andersen — "In all respect there, friend, there *are* a lot of skinny little dogs out there."

"Don't I know it. No feelings hurt; I agree with you, Laura." The Navajo smiled at me.

"No, but we're going to look for some riding around here, in New Mexico." Bette said.

"Heh, we are, too! We're thinking of doing an overnighter around El Capitan, in Arizona, with Navajo guides taking us out to some cliffs with petroglyphs that they know of. There will be a full moon…doesn't that sound romantic?" I was kind of daydreaming aloud now.

"It sure does. Maybe they'll have something like that around this area?" Bette asked, turning to Johnny. She continued. "Fred and I often ride in Central Park."

The cowboys immediately made some suggestions as to who to call about rounding up some trail rides, especially around the 'Enchanted Circle,' with a number of dude ranches and the year-round resorts, like Angel Fire or Red River. Bette and Fred were appreciative of the suggestions, and said they'd make some calls when they got back to their Bed and Breakfast.

"When were the two of you married?" I turned to the newlyweds.

"On September 22nd. It was very strange, just eleven days after the terrorist's attacks. A lot of our friends wouldn't fly. My aunt, who didn't like planes be*fore*hand, refused to fly up from Florida; she drove, instead." Fred told us.

"That's understandable," Pete said. "When did you fly west?"

"Shortly afterwards, in fact the next day – September 23rd. Sunday." Bette answered.

"We came out on the 22nd," I added, "the day you were married. There's got to be a connection in that. Our actual anniversary date was September 11th – our 25th. Unreal."

"Oh, my God – I don't know whether to congratulate you, or say I'm sorry," Fred said.

"Thank you. We know the feeling. But we decided to try to celebrate, anyway, after the initial – tremendous – shock." Pete shared. "Laura and I had worked so hard on all the planning and had looked forward to celebrating our 25th for years. We couldn't *not* come. Thankfully, we had lots of support and encouragement at home."

I added: "Pete's folks are there with the kiddos during the weekdays and one of my sister's is handling this up-coming weekend."

"That's wonderful to have such family support. How many children do you have?" Bette asked, turning to me.

"Three. Skye is 17½ , Jared is 15½, and Natalie will be turning 13 in early November."

"Oh boy! All teenagers – lucky you! You both have your hands full!" Bette exclaimed. "I have two sons, Parker, who's 36, lives in Ramsey, New Jersey, and Jason, who's 34, lives in Charlotte, North Carolina, with his wife, Karen. But he was in town at the time on business. He watched the Towers go down. It was ungodly."

"That must have been an awful sight." Johnny, who had been quietly listening, spoke. His voice was the most serious I'd heard it since we had met him. He leaned on the table, resting his elbow, a hand lightly holding his coffee cup.

"Yes, it was," Bette agreed. "Fred has two daughters, also from a previous marriage. Suzanna is 32 and Mary Jane is 30. They were traveling together on the New Jersey side of the Hudson River and saw everything. Their car was stopped on the bridge. They watched the planes hit the Towers, saw the explosions, watched the Trade Center collapse, first the South Tower, and then the North —"

"Of course, it was pure chaos," interjected Fred. "People were everywhere, there was mass confusion and their minivan wasn't moving. It was like a front row seat in a horror film. We couldn't get in touch with them until early afternoon to know they were okay. It was awful." This time Bette comforted him — reaching over for his hand. They'd experienced so much trauma together just before their marriage, and it seemed only to cement their relationship. And to remind them, too, of how very tenuous life is....

"So you both were in New York on the 11th?" I asked, tentatively.

"Well, actually I was working in New Jersey — ironically, I sell plane engine parts — and spent hours afterwards trying to connect with Bette, Jason, and the girls. It was a madhouse."

"I was in the Lincoln Building, watching the Trade Centers be hit, *and* watching the coverage on TV. It was surreal — I just could not believe any of it was happening." Bette stirred her tea absently, wandering back in time and reliving the day. Her expression became misted and veiled. Fred laid a large and gentle hand over hers, both of them reliving the recent trauma.

"Bette had a very hard time of it. The Wednesday before she had been on the 74th floor of Tower Two with a client, who is also a close friend. Bette is an interior decorator, you see. Thank the stars her client was out of town when they collapsed, but it was two weeks before her client got Bette's frantic message and returned her call. We *just* found out she was okay." Fred squeezed her hand, and Bette smiled at him and then at us, sadness in her warm brown eyes.

"It was awful. But it's a miracle we didn't know others. Imagine, the *entire* office of Cantor-Fitzgerald — gone. Just like that. All those people..." Bette's voice trailed off.

"And all the medics, the EMTs, the firefighters..." Russ broke into the conversation.

"I watched them run into the second Tower. I was talking with my sister, Elizabeth, in the hospital. Poor thing, here she is in for major tests on her gallbladder and watching this horrendous coverage on TV of the world turning inside out. We were thinking of all of the wounded that would be needing hospital space." Silence. "But then, the most horrible thing of all was there were barely any wounded…" I continued. "So we watched on our TVs, and talked over the phone and watched all the medics and police and firefighters run in –"

"And none come out." Bette finished, simply. "All those brave souls ready to help. I just can't imagine what it was like for their families."

"For all the families. For all the people involved." Pete added. We sat and shook our heads. Everyone was quiet for a bit, lost in his or her own memories of sixteen days earlier. Another bizarre moment came to mind.

"One of my old high-school buddies, Kathy Konkle, called me from New York to let me know she was okay. She said that she and the people in her apartment went to the roof of their building after the first plane hit, to see what was going on. She said that it was absolutely surreal. Thousands of people made their way to the rooftops of buildings throughout the city to watch this attack unfold before their eyes." I stopped talking and drew in a breath, trying to imagine this view, as I shared this strange story with the eclectic mix at the table, intently listening to one of the many recollections from that day. "People were literally milling about on rooftops, trying to figure out what was happening in their world. Once the first tower started to implode, Kathy said she heard a collective and audible *'Oh my God'* reverberate over the rooftops… She said it was like being in a futuristic sci-fi movie."

"What a story," Fred said. "There are so many perspectives. Everyone in New York was impacted so differently that day. And everyone so profoundly."

"I don't know of anything that has impacted this country so profoundly," Russ added.

We'd been watching Rocky fiddling with the tops of the champagne bottles, as we had shared these stories. "What *are* you doing there, Rocky?" I asked.

"Oh, you'll see soon enough, Laura." He was leaning back in his chair, halfway listening, and halfway off in his own thoughts, his muscular hands and arms working away on the project, his hat perched back on his head. Then he looked up, brightened, and changed the subject, altogether. "I have one of these for each of you couples," he said, handing a champagne top to Bette and Fred, and one to Pete and me. "See

– they're miniature balloons. This is the basket," – showing us the long cork that had stopped the bottle – and these are the Kevlar ropes." He knotted his dark brows and looked meaningfully at me: "Just go with it, Laura," he said, before I could open my mouth, "and this is the top of the balloon."

"But, Rocky, the balloon's not *nearly* big enough!" I jumped in, teasing him.

We all laughed, glad to lighten up and claim our souvenirs, of both the flight and of our brunch with our comrades, on this fine day. Thelma brought out my doggy bag and I thanked her. We talked about this and that, while Rocky and Johnny filled out official looking blue certificates claiming each of us now to be 'Hot-Air Balloon Aficionados.' "Well, we can all agree on the hot-air part of it, anyway," deadpanned Pete.

We laughed, and Johnny said, with his Texas drawl: "Yup. I'll second that!" and he raised his empty glass.

Time to get on with our day. It was early afternoon by now. Our champagne brunch had ended, mostly on high-notes, and it was time to return to the Sagebrush Inn and get on with our exploration of Taos.

Johnny had to go elsewhere, too, and took Russell and Andersen with him, along with the Hispanic fellows, who he'd drop back at the gas station. They had been inside, breakfasting with friends. Bette and Fred squeezed into Rocky's truck with Pete and me, and we headed on back. Rocky became our taxi return. On the way we traded addresses with them and gave the two of them big good-bye hugs at our hotel, wishing the newlyweds a safe continuation of their honeymoon explorations. They were a couple with whom we would like to stay in touch. After big waves to all, I remembered who it was that they reminded me of, and turned to Pete: "Don't they make you think of Phyllis and Tom?"

"*That's* who it is! They've reminded me of someone we know all day," Pete agreed. Phyllis and Tom were from New Jersey and had moved to Virginia years ago. We met them when they rented 'Canterbury Farm,' a beautiful place down the road. They, too, were a little older than us, both professionals, and both had the well-traveled, educated and calm demeanors that Fred and Bette had emanated. That's exactly who it was. No wonder we felt so relaxed around them. Again, I felt a piece of the kismet fall into place, subtly, as if we were right on track with wherever it was we were heading.

(I've found since this great adventure that Johnny was offered an offer he couldn't refuse and sold Pueblo Balloon Co. He now owns Santa Fe Balloon Co., in Santa Fe. Rocky flies for both.)

Return to the Sagebrush, mid-day, September 27th

When the Wop and I got back to our room we weighed our options, as we flopped back against the pillows of the bed, my head resting against his chest, and his arm cradling it. "Well, we could go down to the Taos Plaza," Pete suggested, "kick around there a while and explore. Basically, according to my itinerary, we have just under 24 hours left here in Taos."

"Your itinerary, *schminerary*!" I scowled at him, hating these limits on letting spontaneity into our lives. "I'm thinking we go over to the pool on this beautiful day and relax a bit. We've already lived a lifetime in a day, and we're only halfway through. Let's rest up… "

He glanced down at me. I smiled up at him. He didn't look as if he'd struggle with the suggestion of resting too much. "Okay, I'm tired, I'll admit. I was trying to catch a catnap on the way to brunch, but your conversations were too insane to let me sleep."

"They were designed to keep you awake," I kidded him. "How 'bout if we take a couple of Coronas over, in plastic cups, to sip on while we relax?"

"Twist my arm," and he willingly handed over his arm to me, a game we play with one another. I twisted gently, pretending to use big force. "*Uncle!*" he said, "I'll go get 'em," and Pete popped up and off the bed, padding over to the cooler for a couple of cold brews.

Bathing suits on, sunscreen smeared, towels and books in one hand and our beers and the key in the other, we headed over to the pool for a couple of hours break from our vigorous vacationing. I had my kickboard under my arm and the safari hat over my shoulders. Pete wore his "Silverton Railroad" ball cap from our trip to Durango last summer, when we'd spent the weekend with Gary and Cynthia and their kids, on our family jaunt West.

Pete was reading Nevada Barr's *Ill Wind*, a mystery centering on a ranger ending up dead in Mesa Verde, the Anasazi ruin over in southwest Colorado. I had read it and was trying not to give him clues as to who-dun-it. I was reading Tony Hillerman's mystery, *Hunting Badger*, based around the Four Corners general area, and Bluff, Utah, where we were headed next. The way Hillerman described the rugged land where the bad guys hid, one could feel the sun bake the cliffs and rock faces of those remote reaches into southern Utah, and northern Arizona. He and I enjoyed reading both of these authors, sharing tidbits from the various books, and learning about the areas we were now exploring. Anna Pigeon, the diminutive park ranger/sleuth who imperiled herself with her insatiable curiosity and fearless encounters with the killers, in Barr's books, was something of a role model for me. I liked Anna. I liked her gumption, her love of animals, and her never-say-die attitude.

Hillerman's main characters, 'Legendary Lieutenant' Joe Leaphorn, Jim Chee, Sergeant of the Navajo Tribal Police, and Janet Pete, a defense attorney caught between the world of the rez that she was born into, and the expansive, glamorous world of Washington, DC, where she practiced, were all larger than life. In later mysteries, Officer Bernadette (Bernie) Manuelito has joined the gang as a rookie cop out to prove herself, and another potential love-interest for Chee. I secretly had a crush on Jim Chee, and was pretty sure that Pete had a thing for Janet (maybe because her name was 'Pete,' but I don't think so). It just made the reading all the more intriguing.

The pool, surprisingly for this beautiful day, was just about empty. One other lady lay tanning herself on a chase lounge beside it, a languid lizard in the hot mid-day sun, basking in its rays. Pete immediately settled in to read, to see what Anna was up to now.

I wanted to move my body parts – we'd been on the go the last couple of days and I was stiffening. "Enjoy your swim," he smiled over his sun-glasses. "I'll join you in a while."

"Let me know where you are, okay?" I pointed to *Ill Wind*. He smiled again, nodded and began reading, his sunglasses perched on his nose and his visor pulled down.

The cool water was delightful in the dappled, azure pool. I lazed around the waters at first, just feeling the tactile sensations glide over my body and looking around, enjoying the gracious courtyard and the little touches Louise had done here and there to make one feel at home. I treaded water a bit to warm up, then – kickboard in hand – went through the full routine, ending up vigorously, which caused the lazy lizard lady to raise her head and sneak a peek to see just what in the world could make me want to exert myself so much on such a languid afternoon. I smiled at her and began some cool down stretches in the water. By now PeterWop had joined me, swimming around like a dolphin or otter underwater, being a teasing rascal, in general. This was a side of the man I loved, when the boy in him forgot about the almighty watch and he lived in the Now. He was good at it when he let go. We cavorted and splashed and laughed, causing lazy lizard lady to pack up and leave. Oh well. Guess the little kid in her wasn't on vacation. Or *she* was vacationing from *her* little kids, and suddenly the adults around her had reverted. She just couldn't win.

But soon we settled down and climbed up out of the water to become lazy lizard people, ourselves, sunning in the warm fall rays, reading our books, sipping our now-tepid beers, until we fell fast asleep, side by side in our chase lounges, holding hands and dreaming of drifting effortlessly through the clouds.

TAOS

In the afternoon Pete and I checked out the Taos Plaza, visiting little shops and looking into the window of Pueblo Drums, which had closed early that day. We'd come back in the morning before leaving, and look into taking one back to the kiddos for Christmas. I photographed the turquoise pony, painted with the local mountain ranges along its side, and carrying the young girl on his back, for Natalie. I was collecting a series of 'Painted Ponies' photos for her, as we traveled along.

I marveled at how much Taos had a little-sister feel to Santa Fe, with her collection of fine art galleries, the elaborate window displays, the mix of Indian and Hispanic overtones and eclectic Old-West art. Adobe structures abounded here, as well, but I did not see the array of imaginative fences and gates that Santa Fe offered. Of course, Taos was on a much smaller and more intimate scale.

The Taos Pueblo, for which Johnny had named his balloon company, was close by. It is the largest existing multi-storied Pueblo structure in the United States. The Spanish first found it in 1540, when Herando de Alvardo led Coronado's first expedition to this area, searching for the fabled "Seven Cities of Cibola." It sits at the base of Taos Pueblo Peak. The Taos Indians have lived here for nearly 1,000 years and some of the communal dwellings are 4-5 stories high. Here the Taos Pueblo drums are made by hand, as they have always been, beautiful, hand-painted, and original, every one of them. The next morning we did buy a drum, with five long black rectangular Indian figures painted on the front, and signed on the back by Phillip C. Martinez, sounding much more Hispanic than Indian to me. This was the 'YA YE Spirit,' protecting the family, something we very much wanted to do at this time of danger and uncertainty. We passed this time on the Kokopelli character, carrying his bag of seeds in the hunch on his back, opting instead, for this other drum. It would be a family gift from Santa to bless our home.

Taos is actually three villages, representing the history and diversity of this area, with its American Indian, Spanish and Anglo influences. Taos proper (legally Don Fernando de Taos) was the original Spanish town that is now the plaza, the center of art and tourism. Pueblo de Taos (San Geronimo de Taos) is home to the native Taos Indians. And south of town Ranchos de Taos sits. It was formerly a farming community. Its beautiful church – the Mission of St. Francis of Assisi – is one of the most photographed structures in New Mexico. I understand that the Mission displays a very old and unusual painting of Christ; we must be sure to see this church on our next trip.

Not only is Taos (proper) a thriving artist's colony like Santa Fe, Indian scout and frontiersman, Kit Carson made his home here. This home is now a museum, which Pete and I saw with the kiddos last year. He, himself, is buried in Kit Carson State Park. I'm sure the Natives love this fact. The writer D.H. Lawrence lived in this area, as well. He wrote of the Indians of the Taos Pueblo: *"All is God. The whole life-effort of man is to get his life into direct contact with the elemental life of the cosmos."* D.H. Lawrence is buried on a knoll on his Kiowa Ranch, which is now a facility of the University of New Mexico, 15 miles north of Taos. I understand that the vivacious actress, Julia Roberts, and the current Secretary of Defense, Donald Rumsfeld, both own ranches outside of Taos.

"We had no churches, no religious organizations, no sabbath day, no holidays, and yet we worshiped." Geronimo (Goyathlay) (1829-1909)
Chiricahua Apache Chief

The Enchanted Circle, northeast of Taos, is a loop offering tourists a real taste of the area. One might head east on U.S. Highway 64, towards Shady Brook and Angel Fire, one of the ski and year 'round resorts in the mountains. Further up is the Vietnam Veterans National Memorial, which I haven't yet seen, with Pete's stringent planning, but very much want to; I've read that it is a 6,000 square foot shrine, constructed by Dr. Victor Westphall, for his son, who was killed in 1968 in Vietnam. It stands to honor the memory of this fallen son, and veterans of Vietnam and other wars. From photos, it looks to be a beautiful and modern memorial, standing there high and tall against the spacious western skies.

Further north 64 takes one to Eagle Nest, where NM 38 intersects, and highway 64 then takes one to Cimarron, meaning "wild" or "untamed." In the mid- to late-1800s Cimarron was a magnet for outlaws such as Clay Allison, Billy the Kid and Black Jack Ketchum. New Mexico's first printing press was dumped into the Cimarron River, and the *Las Vegas Gazette* once claimed: *"Things are quiet in Cimarron; nobody has been killed in 3 days."* The town has now settled down. The Philmont

Scout Ranch lies 4 miles south. It is a 137, 493-acre national camping center operated by the National Council of the Boy Scouts of America. *Where do the girl scouts go?* I wondered.

Cindy wrote to me about this area, her stomping grounds. The 3,600-acre Maxwell National Wildlife Refuge, outside of Cimarron, protects a number of hawks, falcons and eagles. She also told me that Maxwell was very close to the Capulin Volcano National Monument, which is one of the best examples of a volcanic cinder cone in the nation. It was formed about 60,000 years ago. Cindy said that from the summit, 1,000 feet high, one could see the Rocky Mountains, and on a clear day the distant horizons of Colorado, Oklahoma – and even Texas! She must have great eyes – I don't know why she ever even considered Lasik surgery! She told me of fly-fishing for trout on the Red River, riding Smiley over from there to Eagle Nest. We had wanted to visit Cindy on her home-turf, but with our jam-packed itinerary never made it that trip. We figured another trip, for sure, but Cindy and her family have since moved to Hawaii. Guess they wanted lush growth and humidity, and that's okay; Pete and I have a standing invitation to visit…

As Rocky said, Wheeler's Peak stands proudly in the center of the Enchanted Circle, at 13,161 feet; it is the highest point in all of New Mexico. One continues the loop from Eagle Nest to Red River and the Taos Ski Valley, two more year 'round resorts, on over to Questa and down to the Arroyo Hondo, close to where we hot air ballooned, on the Arroyo Mesa, northwest of Taos. This is all to be saved and savored for another time…

"This strong primitive appeal (of New Mexico) calls out the side of art that is not derivative; it urges the painter to get his subjects, his coloring, his tone from real life about him, not from the wisdom of the studios. Coupled with this impressive simplicity, the country makes its inhabitants daring and lovers of the 'chance.' In the cities men are careful, doing what others have done, bound by conventions, ringed round by traditions. The very air of Taos country, its nearness to works of nature, drives caution from man's brain. He takes a chance." Victor Higgins, 1917

For now, our time in Taos was coming to an end. We left the plaza to return to the hotel and find our cowboy buddies working on *The Line Shack*. They were finally getting the lighting right. We watched them a while and were asked if we would like to join the gang for dinner at El Taoseño, a restaurant for locals that would have had Art feeling right at home. Pete and I listened to more of their adventures of the Wild Wild West, laughing our heads off, and sharing some more of our lives.

I watched in amazement at Johnny pouring *13* packets of sugar into a single iced tea and marveled once again at his weight – or lack of it. After our dinner of chili rellenos and Navajo tacos, we shot a couple of last photographs of Johnny and Rocky, Andersen and Dawn, Russell and Noel, who had joined the crew for the shooting of *The Line Shack*. I don't know where Geri was that night; I asked Rocky to tell her adios for us. And then we shook hands and/or hugged all around, were wished health and adventure for the rest of our trip west, and Pete and I headed back for our last evening in New Mexico (on this trip).

Pete and I returned to the Sagebrush Inn. As we walked under the softly lit trees past the pool, shimmering invitingly in the crisp fall night, I suggested to Pete that we take a second dip, as this would be our last before leaving. It took a little coaxing and cajoling, reminding him that it was heated and that we had discovered a hot tub in an adjacent building in which we could warm up afterwards. He finally agreed to swim. Once in, he never looked back. The pool was a warm quicksilver liquid blanket under a chilly sky. As long as our shoulders were in we were fine, so we glided and played and twirled through the pool, the only guests enjoying the beauty of the night. Indeed, we had this whole area all to ourselves as long as we liked. The burgeoning moon peaked in and out of the tree line down at us, watching us play, a Peeping Tom to our antics. This pool had looked enchanting that first evening here in Taos, and it had not disappointed. In my mind, I heard Dean Martin crooning to us:

"When the moon hits your eye like a big pizza pie, that's Amore'…/ When the world seems to shine, like you've had too much wine, that's Amore'…"

After our late night dip we warmed in the hot tub a bit and then braced ourselves for a run through the chilly evening, making a mad dash for our bath towels to high tail it back to our room, to light a final fire in the adobe fireplace and sip a glass of Merlot. While the logs caught fire, we showered and then dried and lay naked, like the lizards of afternoon, in the heat of the crackling flames. Our lovemaking that night was slower, lazier and languid, as we savored the warm glow of this fire and the wine and the memories of the day. We simply enjoyed the others' touch and feel and scent, enjoyed slowing down from our craziness of home, and our constant goings-on. We enjoyed the chance to be together, to remember all the things we loved about one another and set aside the things we didn't, for now. Our time, thus far, had been magical. And we still had over a week to go.

THIRTEEN

Journey on to Utah

"Everything is changing. People are taking their comedians seriously and the politicians as a joke." Will Rogers

Friday, September 28th

The next day we headed north on NM 522, towards the Arroyo Hondo and – and, if we drove long enough – a straight shot up to the Colorado border. Pete and I talked about and relived our last couple of days in Taos. We were so busy chatting that we totally overlooked our turn west onto U.S. Highway 64, and had to retrace ten miles or so, after Pete commented that "The Sangre de Cristos should *not* be getting closer; we've done something wrong." So we turned around and remedied our mistake. *Now* we were headed to the Rio Grande River Gorge Bridge, and were back on our trek out of New Mexico towards Utah, our destination for the next two nights.

Even from the ground this bridge is impressive, perhaps more so, as it is *huge*, spanning 1,200 feet, and joining the east and west sides of the gorge. Built in 1965, the Rio Grande River Gorge Bridge is 650'over the water – one of the highest bridges in the nation – a 3-span continuous truss marvel. It is also a popular place to commit suicide in the region. While Pete and I were visiting, a man's body was found at the bottom, his car parked in an adjoining lot. Authorities were checking into both suicide and the possibility of murder, at the time of our departure.

It is *not* for the squeamish; if one gets queasy at heights, close your eyes and think of something else when you cross it. Of course, being fearless balloonists by now, this was a piece of cake. Pete and I parked on the west side of the bridge and walked out onto the reverberating steel structure to get photographs looking straight down into the Rio Grande river and of each other, with the distant mountains behind us. As cars passed us, the bridge became a dull, repetitive, vibrating pathway of sound, coupling with the winds billowing against us in this immense vacuum of space. It was an awesome and surreal experience to be standing out over this noisy nothingness, one altogether different from floating lazily over it in a lighter-than-air balloon.

This day was beautiful, in the upper 70s or lower 80s, with cloud layers flying low over the Sangre de Cristos behind Taos, far away. The sun was high in the soft blue sky, illuminating the sheer rocky walls of the gorge that we had flown down into but the day before, and reflected a clear mossy green off the river below us. The Rio Grande was again dwarfed by distance.

As we headed back to the car, after our tourist shots, I realized that nature was calling and she seemed urgent. With years of practice at finding a place to pee in a pinch I figured the closest and most unobtrusive would be under the edge of the great bridge, itself. So Pete kindly said he'd study the map, while I slipped and slid down the rocky underside of the bridge, my camera swaying around my neck, as I ignored the warning signs of "Danger" and concentrated on the welcoming orange mesh fencing that promised to catch any falls, *just* in case gravity got the better of my busy feet. Not to worry. Once under this grand metallic feat of engineering, I realized I had by far not been the first to visit. Bits of trash lay on the rocky ground and graffiti was painted on support beams beneath the surface. Indeed, the further out the sprawled words had been sprayed the more ragged they became, and I wondered if some might not have been finished with a deafening scream, leaving Romeo or Juliet sprawled far below, lost and lovelorn and eaten by coyotes. Poor kids; I really needed to cool it with my imagination sometimes…

I took a photograph of this uncommon perspective, before heading back to safety – a little extra memento of the intimate landscapes I get to see because of my quirky plumbing. Once atop the road again, Pete decided he may as well check out the underside of the bridge, and so slipped and slid on down, and I laughed and got a shot of his negotiations.

Okay, *now* we could put some ground behind us. We headed to Tres Piedras, on the edge of the Carson National Forest, with signs that warned it was "Closed in winter." *Hmm.* Might they be expecting snow? This area is considered high alpine meadowland, and it is breathtaking.

We drove across frost-killed grasses in spacious meadows, alert for mule deer or elk, which we did not see. I have read that if global warming continued at the pace it was currently going, these highland meadows might greatly disappear in North America; they would become more temperate zones. Deserts would receive more rain, and the coastal areas of the world stand to be swallowed by the sea, as polar ice caps melt because of these temperature changes causing the oceans to rise. Try buying "Global Warming Insurance" for coastal living...

There goes our beloved Outer Banks, I thought sadly, *not to hurricanes or Nor'easters, after all these centuries, but to mankind's love of fossil fuels and partially to our own federal government's ostrich-in-the-sand approach, in refusing to take the bull by the horns, while we might still contain the beast and join in with the Kyoto Treaty. Much of the rest of the world has the sense to see the climate changes – why can't we? Damnit, Bush, wake up and* stand *up for our environment! Our country must drastically cut back on the burning of fossil fuels and we must curtail industrial emissions and curb vehicle exhaust. Think of the future and wipe your hands clean, for once, of the almighty crude. See that alternative renewable, cleaner energy use is funded: solar, wind, hydroelectric and geothermal – while we still might turn back the clock. Germany – leading the world in the use of wind energy – uses modern wind turbines that produce power enough for five million homes. We have the technology, but then you and your buddy, the Vice President, have clearly conflicted interests. Shouldn't this definitive conflict of interest be illegal in our political system? Shouldn't the interest of* all *of our country – its present and its future – in fact, the long-term environmental impact to the world – be driven not by the almighty dollar that lines your and your high-powered cronies pockets, but, instead, the long-term health of our planet? But then hell, who am I to think these thoughts. I am but a solitary traveler on the planet earth, a mother, a wife, an artist and an eye – you are the President of the United States of America, perhaps the most powerful man in the entire world – at the moment, anyway. Perhaps I should shut up before I end up in one of your internment camps. But I won't. You might silence me, but you won't silence the growing unrest of millions of people in America tired of seeing this country's air, land, trees and water be sucked up like there's no tomorrow, polluted, pillaged and raped, all for the God-almighty bottom line profit of Corporate America. Greed and politics. Your blindness to this environmental crisis now affects the world. Your administration acts as if you personally own the United States and her 'commodities:' the land and her riches, the water, air, and the oceans – and all that dwell on and within.*

"We have not inherited the earth from our ancestors;
we have borrowed it from our children." Chief Seattle, 1854.

This simple statement speaks volumes for our need for environmental responsibility.

"One thing we know which the white man may one day discover. Our God is the
same God. You may think now that you own Him as you wish to own our land.
But you cannot. He is the body of man. And His compassion is equal for the
red man and the white. This earth is precious to Him. And to harm the earth is
to heap contempt on its creator. The whites too shall pass — perhaps sooner than
other tribes. Continue to contaminate your bed, and you will one night suffocate in
your own waste. When the buffalo are all slaughtered, the wild horses all tamed,
the secret corners of the forest heavy with the scent of many men, and the view
of the ripe hills blotted by talking wires, where is the thicket? Gone. Where is
the eagle? Gone. And what is it to say good-bye to the swift and the hunt, the end
of living and the beginning of survival?" Chief Seattle (1786 – 1866), of the
Suquamish Tribe, Washington Territory, both written in 1854:

"This we know.
The earth does not belong to man;
man belongs to the earth…
All things are connected,
like the blood which unites
one family…
Man did not weave the web of life;
he is merely a strand in it.
Whatever he does to the web,
he does to himself."

"If we're to be responsible,
we must accept the fact
that we owe a massive debt
to our environment.
It won't be settled in a
matter of months,
and it won't be forgiven us." Russell E. Train, 1970, over a hundred years later.

The Seven Life Zones:

I'm getting hot under the collar now, so Journal, I will change the subject. I will write, instead, of the Seven Life Zones formulated by a man named Clinton Hurt Merriam, as we headed into the 20th Century. He worked for the U.S. Department of Agriculture and was considered one of the world's greatest naturalists. In studying ecology – the science of all living things – he established seven zones between the equator and the North Pole.

The main determinants of climate are temperature and rainfall on an average, from year to year. In general terms, the distance from the Equator – the latitude – is one of the main influences of climate. The areas closest to the Equator receive more solar radiation than those closer to the poles, thus making these environs progressively warmer.

The Seven Life Zones of the American Southwest: *range from Artic-Alpine of 11,500' above sea level, or higher (alpine grasses); Hudsonian, of 9,500', or higher (spruce & fir); Canadian of 8,000' – 9,500' (Douglas fir, white fir & aspen); Transition at 5,500' – 8,500' (Ponderosa pine); Upper Sonoran, 3,500' – 7,000'(piñon, juniper, chaparral, oaks, sagebrush & grasses); Lower Sonoran, 500' – 5,000' (desert grasses, creosote bush, mesquite, saltbrush, palo verde trees & cacti); Dry-Desert, below 500', (mostly barren).*

When traveling through the Four Corner states, one passes through all Seven Life Zones, the equivalent of a sojourn from the North Pole to the Equator, although this area, of course, is much more arid than the Equator. I believe New Mexico hosts six of these climatic changes, and Arizona, all seven, ranging from the mountains of the Grand Canyon, around the Flagstaff area, to the depths of the Sonoran Desert. That's really an astounding fluxuation in highs and lows, when one stops and considers the diversity of flora and fauna living in one state that result.

We passed standing ponds – welcome water sources in the high mountain terrain – flatly reflecting the quiet blue skies. In coulees, cottonwoods glowed golden, refusing yet to shed their leaves, and small homesteads claimed space in clusters of trees, here and there in these meadowlands. I guessed the hardy landowners must have special permits, four-by-fours, and snowshoes to stay out the winters here, else they migrated to Florida, like the birds. This area would fall within the Canadian/Transitional Life Zone range, I would imagine. I thought of John Muir, who founded the *Sierra Club*, in 1892, another visionary who so loved the natural world, and a statement he wrote: *"Tired, nerve-shaken, over-civilized people are beginning to find out that going to the mountains is going home; that wilderness is a necessity; and that mountain parks and reservations are useful not only as fountains of timber and irrigating rivers, but as fountains of life."* This was written over a century ago; it is immeasurably valid today. We must be sure that We, the People, protect our remaining wild spaces, for they do not revert. Protect them, even if it is from our own political leaders, themselves.

We have been up and over the lower San Juans and headed on to the Brazos Peak. We drove into a large gravel lot that offered huge, sloping shelters against the battering high country winds that can be found here. Last year the beauty of the scenery before us took back seat to our bracing ourselves against the winds and my protecting my newly corrected eyesight from flying debris. The kids had huddled behind the shelters then, only Skye venturing out long enough to appreciate the magnificence of these wild and ancient mountains. We have a photo of her, braced and wind-whipped, against this beauty.

Today the winds were resting, just blowing enough to billow our hair a little. They left the ragged aspens alone. Again, evergreens stood as conical counterpoints before these tattered aspens, some still yellow, but many almost naked now at this altitude of 10,000+ feet, falling in the Hudsonian/Canadian Life Zone range. Far away mountain faces and stands of unleaved aspens shimmered in lavender tones, as distance and disrobing claimed their recent glorious intensity. We stayed and enjoyed the overlook a while, taking some photographs of the echoing layers of San Juan Mountains, breathing it all in, then headed on to Tierra Amarilla, a beautiful, small farming community, after which we would head north on NM 84/64 towards Chama.

This is where we had met Cynthia over a year ago, at the Dairy Queen, sitting smack in the middle of this small town. She had passed Chama heading for Tierra Amarilla for gas, then decided she wouldn't make it that far, so had turned around. If she hadn't returned for gas for Smiley, and then decided to quench her own thirst, we would not have met at all that hot summer's day in June of 2000, with all of our family in tow. This was the Cosmic Dance of circles and friends and kismet taking place before our eyes — which happened to be opened and our antennae receptive — at that time and place. As Joe Leaphorn reminds us, in Tony Hillerman's mysteries: "There are no coincidences."

I've since read that Chama, a small town in the 1880s, boomed as silver mining took hold, and the railway came in. The railroad became a hub and popular attraction, as railroad yards, shops, and a roundhouse offered up one of the nation's last coal tipples. The Cumbres & Toltec Scenic Railroad operates the New Mexico Express from Chama to Osier (which is inaccessible by automobile). This railroad, outdoor recreation and lumber are now the backbone of this little town's economy today.

Pete and I arrived here this beautiful clear fall day, crossing the Chama River, which ran low and dry, on to 'our' Dairy Queen, where we bought iced teas and made a toast to Cynthia's health, happiness, and finding all the things she was seeking in her life. We lingered a bit, made our pit stops, and then roamed out to the airy and colorful Farmer's Market under large umbrellas, just behind the restaurant. This hadn't been here last year. I photographed the bright ruby red chili ristras, freshly hanging full and ripe, over displays of corn, potatoes, watermelon, and large straw baskets of produce.

I could just picture Virginia now, in late September, with her country roadside stands brimming over with a bounty of apples – reds and golds and greens – glass jugs of sweet cider beside them. Yellow jackets would be abuzz above the apples, lazy and intoxicated with their sweet scents. Apple butter would soon be available. Huge fat rounds of deep rich cheddar cheese wheels would beckon, a heavy red wax coating protecting the inner bounty, the all of it glistening, waiting to be sold by the ounces or pounds. Plump perfect orange pumpkins would sit in leaves at the foot of these displays: a harbinger of fall. Crisp, gorgeous, tantaliz-ing deep blue-sky days in the 70s, set against a fruit-loop fiesta of color, as deciduous trees wrapped themselves in a gaudy blanket of color – their last hurrah, once more, before November and December claimed their warmth.

West of Chama and east of the tiny town of Dulce, lies the Great Continental Divide. On the map it looks like a ridge running atop the Cumbres Pass, following the San Juans in a zigzag pattern, northwest up towards Silverton, Colorado, then it heads almost due east. As we drove, a small sign announced the Divide at a rise in the road west – an anti-climax to what one might have expected. Rainfall divides at this apex – to the west the watershed drains to the Pacific Ocean; to the east, towards the Atlantic. This is one of those fascinating geological fancies that add life to such a trip as ours. We, of course, stopped and took photos of one another here. *Tourists.*

Dulce is tiny. It is the capital and principal town of the Jicarilla (Hee-ka-re-ya) Apache Indian Reservation on 850,000 acres, which extends south and west in a zigzag rectangular pattern; the Continental Divide continues to follow the mountain ridges in and out of this rez. The Spanish name means "little baskets;" the Jicarillas are renowned for their woven baskets and ornate craftwork that can be purchased in Dulce. Located at the northeastern corner of the rez, Dulce is also a popular place to restock provisions for anglers, hunters, and other outdoorsmen and women. Once a fierce nomadic tribe in this area, the Jicarilla Apache is now contained on this reservation. Various Apache tribal groups live on other reservations in New Mexico and Arizona.

We stopped just past a dam, a sign above it reading "Dulce Lake." The lake was but a memory of better years that had seen much more rain; the sign was wishful thinking. We took a couple shots of the area and of Pete beside our car, a sheer cutout of rock face across the road and behind him where dynamite must have cleaved the rock to make this road that would take humanity on their travels.

From Dulce we continued on NM 64 through the Jicarilla rez, towards Blanco and Bloomfield, intent on picking up our pace now as the afternoon aged. We had many miles to go yet before we'd be laying down our road-weary bodies in Bluff. We put on Sheryl Crow's *The Globe Sessions* CD to snazz things up a bit, buckled our belts, and readied for the long haul. Time to pull out some of our "World's finest pistachios," load up the shells with the red and green chili powders and "down the hatch 'em," as we drove. We'd refilled our iced teas at the Dairy Queen and could chase them with this cool liquid.

Between Chama and the Four Corners, Gary tells me, in the San Juan Basin, we passed the largest coal bed methane gas field in the lower '48. Driving the long highways across the upper reaches of northwest New Mexico, out of the Carson National Park and on to Bloomfield, where – 25 miles N.E. of town – lies the Navajo Reservoir and Dam, in Navajo Lake State Park. This dam provides much of the water that is needed to support this agricultural area. I've read, however, that years ago Bloomfield wasn't so docile. Settled in 1876, this was a Wild West town with a gang of cattle rustler's that was headed by its own sheriff! (I just love these juicy historical tidbits…)

Bloomfield led us on to Farmington, which is the major industrial and retail center of the Four Corners states. West of town, Navajo Mine is one of the largest coal mining operations in the world, fueling the adjacent Four Corners Power Plant. In fact, Farmington is known to be *"The largest energy-generating power grid in the world, transmitting electricity through an ugly web of lines and towers as far away as Texas and southern California. Farmington's power grid and the Great Wall of China were the two man-made phe-*

nomenons seen by the … astronauts in 1966," according to Peter Matthiessen's book, *Indian Country*, originally published in 1979. What I remembered of Farmington, as we passed through it late Friday afternoon, was that it was a dirty industrial town – with the armpit feel and smell of big ugly civilization that had gone too far in the name of profit, under the guise of progress. We couldn't get in and out of this area fast enough for my tastes. I remembered something Ansel Adams had said: *"My world has been a world too few people are lucky enough to live in – one of peace and beauty. I believe in stones and water, air and soil, people and their future and their fate."*

Bisti Badlands & Shiprock

An interesting aside is that forty miles south of Farmington, on SR 371 (ironically, the 'Vietnam Memorial Highway') lies the De-Na-Zin Wilderness and the Bisti Badlands Wilderness Area. Some 65 million years old, and once fresh-water delta lake deposits, this region may well have witnessed the evolution of the dinosaur. It is now a barren of bizarre and eroded hoodoos, as if on the surface of a strange new planet – a moon valley of one's dreams. It is bleak and windswept, the soft clay mesitas, made of sandstone and shale, might shape-change before your eyes under winds and rain. This ancient geological oddity was thought by the Navajo to be a sacred dwelling place of spirits gone before.

We continued on to Shiprock, of which Tony Hillerman wrote a mystery called *The Fallen Man*. Shiprock is known to the Navajo as "Tse Bitai," or 'Rock with Wings.' Legend has it that they were attacked by a hostile tribe and fled to this rock for haven, whereupon, the story goes, the huge rock 'grew' wings and carried the Navajo to safety. To this day, it is considered to be sacred; at sunset, it is said, it appears to shimmer and float from afar, still loosely anchored to its moorings. The 'moorings' just happen to be the center of three volcanic dikes formed when magma shot skyward and radiated out, forming the basalt core of this gigantic rock millions of years ago. It now towers over 1,700' above the desert floor.

PeterWop and I approached "Tse Bitai" at dusk, intent on capturing this massive structure standing against the fading sun, with the nearly full fleeting moon rising just above, as it had done some thirteen times a year for what would be eternities to a white man. We pulled the Camry up an old road, bordering NM 64, and drove as high as this would take us. I had to make do with my built-in zoom, shooting from afar and capturing much of the general Shiprock area, as well. We ended up buying a postcard entitled "Shiprock," with the magnificent jagged monolith in profile, a full moon rising off to the side, like a free-floating omnipotent golden eye in a lavender sky. But I treasure our own Shiprock photos, for I remember our attempts and the escapade, and the skyline we did catch was a billowing mix of dramatic fiery orange and shrimp tones, blended in with the smoky lower clouds and deeper steelier blues drifting high and haughty above the blaze below. The great rock might be dwarfed by this distance, but the memories we will have of that sky are enhanced by our making the stop and going for the moon (which, incidentally, I cannot locate in our photos). Later I sadly read in a book of weather that these brilliant hot colors on the horizon at sunset are the hallmark of a polluted sky.

Also, while high on this hillside in Shiprock, where we could get a signal on Pete's cell and as it was early enough to call home, we did so and spoke with Jean a while, then with Mary, who was there and ready for the trade-off of our crew. The two had been visiting over tea. All was well on the home front. Everyone was looking forward to a good visit over the weekend, and I smiled inwardly, knowing of the birthday party plans the kids had in store for Mary for Sunday. Now that it was dark and we were alone on this high side road leading to the sky, we made discreet pit stops before heading on into Shiprock, proper, to see if we might find fast food for dinner to hasten our trip along.

(Another aside for fun is that NM 666 intersects Shiprock, heading due north/south. Navajo Detective Jim Chee, in Hillerman's books, talks of the straight shot he takes on 'Triple 6,' down through the Diné territory, often to Window Rock, headquarters to the Navajo Nation. Pete and I actually followed in Chee's steps, as we took a wrong turn out of a Taco Bell in Shiprock, after we'd eaten a little dinner. Fooled by the intersection and the light, we turned around when "Tse Bitai" started, once again, to loom closer.)

Beclabito would be the last town we would pass through on NM 64 before crossing the border into Arizona, where we would soon be in Teec Nos Pos (where Highway 64 ends, after a run across the entire country, starting in Nags Head, North Carolina, on the east coast). On this anniversary trip we would be skipping Colorado, altogether, as Gary and Cynthia would be leading a geology expedition in the Grand Canyon. (Even then, we weren't able to get our schedules to converge although we, also, were heading to the Canyon.) So we'd have to say we saw 'three-quarters of the Four Corners' this time out.

Four Corners, USA

It was the Europeans who mapped the Four Corners of the burgeoning Southwest into a grid of squares. Here is the only region in the United States that you will find the corners of four huge states – of any size, for that matter – converging in perfectly square angles. In June of 2000, Pete and I took our children to the "Four Corners Navajo Tribal Park," paying our $10 fee for a vehicle. This surprised Pete, who – 26 years prior – had visited this (then even more remote) area with only a marker in the sand proclaiming how unique it was. One of my old hippie friends back at home, Cynthia E., tells me how she and a bud stood at this same marker years ago, 'toasting' as they did back then. Not today. The Navajo charge admission to visit this oddity, and have built a very nice brass circular plate, divided into quadrants, each quarter 'housing' a state, set in the center of a large concrete pad. The flags of each of the states – Colorado, New Mexico, Utah and Arizona – fly proudly above their quadrant, each beside a Navajo flag. One Old Glory, with a brass eagle perched on top, flew in between the New Mexico and Navajo Nations flag. This year I imagined that this one was probably flying at half-mast between the others, but I do not know this for sure, as we bypassed this stop.

The Indians built a platform especially for capturing photos of loved ones, sprawled or draped in poses, touching four states at one time. There were clean port-o-potties available in this remote reach of the desert, a visitor's center, and displays of tables of Navajo jewelry under shade tents. I surely recommend that travelers partake in this extraordinary experience at least once in their journey to this region.

The Indians of the Southwest consider the Four Corners area – Mesa Verde, Shiprock, Chaco Canyon, Canyon de Chelly, the Bisti Badlands, Bluff and Moab, etc. – a sacred center of the earth, a place of mystic power, where the Old Ones dwell. It is a place of spiritual abundance to them, home to many shrines and burial grounds. Unfortunately "Bahana" (Hopi for 'White Man') does not hold these sacred places in such esteem. If there are ores of value, or fuels in the earth to be taken, the natives are, once again, forced to step aside – or are hired as labor to reap the profits that will line Bahana's pockets. The Indians are then left with the spent mines, the uranium tailings, the water now deadened from waste products, and the poisoned air. They are left with the refuse of the ravaged lands, which was once their endless hunting ground. It is the story of time eternal.

As we leave New Mexico now, I reflect on this "Land of Enchantment," home to volcanic ruins gazillions of years old, and glorious extended mountain ranges that resulted from the heave and haw of geological change. This is the land of the Anasazis and Mogollon, dating back hundreds of years to the present, whose descendants – the Pueblo Indians – witnessed the influx of the Spaniards, the Mexicans, and the Anglos who, each in their turn, driven by their own cultures and beliefs, left an indelible impression on the history of New Mexico that we see merged to this day. This is the land of the dry depths of deserts long ago under the sea, to towering mountain heights, thus the variety of Life Zones. Magnificent rivers: the Rio Grande, the Little Colorado, the Pecos, the Red River, the Rio Chama, the Canadian, and others, bring welcome water to this thirsty land. Breathtaking wind-whipped monoliths rise defiant and ancient throughout this beautiful state; many pictographs and petroglyphs are painted and etched into the ancient stone, speaking volumes by natives who originally had no tongue. The great Continental Divide weaves its way through the state. From horseback expeditions – in which the proud equine was introduced to the Indian people, and thus changed their lifestyle completely by Spaniards in their quest for "God, gold and glory" – on to the Santa Fe Trail, later to the endless railroads that crisscrossed these open lands and finally to highways and interstates, civilization has left its indelible mark. Today the mines are coal, silver and uranium. Turquoise has been almost depleted. Telescopes sit high in the heavens, exploring the mysteries of the sky and planets. This kaleidoscope of the ancient lands of lore, bridging to the present and the future in this colorful, sprawling, rowdy mix of cultures is what continues to lure and captivate New Mexico's residents and her guests.

Pete and I have now crossed into Arizona. We still have thirty-some lonesome miles of open road to go along this upper northeastern corner of the state, as we travel through Red Mesa and on to Mexican Water, where we will then take Highway 12 North, over the Utah border, heading on up to Bluff. We've put on a Louis Armstrong and Ella Fitzgerald mix I burned from CD's at home, listening to Satchmo's deep liquor-warm and smooth old voice crone "What a Wonderful World" and "Butter and Eggs Man." Ella's wry humor is evident in "Bewitched, Bothered & Bewildered" and "The Lady is a Tramp." What a clear, rich voice… what wonderful, ageless, soulful music.

Deep in the heart of Indian Country, my head back against the seat watching Pete's unshaven profile before dark landscapes flashing by, I started thinking of my own Indian heritage. Or the Indian heritage I *should* have had, had my family not descended from English and German immigrants. When I was a child, roaming wild in the foothills of the Blue Ridge Mountains of Greenwood, Virginia, riding my pony bareback as Indians did, my imagination knew no boundaries. What I knew of my family was that my father's family came from stuffy old bluebloods of the Dawes fortune, directly out of England. They were haughty and strict and would have lived a fine life in the Puritan colonies of New England, only they were born at the wrong time and in the wrong place. Instead, my paternal grandfather and grandmother were Jehovah's Witnesses, she tall and straight as the pitchfork in Grant Woods' *American Gothic*, from 1930. (This is the portrait of the staunch farm couple in front of their farmhouse that looks like a church.) In fact, this painting could have *been* my paternal grandparents. Poor dad. The biggest difference between that couple and my grandparents was that my grandmother was much taller than her husband. I did not particularly care for my grandparents as they did not particularly care for my mother. She was not the socialite that my father – *Dr.* Frank O'Neil Cockerille – was supposed to have married. No, Virginia Eloise Henkel was ten years younger than my father, and although she had no formal education beyond high school, she was intelligent and talented and refused to ever stop learning. My mother's family was German. Her maiden name was Henkel; her great-great-grandfather invented the Henkel Press.

It wasn't until her later years in life, as she researched our family trees and shared this information with us, that I realized how truly interesting a history her family had, and how much the Henkel family had influenced the Shenandoah Valley of Virginia. Her great-grandfather, Sirim Peter Henkel, established the Lutheran Church in New Market, where my mother is now buried; he also established the Lutheran religion throughout the Valley. This was an industrious, inventive, enterprising group of people. True pilgrims.

But I was young and dumb and did not want to be English and German. What I *related* to were the colorful Irish, with their musical lilting voices and their red hair and fiery tempers. In fact, in growing up, I became quite good in my youth in speaking in a brogue, but lost it, unfortunately, as I aged in America. I had a red cast to my long chestnut hair, befitting the Irish, and my eyes were a hazel green – and I had high cheek-bones, which lent themselves well to my 'inherited' Indian heritage... so I choose the Cherokee tribe, not realizing in these earlier years that the Cherokees were found further south, in North Carolina and the like.

It did not matter; I could ride my 'Indian' mount with the best of them. He was a Roman-nosed dark paint pony, with a roach-clipped mane and independent spirit that matched my own. He allowed very few people to ride him, and those that did took their chances. I remember many a mobile mount, as 'Tag-a-Long' – as he was so inaptly called – charged on ahead. I loped along beside him, my left hand entwined in what there was of his cropped mane and the rest of me valiantly trying to spring aboard, as my little sister nearly fell off her own pony, laughing at the two of us. Once on, I'd settle in with a whooping war cry of triumph and off we'd gallop.

Yes, these were the wild, carefree days of my youth; how I/we survived them, I will never know. I'm suspecting God had posted Guardian Angels especially appointed to Marcy and me, and we kept their little wings busily flapping behind us. My little sister, Martha, and I rode together. She prefers the name Marcy, and is the true (Irish?) redhead in our family (dubbed the 'Little Red Caboose,' as she was the last of the bunch of us kids). Her mount, after we outgrew our fat, short-legged Shetland ponies, 'HeMan' and 'Nibbles,' was a palomino pasture mate to Tag, named 'Duffy.' Why Duffy, I don't know, but he was a handsome, gentlemanly equine, much more along the lines of Ashley Wilkes; Tag-a-Long was most definitely the rogue, Rhett Butler. And I was Scarlett (who *did* happen to be Irish), wild and willful and headstrong. (Did this make Marcy Melanie? I don't *think* so...)

So anyways, there you have it. Here we were, smack in the middle of Indian Country, and the latent Indian in me was trying hard to reemerge. I love the land, the flora and fauna, respect the earth, her beauty and her gifts, as the ancients did. I take the time to see her beauty, as the Navajo say: 'Nih zhonigo:' "Walk in Beauty" – and I try, I do try hard, to step lightly on this fragile Mother Earth. To see her many gifts as gifts to us all, to be shared and replenished, and then shared again. Not be to be taken, raped and pillaged by the few, the wealthy, to line their shallow, soulless pockets at the detriment of the many.

As I glanced over at my handsome husband, who was also lost in thought, I took his hand and smiled. We said nothing, except with an exchange of glances. I thought of his heritage and how he'd accepted it without question: the Giannini/y's side, of course, directly descended from Italy over 200 years ago, when Filippo Mazzei brought over Antonio Giannini as an indentured servant to establish early grape vineyards at Colle, a neighboring plantation to Monticello, the home of Thomas Jefferson. When Mazzei returned to Italy, Antonio Giannini later worked directly for Thomas Jefferson, at Monticello, as he was a horticulturist. Of all the languages Pete knew – English, German, some French and some Swedish – he did not know Italian, and for this I will always kid him, until he learns his mother tongue. But PeterWop did inherit the dark hair and gorgeous brown eyes of the Italian gene pool.

Peter's mother's maiden name was Post, a German or Dutch name and her mother was a Westervelt, which is very Dutch. They had come from New Amsterdam, before it became New York. So here you have a fine example of how America was blended into the great mix of individuals and communities and cultures that paint the broad and ever-changing canvas of our times. It is phenomenal to me the diversity in land and people between our shining seas…

And so it goes, the age-old stalemate, this clash of cultures that abound within one blanket society that consists of a kaleidoscope of smaller cultures that make up the United States of America. The great mixing bowl of the world. Our own tossed salad, whose colorful turbulent history is as diverse as the nationalities that paint the past.

It's funny, this mix of cultures, and our heritage in this country. By the time most of us in these generations are born, over two hundred years now from the original European immigrants that came to this newfound land, we are as mixed a mutt as any found in an animal shelter. And we have the hearty genes and stalwart spirit that goes with this blending of bloods. After all, this is what America is all about – a blend of cultures, of ideas, independent pioneers that came to this great country, looking for freedom from oppression in religion and taxes, in whatever forms, and were willing to start a new life in this untamed and promised land in that search. We are descended from pilgrims or rogues, wayfarers who believed in a better life, for themselves and their families, and were willing to trade that which was known and onerous, for the unknown promise of what could be. Our forefathers and mothers were adventurers – for the most part – and they were heroic.

As we headed north out of Mexican Water, up Highway 12 into Utah, I began to doze. The night here was very dark despite the waxing moon, as clouds covered the sky, crowding her out. Pete's voice suddenly rose beside me, excitedly exclaiming: "I *saw* one, Laura! I really *saw* one! A tara*n*tula just scuttled across the road, *right* in front of the headlights!"

"Was it carrying a spider-caller thingy to lure mates?" I asked sleepily, forgetting I hadn't filled him in on my Larson-fantasies.

"*What?…*" he turned and looked at me like I'd gone nuts. "Ra, you're dreaming – go back to sleep. We'll be in Bluff soon, and I'll tell you about the tarantula in the morning."

"That's okay; I heard you, Pete. I'll explain that comment later." I was too somnolent to even try just then.

But soon after Pete braked again, and this time seriously so, as he cursed under his breath: "*Goddamnit* – I forget we're on the Navajo rez now and those free-range animals just roam the roads! See that black shadow beside the road?" He pointed to the right. Our car was now at a dead stop and angled in the road, headlights highlighting the beast; I was now wide-awake. "*That's* a steer that I damn near hit. It just, casually, walked across the road right in front of us." The 'shadow' grazed there calmly, looking for grass patches on the side of the highway, oblivious to his near demise… (and ours?)

Gulp. I'd forgotten about these free-range beasties, too. The Indians grazed them anywhere, inside and outside fencing, in the continual search for grass out here. They depended on their brands to identify them. Last summer, while driving past Kayenta towards the Grand Canyon, we were alarmed when a Range Rover in front of us suddenly braked and then started quickly backing up towards us. Turns out it was an officer from the Navajo Tribal Police and she had spotted a dead horse lying on the side of the highway. Apparently this is a fairly common occurrence out here.

This time we'd gotten lucky, thanks to Pete's sharp eyes. I was certainly impressed by his quick reactions after all these hours behind the wheel. From there on in we took it real easy, still jittery from that close call. Since we were both now wide awake, and to pass the last few miles to Bluff, I shared with my husband how a tarantula might fine-tune his mating practices to better his chances in this Godforsaken country. *That* kept him awake until we pulled into Recapture Lodge sometime around 10 PM.

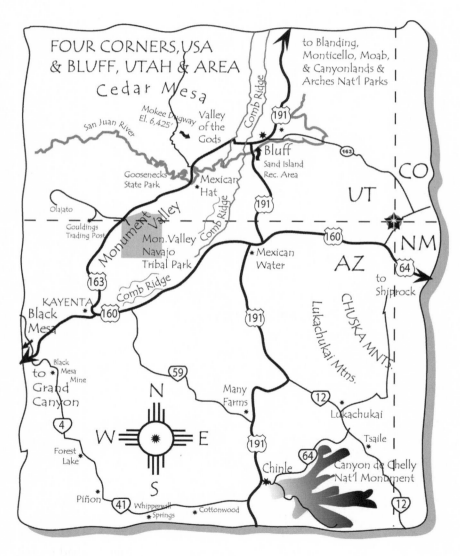

FOURTEEN

Bluff, Utah

"A vasectomy is never having to say you're sorry."
Rubin Carson (but okra does...)

Pete and I checked in, by now wide awake again, the both of us. We were given a room for our two-night stay on the first floor of this small hotel. Jim and Luanne Hook, who own and manage the Recapture Lodge, are good friends of Gary and Cynthia's. The hotel was given its name by the Foushee's, who originally built it in 1959, after one of these charming Wild West stories of which we keep hearing. The story goes that the first people to come survey this area were from the U.S. government, in what was called the Hayden Survey, in the 1860s. They camped 14 or 15 miles east of Bluff. During the night a group of Paiute Indians, native to this area, made off with all the livestock this group had tethered. Undaunted, the surveyors followed the trail to what has now become known as Recapture Wash, and reclaimed their animals. The Hooks bought the lodge and kept the name that the Foushee's had used from this bit of local history.

Recapture Lodge is not a fancy hotel. It is a two-story building with 20 or 30 rooms all opening to the outside. They are simple and clean and provide the multitude of naturalists that visit Bluff an inexpensive and comfortable place to rest their bones after a day of exploring the great open spaces that surround this community. Slide shows are given in the evening – covering topics of interest of the area – by Jim, or his kind and knowledgeable father-in-law, Stan. One of the things that Pete and I remembered most about this lodge from last year when we had rented two rooms, giving one to the children to share, was that the walls were not thick. One could hear just about anything going on in the neighboring room, which made it easy, then, to keep tabs on the kiddos. On an anniversary trip, this was not so good. But heh, it was for two nights, the owners were great, the pool amenities were most inviting, *and* the pool was still open at this time of year.

After settling into our room, Pete and I answered a knock at our door. It was Luanne, who brought to us a gift from Gary and Cynthia for our anniversary. Apparently they had stopped his big old school bus, full of students heading to the Grand Canyon for their geological expedition out of Durango, to drop this off. It was not a bottle of good wine, flowers, or even a card. No, it was a pod of okra. Pete and I looked at each other and laughed.

For, you see, each time our children were conceived okra was involved. For many people around the world, sex seems to be the ultimate method of conception. But not for the Wop and me. (Else, we could have populated the state of Rhode Island, by now.) No, each time okra was eaten, we conceived; for us, conception was vegetable-induced. (Perhaps *this* explains the Virgin Mary's Immaculate Conception?) By the time Skye and Jared were born, we had figured the okra out. So, when in Ft. Lauderdale – 1,000 miles away from my husband over a decade ago – I was offered a Cajun dish with blackened okra by one of my mother's good friends, I felt it safe to indulge. *Wrong.* Little did I know that okra would also have a residual effect. I came home a week later and Pete and I conceived Natalie, our third – and last – child.

Now please don't get me wrong, we love them all dearly, but from then on we have refused to eat okra-*any*thing, not even in a gumbo or stew, and not even after PeterWop had participated in the 'Big V.' Nope, we don't fool around with this potent, innocent-looking little vegetable; we were even careful how we took it from Luanne's hands, as we explained to her the significance of this gift. She walked away laughing her head off. She already had an idea, from knowing Gary and Cynthia, that this was an unusual family – now I'm sure she was sure.

After we closed the door and finished unpacking, I suggested to Pete a swim to unkink from our endless miles on the road. He told me I was nuts, but that didn't phase me at all, as I reminded him of the almost full moon peaking through the clouds (the cloud layer here was not as thick as it had been further south). I *also* reminded him of the cozy little hot tub in the corner of the pool area that I'd remembered from a year ago. *Bingo!* So we changed into our bathing suits, grabbed all the towels we could find, and our jackets, too, for this chilly fall night in southeast Utah, and headed for the water.

The fenced pool area was off in the corner, surrounded by shrubbery. This pool was small, heated by solar panels, and shone a soft aquamarine blue – all very inviting, indeed. A large mulberry tree stood sentry beside it, and again a happy moon peeked at us through the limbs and clouds, waiting to witness more play. It reminded me of last evening at the Sagebrush pool, on a smaller and more intimate scale. But no, the night tonight was too chilly and PeterWop did not want to play – he opted instead for the frothing and bubbling hot tub. Fine. I wanted to swim, so I threw in my kickboard ahead and then, braced on one arm, jumped into the edge of the pool, trying not to get my hair too wet at this late hour. *Daggone, it was chilly!* But it didn't take too long with treading water warm-ups to acclimate, and after this it was bracing and invigorating. The area was so private and the night so late that at this point I came very close to slipping out of my suit altogether, to swim freely under the western evening sky. But my very proper husband, who puts his turn signal on when he leaves our driveway at home, would have had a heart attack if I had done so. Not wanting to break the spell, I behaved while he enjoyed the bubbling suds; I got lost in my thoughts and enjoyed a full water workout before climbing out to join my man, who now sat on the side of the hot tub, waiting for his woman. Together we snuggled down with the energetic jets throbbing at our backs, recapped our day and planned our tomorrow, as the warm golden moon looked approvingly on.

In a while, we bundled up to head back through the brisk fall night to our room. We were by now in the mood for a little late-night loving, but quickly decided to refrain because of the echoing walls. I decided my final unwinding would be to start long letters to each of the children on special photo note cards we had bought for them. Pete read in *Ill Wind*, and soon we were snuggled up and sleeping our first night through in Bluff – only to be awakened by a gang of motorcycle travelers revving their bikes outside, ready to start their explorations. We pulled pillows over heads; I snuggled into my fuzzy bone pillow, and we dozed a little longer before allowing the day to officially start.

Bluff

Bluff, Utah, is known as a 'border town.' It edges three Native homelands – the Ute (from which Utah derived its name), Paiute, and the Navajo. In an ancient river trace above the valley, around 1100 AD, a 'Great House' was built by the Anasazi, predecessors by centuries to all the other tribes. Ruins still remain outside Bluff, proper. The huge sandstone bluffs that give the town its name date back to Jurassic times, over a *hundred million years* ago. Bluff was the first Anglo community in southeast Utah, founded by Mormon settlers in 1880. Winston Hurst, an archeologist of the area, wrote:

"When the Europeans first bounced their wagons into the rocky gulches and dry mesas of southeast Utah around 1880, they found encampments of Navajo and Ute people, about whose history they knew virtually nothing, surrounded by extensive evidence of earlier inhabitants about whom they knew even less... Unrecorded ('deep') history represents about ninety-nine one-hundredths of the human experience in San Juan County." **Historic Bluff City** by Bicycle & Foot, the Bluff City Historic Preservation, © 2002

Bluff's elevation is 4,380' above sea level, placing it in the Upper Sonoran Life Zone (sagebrush, cottonwoods, locust, desert-hardy rabbitbrush, greasewood, piñon, junipers and the like). It teams with birds – even ducks (which one normally doesn't find in the high desert...) – like teals, grebes, goldeneyes, and Canada geese. Seasonal migrants include the white-faced ibis and the American white pelican. Western bluebirds and tanagers visit Bluff and, in the evening, western big-eared bats swoop low after the mosquitoes, over the flood planes of the San Juan. Raptors such as the red-tailed hawk, kestrels, the northern harrier and the golden eagle, live in this region.

Roughly 250 residents enjoy this remote and historic little town's slow and easy way of life, calling it, "The land of room enough and time enough." Indeed the citizens, themselves, claim: "Bluff likely has the highest per capita population of archaeologists, geologists, naturalists, writers and artists of any town in the country." Tens of thousands of acres of public lands surround this community and offer an array of sights such as Comb Ridge, Cedar Mesa and Sand Island, the Valley of the Gods, Mexican Hat, Natural Bridges, Monument Valley, Goosenecks

Canyons and Hovenweep. There are plenty more of the wild desert sights and phenomenon's, too numerous to mention, surrounding this tiny, isolated town set back in time.

Saturday, September 29th

Pete and I dressed for our days outing, intending to explore Valley of the Gods, after a hearty breakfast at the Twin Rock Trading Post Café. This is a sprawling restaurant that offers generous dining, outside or in, beneath two gigantic landmark sandstone pillars known as the 'Navajo Twins,' a sacred site to this tribe. The Navajo Twins, the sons of Changing Woman, are integral in Navajo evolution mythology.

The Twins rose high and embraced, hovering over the building, against the cloud-laced sky. They reminded me of the Twin Towers for a moment, some wind- and water-etched Southwestern sentries, refusing to believe their east coast brethren had fallen. I shook my head at the thought, all of the madness of the Taliban and al-Qaida rushing back now. Still no sign of bin Laden, but George W. was threatening war on Afghanistan at any time, and our government was in chaos. Pete and I had succeeded, for a short time anyway, to put this insanity on the back burner for our anniversary. These Twin Rocks brought it all back. We bought a copy of *USA Today,* and had others from Tuesday, Wednesday and Thursday, that we'd brought to breakfast with us, to catch up. We also had a copy of *The Daily Times*, out of Farmington, and a *Wall Street Journal,* from Tuesday, to update ourselves with what was going on in Washington and the rest of the world; here, one felt isolated and outside of it all. Perhaps we should leave well enough alone and not bother with the papers, at all…

The long, low porch of the Twin Rocks Trading Post & Café extended the length of it, supported by a dozen massive Ponderosa pine pillars. It reminded me of the sturdy old homestead in the TV western *Bonanza,* of years ago. Towering above and behind the café, dwarfing the huge building, a tremendous sweep of stratified sandstone formed an immense backdrop of solid wall. It was here that the Navajo Twins sat high atop this fortress, and off to the right other large square rock formations perched, like our giant's molars, plucked from his mouth. It was a spectacular sight, making one feel puny; I felt we were viewing the world from an ant's perspective.

Pete and I opted to breakfast outside on this gorgeous fall day, nearly the last day in September. Beside us the wacky and enormous 'Sunbonnet Rock' stood, a madcap mushroom of a thing, this many-toed stone with a large horizontal 'hat' tilted precariously atop. It looked like a Jim Henson character, solidified. I felt we were vacationing on another planet. I had brought my letters to the children, and while Pete read the paper and leafed through visitor's guides to the area, I continued to write to each of them about our travels thus far: the hot-air ballooning experience; meeting the cowboys; and of seeing Art and Cindy; the Trail of the Painted Ponies; the Turquoise Trail, etc. With each of them I'd share a different part of the trip, thinking of what they would like to know. Our food came and we set aside our doings to enjoy this generous sustenance.

After we ate, we read the paper together, discussing the turmoil our country was in. Headlines like these were rampant: From *USA Today*, Tuesday, September 25th: **U.S. targets terrorists' cash:** *White House order aims to freeze bin Laden's assets in U.S., abroad.* **Should the twin towers rise again?** *Americans are split on whether to rebuild these icons of success or create a memorial.* **Write-in movement is pushing Giuliani for a 3rd term: Popularity of NYC mayor fuels talk. Magnitude of loss revealed in details of lives. A look at Ground Zero:** *Rescue efforts ... continue toward recovery and stabilization of the underlying foundation. Now a network of systems and people has taken shape.* **Pilots ready to fight to defend friendly skies. Oil prices plummet on global sell-off:** *Plunge could help boost economy as consumer costs fall.* **Stocks soar out of losing streak:** *Some experts predict end of bear market near.* **Workers' task as painstaking as it is painful. Unlike Pearl Harbor, this tragedy was live.**

From *The Wall Street Journal*, Tuesday, the 25th: **Aiding and Abetting:** *Bush's Financial War on Terrorism strikes at Islamic Charities.* **'Porkchop' is among hero dogs combing Trade Center rubble:** *Trained to sniff out the living and the dead, hundreds gladly work 12-hour shifts.* **CIA finds itself at center stage in Bush's war on terror.** From The *Albuquerque Journal*, Wednesday, September 26th: **More Attacks are Possible: AG** [Attorney General] **Cites Hazardous Chemicals. Ashcroft warns of more attacks. More reservists called up, big offensive unlikely. Israel, Palestinians reportedly set truce-talk date. Afghans flee to safer lands within or across borders.**

And from this latest *USA Today:* **Terrorism fight, relief efforts could deplete budget surplus. Amtrak plans tighter security due to attacks. Bush seeks 'cooperation' of Afghan people. Russia rallies 'Stand' in support of U.S. fight. Terrorists tasted lusty lifestyle they so despised. Truckers who carry hazardous material are be-**

ing scrutinized… The news continued, but most attention was focused on the upcoming war and the terrorists, our new and invisible, enemy.

The Daily Times read: **Navajo Code Talkers to receive silver medals in November: Proclamation issued in response to Sept. 11 attacks.** *"The Navajo Code Talkers Association chose Nov. 24 – two days after Thanksgiving – for 380 Navajo Code Talkers to receive their silver medals during a ceremony at the fairgrounds in Window Rock, AZ."* We read over coffee for a couple of hours, in the tranquility of Twin Rocks Café, lost in another time zone, in another place and time, the news of life in America post 9/11.

I hadn't finished the letters yet, and planned to do so later that day or evening. I wanted to be sure they'd be postmarked in Bluff, to remind the kids of our trip last year, so we headed on through the little community to find the post office. Here there was no flag flying at all – I guess they'd taken it down for the weekend, as they were about to close. The kind older gentleman inside weighed the envelopes for us, stamped them, and I assured him I was only adding one more page to each, and a bit of desert sand after our trip to Valley of the Gods today, before sending them on. He told us that if we were to bundle them with a rubber band, after I finished, he'd look for them on Monday morning and would be sure to get them postmarked and sent, as we'd be long gone.

I thanked the gentleman for his patience and help and then stopped outside the post office to get a photograph of the fencing across the road – one of those imaginative creations where one makes do with materials on hand. In this case cedar or juniper trunks were interlaced in a crisscross fashion, braced up against one another and balanced, to form a sturdy, see-through, shoulder height fence that ran the length of this road. An old brass headboard was mounted there, strapped to a post, as a makeshift gate. An aged black gentleman wearing coveralls, a white tee shirt, and a straw hat, rode by on a small bicycle as I shot one of the photos, adding local flavor. Sandstone cliffs rose behind as a solid stone wall in the background, and below them were the remains of a stone home, or fort, only broken corner walls rising up to the roofless reaches of the sky. Weeds and faded grass tufts lay ragged at the base of this forgotten ruin. This tiny town breathed history, promising up her secrets if only we slowed to listen to her whisperings.

Pete and I left the area then, with our cooler packed with regenerated ice packs that Luanne had kindly refrozen for us. We had tea, some ice from the café, a couple of Coronas and limes, fruit, and doggy bags of omelets and homemade biscuits from breakfast. We'd be good to go for a long while. The day was warm enough to wear cargo shorts and we wore hiking boots to protect ourselves in our explorations, as we knew rattlesnakes were endemic to the desert scenery. Short-sleeved shirts were the ticket that day, but we kept jackets in the backseat for the inevitable temperature drop of the evening desert. Later that night we'd be back to tackle the past weeks laundry. We had plenty of film, a couple of disposable cameras for the Wop and we were set to go roam.

Sand Island

Our first stop on the way out was Sand Island to see the petroglyphs carved up to two thousand years before us, by the prehistoric Anasazi that had lived here along the San Juan. These natives of yesteryear had farmed this floodplain site. Early weaving, basket making, and jewelry making began with the native migration about 100 B.C.- 400 A.D. The Mogollon Indians, from the south – the great potters – and the Anasazi, from the north – the basket makers – appeared before 500 A.D.; their complex societies left ruins and artifacts. Around 600 A.D. elaborate pottery designs were created by the evolving native cultures. In 800 A.D. the Indians made homes in villages of pit houses.

By 1150 A.D. Chaco Canyon – the Anasazi culture – was at its peak, as a trading and cultural center. These are the 'cliff dwellers,' found in many areas throughout the Four Corner region of the Southwest, who disappeared without a trace, leaving historians and anthropologists speculating on various theories since then. 1250 -1400 A.D. found ancient sites abandoned as modern pueblos were founded.

Today Sand Island is used as a boat ramp and campground for adventurers to enjoy the wonders of the natural world found here. Huge walls of sandstone, that looked as if they had been sliced in half by our giant's knife to expose the swirling buff-colored stone inside, formed formidable fortresses around us. We hiked down around the cottonwoods and Russian olives looking for these ancient carvings, blackened by age and etched in the ancient stone, watching our step falls all the while for snakes. Mischievous Kokopelli, the musical man of myth playing his eternal flute, was carved many times on these walls of art.

From Sand Island, which is the main boat launch area for this length of the San Juan River, we headed out of Bluff on highway 163, past Comb Ridge, a long serrated hogback ridge of sandstone that extends 80 miles south, southwest to Kayenta. It was an impressive length of rock, jagged at the top with the cool blue of the sky contrasting against the warm manila below.

Past Comb Ridge, Pete and I were awed by a vast sweep of mounded rock formed as if, once again, our giant had been on the scene. He had taken a brush loaded with color – or perhaps he had used a palette knife this time – and, in one deft swoop of his hand had left a tawny mound of pigment to harden. Hardy sap-colored junipers, rabbitbrush and cedars dotted the base, in deep counterpoint greens. An amazingly beautiful cerulean sky full of cottony cirrocumulus clouds completed this landscape of rich, pure hues. I was thunderstruck by this beauty and insisted we stop roadside to absorb it all – let it osmose into our memory and into our souls. To help that process, I also took about five photographs, one frame leading to the next, to capture the panoramic sweep of rock laid low over the earth's surface. This was a magical canvas of pure golds, earthy greens, and deep blue sky full of mackerel clouds suspended above – like a huge rift of cotton candy that had burst in exhilaration and then been left to drift aimlessly over our heads, with nothing else to be but beautiful.

FIFTEEN

Valley of the Gods/Footloose & Fancy Free

"Don't cross this field unless you can do it in 9.9 seconds. The bull can do it in 10." (Sign on a bison range)

Valley of the Gods

After our Cosmic communing with nature we tore ourselves away to continue on to the Valley of the Gods, off to the west of Bluff, out in the middle of this nowhere. Pete, in an adventurous moment, decided to bushwhack with our Camry, pretending it was a rugged off-road vehicle with all-wheel drive that could handle the deep soft sands of the back country desert. Oh yeah. We inched along, imagining a road to be where we weren't for sure there was one, and hoping like crazy we wouldn't be dead-ended and thus need to reverse our way back through these near invisible ruts of sand. No such luck. We reached a dead-end at the mouth of a deep, dry arroyo and there was no choice but to close our eyes a moment and pray that we'd be able to find again this path from whence we'd so bravely tiptoed. We slowly, carefully, undid this spontaneous deed, with Pete bent around in his seat, his hand on the back of my seat, half the time his sunglasses resting on the tip of his nose for a better view out the rear window. Occasionally, I'd open my door to see if it looked anything like a road. Eventually we retraced our way to hard surface and that felt grand. We sat for a minute, thoroughly relieved, looked at each other and laughed.

"Wanna' try that again, Cowboy, just using a different road?" I asked him, impishly, "Or do you want to go on in like most sane people do, and use the entrance?"

The Wop just gave me a look over his dipped-down sunglasses, letting me know I was pushing it, and said: "Let's choose the sane route and get there." He flipped his glasses back up over his eyes, pulled the Camry on to the main road and we headed to the official entrance of the Valley of the Gods, off U.S. 163.

I would love to know how this land got its name. My guess it is for the mammoth sandstone structures left standing triumphantly after millennia's of wear from weather. They are the Gods. This land is known as "Cedar Mesa Cultural & Recreational Management Area," part of a 360,000 acre spread. Valley of the Gods is not as commercial as Monument Valley, and therefore not as well known. The monoliths, overall, are not as dynamic, but still it is an awesome place. And that particular Saturday, it was ours. We braced ourselves to be bombarded by the ultra fine red granules, like brick dust that has been pulverized, that permeates every crevice and pore it touches. Not long into the trip our car was covered by the fine red sands. Each time we got out to trek up or around a butte, we'd come back a little dustier, covered in rouge, with more sand on and in our socks. Our hiking boots and legs were rust-colored, and I shuddered to think what these minute particles were doing to the inner workings of my Canon.

Despite the dusting, Pete and I thoroughly enjoyed our couple of hours driving quietly through this sprawl of massive geological remnants, listening to a *Coyote Oldman* CD a client had given me years ago. What a perfect backdrop for the whisper of the ancients in our ears. I filled a couple of film canisters with this powdery red sand, planning to take some home as a souvenir and to put a pinch of it in each of the letters I'd be sending east, to share the trip with its recipient. Each time we got out of the car, we laughed – or grimaced – at how it had left a film on the inside doors, on the carpets, just everywhere. (The rental agency would *love* us for this! I don't believe 'bush-whacking' was in the contract.) But the damage was done, and I was beginning to suspect this was how the Indians had become known as 'redskins.'

In the middle of the desert, near the west end of the road through Valley of the Gods, lies a small B & B called, appropriately, "Valley of the Gods Bed & Breakfast." It is a stone lodge literally in the middle of nowhere, where one can truly get away from the madcap world of humanity. It is solar and wind powered, and thus off the grid, like the earth ships back in Taos. Don't expect a color TV or a cappuccino; here one has left behind the civilized world of such offerings.

Moqui Dugway

Off to the far edge of Valley of the Gods, Cedar Mesa rises 1,000 feet grandly above the desert floor. The road to the top is called Moqui Dugway (highway 261). One reaches the top by steadily driving round and round a series of switchbacks that leave one with the feeling they're motoring their way directly to heaven. It is quite the experience. This was built during the uranium boom to aid trucks hauling this radioactive ore from mines on Cedar Mesa to the mill at Halchita, near Mexican Hat. We had poured waters a ways back to soothe our dust-parched throats, and sipped these as we wound our way up and around Moqui Dugway, stopping to 'ooh' and 'aah' and take photographs at pull-offs up this highway to heaven. On a clear day such as this you feel you can see to the borders of neighboring states – in fact, I'd lay a bet you could see *way* down into Arizona – maybe clear down through this state and on to Texas – if you covered your eyes from the glaring sun and had the vision of an eagle. Sometimes we'd see, far down below us, the rusted carcass of a car or truck that had careened off the edge of these switchback cliffs, to be left there, then, for eternity, as there was no way back up to salvation. From our towering perspective, high, high above, the B & B looked lost and lonesome way down below us, in the midst of these sandstone deities.

At the top of Moqui Dugway we found a pull-off, where we could perch above the desert lands far below, and popped open our Coronas. We toasted to braving the red sands and the drying sun that wicks moisture from your body by the millisecond in this arid desert heat. In summer it would be just unbearable, which is why anything, or anyone, with a lick of sense finds a cool place under a rock or in a hotel, to siesta for the afternoon. Keeping an eye out for scorpions and/or rattlesnakes, Pete and I carefully found a place to sit to picnic and then we finished the doggy bag breakfast from the café from this morning, along with a couple of oranges, and savored the sights. We tried to locate the back road we had tried to come in on earlier, but from this distance it was impossible. It had been hard enough to see the ruts when overtop them! But we could see the tiny ribbon of U.S. 163, leading into the Valley *way* down below.

It was time to move on and try to locate the old Oljato Trading Post, at Goulding, where we had hoped to arrange an overnight ride into a place called Mystery Valley for Sunday. We'd found it on the Internet and called them for details. Now we'd drive down and check into making the arrangements. We packed up our picnic and rewound our way back down the multiple steep switchback roads of Moqui Dugway, listening to some Joni Mitchell and Van Morrison tunes from yesteryear, enjoying this freedom and the vast cloud-studded skies.

Goosenecks and Mexican Hat

Soon after leaving Valley of the Gods one comes upon both Goosenecks State Park and Mexican Hat. Both are fascinating. Goosenecks is another must-see off of U.S. 163, providing a wondrous overlook of the lazy San Juan River far below. The distance across these canyons is 1 mile, but floating down the San Juan one must traverse in and around these massive fingerlike canyons for 6 miles. They looked to me like alligator heads resting atop green bodies of water – just the top of the head and eyes seen – ready to spring up and take ones head off. Goosenecks Canyons are called 'entrenched meanders,' dug out over time by the silt-laden river. We stopped here last year with our teenage trio, who had wandered around in awe of the deep ravines holding the slow and sparkling water below. Navajo artisans had sat at the top behind long tables selling their handmade jewelry, captivating Skye and Natalie. Jared had walked around with my camera around his neck, carefully framing monumental photos, his expression intense, a young Ansel Adams at work.

A little further south(east) Mexican Hat is set back off the main highway, but can be seen from a distance, as it is immense. It is named because it has a 2,500-ton 'sombrero' that sits precariously above a 200' cliff. The hat, itself, is 60' wide and 12' thick. There is a special road to take one back in to loop around and see Mexican Hat. We drove in to get photographs, as the light was so dynamic in the deepening afternoon, and we had not driven this loop with the family last year. Behind the red rock balancing act one is awed by a fine example of the 'painted desert.' As we drove further south, deeper into Arizona, more and more often we see these monumental, undulating, shifting mountains of striated sand art. Layers of soft southwest colors are 'painted' – as if with sure horizontal brush-strokes of our creative giant's hand – into colossal dunes, echoing the soft, flowing curvatures of these miraculous mountains. Light plays upon the painted dunes leave one mesmerized by this artistic sweep of nature before them. This was the backdrop of the Mexican Hat landmark, its dusty brick colors warm before the varied grays and softer peach sands of these striated dunes. In the foreground, sage and desert grasses sang sweetly golden in the afternoon air. In the front of this preposterous oddity small oil wells pumped away, like pre-historic skinny black birds, pecking endlessly for bugs in the sand. This became another of our postcard cameos of what we felt the Southwest is all about.

Oljato Trading Post

The Wop and I continued our journey on to check into our overnight ride for Sunday. We soon found the turn-off for the Oljato Trading Post across from the entry to Monument Valley, our Monday destination; a small sign directed us to turn west and follow our faith that this dusty little road led anywhere. To our left a vast sandstone cliff rose far above our heads – I later found this to be the famous Mitchell Butte, from our AAA "Indian Country" map. At the base of it grazed a herd of Indian ponies in assorted colors – I went bananas as the light was on them in the settling sun, and the picture was ripe for photographs.

But Pete insisted in driving on and past them, saying he didn't want to risk the place closing before we could talk to those that ran this show. He had a point. But still, I squirmed and fidgeted – the whole scene had been unbelievably perfect for Wild West shots – I could see them as a basis for a painting. "You can catch this shot when we leave." Pete said.

"No, the light will have changed completely, – haven't you noticed the sun is setting? We'll lose this moment, Pete." I was aggravated. *I wanted the keys to the car, for once; this was too much like the remote control wars at home.*

"Yes, I have, Laura, which is why I want to get to the trading post – they're probably getting ready to close."

"*Humph.*" was my only comment, as I set my jaw. The photographs *might* have taken all of five minutes.

We found the old trading post sitting there close to a series of swirling, rounded, tawny cliffs that sloped down to the sands. Painted on them in white letters were the words 'Oljato, Utah.' Guess this was the place; Pete and I got out to look around. I'll be darned if there wasn't a road leading off into the desert that Pete insisted was a landing strip; it looked as if it tapered off into nowhere. Funny, I just don't picture reservations and Indians and planes in the same thought. The building, itself, looked very old, the front of it a faded rock structure, with a Ponderosa pine beam header wedged in between these rocks, and under this a whitewashed screen door flanked by four windows set into the stone. The mullions were painted a turquoise blue. In the upper part of a window to the left of the door a room air-conditioning unit rested, just beneath the header. Centered above this was a sign reading 'Oljato Trading Post.' A wooden sign in front of the dirt lot said: Est. 1921. A large white ice machine stood to the side. There were also a couple of hitching posts in front to offer the more authentic old-west visitor parking.

Two mongrel dogs that looked as if they were littermates came around the corner to greet us. I was thrilled – I hadn't had an 'animal fix' since Wednesday, so the first thing on my agenda was to kneel down to greet the little fellas while Pete went inside to talk business. What *sweet* little dogs! One was predominantly white, with black ears, a freckled face, and a tail that waved and billowed over her body, like a flag. The other was predominantly a map of black over white, again with black ears over a white face, and her tail was not nearly as endowed. Both were well cared for. They happily lapped up the attention, as I sat and talked to each of them. For me, this loving the little mutts was worth the trip to Oljato, altogether. How I missed our menagerie…

After a bit I stood up, brushed the seat of my shorts off, dusted my hands together, and went on inside to see how Pete was coming along. Walking through that door was a walk back into time. Like the Santuario at Chimayó, everything inside smacked of yesteryear. The floor was old and dusty, large countertops were built into the small store, and wound an 'L' to the left. Items that might have been sold at the turn of the century were on display. Shelves lined the whitewashed wall at the back of room, full of bottled and canned goods, where a large white sign said: "Oljato – Utah, Elevation 4838 Ft. –Runway 2600 ft." Beside it were antlers from a large buck and below it another Ponderosa pine header ran the length of the room. On the beam a horseshoe hung upside down (to hold luck) and below it another sign was painted with a bright blue sky, a sun dazzling in the middle, and a butte to the right and the left of a pool of water, reflecting the sun. Like a rainbow, it read "Oljatoh

Trading Post" in an arch of letters. Underneath, beside one butte read 'Oljato, Utah' off to the right, above the other butte, read 'Kayenta, Arizona.' *Was there a second trading post, or could they not decide where this place was?* I thought. *Or did it fall between the two?*

Pete was talking to a man behind the counter, asking him questions about the ride. This man was of medium height, roughly our age, and nice looking. Said his name was Kyle. Yeah, he could help us with the overnight camping ride; it would begin around El Capitan, and we'd need to be there mid-afternoon tomorrow if we were going to ride into Mystery Valley by sundown. As he was talking, a Navajo fellow came in and told Kyle that he had a flat tire – could he give him a hand? Kyle looked at us and said: "This won't take long. Let me change the flat, and I'll be right back. We'll work out details."

"But wait a minute, we haven't decided we're going for sure. Can't you just answer a couple more questions, and then we'll be on our way?" I asked, perturbed with the interruption, when we'd have completed our questions in five, maybe ten minutes, max.

"Listen," he said as he walked out the door. "Hang tight. I'll be right back, and then we can make the arrangements. If you want, you can go in and look at the artifacts in the back room. It's something of a history museum. I won't be long," the man assured us again.

"Well," Pete looked at me, "I think that was rude; we were here first, and we weren't going to be much longer. Now we'll just have to twiddle our thumbs. Let's go on back and see what he's talking about." He gestured towards the back room, and opened the swinging door between the counters for me to pass on through, but I could see that he was also perturbed.

We walked on back to a small room with very old framed sepia photographs on the walls of what looked like frontiersmen, and some faces of the Navajo. Dust had settled over them. A skull of a steer was painted scarlet and black with a circular Indian painting in the forehead, and two eagle feathers draped down between the horns. Beside this a large bow hung vertically from the wall. Various arrows with feathered ends rested against the textured beige walls. An old table held bits of antlers and a mirror; atop this was a gold and mahogany sign – looking out of place, as it was far too new – that claimed this to be a Utah Historic Site. Beams ran across the ceiling, and the floor was, incongruously, a gray linoleum design, which was entirely out of place. An old Singer sewing machine stood against a side wall, with a blue and gray striped Navajo blanket folded over the middle. An Indian doll, her pale blue skirt swirled around her, was working away weaving a blanket at a loom made of a deer antler. I had to hand it to them for their imagination. To the left side were gaily-colored yarns, and off to the right above two drawers a wooly sheep doll stood. I'm sure this was all symbolic of the Navajo's reliance on sheep for its wool, leading to their livelihood of weaving.

We spent about twenty minutes looking around in the back and then I told Pete, since Kyle hadn't showed up yet, I was taking the car back out to the horses and see if I might still have enough light to get my shots. "Yup. You always gotta' hurry up, so we can wait. I'd have had the shots and that would have been the end of it, you know; I wouldn't be fussing now."

"Just go. I'm sorry – I *could* have stopped just a minute, but I really thought they'd close on us."

"Who knew," both of us were miffed at this wait. "I'll be right back." He gave me the keys and smiled sheepishly. I returned his smile and took off.

Camera around my neck, I spoke to the startled pups as I ran to the car and hopped in. There was still some daylight now, but not much. The light would be altogether different for these photographs. I backed out, careful not to hit either of the dogs, then shot down the straight stretch of road ahead, looking out for the big cliff and the little horses. It felt good to be driving again. Funny, I didn't remember the road being this straight. And then it was I realized that I was on the runway – a straight shot to nowhere! Well, didn't I feel stupid. I made a face of contrition, and put my hand on the back of the passenger seat, to see if I might be able to turn around. Sure, and get stuck in deep sand. My only option was to back up to the trading post. *Oh well, I need practice*, I thought; *it's been a while*. So I backed up the long road, and turned around only to see my husband standing there with a righteous smirk on his face, his hands on his hips, shaking his head and trying not to laugh out loud at my blunder. "I *tried* to wave you down," he said, as he stuck his head in the window, "but you never even looked back."

"Oh. Shut. Up. I had a goal, and, if you'll excuse me, I still do…" I knitted my brows and tried to look cool, but inside I was feeling fairly blonde. Here, my first opportunity – *finally* – to drive, and I had opted to fly, instead. *Oh well…* "Pete, Yogi Berra once said, 'When you come to a fork in the road, take it.' So I did. Bet *you*'ve never made such a blunder, Wop."

"Never."

"Uh huh." Condescending son of a gun. Sometimes I wondered why

I stayed married to the man. A saying by H.L.Mencken, *"Getting married, like getting hanged, is a great deal less dreadful than it has been made out,"* flashed through my mind. *Ha!* But here he stood, charming me all the while he playfully mocked my faux pas, arms crossed on his chest, that smug smile on his face, standing there rocking on his heels... "I'm leaving you, Pete. I'm going to go get those photos of the ponies. I may just leave you here stranded, you know..." And off I went, on my way.

There weren't many options, so, as Robert Frost so eloquently said: I choose the road not taken and, once again, found the small heard of Navajo ponies scattered out into the scrub nowhere near the scenic butte as backdrop. I got out slowly, talking to them quietly, and popped the lens cap off my Canon, checking the light settings as I eyed the horses and eased as close to them as they felt comfortable. The best shots now would be backlit ones, all golden-edged, as the sun called it a day behind them. There were paints and bays and sorrels, all a fine example of the small-boned, short-legged Indian ponies of which I'd read. They had shaggy, unkept manes, curious eyes, and common heads. They were more utilitarian than beautiful, but they were sturdy, rugged, and priceless to the Navajo.

After my successful photographic session, I joined PeterWop back at Oljato. He was still giving me a superior male air about my driving snafu; I ignored the man. Kyle was still nowhere in sight; by now we'd waited 40-45 minutes. "Let's just leave him a note with our hotel number. I'm hungry and tired of waiting." Pete said.

I had to agree. "It's a sign, Pete. Maybe we weren't meant to do this." He arched an eyebrow at me. "But let's at least buy a couple of those apples for the road." On the counter was a bowl of red delicious for 50¢ each, looking as incongruous as the patterned gray linoleum floor. We penned a note telling Kyle we had tired of waiting, please call us, left him a buck for the apples and left, saying goodbye to the dogs.

By the time we got back to Bluff it was dark, except for the golden moon rising low in the deep blue starry sky. We chose a place called The Cottonwood Steakhouse, on the right as we entered Bluff. We walked beneath an arched ranch sign to find a long over-hang under which picnic tables, covered in red & white checkered clothes, sat. More tables were placed throughout a big, open yard. Lanterns were hung all around, and long strands of lights hung from trees. Steer skulls, including Longhorns, were mounted to every hangable surface. To the right, as one entered, a boxed-in building housed an open-air grill, where a couple of men in white aprons over flannel shirts, jeans, and cowboy boots, flipped huge steaks. White chef hats had replaced the probable Stetsons.

The place was packed. It looked like everyone that lived in Bluff, and their uncles, had come here for dinner tonight. We were finally seated at a table under the overhang and a pleasant older waitress that had the down-home charm of Thelma came to get our order quickly. We got a couple of steaks, with the ranch fries and homemade coleslaw, and a couple of brews. We were famished; it was later than we'd expected to get back with the hold-up at Oljato and all. Our week's worth of laundry still lay ahead, and we'd want to pack up a lot of our things tonight to take some pressure off the morning. *Ugh. Back to the clock.* We waited for our dinner, sipped our beers and discussed Oljato, Kyle, and our possible overnight ride out of El Capitan, in Mystery Valley.

"Well, what do you think about all this now, Ra? You still want to ride?" Pete sat on his bench across from me, willing to lean one way or another. This long stretch in the saddle was much more for me than for him; horses did not come naturally to the man. Hand him a trumpet or a golf club and he would be in heaven. He took a big swig of his beer, his warm brown eyes questioning mine intently.

"I don't know, Pete. You *know* I want to ride and how much I — and I hope *we* — have been looking forward to this. But from what this Kyle fellow was hinting at before he disappeared, it seems it'll be awfully expensive. And maybe disorganized."

"Yeah, I was getting that impression, too."

"Maybe, you think, a little too disorganized to be so expensive?" I queried, an eyebrow raised. "I *really* had wanted to go, but this money sure would buy a lot of hay to feed our own horses back home this winter, anniversary, or not."

"Listen, Laura, it's your call. I'll support you one way or another. I know how much you were looking forward to a long ride out here, and the overnight camping — all of it. But it will be expensive, and Kyle kind of blew it, in my book, by letting us hang to dry like that."

I smiled at my husband and friend. He really would go one way or another. "I agree with you, PeterWop — I think Kyle blew it, too, frankly. I've got a gut feeling that says keep going, we'll ride in Canyon de Chelly. I don't know if I could feel comfortable handing over all that money to whatever it is they want to offer up now. Let's just skip this, okay? I still think it's a 'sign'." I added and winked at him…

"Yeah, yeah. Maybe it's a 'sign.' If we skipped on the ride, this would put us in Monument Valley tomorrow, instead of Monday, you know

– and on to the Grand Canyon a day early. That'd be fine by me." The Planner of the Itinerary had returned.

"I thought so," and smiled at him, leaning back out of the way, as our waitress served our dinners. Large platters of food were laid before us, the steaks sizzling beside our fries and coleslaw.

"You two need anything else now, you just holler at me, awright?" our waitress told us and grinned in our direction before she took off to wait a new table that had been seated.

"Alright then, case closed. We'll add another day to our itinerary. That looks *great*." Pete eyeballed his meal. I think the subject was absolutely closed. The Wop had a steak laid out before him; we had an extra day in the Grand Canyon, and much less time in the saddle. All around, the man was pleased.

Dinner at the Cottonwood was delicious – a mite on the heavy side, but we didn't indulge in this down-home cookin' too often. So we enjoyed our steaks and home fries, sipped our beer, had coffees but passed on the rhubarb pie, and headed on back to the Recapture Lodge to gather our grubbies. When we got back to our room, Jim told us somebody named Kyle had called and left a message. It was too late to call him back tonight – we'd reach him in the morning before leaving. We gathered our clothes and headed on to the laundromat.

While the wash loads ran at the Cottonwood Laundry across from our hotel, Pete read more of *Ill Wind*. I finished the letters to the kiddos during the washing process and, during the dry cycle, wrote a long letter to Jean and Allan on a beautiful photographic note card I'd bought of one of the old Spanish churches, telling them of our trip. Next would be a long letter to Mary, but that would have to wait. I wanted time to think about what I'd be writing to her. October 1st was Monday, and I'd always tried to be supportive after Galen's death. I would want to be thinking carefully about what I wrote, and concentration here was too broken up with all the stopping and starting of the machines. Maybe I could get her letter started and a few postcards in at breakfast, though.

Before leaving home I had arranged with the children to have them throw a surprise birthday party for Mary on the Sunday of her stay. They would work in cohort: Skye would slip Mary out of the house a while to take her for ice cream, and to show her the coffee shop where she worked; Natalie would stay at home, bake the cake, and decorate. Jared would do his part in helping by never leaving the computer… thus keeping him out of Nattie's hair. This was the plan, at least; it would have

Mary feeling loved and hopefully make the 1ˢᵗ, her day of departure from her nieces and nephew, and the anniversary of her son's death, much easier to face.

Sunday morning, September 30th

We were greeted by another beautiful day as we packed our freshly laundered clothes, bags of gifts we had bought, our cooler and food supplies, the last of the bedraggled bouquet of flowers, and our pod of okra. When we went to the office to check out, Luanne told us that this fellow Kyle had called again, and again had left his number. Pete and I looked at each other; our decision was made, but we'd give the man a call at breakfast. We thanked Jim, Luanne, and Stan for our stay, said our goodbyes, and headed on to the Twin Rocks Trading Post and Café for another hearty breakfast to fuel the day ahead. After last night's dinner, I wasn't especially hungry. It'd probably be another doggy bag.

We ordered, eating outside on the big covered porch again, surrounded by the enormous red rock cliffs and the 'Sunbonnet Rock.' Pete tried his cell phone to call Kyle while we waited for breakfast, but couldn't get a signal. Out here it was hit and miss. Trying to find a signal kept reminding me of the scene from the original *City Slickers* movie, with Billy Crystal and the ice cream guys trying to conduct business back east from horseback. Every time they rode behind a butte they lost the call.

Part of the 'personality' of this trip had been our frustration with phone calls. Before leaving home I had arranged for an 800# to be placed on our phone, so the kids or we could call in at any time, from pretty much any state, and the call would be charged to our phone. This had worked well. I had also arranged for a long-distance calling number, so that we could dial the series of access numbers and charge other long-distance calls to our home bill. This hadn't worked so well. Despite numerous calls in the past week, Verizon had blocked World XChange's long distance and could *not* get this straight for the life of them. We'd have to call them once more and go through the whole spiel and complaint again. Just what we wanted to be doing on vacation…

Before leaving home we had also purchased a calling card from Lowe's with a hundred minutes on it. The cashier told us she had activated it and it was all set to go. What she *hadn't* told us – and we never found out until we returned to Virginia and to Lowe's claiming the card to be faulty – was that one had to take a coin and remove the black strip that covered the access number on the back. Live and learn. So the entire trip, we had a hundred minutes of long distance in our pockets, and were too hi-tech inept to use them. Instead we stayed frustrated. Unless we called home on our 800#, or located a place high enough to catch a signal close enough to a cell tower, we were up a creek when it came to long-distance communications that required other than an 800#. All of this would have special significance to us in just a couple of days.

After breakfast I used the pay phone to call home and say hey to Mary and to the family, to see how all were doing. Our time was two hours behind, so it was about 9AM out east, early enough that Skye and Jared were still sleeping. Only Mary and Natalie were up, visiting over tea. Mary still had no inkling of the birthday party in store for her. I asked her to change our itinerary, that we'd be nixing the ride, and move everything up by a day – to please let Jean and Al know, too. We talked for a while, and then Pete was able to get through to Verizon on the pay phone, on their 800# for service. While he lambasted them for mishandling this situation all week, I paid our bill and went into the gift shop to get a few more post cards of Bluff, a couple pairs of turquoise earrings for friends, and a *Spiritlands* CD by John Huling, to play en route. *What fitting music as a backdrop for Monument Valley,* I thought. *I'll surprise Pete.*

He was still on the phone, his body language telling me he was extremely aggravated by the ineptitude. When he finally got off, I suggested he take a deep breath. He stood for a moment, closed his eyes and let out a long, slow expulsion of air. As he exhaled, he said, eyes still closed: "They'll have it working by Tuesday – they *promise.*"

"Yeah. Like they promised us Friday. And last Tuesday, as well. We'll see. We're paid up – you ready to roll?" I asked him.

"Sure. Let me make a pit stop. I'm suspecting you've done that already?"

"You betcha'. And I've got a little surprise for our trip that will help you relax," referring to the CD. "While you're in there, I'll get the letters ready to mail at the post office."

"Good idea. I'll be right back," and with that his long blue-jean clad legs carried him up the steps and across the porch, out of sight.

I had added a pinch of the soft red desert sands, collected in the film canister at Valley of the Gods, to each of the letters to the children and the one to Pete's folks. I'd add some, too, when I wrote that letter to Mary, and some for Elizabeth, when I wrote her. I bundled up the finished envelopes with a rubber band and added a slip of paper for the kind old postmaster, reminding him to hand-stamp them for "Bluff, Utah," and thanked him again for his trouble. We dropped them by the post office and were on our way. As we approached Comb Ridge, heading out of Bluff, I remembered that we hadn't called Kyle.

"Oh, right. Let's get to the top and see if we have a signal." We found his number on our itinerary up front and dialed. Kyle answered and he was not happy that 'we had reneged on the riding.' He said that 'he was getting the horses ready.' We told him that we'd never had the chance to finish our conversation, much less commit to anything, so had made other plans. Maybe another time. I bet *another time* he'd finish his discussion with potential customers before he went off to something new…

As the signal was clear from atop this ridge, I asked Pete if there were any other calls we needed to make while we could still get out. He thought a minute, and said: "Of course. We need to call The Red Feather Lodge and let them know we'll be coming into the Canyon a night early. They have us down for Monday night, only."

"Good idea. Do you want me to call them while you look at the map, Pete?" I knew how much he liked to get his bearings before we traveled.

"Sure, Ra. Thanks. Here's the number," he handed me the itinerary again, put on his reading glasses, and pointed to the hotel. Then he got out the Indian Country map, spread it open to study it, resting it against the steering wheel.

I pressed the digits on the cell. Soon a lady answered, saying brightly: "The Red Feather Lodge in the Grand Canyon, how may I help you?"

"Yes, we have a room booked for tomorrow night, but we've changed our trip plans and we now plan to get in a day earlier than we thought. Would you also have a room available for us tonight, as well?"

She checked her roster. "Oh sure. What's the name?" I told her. "Would you want two queens or a king? Smoking or non? And do you have children or pets traveling with you?"

"Non-smoking, please. Queens will be fine – and no, no children *or* pets," I said, "They're all back in Virginia. We're out here on our anniversary, just the two of us. We're foot loose and fancy free." Famous last words.

Part II
Week 2 in the Four Corners

*"We Americans cannot save the world.
Even Christ failed on that.
We Americans have our hands full
trying to save ourselves."*
Edward Abbey

The Navajo/Monument Valley

"In the skin of our fingers
we can see the hail of the wind;
it shows us where the wind blew
when our ancestors were created."
Navajo legend

Pete and I drive through the endless open starkness that make up the Southwest deserts. Everywhere sands in warm soft tones of ochre and ecru, gold and taupe, undulate before and around us, ever changing patterns against the stoic, solid sandstone structures rising majestically to the heavens. Deities of the desert.

On a daily basis, against an ever-changing sky, and as the earth rotates steadily on her constant axis, the sun caresses this epic stone, misses the crevices but kisses the varying surfaces, lights their magnificence as royal crown jewels interspersed through the shifting desert sands humbly at their feet. The monuments are in highlight or in shadow at the omnipotent sun's whim. Everyday the desert is different. Everyday the story is retold. And yet…

There is constancy in the Southwest that winds and time have not changed. It is in the inhabitants of the environment, itself. It is the Indian that still makes this beautiful and brutal environ their home; for decades, indeed, centuries, many still live the 'Old Way.'

THE NAVAJO

Diné Bikéyah – Navajoland – is home to the largest population of Native Americans in the United States. Dinétah – the Land of the People – is, indeed, a nation within a nation. Their reservation is roughly the size of West Virginia. As with all reservations, this land is held in a public trust, managed by The Bureau of Indian Affairs (BIA) and the U.S. Government. Although the non-Navajo public may cross Dinétah, non-Navajo may not live on the rez unless they work there. Navajo call themselves "Diné," meaning "The People," and number well over 200,000. Diné descend from the nomadic Athabascan tribes that migrated from Asia over the Bering Strait into Alaska and Canada during the glaciation period, more than 11,000 years ago.

The Athabascans resided in Alaska and northwestern Canada for centuries before continuing their migration south to the Four Corners area of the American Southwest. Here, they encountered the ancient Pueblo cultures – descendants of the cliff-dwelling Anasazi and the Mogollon – already firmly ensconced and living a life off the land.

The Pueblo Indians grew corn, beans, melon and squash crops, using the 'dry farming' technique that enabled them to grow food in this harsh environment that offered very little annual rainfall. The Athabascan people, being a nomadic culture always in search of game and plants for their daily existence, learned from this farming community the value of a steady supply of food – and thus stability.

The roaming Athabascan descendents frequently conducted raids against other tribes, including the peaceful Pueblo culture. The Utes continually tried to force the marauding Indians from the Four Corners geographical area long before it was even a U.S. territory, but were not successful. It is believed that the Zuni Pueblo Indians called the newcomers "apacu," meaning "enemy" or "stranger" in the Zuni tongue, which the Spaniards later changed to "Apache." Distinct tribes developed over time and the Spanish, who began to arrive in the mid-16th century, came to call those Indians of the northern borders of New Mexico and Arizona "Apaches de Nabajo" ("Nabajo" may have been a term originally meaning "planted fields" and was used for those clans that had settled down); this was later shortened to "Navajo."

The Navajo language is part of a related group of languages known as the Athapaskan tongue. (The name originating from a lake, Athapaska, found in northwestern Canada.) This language has managed to remain intact, with little outside influence. As with other Native American cultures, storytelling is an integral part of tradition, teaching new generations both the language and their history through their elaborate myths and beliefs. This method of passing such history verbally, from one generation to the next, reaffirms these beliefs and teaches lessons of the Old Way. The Navajo tongue is a complex language that was not written down until well into the 20th Century.

The Spaniards first came north out of Mexico in the mid-1500s, in search of the fabled "Seven Cities of Cibola," rumored to have been built far to the west of Europe by Catholic bishops escaping Muslim rule. These cities were thought to be so rich that 'the streets were paved with gold and jewels.' These newcomers interrupted centuries of Native American living. Indians had never seen such a sight as horses, or sheep, cattle and goats. The Zuni Indians at first drove the Spaniards away, but a year later Francisco Vasquez de Coronado, sent by the viceroy of Mexico, arrived with enforcements to continue the search for the legendary golden cities. The Zuni Pueblo Indians, playing on the legend of these cities, led Coronado to believe that they were to be found further east, and sent Coronado on to Kansas, but the conquistadors had discovered the American Southwest and it would never be the same. They would continue to return, riding up from Mexico, in search of riches for their Mother Country.

The Apache (and some that became Navajo) tribes in this area were more mobile and more aggressive, thus more difficult to 'persuade' to the Spaniards' desires. This clash of cultures paved the way for much bloodshed in the next two centuries, especially as these Indians had acquired a liking for the mobility of the Spaniard's main mode of transportation: the horse. In the 1540s the Conquistadors first introduced the horse to the Southwest. This swift four-legged creature came to have a tremendous impact on the mobility of the newly mounted Indian, especially in raiding jaunts for additional horses and other livestock. It was said amongst Native Americans, "Stealing horses is stealing power." By the 1650s these Indians were well mounted, but not welcomed, and the Spaniards were out for revenge. Fierce battles were fought over territory, livestock, and the Spanish lust for Indian slaves, including the Apache and Navajo.

During this cultural clash with the Spanish, in a course of roughly 200 years, much of the way in which we identify the Navajo people of today was developing. Being the resourceful and adaptable people they are, the Navajo readily absorbed the ways of these newcomers that would strengthen their own existence. The Spaniards had introduced a variety of animals that the Navajo would adapt into their own culture. Acculturation continued as European vegetables and fruits such as wheat, potatoes and peaches were presented, along with the know-how to plant these crops, from earlier days of better times between the divergent cultures. The various Indian cultures, in return, taught the Spanish skills to dry farm and live in this arid land; they traded animal skins for livestock and tools and for a time the cultures were reciprocal.

But the Spaniards were unquenchable in their quest for "God, gold and glory." They wanted to convert the 'heathens' to Catholicism; they coveted their lands and the ores within. Soon they wanted the Indians, themselves – at first the more peaceful Pueblo dwellers, but eventually any tribe available – for slave labor to unearth the loot of the land. And, of course, the Indians – of all tribes, eventually – fought back. So the cultures mixed – that of the many Native tribes, the incoming Spanish, later Mexican, and eventually Anglo – and, as the course of history and humankind has shown, they at first taught one another, and then they fought one another, for rights to the bounties and resources offered by the most generous mother of them all, this great earth.

The sheep introduced by the Spaniards are now a staple to Diné life; they are a source of food and the provider of wool, which has become synonymous with Navajo weaving and the fine blankets, for which this tribe has become famous. Sheep and other livestock are tantamount to wealth in Diné culture, notably the hardy churro breed of sheep the Navajo so prize. Parents give their youngsters lambs to raise, explaining to them that they are the beginning of the flock of their own sheep they will have as adults. By caring for these lambs, the young children become working and involved members of the larger community early in life. By the late 1700s, the Navajo way of life revolved around the tribes' herds of sheep.

Silverwork is also synonymous with the Navajo. Some learned silversmithing from Mexicans years before the Navajo were subjected to the Long Walk and life at Fort Sumner. But it was here that they learned the skill from the Spanish, and – once again – the adaptable culture incorporated a skill into their society that would benefit and strengthen the whole for upcoming generations. Using Mexican and U.S. coins (such as silver dollars) as raw material, Diné would melt the metal and mold the silver into ornate earrings, necklaces, belt buckles, buttons, bridle parts, boot tips and spurs, etc. By the late 1890s the Navajo had started combining silver with turquoise, mined in New Mexico and Arizona, into their jewelry. This has become a trademark of Diné artisans worldwide; the combination has become a distinctively Southwest look. The large and elaborate 'Squash Blossom' necklace, so often worn by Navajo women, is distinctly their design and a symbol of wealth.

As we drove towards Monument Valley I read to Pete from **Discover Navajo –The Official Navajo Nation's Visitor Guide**:

"The Navajo people, the Diné, passed three different worlds before emerging into this world, The Fourth World, or Glittering World.

"The Diné believe there are two classes of beings: the Earth People and the Holy People. The Holy People are believed to have the power to aid or harm Earth people. Since Earth People of the Diné are an integral part of the universe, they must do everything they can to maintain harmony or balance on Mother Earth.

"It is believed that centuries ago the Holy People taught the Diné how to live the right way and to conduct their many acts of everyday life. They were taught to live in harmony with Mother Earth, Father Sky and the many other elements such as man, animals, plants, and insects.

"The Holy People put four sacred mountains in four different directions: Mt. Blanca to the east; Mt. Taylor to the south; San Francisco Peak to the west; and Mt. Hesperus to the north, near Durango, Colorado, thus creating Navajoland. The four directions are represented by four colors: White Shell represents the east; Turquoise the south; Yellow Abalone the west; and jet Black the north.

"The number four permeates traditional Navajo philosophy. In the Navajo culture there are four directions, four seasons, the first four clans and four colors that are associated with the four sacred mountains. In most Navajo rituals there are four songs and multiples thereof, as well as many other symbolic uses of four.

"When disorder evolves in a Navajo's life, such as an illness, medicinemen use herbs, prayers, songs and ceremonies to help cure patients. Some tribal members choose to be cured at the many hospitals on the Navajo Nation. Some will seek the assistance of a traditional Navajo medicineman. A qualified medicineman (ha'athali) is a unique individual bestowed with supernatural powers to diagnose a person's problem and to heal or cure an illness and restore harmony (hózhó) to the patient.

"There are more than 50 different kinds of ceremonies that may be used in the Navajo culture – all performed at various times for a specific reason. Some ceremonies last several hours, while others may last as long as nine days."

The Navajo beliefs are as devout and complex as any religious creed. For centuries the Spanish tried to force their Catholic doctrine upon the

Native Americans. After this Christian missionaries have tried, and are continuing to try, to do the same. The endemic cultures are stubbornly resisting this outside influence; the Pueblo, Hopi, Navajo, Zuni, Apache, Havasupai, and other tribes of the great Southwest quietly continue their individual faith, in their own version of "The Great Spirit." As a favorite bumper sticker of mine suggests: **GOD IS TOO BIG TO FIT INSIDE ONE RELIGION**. To each his or her own, I say; wouldn't it be a more peaceful world if we would practice this tolerance? Think of what we might learn from, and teach to, one another if we kept our minds, and our hearts, open to this pulse of life from culture to culture.

Monument Valley, Utah & Arizona

For centuries prehistoric Anasazi Indians lived frugally upon this bone-dry land, aided by aquifers deep beneath the desert sands in Monument Valley. By the 1300s the Anasazi had disappeared from this area. It is unknown as to when the Navajo first settled here, but – as in Canyon de Chelly – they have made it their home, herding sheep to be used for wool for their famous blankets, making their turquoise and silver jewelry, growing limited crops in sparse gardens, and now hosting these sights to visitors.

Monument Valley, known to the Navajo as "Tsè Biì Ndzisgaii" (meaning "Clearing's Among the Rocks) is 5,564' above sea level – more of the high desert country through which we have been traveling. It sprawls across northern Arizona into Utah, with no division between the states, as it is all part of the Navajo Indian Reservation. In fact, it was the first Navajo Tribal Park, established in July 1958, by the Navajo Tribal Council.

What was at one time a basin became a plateau, as Monument Valley was once a solid 1,000' layer of sandstone. For hundreds of millions of years, debris eroded from the early Rocky Mountains that deposited multitudes of layers of sediments, which cemented over the years, to become sandstone, limestone and shale. Ceaseless pressure from stresses below caused the surface to bulge and crack, causing uplifts of these stones, as well as gullies and canyons. These monoliths have been continually wind-, rain-, and sand-whipped over the millennia, shaped by ongoing erosion, as well as by extreme temperature fluctuations that caused the rock to crack, creating the astounding buttes and mesas that lure 400,000 tourists annually to Monument Valley. Two of its buttes, Merrick and Mitchell, were named after eager prospectors who claimed that they had found hidden treasures of silver lodes in this valley. Ute Indians killed them both for trespassing into forbidden country, intent on stealing its riches.

The erosion of these alternating layers of soft and hard rock slowly shape these grand structures. Harder Shinarump formation caps and protects underlying De Chelly (pronounced de-shay) sandstone that shape the spectular mesas and buttes. Softer Organ Rock Shale is found at the base of these monoliths; it erodes outward in step-like horizontal terraces, which form the sloping foundations of these ancient creations of nature.

Monument Valley was 'put on the map' in 1938 by the persistence of Harry Goulding, who introduced this wild western landscape to Hollywood, specifically John Ford, in the production of *"Stagecoach."* Harry Goulding was born in Durango, Colorado, in 1897. In 1923 he moved from a ranch near Aztec, New Mexico, to Monument Valley, making his living as a sheepherder beside his friends, the Navajo, and his beloved wife, 'Mike.'

In 1928 he opened Goulding's Trading Post, where people in a vast country converged to buy, sell, barter and trade goods needed to live and survive in these barren lands. Goulding's Trading Post is now a prominent National Landmark and museum on the border of Arizona and Utah. The old Oljato Trading Post is just down the road.

"Like the fine rugs that the Navajo women weave, so too are the finest of people associated with Monument Valley — Harry and Mike (Leona) Goulding. They settled here as traders in 1923 and put names to many of the monuments in this, the heart of Navajoland." Joseph Muench

Joseph Muench was born in Schweinfurt, Germany, on February 8th, 1904. He was given a box-style camera by his mother when he was a young boy. Who knew then that this gift would eventually lead to his deep and abiding love of the Diné, Arizona, Monument Valley, and his longtime friendship with Harry and Mike Goulding. But an unfortunate incident with Adolph Hitler – in which Muench hit the rising young radical with a tomato he had thrown to boycott Hitler's politics (even then) – led him to flee his Mother country in 1928. Muench felt he was a marked man.

Joseph Muench's estrangement from Nazi Germany became a gift to the United States, especially the American Southwest. After working for the Ford Motor Company he saved cash enough for a Model-A roadster and money to head west during the Great Depression, with nothing much more than hope and a dream of becoming a photographer.

Eventually Joseph Muench met and collaborated with Raymond Carlson, the man with the vision behind "Arizona Highways," which had originally been a state road construction magazine. He, like Ansel Adams, worked in black and white photography for years. But in 1937 Eastman Kodak introduced Kodachrome (color) film and Joseph Muench shot his first roll in Monument Valley. One of these photographs – of Totem pole and the Yeibichai monuments, two rugged red rock sandstone giants, against an unbelievably deep cerulean blue sky, with snowy clouds drifting through as lazy counterpoints – ended up on the cover of "Arizona Highways." It put Muench – and the magazine – on the map. He and his wife, Joyce, a writer, teamed up to do a photojournalist piece for "Arizona Highways" in 1939, after Harry Goulding – with his buddy, Joseph Muench's help – had already introduced Monument Valley to Hollywood in 1938, to be the setting for the movie *"Stagecoach,"* with a young John Wayne.

Other movies followed: *"My Darling Clementine"* (1946); *"The Searchers"* (1956); *"How the West was Won"* (1962); *"The Trials of Billy Jack"* (1973); *"The Legend of the Lone Ranger"* (1980); and *"Back to the Future III"* (1988). Of course, this doesn't include all the macho SUV commercials used to show the prowess of their aggressive off-road vehicles blasting through the sands here, as they climb the silent and mighty – but still fragile – sandstone structures.

In 2002, *"Windtalkers,"* poetically, opened in Monument Valley. Starring the almost indestructible Nicholas Cage, it portrayed all too vividly how the U.S. Government used the Navajo in World War II to turn the tide for the Allies, as the only code that the Japanese could not break.

The "Code Talkers" were responsible for communications in every major assault in the Pacific (Iwo Jima, Tarawa, Guadalcanal, Peleliu, Okinawa, Guam, etc.). The United States Marines considered them to be their 'secret weapon.' The Navajo ironically – but rightfully so – became American heroes. A statue was erected in Phoenix in 1989 to honor the 420 Navajo men who contributed their complex verbal skills in bringing an end to the war.

In their plan to introduce Monument Valley to Hollywood, Joseph Muench made two handsome black & white photograph albums of these sights that would have given Ansel Adams a run for his money. These were presented by Harry Goulding to John Ford and his production chief, Walter Wanger. The Goulding family has one of these albums, and the Muench family kept the other. They are likely now priceless heirlooms.

Thanks to Harry and Mike Goulding's foresight, the photographic eye of Joseph Muench, John Ford's vision, and the megamoney of Hollywood, roads were paved from Tuba City through the deserts to this quiet and wondrous Navajo Tribal Park. Monument Valley was discovered for all the world to see – and to be astounded by – the ageless monoliths standing sentry above the shifting sands of time and the ever-changing skies above.

*See map, page 152.

Laura
Cockerille
Giannini
© 2004
Finding Dingo
in the desert –
Monument
Valley

SIXTEEN

Change of Plans (Enter, Dingo)

*"The American Indian is of the soil, whether it be the region of forests, plains,
pueblos, or mesas. He fits into the landscape, for the hand that fashioned
the continent also fashioned the man for his surroundings."*
Luther Standing Bear (1868-1939) Oglala Sioux Chief

Our excursion through Monument Valley was but a grander version
of our excursion through Valley of the Gods, the day before. The Navajo had built a fine visitor's center inside the entrance, complete with
history, artifacts, and clean restrooms. It was here, for the first time
in a week, that we saw the American flag flying at full mast, high and
proud against the brilliant blue western sky. Pete and I paid a small fee
and told them no thank you, we didn't need a guide — we'd rather go
it on our lonesome. The Diné then reminded us to stay on the 'main
road' (they must have seen us bushwhacking yesterday). Of course,
this road was a dusty version of the day before, the sands being much
the same.

There were few clouds today in this late September sky. Indeed, it
looked as if it had been hired, or danced up, by the Navajo as a turquoise backdrop to the magnificent deities that graced their homeland.
As harsh and barren as this land is — still, *what* a place it would be to call
home! It would sear into one's soul over time. Pete and I spent the afternoon enthralled by the various shapes and forms that made up these
famous sandstone monuments that one usually saw only in Western
movie backdrops. How I wish we had brought the kiddos here last year!
But Pete's itinerary had been full to overflowing then, too; we probably
hadn't allowed that time. For pity's sake. We had driven our family right
past Monument Valley.

Pete and I drove through the sprawl of interconnected dirt-sand roads that lead to and around these monumental monoliths millions of years old. The Diné say "the gods use the valley's mesa tops as stepping stones when they walk the Earth." They all have names given them by the Navajo, but are known more commonly by the white man's monikers. Many were named by Harry Goulding. There are Merrick and Mitchell Buttes, named in post mortem, after the old prospector's with gold dust in their eyes – and no time to spend it. There are others. "The Mittens" are huge rocks with 'single opposable thumb's looming separately from the main mass.' "Full Moon Arch" opens a huge peephole to the sky. "The Three Sisters" refers to a trio of upright finger rocks, larger ones on either side of the small, thin one; they represent older nuns initiating the younger one to her calling. There is "The Stagecoach," the "King and His Throne," and the "Bear and the Rabbit" monument. "Yeibichai" maintains its Indian name, from Navajo mythology. There is "Rooster Rock" and the massive wall of "Meridian Butte," next door to it.

We spent the better part of three hours driving through Monument Valley, getting out often enough to get better angles for our photographs of this foreign world. We stopped at a jewelry table with a pleasant Indian woman named Mary Stanley selling her wares and bought a ring seen in this area quite frequently. It was not expensive and this might well have been made in China, but it looked authentic, with turquoise triangles opposing coral triangles, on some type of ring that was certainly not silver. We bought one for each of us, a token of this visit, a small anniversary memento. We found necklaces there for the girls, and a leather bracelet with a silver bear on it for Jared. At one point we watched a man, mounted on his slim Navajo painted pony, ride to the end of a cliff and pose there to be photographed against the western sky. A postcard shot. We shot one of him, too. Then we poured a couple of teas from the cooler, with precious ice coveted from the Café, for our dusty drive out of the Tribal Park, and to begin our journey on to the Grand Canyon.

As we passed the last of the pull-offs, I glimpsed an old Navajo woman sitting behind a long table filled with her jewelry. One of the buttes of the Valley sat in the background. "Pete, let's back up to take this shot. It's so 'Old West' it looks like another postcard photo."

Pete gave me a quizzical eye, not sure if he wanted to, or not. We had spent a lot of time here and the man was ready to strap on his seatbelt, forget capturing the scenery for a while, and put some miles behind us. "Okay," he said finally, "but let's not make this a habit today. I'm ready to get to the Canyon and we've got a *lot* of miles ahead."

Uh oh. Military mode. Back to the clock again. *Some*body had flipped his switch. Peter backed up and pulled into the parking area at this overlook and brought out the Indian Country map, uninterested in the Navajo woman, her jewelry, or the view, at this point. I patted his knee, located under the map, secured my camera and left the car. From a distance, so it would be candid, I took a photograph of the elder behind her jewelry-laden table. To my right was another table that I hadn't noticed until we turned in; behind this one sat a young Navajo girl, about Skye's age. She had on the long velveteen shirt and full skirt of native attire. She wore silver and turquoise necklaces and bracelets – and headphones over her sleek, long black hair, her head bopping to the rhythm in her ears. She was oblivious to the world around her. A typical teenager. What a study of the old and the new, of age and culture's clashing. How purely ironic…

I walked closer to inspect the older woman's table. In the corner of my eye, under a sagebrush between the two tables, I saw a movement, a yellow 'swish' of color. Curious, I walked a little closer to the sagebrush to check it out, thinking it might be some bird or other native wildlife. Close. There in the deep shade thrown by the dense bush lay a small straw-colored puppy. She cowered down as I came closer. I knelt and called to her softly. The pup crouched down timidly and made her way over to me, in a defensive posture, low to the ground with her tail tucked under her; she reached out to sniff my hand.

"It's okay, baby. I won't hurt you. It's okay there." I put my hand quietly on her head. She looked to be just a few months old. I ran my hand down her scant body; her coat felt dry, like old straw, and her ribs and haunches protruded. She was starving. I talked to her quietly as she lay cowering below my gentle hand.

I looked over at the old woman, who was ignoring us. "Excuse me, is this your dog?" I asked her as I rose and walked to her table.

"No."

"Do you mind if I feed her or give her water?"

She shook her head "No," and asked if I wanted to buy her jewelry. I told her maybe later, and went to the car.

"Pete, you know that breakfast burrito we've been hauling around in the cooler, that I saved for 'some poor dog on the rez' – well, I've found 'the dog.' There's a pup over here starving to death. I'm going to give her the doggy bag and some water. Wanna' see her?"

He was intently studying the map and absent-mindedly shook his head 'no.' I fished through the large cooler, retrieved the Styrofoam container from the bottom, and hoisted the gallon jug of water we kept behind the passenger seat. I'd use the top flap of the Styrofoam for a bowl. I returned to the puppy that had returned to her shady protective cover. "Hey, girl, I've got something for you here. Come on out again – you'll be glad you did." I called to her softly.

Once again she came to me timidly, but had caught the scent of food. Her ears perked up. "Yes, yes, it's something for you to eat. I don't know how you'll like the green chilies, but here – go for it." I opened the box and put it on the ground.

The pup reached down and bloody well inhaled the burrito. She could not eat it fast enough. The small dog didn't stop to sniff or taste or pick through the chilies, she just flat-out absorbed the food. Immediately her little stomach distended. She licked the Styrofoam container vigorously, looking for any remaining morsel. *Well, damn. Here I thought I'd only feed her and leave, but obviously she hadn't eaten anything in some time. When would she get food again?*

I walked over to the young Navajo teen and knocked on the table to get her attention. She pushed back her headphones and looked up. "Excuse me – sorry to bother you – but do you know if anybody owns, or feeds, this dog?"

"Nobody owns her. She just hangs around. Sometimes a tourist will give her something."

"You don't feed her?" I asked.

"No."

"Then I'm taking her with me to find her a home, so she won't finish starving." (*Where'd* that *come from?!*)

"Go ahead. I don't care." She put her headphones back on. So much for the Indians being one with all living things.

I went back to the puppy. A tall, stout blond man and his pretty dark-haired companion were standing over her. "I just fed the little thing," I said to them. "Apparently, she's a stray. The Indians don't want her, and don't care if she lives or dies. Would you want her?" I asked, tentatively. "She's just going to starve to death out here."

"Ha! Nein, nein, ve are traveling here von *Germany*. I just vanted to see her." The man said with his singsong voice; the German was obvious now.

"Well, I can't leave the pup. She just gulped down the food I gave her. Who knows when she'll eat again."

"Here, let me give her vater." He said, vanting to help, and he reached for a canteen strapped to his waist. He poured it into one of the Styrofoam compartments. The yellow puppy started to lap it right up.

"Here, I've got a jug of water here – let me put some in your canteen. We have plenty more in the car." I pointed to the Camry. Pete and I had learned something about driving through the desert. They let me do this and he said: "Danke schön." And "Viel Glück in finding her a home." And they were on their way.

Hmm… Now what? She had finished the water and was headed back to the safety of her sagebrush. I headed back to the car, walking around to the driver's side, and braced myself for a showdown. Pete would already be perturbed I'd taken this long. He saw me coming and rolled his window the rest of the way down. "Yes?" he asked, peering over his glasses, an impatient look on his face.

"Pete, she's starving. Nobody wants her. We'll have to bring her out of here and find her a home." There, I'd said it.

"No. No, Laura, we don't *have* to do that. Remember, we're on vacation – 'foot loose and fancy free'? You said that yourself, just a few hours ago."

"Yeah, well, things change. I cannot just leave her here to finish starving."

"Yes, Laura, you *can*. It doesn't always *have* to be you."

"Okay, Pete, just **who** will that 'somebody else' be, then? She's halfway gone, already. She's skin and bones. 'Somebody else' hasn't shown up yet. So at what point in the starvation process do you think they'll show up? And when will it be too late?" I was getting angry; I put down the water jug and crossed my arms over my chest, going into mule-gear.

"**No**. No, no, **no!** We're headed to the Grand Canyon. They probably don't even *allow* dogs there. Remember how romantic this was going to be, hiking down in by the light of the full moon? All those walks? A puppy just doesn't fit into this equation, Laura." He had taken off his reading glasses and folded the map, ready for battle. This was quickly becoming a Mexican Standoff, one of those defining 'marital moments,' where a couple is light-years apart in mutual motivation. Love was now a many-splintered thing.

I thought quickly. "Pete, listen. It's like this. If you don't take this *puppy* out of here, you don't take *me*." I stood taller and locked my arms. "I'm not going without her." *Well, damn. Listen to my ultimatum.* Later on, I thought: *that probably wasn't the brightest thing to have said, being that we were in high desert country, the day was on its way out, and this man held the car keys. Here was a test of true love.*

Testing, testing… He glared at me from the car, but we had been through 'marital moments' before. He knew I wasn't going to back down. Clearly furious, he opened his door and stormed out, keys in hand. He silently opened the trunk. "Okay, you win. I know you aren't going to change your mind. So what are you going to use as a leash?" He was opening my suitcase.

Great! She'd be going out with us and would have a chance at a home, after all!

"Wait a minute," he stopped his search and looked at me. "What if somebody owns her? What if they're looking for her?"

"Out here? Out in the middle of this *no*where*?!* How in the world are we supposed to find *that* out?" I asked. "It's not as if she has a collar on it with identification tags, or a tattoo. Good try, but I don't buy it. Let's find her a good home." Now I was scrounging through my suitcase. *Ta dah!* There was my maroon and navy nylon belt with the adjustable buckle and little Kokopelli flute players marching across it. Perfect. "Here, we can use this as both collar and leash for now, until we can find the real thing."

"What's this '*we*?' Don't start saying '*we*' – this is your gig." He growled at me.

We walked over to the sagebrush. I told the old woman we were taking her out of here to find her a home. She said: "Okay, do you want to buy my jewelry now?" I told her "Not today, but thanks." And I showed Pete the pup that was crawling from under her cover to me. She had a slim face with upright ears and a small blaze running between her golden brown eyes. Her markings and color were those of a yellow Labrador Retriever, complete with the lemony shoulders, but there the similarity with a Lab stopped. She had a small-boned body, with a tail that trailed low behind her, with something of a curl in it. The pup was skinny and her coat was dull, but she was a pretty little thing and didn't look mangy or diseased.

"Just where do you suggest she ride?" Pete asked, as I quietly put my belt around her neck, slipping the end through to make a collar, and then secured the buckle, reassuring her as I worked.

"On my lap, I guess. That way I can talk to her and settle her down."

"And she just ate? You're living dangerously. You'd better put something on your lap to cover your legs – and catch the car sickness." (He cared!)

Leaving the dog with the 'leash' on her a moment, we looked in the trunk again and I found my old denim jacket, the one with the round black patch left over from my hippie days that said: **"Give a damn"** in white lettering. This seemed appropriate.

"Perfect." Pete said sarcastically. He was trying his best to be a tough guy and stick to his original guns, but now that he'd actually seen the puppy, he realized I wasn't exaggerating on her poor condition. We put the jacket on my seat.

The little dog seemed to have never had a leash on her in her life. She panicked with the pressure around her neck and I knelt down and soothed her. "It's okay… *Shhhh*… You'll get used to it, girl. There are some trade-offs to being cared for."

Pete opened the passenger door, picking up the jacket. I ended up coaxing and halfway dragging her over. He picked up the Styrofoam container and went around to the other side for the water jug I had left on the ground in our standoff. He nodded to the old Indian woman in passing and then came back around to put both items behind my seat. "Get in, put the jacket on your lap, and I'll hand you the dog," he said gruffly. I cooperated, spreading the jean coat over my lap and knees to protect my bare legs. He picked her up and she wiggled and squirmed in a panic over being handled.

Pete laid her gently on my lap. "It's okay, pup. We won't hurt you." He spoke to her calmly; maybe he was coming around. Pete closed the door and walked to the other side.

The pup panicked. Apparently she had also never been in a car in her life. As Pete got in she bolted for his open door, scrambling over and nearly upsetting our iced teas in the console between us. Then she tried to go out my closed window as I held her wriggling body. She dug a nail in my left pointer finger knuckle, opening a quarter-inch gash that went immediately red with blood. I didn't have time to think of this in trying to soothe and control her.

"Yeah, this is a *great* idea, Laura. Let's bring a wild desert dog on our vacation. Liven it up a bit." He was saying smugly, his arms crossed over his chest now, leaning back against his door, watching the show.

"She'll settle down, damnit Pete." I said through clinched teeth, as she headed for the windshield, digging her hind legs in the jacket on my lap and twisting it around. "Come *on*, girl, show him I'm *right*. Settle down now…" I tried to be comforting, under her busy, frightened body. She was quieting down some, realizing there wasn't a way out, despite all the promising views. Her little body trembled. I stroked her and told her it was okay, we'd take good care of her. There'd be more food, safety, all that.

Pete got back into driving position and turned the ignition on. "Don't ask me to stop again for a while, Laura. I wish to hell I'd passed on this one. Hold her tight now."

The car started and she started, as well, but she soon realized there was nowhere to go.

I managed to get my jacket rearranged beneath me again to protect my legs, and the pup halfway sat on my lap, with her left leg braced on the floorboard, her paws on the door, watching the desert roll away. After a bit she gave a big sigh of resignation. Within fifteen minutes, she was resting fairly comfortably, content with the movement of the car and watching the world go by. I stroked her skeletal body and talked to her. Pete had grown silent, his face was in profile and his jaw was set; I could only imagine his thoughts.

We drove the twenty-some miles to Kayenta without further incident. I talked with the pup quietly and soothed her thin, frail body, assuring her we were her buddies. What I was thinking was: *Please, baby, hold onto your dinner. We don't want to have breakfast burrito come back all over us in an 'I told you so' moment.* Not a problem; she was a trooper. Pete said next to nothing, except that we could start looking for a home for her in Kayenta. Later he glanced over at my hand, still bleeding from her toenail digging into it. "You'd better mop that up. It'll get blood over everything."

"Gee, I appreciate your concern there, fella'," and found a napkin to clean the wound. It wasn't terribly deep, but hand injuries bleed profusely. I'd have to keep it clean and be careful of infection, but it would heal soon enough, probably with a small scar. It was just another badge of living life; another story to tell.

Pete was saying very little. The truth of the matter was that he was so mad that he sat there driving while I watched steam come from his ears. So I turned the *Spiritlands* CD up a little, hoping the quiet Native American music would calm them both, and turned my focus on the puppy, petting and talking to her. She now lay on my lap. As I stroked her, my attention turned to the sky out my window to the west. Huge cumulus clouds had gathered high, backlit completely by the sun. Streams of light majestically radiated to the ground, as if blessing all they touched. I've always been awed by these magnificent late afternoon backlit cloud formations and call them, simply, 'God.' I watched for a moment, mesmerized by this beauty, the haunting pan flute in *Spiritlands* as background.

I turned to my silent husband and said: "*You* may not be talking to me, but that's okay. God is," and I pointed to the holy cloud mass vibrantly aglow. "And he's telling us that we're doing the right thing."

Pete looked at the clouds high in the sky, with their perfect halo of light, then at me, and actually smiled. "Laura, you *are* impossible. But how can I argue with 'God'?"

"It's usually not a good idea. Does this mean, then, that we could actually stop for a second so that I can get a photograph?"

"Laura, you're pushing it. You are *pushing* the envelope. But okay – *one* photo." Pete shook his head, grimaced, and tried to continue being a Grinch, but the man was just too good-natured to carry off this gruffness too long.

"That's all I want. Thanks." He pulled the car over and steadied the pup while I rolled my window down and took the one shot of 'God.'

Pete and I passed El Capitan on the left, shortly before we entered Kayenta. From here is where we were to have ridden to find our way to Mystery Valley, past Wetherill Mesa and Natural Arches, in the southern end of Monument Valley, for our thwarted overnight ride. I had a quick thought that if we *had* taken that ride, then the puppy might well still be under the sagebrush waiting for that 'somebody else.'

El Capitan, like Shiprock, is another volcanic core, this one rising 1,400' out of the desert floor, reminding us again of the intense volcanic activity that formed so much of the Southwest zillions of millions of years ago. The Navajo called this lofty creation "Agathlan," meaning "the place of the scraping of the hides." One can see it looming high above all else as El Capitan is approached. Sands of the desert, dotted with sagebrush and creosote bush, sweep ones eyes to the massive heights of dark volcanic rock. At its base flowing taupe sands spill down and away, carving out the horizon. A small corral sat there with two trucks, a horse trailer, and an RV. Perhaps Kyle was still waiting for us to show up, not willing to take no for an answer...

Peter and the pup had both settled down. Basically, Pete hadn't spoken fifty words to me since we'd left Monument Valley, so I had a lot of time to go one-on-one with her. By the time we reached Kayenta he was softening, realizing that maybe she truly *would* have starved, had we not intervened. As we entered this small Navajo town the sad fate of dogs on the rez became more evident. Spaying and neutering is not something they seem to do out here, and – in all fairness, with the abject poverty we've seen on the rez – priorities are shifted to their own survival and necessities first. Vetting dogs is not one of them.

As we drove south down U.S. 163 into Kayenta, thinking of a game plan to locate a home for her here, we watched a dog be hit by a tractor-trailer heading north. The truck did not stop; the poor dog lay in the road, writhing in pain and, as he did, two more scrawny adolescent Dalmatian pups – probably littermates – came to him. Pete pulled the car over to the right shoulder and cut on the hazard lights. "Let me move the poor animal out of the road. These other two dogs are sitting ducks to be hit next." I held the pup as Pete got out and she saw an opening for escape.

"No, girl, you stay here. Let him take care of that, and be glad it's not you." I soothed her quivering body as we both watched Pete carry the now limp dog well into a yard opposite us. A lady had stopped her vehicle to see if she might help. She and Pete were looking around, pointing to different trailers and hogans. The bedraggled Dalmatian pups were sniffing around their buddy's body. Pete pointed to us, and the lady nodded and waved over to me. I waved back, not sure what this meant.

Pete came back across the road, looking grim. "The dog died in my arms as I was setting him down," he told me, "it was an unnerving experience. Maybe those other two won't get hit, at least for now." He looked at the puppy and me strangely.

"See, you do have a heart – I knew it. What did that lady say?" I asked, and put a hand on his arm and squeezed. He gave me a weak smile.

"She said she'd see if she might be able to find an owner. There was no collar. I told her we already had a stray pup from Monument Valley that we were trying to find a home for."(I noticed that he now used 'we,' but kept this observation to myself.)

"Oh. Okay. Pete, you know, I think seeing this dog get hit as we were driving in is a sign that she wasn't meant to be left off here. There are skinny dogs all over the place – she'd just end up being another unspayed mongrel running around with all the others."

He looked over at the scrawny yellow puppy on my lap and then at me. His face softened. "I know, Laura. I was thinking the same thing. This isn't the place."

"Let's take this one step at a time. Let's try to find a grocery store around here to see if we can find some food for her, and maybe a real collar and leash, alright?" I suggested.

"That sounds like a plan. This place is pretty small – it shouldn't be hard." And it wasn't. Further up the road, to our right, was a shopping complex with a Diné "Basha" (Navajo owned and run) market, and a sporting goods store beside it.

Not wanting to leave the wild dog alone in the car, I asked: "Do you want me to hold the puppy while you look for the supplies, or would you like me to look?"

Pete replied: "I'll hold the dog out here. You know what you want for her." He walked over, carrying her with him, to a seating cluster in front of the stores. The small pup was all akimbo, splayed out in his arms, looking like a petrified deer in headlights.

"Good. It'll give you two a chance to bond." I smiled at them and walked into the sporting goods store, first. No collars, no leashes, but lots of coolers, lanterns, sleeping bags, and the like. I'd try the "Basha" market next. "Pete, they didn't have anything we need. I've got to go in here. I'll make it fast, okay?" He was leaning down, talking to the unsettled puppy that apparently had never seen so much 'civilization.' "She's been checking out all the paper trash on the ground, looking for food," he called after me.

I stopped in the produce section long enough to put some apples and oranges into the basket, and a couple of limes for our Coronas. Then I found the pet isle. They had no puppy chow, but there was Purina dog chow in a 5-pound bag, in small nuggets, so I hoisted that into the cart. There were plenty of leashes, but strangely, no collars. *Perhaps it went back to an Indian's sense of freedom?* I put a slim blue leash in the cart, and found the area for dog bowls. I added a small stainless steel double dish for food and water. *Okay – anything else?* I stood there, surrounded by the tall shelves full of goods of every kind, closed my eyes and thought. *Food. Water – oh yeah, water – maybe I'll get a couple more jugs. Leash – got it, collar – nope… Maybe some more beer, while here. No – a store on the rez wouldn't be selling alcohol. We can get more Coronas at the Canyon. Let's see? Anything else? No, no, we're okay.* I ended up adding a bottle of cranberry juice to the goods. When I got to the register the young Indian checker looked at me skeptically – *what is a Belagaana doing out here buying dog food?* I bet she thought.

"Do you have a "Basha" club card?" she asked.

"No, I don't." *I thought not*, her face said. "Would you like an application?" she asked.

"Sure, why not. It won't take long to fill it out, will it?" I asked, Belagaana-style.

"Not very." She looked a little surprised. As she rang up the few items, I filled the information out, and she scanned my brand new card. Two dollars came off. Modern technology meets ancient cultures. Cool.

I thanked her and rolled the cart outside to meet my husband and our new friend. The pup was calmly sitting at his feet now, and Pete was pointing to me, saying: "Who is that?" She actually wagged her body a little in recognition.

"You just know I have more food," I grinned down at her. "Suck up."

After this we found a McDonald's nearby and bought hot coffees, then sat outside to eat a couple of pb&j's and apples on an outside bench. We gave the pup dry food and water in her new dish set. Once again, she inhaled the meal – and then she looked up at us, begging ours. "Nope. You're not getting this, and you are *not* going to learn to beg, kiddo." I added a little more dry food to her dish. "But we've got to go easy with you – we don't want to put your system in shock with *too* much of a good thing, all at once."

Pete was eating his sandwich and looking around. "Well, we've got another couple of hours before it's dark. We should get to the Canyon around 8 PM, I'm guessing. It'll be too late to see the sunset on the rim tonight." He looked at me sternly.

I ignored the look. "I'm thinking we oughta' call her 'Dingo' for now, Pete. Look at her build and her face – and, oh my God – look at that curl in her tail! She didn't have *that* when we first found her! Doesn't she remind you for all the world of a wild dingo?"

"Call her whatever you want. We won't have her long enough for it to matter," he responded. Uh oh. Back to hardass, hit-the-road, no-non-sense-travel-guy mode.

"Okay, Dingo," I said brightly. "Dad wants to go." I glanced over at him for a response, and grinned impishly. He just scowled. "Make your pit stop; I'll hold the dog."

Black Mesa

"Professional ambition, financial gain, social aggrandizement: too often these seem to drive short-term decisions that must then be lived with by those who come after. The people making those decisions should be more mindful of the value of what we already have, since the nation's idea of itself resides in land and in structures, as well as in ideas…By altering the symbols of the past, we deny the future both inspiration and choice."
James Conaway, Editor, Preservation magazine, March/April 2003

We left Kayenta in the late afternoon, ready to travel the long lonesome miles down through the desert on highway 160, past Black Mesa, an extremely controversial area of the Big Mountain, sacred to both the

Hopi and Navajo Indian. Here, decades of controversy over Peabody Coal Company laying claim to the only known coal reserves in Arizona – which happen to also be one of the largest coal reserves in the world – have resulted in a clash of cultures like no other. Both the Hopi and Navajo are employed here, and need the income desperately. But even more importantly in the desert is clean water, upon which they depend to survive, and so they are caught between a rock and a hard place. The indigent Navajo and Hopi tribes do not stand a chance to protect themselves, and their simple way of life, from the voracious appetites of cultures that can never acquire enough resources to meet gluttonous and endless energy needs for a society that always wants, expects, and feels entitled to more. Once again, the bottom line is huge money and corporate greed, condoned by the federal government and franchised by too many in the Bureau of Indian Affairs (a branch of the former), that conveniently lays aside rights to the land held in treaties, that are usurped through the desire for the resources by our government, and the big-business mentality that feeds its hungry face.

"Black Mesa coal came to be viewed as the engine that could power the Central Arizona Project (CAP), a massive network of aqueducts, tunnels, pumping plants, and pipelines designed to transport billions of gallons of water each year from the Colorado River to arid lands in the American southwest..." * Wells have been dug 3,500 feet deep into pure water aquifers in the desert to pump this lifeblood of the Native out of the ground at the rate of 2,300 gallons per minute to wash the 'slurry' (mixture of coal particulate and this pristine groundwater) to the Mojave Power Plant in Nevada – almost 300 miles away – which, in turn, provides electricity to huge cities like Los Angeles, Las Vegas and Phoenix. *"The Navajo Aquifer, this groundwater in dispute, known as the N-aquifer, is the most significant water source in the region. Insulated by a barrier of mudstone and sandstone, it naturally satisfies EPA standards for drinking water – unlike the region's other aquifers, whose contents are brackish or contaminated by uranium or coal. And the springs it feeds along its southern front are sacred to the Hopi people and essential to their religious practice. Ultimately, the debate over Peabody's use of N-aquifer water cuts to the sustainability of one of North America's oldest cultures, the Hopi, and implicates many similar issues for the Hopi's neighbors, the Navajo Nation..."* *

*Information from Natural Resources Defense Council Report entitled "Draw down: Groundwater Mining on Black Mesa," October 2000

"...*The battle over sacred sites predates the Bush administration but has intensified under the current Interior Department. Most of the sites lie on public lands, and the administration's determination to accommodate energy and mining interests on these lands has threatened several sacred places. The administration has sought to roll back environmental regulations limiting what can be done on public lands, in some cases appearing to work hand-in-glove with the corporations it is supposedly regulating. Interior Secretary Gale Norton and the department's lead attorney, William G. Myers, have reversed legal rulings by the previous administration that closed ... sites to development...*

"*The overall situation has so alarmed many Native Americans that Tex G. Hall, president of the National Congress of American Indians, says tribes should consider 'a declaration of some kind of war to protect our sacred sites.'*

"*The defiant rhetoric is a purposeful, but also melancholy, echo of battles lost and remembered, of the long history of Anglo disregard for Indian customs and rights. But today is not yesterday. Groups that extend beyond the Native American community have come together to protect sacred sites. The alliance includes preservation and environmental organizations – among them the National Trust for Historic Preservation and in several cases the Sierra Club.*

"*Native American faiths have been so co-opted by New Agers and so simplified by Hollywood that they can seem from the outside like a vague, spiritual environmentalism, a pseudo-hippy reverence for nature, man. But this view, however sympathetically intended, is a simplistic caricature of religions that usually have creation stories and cosmologies as complicated and resonant as any of the world's larger faiths.*

"*My experience covering Indian issues since the mid-1980s leads me to believe that the distortion also doesn't capture the attitude of most Native Americans who adhere to traditional beliefs. What always strikes me most forcefully is the matter-of-factness about the way Indians – whether Sioux, Navajo, Apache, or Quechan – pursue their faith. It seems woven into the fabric of life with a devotion that doesn't need to proclaim its righteousness.*

"*Perhaps that's part of the reason the U.S. government has had so much trouble accepting these faiths. The sad history of federal policies intended to sever the connection between Native Americans and their traditional cultures is well known. The forced resettlements, the boarding schools, the 200-year imposition of Christianity by a government that has one of its central tenets a separation of church and state are all part of the chronology... In 1978, Jimmy Carter signed the American Indian Religious Freedom Act, which states that 'henceforth it shall be the policy of the United States to protect and preserve for American Indians their inherent right of freedom to believe, express and exercise traditional religions... including but not limited to access to sites...'*

"*The act was a welcome repudiation of past policy, but it did not specify how access to sites was to be protected. Without a cause of action established by law,*

Native Americans were left only with a hearty endorsement of the sentiment that they should be free to worship how and where they pleased. The Clinton administration followed up with an executive order directing federal agencies to institute policies ensuring Native Americans access to sacred places and to protect them when possible.

"But public lands are subject to a welter of contradictory demands. The nation's national forests, grasslands, and deserts are used for recreation, ranching, logging, and mining, among other things. The federal government attempts to balance conflicting demands through a regulatory process that provides for appeals of land decisions by dissatisfied parties. The system, undergirded by a multitude of laws supporting various parts of the equation, guarantees a perpetual struggle over how federally owned lands are used.

"The underlying principle is that the land should be managed for the benefit of all Americans. In practice that has often meant Americans with the greatest influence with lawmakers...

"The idea of landscape as a repository of the sacred — in effect, landscape as church — is one contemporary western culture has had difficulty taking seriously, although why this is so is puzzling. Wars have been fought over 'sacred ground' by Europeans since they first organized themselves into nations. It's hard to imagine that anyone would suggest drilling for oil at Lourdes or mining Calvary, the hill on which Christians believe Christ was crucified...

"Almost no one in government or corporate America would openly espouse such denigration of another faith these days. However, the secular religion of American industry in the West has always held that natural resources were there to be used, and the land was 'empty' if not filled with people (meaning white folks), towns, roads, and all the bustle of modern commerce. The Bush administration, staffed with former executives from the energy and mining industries, seems resolute and untroubled in this faith...

*"...With little likelihood for stronger laws or even favorable interpretations by the administration of those that exist, the battle on behalf of Native Americans holy places will have to be fought one site at a time... As Tex Hall, the Indian leader with the name of a cowboy, says, 'We're all part of the sacred circle of life... and we all have a duty as a member of the human race to keep the circle intact'."***

**Quoted with permission from the article "Losing Sacred Ground: Values of faith and profit conflict on federally owned land." By Reed Karaim, "Trail of Dreams" issue, March/April 2003, excerpted from <u>Preservation, The Magazine of the National Trust for Historic Preservation</u>.

Ahead of us lay miles upon open miles of flat desert road to bring us eventually to the Grand Canyon National Park. We were traveling on U.S. 160 now, which had intersected at Kayenta, and it took us in a fairly straight southwest shot towards Tuba City, where it intersected with the ancient Hopi village of Moenkopi. Kayenta to Tuba City was about 80 miles. By now Peter and I had resumed communicating, and Dingo was settling into transportation-by-car comfortably. She loved to sit on my lap, that left foot braced on the floorboard, and watch the scenery flash by while I stroked behind her ears. She didn't seem to mind the contraption around her neck any longer, and she loved the attention she was getting. Every so often, Pete even reached over to give her a rub.

It was here, as Pete and I were driving through the perpetual desert listening to *Sting* singing, appropriately "Desert Rose" and "2,000 Years," that we saw her. Or rather, Pete saw her. He slowed and pointed down off to my right. "I'm going to back up, Laura. We're both going to want to see this. Did you see her? Did you see the elder, herding her sheep down in the gorge?"

"No, I was listening to the music, off in my own world." I told Pete, as I craned my head around, looking for the old woman. Pete backed the Camry up the deserted road and located a place to pull over close by. We left the nervous pup in the car and the two of us got out. I popped off my lens cap and checked the settings on my camera as we walked towards the edge of the big rock overhang blocking her from view.

Barbed wire, in 3 tight strands, blocked our immediate paths. As much as the inevitable influx of new civilizations, as much as the railroads and the immigrants, the Calvary and the cattle ranches this new breed of people brought with them, it was this vicious cruel wire, strung throughout the infinite spaces to define and tame the sprawl – while it mangled and maimed unsuspecting beasts that impaled themselves upon it, becoming slashed and entangled and dying horrendously slow, hideous deaths – it was this wicked wire that also helped tame the wide open west.

We both stood and eyed the obstacle. Pete said, "Well, this is as far as I go. I'm not tackling that stuff. It's there for a reason."

"Not me, Pete. Help me through this, will you – I want the photo. From above like this it'll be such a spectacular shot – *if* I can get close enough to her."

Pete eyed the treacherous wire. It was new and it was tautly stretched. "I don't know, Razza – you could get hurt or tear up your clothes trying to get through here."

I stood tall and defiant and looked at him, then over to the edge of the cliff blocking the old Navajo woman from view. She was 'getting away' as we stood there. "I'll take my chances, PeterWop – *please* just see how wide you can stretch this stuff." In a moment of forethought, I slipped my camera over my head and laid it under the bottom string of wicked wire. Pete found safe handholds and gave a mighty heave. Dingo whined in the car behind us, watching us, her pert face intent. I took a deep breath and then let it out, visualizing myself to be Kate Moss or Twiggy. With a body horizontal, I scrunched to 90 degrees and eased between the strands, a leg at a time. One prong grabbed my denim shorts; I was stuck. *Damn!*

"Laura, I can't keep holding this like this; please come or go, but don't lollygag..." he spoke through clinched teeth.

"Pete, I'm snagged, I'm *trying.*" I had to laugh – we probably looked like a couple of morons standing there in this ridiculous situation; too bad somebody didn't have a camera on *us. Tourists.* This crazy memory of a magnet in my studio office came to mind. It said, **"Blessed are we who can laugh at ourselves for we shall never cease to be amused."** Case in point.

I reached back behind me and tried to undo the barb, thinking that Pete might have to let go at any moment and snap these barbs right into my face. *Ouch.* With a ripping sound, the fabric gave but my leg was through, then the rest of me, with but a pinch of wire on my upper arm – just a scratch. "Thanks, Pete! I'll be *right* back! Hope we haven't lost her –" I snatched my camera up from the ground and ran to the edge of the rock, popping off the lens cap and checking the settings as I went. She and her sheep and dog were ahead of us, walking along the arroyo bottom, oblivious to our presence. Pete called for me to hurry.

I ran lightly along the edge of the huge cliff, jumping small rocky gullies, praying that rattlesnakes would feel the vibrations of my footfalls and stay put under their rocks. Okay, now I was just a little bit behind her. Her dog looked up, sensing or smelling my presence, and whined a little, moving closer to the elder. He looked like an Australian Shepherd mix, blue and mottled and short-tailed. *Odd,* I thought, *that a breed like this would be out here...* But I was really watching the old woman, focusing the lens on her as she moved below me with her flock of maybe thirty sheep, as she'd done here on the rez probably for decades.

She was a small and wizened little woman, her heavily grayed hair pulled back in a bun behind her head. She was unaware of my presence, standing above her like this, framing my shots. She wore a heavy maroon velveteen blouse, gathered with a handmade woven belt outside her full black skirt. A turquoise and silver squash-blossom necklace hung around her neck, the central Naja pendant hanging well down her torso. This tiny woman was floating through time before my eyes; this moment was out of photographs of Indians from any number of books I'd seen, or as many postcards. This moment might have been a hundred years ago, with nothing but the breed of dog having changed. I silently thanked Pete for spotting this convoy and for holding the wire. This was not to be missed.

I ran ahead to try to catch a photo of them as they came up the path. The dog was becoming agitated, not happy with my movement above. The old woman looked around, noticing his unease, and then looked up. The wrinkles of her leathery face lay in layers of nut brown creases from years and years of baking sun. I took the shot and waved down at her. Perhaps this was not the respectful thing to do. To wave, or to be here at all, photographing her in her everyday life.

Suddenly I felt like a voyeur in time, that this moment might have been sacred, not meant to be witnessed, or touched by an outsider. I stood there quietly, in respect, and watched them pass, hoping I had not scared the bejesus out of her. *Better me than a crouching cougar*, I rationalized.

Pete was calling, asking why I was taking so long. I pensively walked back over the uneven rock surfaces of this cliff above what now seemed a mirage. "I hope that I didn't scare the old woman in my enthusiasm there, Pete. It was so exciting to see her down there, herding those sheep – I just got lost in the moment and in framing the shots."

"Different cultures, Laura. You probably did startle her – here she thought she was all alone, and then some Belagaana is standing there, like you're from Hollywood, or something. And a woman, no less. She'll be okay. You ready to tackle the fence again?"

"You ready to hold it?" I countered. "Real wide now – that was a pretty wimpy stretch before," I kidded him. *Careful, kiddo, I thought, you don't want to let him have reason to snap it shut around you, like the jaws of a crocodile, for being a Smartass...*

Pete made a mock-mad face and then gave a big macho to-do, grunting to spring the prickly wire open; I tried to ease back through, but this time managed to snag my calf with a barb, drawing blood. Not bad, but I considered it a reprimand, maybe, from one of the Navajo Yei (masked representatives of supernatural beings) for trespassing on their space. Oh well, another scar, another story. It was worth the wound.

As we returned to the car, the pup was wagging her whole petite body, deliriously happy that we had come back to her. We gave Dingo a big reassuring love and then washed off the wound at the car and assessed damages to my shorts. No big deal; one would heal, the other mend. It was time to be on our way.

We continued our free float of miles upon miles of open desert driving, slowing only when we saw a free-range cow or horse ahead, careful to give it plenty of space to react. Generally, it simply stood its ground and lazily watched us pass. We passed the sign that said "Elephant Feet," across from Red Lake. These strange phenomenon's are two towers of sandstone, enlarged at the base, and divided into 'toes,' looking much like pachyderm feet. We did not stop, but I understand that if one takes a photo of someone standing between these structures it looks as if you've been caught under huge, fossilized, elephant legs – a very interesting place for conversational family photos.

"We're getting low enough on gas that we'd better stop in Tuba City to tank up," Pete broke into my pachyderm thoughts.

"Sounds good to me. I look forward to stretching loose the kinks. We can give Little Bits here a chance to unwind, too, and maybe take care of business. Maybe they'll have good coffee," I added, longingly. Coffee at this point was often from sitting pots; who knew when they'd last been made. And finding a Starbuck's, or the like, out here would be as likely as finding a hogan on Wall Street. But a 7-11 would be nice…

"We'll see," said Pete. "Are your legs going to sleep under your dog?"

My dog? Hmm. I kind of liked the sound of that. But wait a minute – I'd just promised the man we'd only be looking for a home for her, and as soon as possible, too, so we could carry on with our vacation… "My dog, eh?" I looked over at him, hopefully.

"No. Let me revise that. And quickly. *The* puppy. *The* puppy that needs a home – ASAP. Don't get any ideas, Razza." Pete looked over at me meaningfully, trying to be stern.

"I actually wasn't. You just planted a little tiny seed."

"Well, dig it up. By the way, how's your hand?" he reached over and took my left hand to take a look. "I see it's stopped bleeding, but you'd better keep it clean. Between your hand, and now your leg, you'll carry home all *kinds* of scars to remember this trip, Ra." He turned to me and actually smiled. "Maybe you can wash them well when we get to the station." (He *did* care!)

"Maybe so." It had long stopped hurting; I'd pretty much forgotten about the hand. "How about my driving a while after we get gas?"

"Nah. And me get to hold the dog? *Forgeddaboutit.* You bond; I'll drive. When we reach Cameron, and turn off to drive through the park, I think it's only another 50 miles, or so. That'll make it about 75 miles from Tuba City. I'm tough – I can handle it."

"I know you're tough, Pete. Just like a Ford truck, and I know you can 'handle it.' I just thought you might like a break, that's all. Maybe we could put her on the jacket behind my seat. You might not have to hold her – she seems pretty sleepy."

"Nope. I'll drive. It keeps me out of trouble."

"Fine, hardhead. You're just like a man. I'm not sure if I'll remember how when we get to Virginia. Skye and Jared will have to be *my* driving coaches, when we get back."

"Yeah, that relearning to drive thing, *and* remembering where you're going," he teased, referring to the airstrip.

"Smartass." Lights at the Tuba City/Moenkopi intersection lay ahead. By now it was late afternoon. We filled the car; Dingo peed; we peed and there was actually fresh (enough) coffee. Life was good.

NON SEQUITUR © 2001 by Wiley Miller. Dist. by UNIVERSAL PRESS SYNDICATE. Reprinted with permission. All rights reserved.

The short stint between Tuba City and the intersection with U.S. 89 was 8 miles. A sign at the tee said "Dinosaur Tracks" to the right, which I read later were perfectly preserved prehistoric footprints of some 200 million-year-old creatures. *Un*believable. 'Million' out here in terms of years was thrown around as commonly as 'million' in D.C., in terms of dollars. And in this Bush administration, 'million' is rapidly being replaced by 'billion,' as America's surplus is spent on firing up the troops for war in the Middle East.

At the tee, one of the many out west, a large sign read **'Grand Canyon.'** Under it was two green signs, one pointing to the right that said **'North Rim,'** and the other pointing left: **'South Rim.'** Beside it another green double sign said **'Page,'** pointing right and **'Flagstaff,'** pointing left. A large black arrow on a yellow sign reminded motorists that this was an intersection – **'Stop!'** And in the background of this tee at highway 89 were rolling mesitas of Painted Desert in cinnamon and ecru sands, offering a soft place to land, if one happened *not* to stop in time. "Well, since our hotel awaits us this way, let's head south." Pete mused. "Cameron's only about 15 miles down the road; this is where we turn off to head into the Grand Canyon parkway."

"Pete, you've *done* your homework – I've gotta' hand it to you. So *that's* what you're doing when you ogle the maps, while I'm off with the camera and you're sitting in the car..."

"Somebody's gotta' do it."

"Well, you know what? The mileage wouldn't change whether or not we check it out – and I get to take all this in on a more intimate basis, while you add up the sums."

"Yeah, well, call it a male thing. I like to know where we're going and how long it's going to take."

"Fine. That's fine. You go right ahead there, baby, and count your miles to kingdom come. I'll watch the scenery," I kidded him, and looked down at the sleeping puppy. The crazy little mutt had both her back paws on the floorboard now, beside my legs, and her scrawny little body and front legs were sprawled over my lap; she was trusting me to brace her while she slept. Dag*gon*it, she was sweet. My maternal instincts were kicking into gear big time now, and I was enjoying this long-term 'animal fix.' It had been a long time since I'd handled a young pup, and this one was awfully sweet...

SEVENTEEN

On to the Grand Canyon

"To keep your marriage brimming
with love from a loving cup,
whenever you're wrong admit it
whenever you're right shut up."
Ogden Nash

We turned onto State Highway 64 at Cameron to begin the long slow trek through the Grand Canyon National Park to reach Tusayan Village. The speed limit in the park was 45 mph, down from 60 mph or better on the open desert highways; it felt like we were crawling as we anticipated finally reaching our destination. It was by now dusk, that twilight time of night that was neither light nor dark.

We drove along what they call the Coconino Rim, north of Gray Mountain. The desert openness gave way to high mountain scrub pine, piñon, and any number of other vegetation. The light made it difficult to discern just what it was we were seeing. Small delicate deer made their way brazenly across the road, as bold in their wildness and rights to the protection of this preserve, as were the free-range domestic beasts bold in their feral world, there on the reservation.

Now and then we would see an elk on the edge of the road glide silently into the woods beyond, enshrouded again in wilderness. At some point Pete pointed out a fox or coyote stealthily vanish into the brush; I just caught a glimpse of his tail before it was swallowed by greenery. "I hope it was a fox, Pete. The Navajo say that you should not continue on your path if a coyote crosses it first. It's bad juju. But if you spread cornmeal and ask him to go in peace, then it will be okay. We *are* in Navajo country, you know."

"What do you want me to do? Turn around and get to the Canyon via the North Rim, Laura? No, don't tell me. You have cornmeal…" he winked at me and continued: "I swear it was a fox, now that I've had time to reconsider."

I laughed at his hedging. "Okay. It was a fox. Let's get along then. But we'll keep our eyes peeled for Wile E. Coyote and we'll add cornmeal to our shopping list in the village."

"Done." We continued our drive, getting closer to the official park entrance station now, and pulling out our National Parks Pass.

"I was thinking, Pete…"

"Uh oh —" he interrupted.

"Didn't I call you 'Smartass' earlier? Don't interrupt me, please." I jabbed his arm lightly, trying not to wake the sleeping pup.

"Ex*cuse* me – go on."

"I was thinking about last year when we were out here with the kids. Do you remember that very nice lady that we met in the village there the day we were leaving? Her name was Jama Davies and she worked in a place called South Rim Travel? She helped us make a copy of my long letter to Mary to keep as a journal of our travels? Well, I bet she might know how to find a good home for Little Bits, here. Or at least where we might start looking."

"You know, that's a good idea, Ra. I'll bet she *might* know something or someone, since she lives here. We'll try to look her up in the morning. Good work."

"Not yet, it's not. Let's see if we can find her first, and *then* see what she has to say…"

The ranger station lay ahead. Pete slowed to show our park pass. The uniformed guard handed us a Grand Canyon newsletter and a folded park guide, as he welcomed us. "Have a good evening, and enjoy your stay at the park. Remember to keep your dog on a leash…" he called after us. Soon after this we passed the entrance to Desert View, one of my favorite places along the rim, but at this point it was far too dark to see anything and the moon had not yet risen high enough to light the earth. We opted to continue to our hotel, eager to get our situation with Dingo figured out and to settle our bones.

We passed the Moran, Grandview, and Yaki Point entrances before we found our turn south to Tusayan Village. We were so ready to be there and lay our heads down. I was beginning to feel like Mary traveling through the desert wilderness with Joseph, following the Star of Bethlehem, looking for an Inn for the night, but with a young babe already in our arms. *Please, please let it be okay that we have a dog with us...* I thought to myself. *It's way too much of a hassle, at this hour, to be looking for other lodging...*

We entered Tusayan; shortly Pete was pulling into the entrance to the Red Feather Lodge. He looked over at the sleeping puppy and me. "Well, here we are. I'm going to let *you* do the talking, 'Foot-loose,' as this was all your bright idea. I'll walk the dog."

"Well, good luck in walking her and getting anywhere. She's zonked out cold." I glanced at him a second, then opened the door and eased my numb legs out into the cold night. *Chilly! This will wake her up...*

I picked up my backpack from the floorboard and headed into the foyer, rehearsing in my head what I might say about that conversation we'd had with the lodge in what felt like weeks earlier that same day. Inside the brightly lit tiled and carpeted interior the main desk stood to the right. Behind it were two young men; one of them was on the phone and the other was busy checking in a guest. I waited my turn quietly, rehearsing in my head.

"Yes, may I help you?" one of the young fellows asked, with an accent that I couldn't quite place. He was a tall and solidly built fellow; he looked as if he might be an athlete or a bodyguard. His shoulders were very broad, his brown hair was cut in a military-looking buzz and he had intense brown eyes in a pleasant face. His badge read 'Marcos.'

"Yes, ah, Marcos. Hi. My husband and I have reservations for tonight and tomorrow. We called in this morning, you see, and the lady asked if we had children or pets."

He looked at me quizzically. "And?" he said, "did you find some children along the way?" he smiled, as he asked and raised a thick dark eyebrow.

"No. But we found a pet. And we don't want to sneak her into the room, or anything. I've got to check with you about your pet policy. You see, we found her starving to death up in Monument Valley. She was lying under a sagebrush, out on the reservation. Nobody wanted her – not the Indians, or tourists. And I couldn't let her starve. So, we brought her with us."

By now the second young man had finished his phone conversation and was listening in. "Oh," he said, "that was so nice of you. What kind of dog is she?"

"Just a little yellow dingo-looking mutt. She's not very old – 4 months max. And she's skin and bones. I couldn't leave her. So, do you take pets?

What's your policy?"

The two exchanged glances and smiled. The second fellow's name was 'Scott.' He was shorter than Marcos, with sandy-brown hair and glasses. He had a very kind face, and walked with a slight limp. "Well, Scooter, whadja' think?" queried Marcos, knitting his brows and trying to look like a tough guy. "Do you think we oughta' let 'em have a room?"

Scott glanced at his buddy and laughed. "Of course we will." *Whew! A weight flew off my shoulders.* "Our policy here is we'll add a $40 pet deposit to your card, refundable if there is no damage, and there is an extra pet fee of $5 a night."

"What a relief – thank you, *thank* you, fellas," I said, then added: "But I'm sure she's not housebroken. Good grief, she'd never even been in a car until this afternoon. But I *promise* we'll keep an eye on her and walk her like crazy. My husband is walking her right now – out there pacing, in fact, worrying about the verdict."

"Well, *don't* worry. We've got you a room, and you just let us know if there is anything at all you need, okay? That really is a kind thing you did. Not a lot of people would have bothered." Marcos told me. He smiled over at Scooter. "Wasn't it?"

"Sure was," said Scott. "We wish you the best of luck. You let us know if you need something."

"Well, how about a home for her for starters?" I kidded them.

"Can't help you there – we both live in employee housing and they don't allow pets. You're going to be finding a lot of that here in the Canyon. But we'll ask around."

"Thanks, guys. Thank you both for your help, and for being so supportive. We were worried." They gave me two room keys and showed me how to find it, putting us on level 2, with easy access to the outside. Mary and Joseph and the baby had found their manger for the night.

"Bring the puppy down when you get the chance; we'd like to see her," called Scott as I walked out to join PeterWop and the pup.

"Mission accomplished, Pete," I grinned, as I found the two of them behind the hotel. Dingo was busily sniffing bushes and stones, deciphering the mysterious canine codes that dogs leave one another.

"Well, I've got to say, I *am* relieved. Good work, Razza. You got the keys?"

"Yup. We're on the 2nd floor, with easy access to the great outdoors. I think they want to make it easy to housebreak her. There are two young fellows at the desk – Marcos and Scott – they're both very nice, and very supportive. They said to let them know if they could help with anything at all."

"How about a home for the dog?" Dingo was straining at the leash and the purple bandana that we had put around her neck as a makeshift collar, pulling heavily on Pete's arm.

"Nope. I asked already. Employee housing; they can't have pets. They said this would be a problem here in the Canyon – lots of transient workers, living in temporary housing."

"Smart guys." Pete glanced over at me, looking for a rise, and hauled her back to him. I scowled at him. "She's been sniffing and sniffing – and pulling and pulling – like this since I woke her up, but do you think there'd be any results? Not on your life. She's too damned thrilled with all these wonderful scents to remember why we're here."

"*She* knows why *she's* here. It is those 'wonderful scents.' The rest is all just an afterthought to her. You've got to remember the perspective, Pete."

"Thanks for your interpretation, Doc. Well, since we aren't getting anywhere outside, how about we find our room and unpack the car?"

So tiny 'Dingo,' all of 3½-4 months old, has started a new life. Taken out of the brutal high mountain desert, where she had scrounged for food and water as best as she could, she – in the course of a single day – had been introduced to a noose around her virgin neck, where she was pulled along the ground; she was hoisted into a mobile prison-on-wheels and forced to travel with us, like it or not; and now we were asking her to enter this gigantic *thing*, full of noises and strange scents, with jaw-like contraptions that snapped shut behind us. The unnerved pup was in a near state of shock as we tried to lead her through the doors. She leaned back and dragged her frail body, that frantic deer-in-headlights look back on her face. "Oh, poor thing, she's scared to death. You'd better carry her to our room, Pete."

"Oh, *I* had better carry her, huh? How come I get the honors?"

"Because you're the tough guy, built like the Ford truck, remember? You can 'take it'."

"This is *not* the way I want to 'be taken'." He looked at the cowering, miserable puppy. "But if we're ever going to get here, I guess I'd better do this dastardly deed." He put down the suitcase. "You get to carry this, then."

"Or come back for it." I shrugged my arms, already full of things from the car. "Nobody's going to bother it for all of two minutes." He looked doubtful. "Come on, Pete."

We found our room, PeterWop with the pup again sprawled and stricken in his arms.

I set down my stuff and swiped the plastic key through the lock gizmo a couple of times until the small light registered green, then I opened the door for Pete to carry her through. He gently set her down in the hallway, beside the bathroom. She looked up at us, trying to believe she could trust us enough for this to be okay. Even Pete had to smile at her expression. She looked about her and then wandered around a minute and – God Bless her – squatted to do *all* of her business on the carpet inside the doorway, as the Wop and I looked on, speechless. *Well, there goes our security deposit. Her first experience inside a building and she has to christen the whole damned thing. Oh well... guess this was no huge surprise; I can now safely say it literally scared the shit out of her.* My thoughts raced. "Oh, my gosh, Pete! The suitcase?!"

"You're thinking of the *suitcase* at a time like this?!!" He glared over at me.

"Sure, aren't you?" I raced back down the hallway and looked out over the railing of the balcony. Below us was the open lobby and the fellows at the front desk. I leaned over the rails. "Hey guys – *yo* – *Scott, Marcos!*" They looked up, startled, at the voice from the sky. "You know how y'all said, 'if I can help with anything, let me know.' Well, '*help!*' Do you have any paper towels and carpet cleaner down there?"

They looked at one another and grinned. Scott said: "Marcos will bring something right up. Won't you, Marcos?" Scott grinned again. Marcos called: "I'll be right up!"

"Thanks!" I turned and looked for the suitcase that sat exactly where we had left it, there in the hallway. I picked it up and headed back to the room, not relishing the idea at all of facing my husband. I tapped on the door. "Pete? It's me –" The door opened. Pete stood there with an, 'I told you so' smirk on his face, the gifts on the rug behind him still. I'm sure he was waiting for me to do the honors. "Where's Dingo?" I ventured the question, hesitantly.

"You mean 'poop-butt'? She's relegated to the bathroom from now on. There's a tile floor in there."

"Good idea. I've got 'room service' coming up with cleaning supplies. They wanted to help... I'll get it all cleaned up, I promise, good as new."

"Well, there goes our security deposit." Pete said testily. "Didn't take any time, at all."

"Not if I can help it – I'll put some elbow grease into it and clean the messes right up. Tomorrow maybe we can find some of that new spray-stuff that's supposed to make furniture and carpet smell like a pine forest."

"A piney forest. A gingerbread house. Apple pie, anything but this…" Pete mumbled. There was a knock behind me; I opened the door to Marcos standing there looking like he'd just been told a good joke.

"We're sorry, Marcos. It's all new to her and she didn't know what to do. Really, we *did* walk her. She's in the bathroom now – and that's where we'll keep her from now on."

"Don't worry about it. These things happen. I've brought some heavy-duty rug shampoo, a whole roll of paper towels, and a couple of extra plastic bags. Do you need newspapers or something else?" he asked helpfully.

"No. No, we have a ton of those in the car that I've been collecting on our trip about the terrorist's attack and all of this chaos since. We'll use some of those. Thank you." I said.

"Sure." He grinned. "It's okay. I'm sure you'll clean it up well. Don't worry about your security deposit – yet." He mock-scowled. "Let me know if you need anything else."

"You're a Saint, thanks. Goodnight."

"Goodnight." And Marcos was gone.

"Okay, while you clean that up all spiffy and nice-like, I'll finish unloading our stuff." Pete headed out the door.

"Please don't say 'unload'," I mumbled after him, doubting that he even heard me.

I faced the messes, first layering down several thicknesses of paper towels to sop up the liquid. Then I gathered up the poop, in another folded towel, opened the bathroom door, frowned down at the pup lying low on the tile floor and plopped it in the toilet, careful not to drop the towel wad in, too. Luckily, and surprisingly, it was a firm stool and did minimal stain-damage to the rug, even before cleaning. Dingo looked so lost and miserable I softened and knelt down beside her, rubbing her ears. "Okay, truce there, kid. It's a lot for you to swallow at once, I know. But we've got to work out some compromises, or you're going to get me in a boat-load – no, correct that, *shit*load –of trouble." I confided to her. "And I know 'compromise' is a big word for you to understand right now, but you're a smart little girl. You'll learn. *Please...*" She looked up at me, relieved to have talked.

I went back to the hall to finish my job, taking the bathroom trashcan with me. *Hmm... I should have asked Marcos for rubber gloves. Oh well, there's soap and water.* Gingerly, I picked up the corner of the soggy paper towels and dropped them into the plastic-lined receptacle. Then I sprayed the rug with the carpet shampoo in both places. It foamed up like shaving cream. *I'll let this sit a minute*, I thought. *Pete should be back soon.* I opened the door and looked down the hallway. My Ford Truck Man was loaded down heavily, making his way to the room. "Pete, for Pete's sake, when I finish mopping this mess up, I'll help you, you know. You don't have to pretend you're a mule."

"I'll leave that to you," he grumped and squeezed past me as I held the door.

"Watch your step. We're on the soak-cycle." I warned. He stepped carefully over the foamy mounds, balancing his burden past the bathroom to drop his cargo on the nearest queen bed. I realized then that we hadn't even looked into the room yet. I joined him.

It was typical: comfortable, double-queen beds separated by the night table between them. Desk, dresser, TV/luggage stand, and a round table under the window, flanked by two chairs, and a floor lamp finished the standing room décor. Prints of Grand Canyon landscapes and Indian artwork graced the walls. The colors were soft, muted pastels. All of it was tastefully done. We'd be very comfortable here for two nights.

I turned to my husband, "Pete, while this is soaking, why don't we take a minute and give the puppy a quick bath. Who knows what might be on, or *in*, her coat – and if she has any fleas we can wash them down the drain.

"Not a bad idea, Laura. But let's make it quick, we still have to unpack and eat."

"Okay. Help me hold her then." We went back into the bathroom, rolling up our sleeves, and called Dingo over. She still looked pretty miserable. "Come here, girl, this will be new to you, probably, but in the end it'll feel *really* good. You're getting what is likely your first bath." While I talked to her, Pete ran warm water in the tub. I unwrapped one of the plastic cups while he gently put her down into the water. As soon as her toes touched she immediately started to scramble for the edge. "Oh no you don't, girl. You're staying in there." She submitted, looking frightened and frail, as we poured cups of water over her body, wetting the hair. "Hand me that hotel shampoo, will you, please, PeterWop?" I held her with one hand and reached around. Pete was a step ahead of me, handing me the opened mini-bottle. He then knelt down beside me to hold her steady.

"Oh man, *look* at that skeleton... She's in worse shape than I thought."

"I see it, Pete. She's pitiful, but we'll fatten her up soon." Dingo looked utterly forlorn.

A few fleas were floating around in the dirty water around her feet. "She'll feel *so* much better after this." Pete unplugged the drain while I ran clean warm water into the cup and rinsed her well. We then closed the curtain while she shook. Pete handed me a towel and we dried her coat in the tub before we let her jump out. When she did, she stood on the bathmat, tiny and bedraggled, her yellow coat fluffed in all directions around her boney body. She stood there, ears out to their side, her tail between her legs, trembling and terrified by this new experience. I knelt down beside Dingo and continued to dry her, talking to her gently, while Pete rinsed the tub. "It's okay, girl. When you dry, you'll feel like a *new* little puppy dog. You'll have an en*tire*ly new lease on life. I promise."

"Alrighty then, we've finished this job. Now let's get something to eat. I don't know about you, RazzaWop, but I am *starved*. Where do you think we can get dinner around here this late?" This was a good sign; he was using one of his endearments.

"I'm not sure. The McDonald's across the street looked open when we pulled in. Maybe they're still open." We washed our hands, left the pup in the bathroom, dodged the foamy carpet, and walked to the window. The Golden Arches were still glowing yellow and lights shown from inside. "That looks hopeful. But do you realize we don't eat at fast-food places so much in a *year*, as we've done out here on this trip?" I marveled. "*Geesh*, the food's starting to taste good."

"That's because we're always starved when we eat it. Like now. I'll run over and see what I can scrounge up. What would you like?"

"Anything with chocolate and no fat."

"Yeah, right. None of those places serve fat *or* calories. I'll be back in a bit."

"I'll finish cleaning this up, Pete, and I'll get some newspapers from the car to lay down in the bathroom. See you soon."

Pete left to cross the street. It was close to 10PM. It looked like they stayed open until at least then. I put the 2nd room key in my pocket and went out to the car, poking my head in the bathroom and telling the startled, wet pup that I'd be right back.

I found the stack of papers collected from the past week in the trunk of the car, put my denim jacket over my arm and grabbed a few more things to bring back to the room. Balancing all this, I opened the door and headed inside, taking the jacket and newspapers into the bathroom. "Hey," I looked down at the damp little dog that lay there under the sink with her head on her paws, her eyes rolled up at me, her hair going every-which-way. She looked utterly depressed. "I brought a friend of yours, girl," and knelt down to put the jacket on the floor. "This should make you feel more at home." Her tail wagged a little as she stood and crept to me. I put the jacket down where she'd been laying. The familiar scents should help make her comfortable. She walked to it, circled a time or two, and lay down to nestle in.

I stood over the bathroom counter to start sorting through the stack of *USA Today's*, *Albuquerque Journals*, *The Navajo News*, and a couple of recent *Wall Street Journals*. My, we had quite a collection of local, state, and federal coverage of general news, as well as the updates and blow-by-blow accounts of the terrorist madness, the domino effect of September 11th, and the government's reaction, all leading to the buzz of war.

I stood there scanning the articles, separating those to save, with those that could be used for potty training. A couple of headshots of bin Laden went into the potty-training stack, for up close and personal use. As I read through the diverse collection, my mood started taking a nosedive. There were a few personal stories of individuals, as told by their family, that had been in one or the other of the Twin Towers, in the Pentagon, or on one of the four planes. There were stories of the policemen and –women and firefighters.

Headlines from the various papers read: **Official: More attacks from Bin Laden likely. U.S. vows to give world proof:** *Economy (Poll shows optimism over the long haul);* **Chemical Threats** *(Cities reveal plans for bio-chem attack);* **The Hunt** *(Officials will soon release evidence of bin Laden network).* **U.S. cities brace for the next acts of terrorism** *(Atop the new fears: Biological and Chemical attacks).* **U.S. Tries to undercut Taliban** *(A move to enlist Iran; Saudis break with Afghan regime).* **Shock waves spreading out in unpredictable directions. Bush outlines new airport security plans;** *Lawmakers unenthusiastic about plan to arm pilots.* **Poetry soothes in** world without rhyme, reason. **Flags will be in style for a while** *(from T-shirts to haute couture, Old Glory is flying everywhere)*. **Taliban admits bin Laden is in Afghanistan. Terrorism war could spur global problems. U.S. shaping plans to fund foes of Taliban.** The list was endless. The only good news was about the poetry and that Michael Jordan, at 38, had decided to return to basketball with the Washington Wizards. It was official; he had signed a 2-year contract for mega-bucks. In a statement, he said: *"Although I am energized by my impending return to the court, I am deeply saddened, and my heart goes out to the victims and their families."*

I stood there a moment in silence, closed my eyes and said a quiet prayer that humans find some core of balance, some stability, and a means to understand one another in this craziness. The world had turned inside out. It was nuts. Please God, let there be peace on earth – some day. I felt like a beauty queen.

Another headline caught my attention, as I was gathering up the papers to be saved: **War on Afghanistan to be called "Operation Enduring Freedom."** One of those snazzy code names that the military uses. Under the title it read: *Pentagon coins new name for battle against terrorism after the first moniker, Operation Infinite Justice, was said to be offensive to Muslims. This name will stick, unless there's a problem with it, too, says Defense Secretary Donald Rumsfeld.* Bush wanted to find bin Laden, Texas-style, 'dead or alive.' *Any moment now we would be plunging into war with the purpose of extracting this man, the Taliban, and al'Qaida from the mountainous regions of this distant country. There were so many questions. God help our men and women going in to fight this war; Allah help the innocent men, women, and children who lived in Afghanistan and had had nothing to do with the Taliban or al'Qaida, and would be at the mercy of our fierce military force. Osama bin Laden and his fanatical thugs had pried open a hornet's nest of retaliation. Damned religious fanaticism,* I thought, sadly. *I remembered one of Mahatma Gandhi's sage quotes:* "An eye for an eye just makes the whole world blind." *I had read this somewhere, and the simplicity of the statement had stayed with me. Look at the Palestinians and the Israelis. Look at Pakistan and India – the Muslims and the Hindus. Look at all the wars, the genocide, the mutilations in so many parts of Africa. Look at racism still here in America. Dear Jesus, it didn't end…*

A tap on the door interrupted my thoughts. I shook my head out of the stupor and opened the bathroom door. Good grief, the foam still lay on the carpet – by now it should be clean under there – *if* the carpet had any color left. "Heh, Pete," I opened the door for him to sidle by me again, his arms loaded with the cardboard tray, a couple of cups and a bag balanced on top.

"You still haven't cleaned up the gobs of gunk down there?"

"No, I got sidetracked with the newspapers. I'll get it now. The papers are sorted."

"Okay, I'll get our banquet laid out," Pete headed into the room with dinner.

I finished mop-up duty, using clean paper towels to scrub, and then watered down even more to 'rinse' the rug. We wouldn't know how the rug had fared until it had dried, but it looked promising, for now. I took the trash can into the bathroom, tied-off the top of the bag and put a fresh one in, set the 'used' one in the hallway and then scrubbed my hands thoroughly a couple of times, rubbing in hand cream for moisture afterwards and to add a fresher scent. Okay, ready for dinner. My, what an appetizer *that* had been.

Pete had gotten a couple of broiled chicken sandwiches, easy-on-the-mayo, a large fry to split, and two milkshakes, a vanilla for him and a chocolate for me. "Your gourmet meal is served, Madame," said he, as he bent at the waist and waved towards the food.

"Looks scrumptious, PeterWop. You must have labored for hours."

"Oh, I did. I did. Sit. Enjoy."

I smiled at him; life was so simple here. We placed the pillows against the headboard, pumped them up, and sat back against them, the food between us. I had not realized that I was famished, but it had been hours and hours since we'd had our pb&j's in Kayenta – I don't remember McDonald's ever tasting like such a feast. We savored every bite. The chocolate shake was exquisite. Criminy, we must have been starved! "Is yours as good as mine?" I looked over at Pete, my mouth full.

"My what?" he asked me mischievously.

"Your anything." I winked at him.

Our deep conversation was interrupted by Dingo whining behind the door. There was a pitiful little scratch. "I'll go talk to her. She's been so quiet, I think we put her into total shock with all this newness and then the bath, to boot." I put my dinner down, climbed out of bed and went into the bathroom. Dingo had gone back to the jacket and laid down. "What's wrong, girl? You lonesome? You wonder where we went? We're here. Let me give you a little more food." I knelt down to add some dry food to her stainless steel bowl. She still had plenty of water in the other side, but she didn't seem interested in a meal. Dingo lay there staring at me intently, as if trying to osmose her thoughts into my head. It struck me then that she had a quiet dignity about her, and a sweetness, that re-minded me of Lakota. There was an aura emanating from her that was so like his. *Whoa, there, Jack,* I shook my head. *Don't be doing that, pup. We're looking for a home for you, remember?* I osmosed back. Her golden-brown eyes never left mine, as she laid her head on her paws. "You be quiet now. We're right outside." I closed the door behind me, stood against it for a moment, and cleared my head before returning to Pete. "She'll be fine — she just needed to know we were close by. Man, she just pulled a Lakota-look on me. It was uncanny — like he was there with me, for a second."

"Uh oh," Pete grimaced. "Don't start that now. You know what we need to do, Razza."

"I know. I know. Keep her and take her back with us, right?" I kidded him.

"Yeah. That's what I meant. Tomorrow, first thing, we find Jama and start looking for that home."

EIGHTEEN

Searching for a Home for Dingo

"Things don't change. You change your way of looking, that's all."
Carlos Castaneda

'Tomorrow first thing' came and I rolled over to find my man and give him a sleepy hug. Instead, there was a rumpled, empty, bed. *Hmm?...* I opened my eyes and looked around the darkened room. The curtains were still drawn, and it was quiet as could be. I got up and padded to the bathroom. "Pete?" I knocked on the door. Nothing. I went in and there was no puppy there, either. He must have walked her, so I answered nature's call, and then washed my face and pulled on some clothes. Just as I was tying my shoes, I heard the key sliding in the lock outside the room. Pete brought the puppy in, took her immediately to the bathroom and closed the door, so there would be no repeat of last night. "Good morning," I called to him. "You're up early. Have a good walk?"

He walked over to the curtains and opened them. "I'm always up earlier than you, Laura." He smiled and asked: "Sleep well? When I left, you were curled up like an angel with a little smile on your face. I sure hope you were dreaming about me. Or one of the kids, maybe. Or one of the pets…"

"*I'll* never tell," I joked, not remembering the dream at all.

"Well, you know, it is a beautiful day out there. You ready to go?" he asked me. "Oh, and by the way, maybe this puppy-thing isn't such a bad idea, after all. You have *no* idea how many women approached me from out of the blue – young, old, it didn't matter. They were just gushing over the dog. She's a real babe-magnet." He decided to elaborate. "In fact, I could swear one of them was Lonnie Andersen…" He peeked over his shoulder to catch my reaction.

"Lonnie, eh? And how old is *she* now? At least you didn't say Drew Barrymore. Oh, and by the way, that's a single man's well-known fact about puppy's being babe-magnets. You've just been out of the loop too long, there, hound-dog. Did you find her a home with all of the 'oohing' and 'aahing'?"

"No, alas, not that. But I *did* get a couple of telephone numbers." He grinned like an imp.

I shook my head and smiled at his nonsense. "Did she do any business?"

"I didn't notice; I was talking to the babes." Pete didn't want to let this one go. His 'babe-magnet' had made his macho day. He'd be impossible for hours now, puffing out his chest and strutting like a peacock. Maybe, at least, he'd stop complaining about her.

Monday morning, October 1st

The day was, indeed, gorgeous. We took light jackets with us as we crossed the road to McDonald's for breakfast. We were becoming downright regulars of Mickey-D's. The flag outside the restaurant here in the Canyon was flying high and full, as it had been in Monument Valley. "You go in and get what you want. You'll know what I like. I'll hold the dog," he teased, "maybe I'll get to meet some more women."

"Oh, God, you're totally impossible now, Wop. I think I liked you better when you were grumping."

The prices inside were typical of a resort town, set to gouge the tourist. No wonder Pete had called it 'gourmet' last night. I bought a couple of breakfast combos, complete with coffee and orange juices and balanced them carefully, as a nice-looking young fellow held the door for me, smiling at my precarious load as I passed. Pete sat at a small table outside. Dingo was eager to see me return, wagging her curved tail happily.

I wasn't sure if the enthusiasm was for me, or the food I brought, as she recognized Styrofoam. As I was leaning down to set the tray on the table, she ducked between my legs and the leash tightened, throwing me off balance. A coffee went flying; Pete quickly saved the rest before it could follow. Some of the airborne liquid scalded my wounded hand. "Damnit, I do believe she's trying to see that this hand will be forever branded!" I shook it out, untangled myself from the pup, and then laid an O.J. against my hand to cool the skin.

Pete was whistling and looking around, nonchalantly. "I'm not saying a thing… But I'll get a refill for that coffee. Was that your decaf, or my high-test? And are you okay?"

"I'm fine. She's got to learn a thing or two about leash etiquette, that's all." I scowled down at Dingo, but she was oblivious to my reprimand as she sniffed around the coffee spill and strained to reach a wadded up paper sack on the ground. "That one was yours, I think, Pete," as I looked closely at the lids. "But if I start zinging, we'll know I was mistaken. Then I'll be sitting on my foot and we'll be looking for bathrooms every half hour."

After an al fresco breakfast our trio walked to the Tusayan Grocery, beside which we remembered "South Rim Travel" to be, but there was no sign of the agency. Dingo was becoming better at following along with us on the leash, but she still was easily intrigued by the array of scents we passed. Sometimes we'd let her sniff and other times we'd insist that she keep moving. "Why don't you go inside and see if they know Jama, Laura. Maybe someone will know where the 'South Rim' moved. While you're in there, will you get some more beer, please?" he added, and gave me a big hopeful grin.

I went in past the registers. On the right side of the store one found grocery items; in the back were chilled items; in the center was a small post office, and to the left was a touristy gift area for Grand Canyon merchandise. I took a right and found some Cascades paper towels (100% recycled), a small bottle of extra-strength Febreze, a pair of medium-sized rubber gloves and Lysol spray for our potty-training adventure. The rug had looked pretty good this morning, and the few areas in the bathroom weren't difficult to clean, although she'd missed bin Laden, altogether. I'd keep the papers down; she would nail him, sooner or later.

A coyote crossed my mind and I grinned to myself, remembering. *Ah, the cooking isle… yes, yes, they had cornmeal, and a small bag, too. We shouldn't need much, and that was good because it was at a ferocious price, but while in Rome… Not only would it ward off bad luck if and when we ran into these critters, it was absorbent. This might come in useful in our potty-training escapade.* I put the bag in the cart. *Oh yeah, the beer.* There was no temperance in the Canyon. Beers and wine of all sorts were offered; I found a bottle of Merlot/Sauvignon cross and put it beside the cornmeal, then decided to surprise Pete with Dos Equis instead of Corona this time. He'd appreciate the change.

Okay, now to locate Jama. I looked around the store for a manager-type. A tall, pretty platinum blond was walking brusquely past me towards the post office. I stopped her. "Excuse me, but I'm looking for someone that worked next door here last year, at the South Rim Travel Agency. You might know her, or of her; her name was Jama Davies." The lady turned. She must have been 5'11"– I felt small next to her at my 5'8". She looked like a mannequin, come to life, everything perfectly in place, born into her makeup, hair coiffed and sprayed. I suddenly felt disheveled, there in my khaki wind pants with the Kokopelli belt, red chamois shirt and hiking boots, my windbreaker tied around my waist, and chestnut hair all amuss. Oh well, not important. Back to the mission.

"Yes, I know South Rim Travel, but they closed six months ago. How is it that you know Jama?" she asked me, guardedly.

"Like I said, we met last year. She helped me copy a letter to my sister. We hit it off – she and I talked a good while and I sent her a letter later on, but never heard from her."

"That's because she moved when the agency closed, but I couldn't tell you where." I had the feeling that 'couldn't' actually meant 'wouldn't', even if she did know. She was a careful type of woman. "Why do you want to know?" she asked me skeptically, raising a perfectly tweezed eyebrow.

"For two reasons – again, like I told you, we hit it off, and I'd like to say hello, since my husband and I are back in the Canyon. The second is that while we were traveling through Monument Valley, on the Navajo rez, we found a puppy out there, starving to death. We brought the pup here with us, hoping to find her a good home. We thought that maybe Jama might have some ideas, knowing the area as she does."

"Oh." Her pale blue eyes narrowed. "Listen, I don't know where Jama is, but let me give you some good advice. If you found a puppy on the reservation, I suggest that you just put a bullet in its head and be done with it. Those rez-dogs are inbred; they're mangy and diseased. You don't know what they might be carrying. Get rid of it." I stepped back in disbelief at what this woman had just said.

"No, the pup isn't diseased. There's no sign of mange, and she is actually a very intelligent little animal. She's just very thin, through no fault of her own." Man, I thought, *this is the type of woman that country crooner wrote about when he claimed, "She never cried when Old Yeller died." She was one cold fish. I wondered what had transpired in Barbie's life to harden her like this.* "Listen, we *are* going to find her a home. If you don't know where Jama might be, might you know of a shelter around here – some SPCA, a vet's office, anything – as a lead?"

"Well, there *is* always the Grand Canyon Kennel, in the big village.

They act as the animal shelter, but they stay full. They board, as well. There are strays from all over the place. I still suggest you just put her down."

I grimaced at the thought. "That's not an option – she's way too precious. If you want to see her, my husband is holding her right outside." She shook her head no, and turned to leave. "Thanks for your help." I called to her, trying not to sound sarcastic.

I cashed a travelers check to pay for the groceries and asked them to double-bag them for the haul back to the lodge and then joined Pete and Dingo outside, relating what Miss Congeniality had said. Even he shook his head at her perception of our reality. "It takes all kinds of people…" his voice trailed off, and then, "Man – I am starting to feel real badly for stray dogs. They sure get to be the dregs of society, don't they? It's not as if spaying and neutering weren't an option."

"I know, Pete, but a lot of people don't believe in it; others don't see the need, or have all kinds of reason why they won't. Some think they can't afford it, although shelters are forever offering affordable rates for low-income families. Unfortunately, it's these guys who get to suffer for all those reasons it doesn't happen. Dogs *and* cats. Damnit, *millions* get euthanized in shelters every year, because there just aren't enough homes. Millions more become road kill – and many more end up like this. Starving to death." My throat constricted; I could feel my pulse quickening. *Damned needless stupidity.* "Come on, let's get this stuff back to the hotel, and then try to locate this shelter." I wanted to change the subject. "By the way there, PeterWop, I got some Dos Equis, for a change." His eyes lit up and he threw a companionable arm over my shoulder and squeezed a thanks.

Back in our room we relegated Dingo to the bathroom again and decided to pack up the cooler for a day's outing, at least along the Canyon rim. We packed our pb&j ingredients, fruit, milk, cheese, dog chow, Wasa Bread, and a couple of the beers. We looked up the number for the kennel and put it on a notepad to take with us, grabbed a couple of jackets and set out for a full day at the Grand Canyon. "Shall we take a rim walk first, before we find the kennel? It won't be out of our way, and I'm ready to see the sights." Pete suggested.

"Fine by me. We can walk Dingo again. See if it's hopeful to find her an owner out here."

We headed over to Yavapai Point, which overlooks sections of the South Kaibab Trail, where we had hiked as a family the year before. I remembered how, when the kids first saw the Canyon at sunset when we had arrived they'd scoffed, saying it wasn't nearly as big or awesome as they'd imagined. These were cool, hip teenagers who had watched countless videos, with their special effects and incredible actions sequences. Been there, done that. Oh yeah? The next day we had hiked several miles along the rim, cameras in action and water bottles on hand. Then, after a rest back at the hotel, we took the bus over to the South Kaibab Trail, each of us loaded up with water, comfortable walking clothing and lots of film. We only hiked a mile and a half or so down, back and forth, back and forth, along the endless switchback trails, deeper and deeper into the severely eroded earth. We made it to what is so aptly called "Ooh-Aah Point."

Somewhere in the course of this hike it dawned on our skeptical, omnipotent teenagers that this place really was pretty magnificent and that it was possible that we were but tiny specks of insignificance amongst the grandeur of this ancient landscape that undulated for miles upon miles of exposed layers of stone. Rock with names like Toroweap Formation (a mere 260 million-years-old sea sediment); Coconino Sandstone (270 million-year-old desert dunes); Supai group (300 million-year-old river swamps and floodplain deposits); Bright Angel Shale (540 million-year-old calm water sediments), down to the "Great Unconformity" (330 million-year-old gap – a period of erosion, not deposition) to the Grand Canyon Supergroup (900 million-year-old to *1.2 billion*-year-old sea sediments)… There is the Vishnu Group, *way* down below even the Colorado River, which runs along the bottom of these colorful stratified layers of history. The Vishnu Group, 1.7 billion-year-old metamorphosed sea sediments that are interspersed vertically with Zoroaster Granite, were molten intrusions in these sediments. *

(*This information comes from **The Grand Canyon** by Stewart Aitchison, The Sierra Press.)

We didn't go into this detail with the kids, as we didn't know it then, ourselves; we just told them we were in sacred lands that were millions of years in the making, and to be respectful. We did not have to say much more – the dawning of the magnitude of nature surrounding us enveloped the each of them, in its own due course. I watched quietly, tears in my eyes, as Jared, Skye or Natalie would stand along this trail, thunderstruck and awed by what he or she beheld. They were finally 'getting it.'

A storm had threatened to blow in; weather here can change on a dime. We had decided to hike on back out. Winds and dust whipped around us; I had put on my protective glasses to guard my newly Lasiked eyes from the particles and bowed my head against the oncoming wrath, shielding the camera inside my jacket. But it was all temporary sound and fury, it did not last. The storm grew tired of threatening our little group and veered north, heading off to find newcomers with which to play. In its wake it left a glowing light that seared unforgettably into each of our memories.

We watched the distant echoes of rock faces turn coral and plum colors, shadows and light kissing the serrated surfaces and moving on, as clouds swept through sun downing skies. And then, as if a light had been switched on inside the canyon, the world turned to shades of vivid gold and the sky deepened to indigo, as we made our way back up the steep switchback trails. When the setting sun hit surfaces it turned them to mountains of gold, shimmering against the darkling sky. Unreal. This illusion of gold here in the West, that had made many a sensible man a fool, was as real as the ancient stone surrounding us at that time. We were drunk and made giddy by the beauty, like brave Ulysses enchanted by the sirens of song, in *The Odyssey*.

Yes, the Canyon can do that to people. It is impossible to describe the sheer magnitude or splendor of this place. Photos are but glimpses into its infinite old soul. Images on the screen are just a tease. All I can do is suggest that each person, in his or her lifetime, make it a goal to experience this wonderment of nature firsthand – have your own hair rise in goose bumps on the nape of your neck, as tears come to your eyes, feeling totally insignificant before this majesty. It is a religious experience that each must absorb on your own, regardless of your God.

"No matter how far you have wandered… the Grand Canyon of the Colorado will seem as novel to you, as unearthly in color and grandeur and quantity of its architecture, as if you had found it after death, on some other star."
John Muir, founder of The Sierra Club, from Our National Parks

Pete and I walked Dingo along the rim a while, looking down into the South Kaibab Trail and reminiscing. If we didn't have the pup in tow we could have hiked down any number of these trails, as we had originally planned. But we did, and dogs are not allowed below the rim for a number of good reasons, so we did not hike in on this trip. In a bit, we decided to locate the animal shelter. After some search in and around the Grand Canyon Village we found it out beyond the train and beyond the corrals and barns where they keep the mules that must trek down these steep rock trails – down and back, down and back – carrying the tourists that do not want to walk. They are beasts of burden in the most literal of terms, but they are well cared-for and are integral to Canyon travel. We found the kennels way back in the woods, hidden away.

It was a small bungalow tucked into the pines, with mesh runs lining the outside of the building. As with any animal shelter, we were greeted by a chorus of barking as we left the car. Little Dingo cringed down and pulled away as we tried to lead her to the door.

She was unnerved by the noise. "I'd better carry her in," Pete volunteered, as he knelt down to gather her up in his arms. Once more, she splayed out and looked stricken, but didn't fight the enveloping arms as she had done only yesterday. I opened the door and held it as Pete edged past. "After you; I'll be a gentleman," I smiled after him.

Behind the desk sat a diminutive woman with a wave of soft strawberry blond hair around her face. Something about her reminded me of Holly Hunter, the actress. She held a vulnerability, a fragility to life, in her expression. Her large gray eyes smiled at us as we entered. "What have we here?" the lady asked, with a Southern lilt in her voice.

"We have a little mutt we found up in Monument Valley lying under a sagebrush, starving to death." I told her.

"Oh, my. Well now. So you brought her all this way to us?" she asked. "How unusual."

"Well, we were coming to the Canyon as part of our anniversary trip," Pete explained, "and so we thought we'd try to locate her a home, so we can get on with our travels."

"I see," said the petite woman, as she came around from behind the desk to take a closer look. Pete knelt down and deposited the scared puppy on the linoleum floor. I knelt down to reassure her. Dingo's tail was not curled at all; it lay tucked between her legs and she was hunched together, her ears horizontal, looking miserable, like at any moment she might be used for target practice. "It's okay, girl, this nice lady is here to help us." The incessant barking continued in the background, and I could feel the pup's body tremble.

"Well now, she's a pretty little thing. Awfully *skinny*...," the woman knelt down to inspect Dingo, running her hands along her coat, lifting a leg, checking her belly. Dingo leaned into me, shaking. "I don't see any signs of mange, or fleas, or disease. Her nose is good and damp; she seems healthy enough – just thin. Y'all are lucky there."

"She shouldn't have fleas – we gave her a bath last night. We thought she looks pretty healthy, too – which is amazing, considering her lack of nourishment. None of the Indians wanted her, and a lady" (I was stretching it there) "in Tusayan Village said that a reservation dog is likely inbred and diseased and she literally suggested we put a bullet in her head." My voice was hard as I related the conversation.

"Oh no," she said, shocked. "Some people out here can be so calloused. No, if y'all have a reservation pup, you've got yourself a real good dog." She said in her lilting voice. "Usually they're as sweet as they come, and sturdy and smart. And they're full of natural immunities. Have you thought about taking her back home with you? Where do y'all come from?" She looked at us.

I could see Pete swallow. I smiled up at him and answered the lady: "We're here from Virginia, out for two weeks for our 25th Anniversary. And it really hadn't occurred to us to take her back. We flew, you see…"

"Don't worry about that. That part's easy – you can just add her to the ticket. And by the way – congratulations on your anniversary. Y'all sure don't look like you possibly could have been married that long. But that's great – not many people make it that far."

"We may not make it a lot farther…" Pete mumbled; now *he* was looking like the deer in headlights…

"Let me make a quick call and see if the airlines still work the same way. Usually, you can just pay like $75 and add her to your ticket, get a travel carrier her size, a vet to check her out and make sure she's healthy to go, and Voila! You're set!"

"*And Voila! You're set!*" Pete singsonged under his breath, barely audible. He looked dejected. I felt hopeful, but torn, as we were sup*posed* to be here to find her a home.

"What's your name?" I asked the woman, as she dialed her friend.

"Karen," she called over her shoulder and then began talking, listening and confirming. She thanked her friend and hung up, turning to us again. "Just as I thought," she verified.

"Well, my name is Laura. This is Pete, and we're calling the pup 'Dingo,' for now."

"Oh, a good name – she looks like one, alright. We have another dog in here, older, that looks like she could be this one's mama. Uncanny. Y'all have to see her. Okay, if you want to consider taking her with you, you'll need to call your airline and pay an extra $75 for a rider on your ticket. That's what most airlines charge. Y'all need to find a travel carrier her size, like I said – or buy one from a vet or the airlines – but they're way more expensive than, say, a Wal-Mart. And y'all need to make an appointment with a veterinarian for a health check within ten days of your flight – and she'll need a rabies shot and certificate while you're there. Then you can take her right back with you."

I looked at Pete; he looked at me; we looked down at Dingo, who by now was considerably more relaxed. She looked up at us.

"Listen, we came in to consider our options. We really hadn't planned to take her home with us. We just wanted to make sure she'd get a good home, and not be left to starve in the desert. What is your policy here? Are you a no-kill shelter?" I asked Karen.

"Well, yes, we are a no-kill, but we're also very small, and – like many shelters – underfunded. We're pretty full right now, but if y'all really get in a pinch and can't work something out, I'll put her in with other dogs roughly her age. Occasionally we take them down to Flagstaff, looking for homes. We have more luck there than here, as there are so many transient workers here – and tourists, like yourselves. This *is* all a seasonal operation."

"Oh, right. That makes sense." *Hmm. This didn't sound too hopeful for a good, long-term home. And in a crowded kennel the chance of her picking up the parvovirus, or distemper, was fairly strong.*

I looked over at Pete again. He looked torn and uneasy. "We were going to take her out this afternoon on a rim walk and talk with tourists – see if we might find her a home there," he looked over at Karen.

"That's a possibility, but remote. Of course, we have tourists from around the world here to see the Canyon, but they would have to deal with the issue of quarantine – *if* they were even interested. Y'all might try it, and I do wish you good luck. If it were me, and I liked the puppy, I'd fly her on home – add another member to the family," she smiled. We chose to ignore this remark.

"Karen, thank you. We'll keep your number here. How late will you be open today? 5:00? – Okay. And will you be here tomorrow?" She nodded a yes. I dug a ten-dollar bill out of my wallet and slipped it in their donation jar on her desk. "This is for your spaying and neutering program. I know the jar is bottomless."

"Oh yes," she gave a small smile. "If only… it all wouldn't always feel like such an uphill battle…"

"We'll call you if we get into a real pinch. Thanks for all your advice and your help." I told her, while Pete scooped Dingo again into his arms, and I – once again – held the door.

"No problem," she called after us – "Enjoy your anniversary trip, Laura, Pete – and 'Dingo'! I hope y'all go home to Virginia to*getha*'!" she added.

As we left, a handler was walking a medium-sized dog that could have been Dingo when she matured. She had the yellow coat, the corkscrew tail, the upraised ears. This dog looked healthy and acted aggressively, jumping at us and barking threateningly.

"Oh boy – it's okay, girl, we're leaving. What's her name?" I asked the handler. "She looks like she could be this one's mother."

"Sunshine," she said and hauled back on the leash. "And Sunshine needs some *manners*."

Our Rim Walk, October 1st

We headed back to the rim for an afternoon walk and picnic lunch. This time we started at the Yavapai Overlook west to the Mather Point – only 1.2 miles round trip, heading in the opposite direction from this morning. We had hoped we'd walk longer and faster than that, but with Dingo in tow, sniffing at everything as we went, and our talks with many of the fellow tourists who stopped to admire her, the goings were slow.

Dingo was a great way to meet people. She was so adorable that individuals from all nationalities would make over her. But because they were from all nationalities – the UK, New Zealand, Japan, Germany, Australia, Canada, France… adopting her on the spot was not a viable option. And, after the September 11th attacks, we found few American citizens, like ourselves, traveling. Several foreigners did consider the option. One delightful older couple from Great Britain strongly considered it, but opted out because of the 6-8 week quarantine. But they were smitten by our precious, scrawny, golden pup. They had just lost a family dog of 15 years to old age, and their hearts were tender. This was exactly the kind of couple I had hoped might adopt her – or maybe a family with gentle children. One woman and her partner grinned at Pete and me and said, "This puppy was destined to become a Virginian." If only she knew…

So we walked along the rim, making over her when she peed, continuing to train the pup to lead, admiring the scenery and stopping to take photographs of one another and our little buddy. Occasionally a fellow tourist would use our camera and take a shot of the three of us – a family photo. I noticed how protective Pete was becoming of Dingo, careful that she didn't wander too close to the edge or reprimanding me if I let her get too close. He'd find a rock with a depression in it and pour water there to be sure our little friend would not get dehydrated. The old hardass was softening, but I kept my mouth shut and just smiled inwardly.

The longer little Dingo was in our company, the more similarities to

Lakota I noticed. She was very intelligent – a quick study, as he had been – and with the same independent manner. Their builds were very similar – both lightweight but strongly built, with the slim body curvature, the neat legs, and the husky faces. His coat had been thicker. Of course his eyes had been ice blue, ringed in black liner and hers were golden brown, ringed in sable. They both were expressive with their ears, mirroring an array of emotions. Dingo's tail corkscrewed up over her back, when she wasn't feeling threatened; Lakota had the husky 'scythe,' arching gracefully over his, with his plume spilling out behind. But it was more in mannerisms and responses to the world around them that I noticed the similarities. I felt her spirit to be so like his… And I noticed, too, that she was responding more and more to Pete's and my voices, trusting us… I began to be less and less enthusiastic about having a stranger walk away with her, and spoke less when we talked with the tourists.

Later we sat at an overlook, made and ate our pb&j's, washed them down with cool milk, and gave Dingo a peanut butter Wasa cracker and some dog food. We watched a French artist painting a huge square canvas of the north rim of Bright Angel gorge. She was using vats of acrylics, a drop cloth laid beneath her. In her hands were large brushes and smaller ones, which she exchanged as needed, taking quick sure strokes. I took several shots of her as she worked, but there was little conversation, as 1) she was concentrating intently and we all understood that, and 2) she only spoke French – or perhaps used this an excuse not to have to stop and gab with curious onlookers, of which she had collected quite a few. I enjoyed watching her work, leaning around her canvas, taking a long think, then swinging around, adding a deft horizontal rim line, or a vertical directional stroke. She mixed colors furiously at her feet, as there was a lot of painting ahead of her before the light changed. This was the challenge of plein-air work. She wore Capri jeans and painted barefoot; I'm sure she had a mix of palette squished in her toes, but she worked on obliviously, lost in the serendipitous moment, a lady after my own heart…

Pete and I watched her a little longer after our picnic lunch, then packed up all of our stuff and led Dingo away. By now it was late afternoon and we had pretty much decided that a tourist taking her home was a long shot, so we opted to take our fresh-air saturated bodies back to the hotel and rest a bit before dinner. Dingo followed right along, hopped up into the car, as if she had been doing this all of her life – and not just for a day – and off we went, our little trio. I loved having her along with us; it was worth all the compromises we had to make. But I knew that

Pete had *not* written painstakingly in his itinerary, his travel Bible: *find dog, bathe dog & clean up messes, train dog & figure out what to do with beast in tow.* He was being a good sport, nonetheless. Bless his heart. He may not want to keep *me* after this, but I sure intended on keeping *him*.

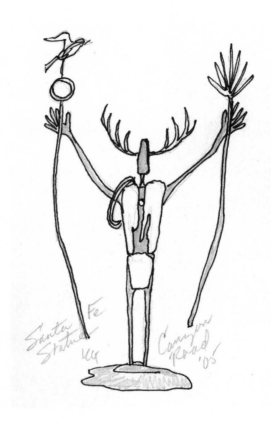

NINETEEN

Entrusting her to Ricardo

"No trumpets sound when the important decisions of our life are made. Destiny is made known silently." Agnes De Mille

Pete and I took Dingo back to the room with us. She was full of fresh air and sunshine and ready to zonk out for a long nap, like the baby she was. We decided to lie down and rest a bit, ourselves, and to discuss the puppy's future. We had no takers, understandably, from all the world travelers we had met that day. So now there was the possibility of taking her with us for the rest of the trip, and then flying her home to join our family full of teenagers and critters (which I preferred, by far), or the alternative of leaving her at the Grand Canyon Shelter, for a future unknown.

I had not slept well the night before, and my eyes would *not* stay open now. I wanted to join Dingo in la-la land in the worst way. Pete was sipping a beer and said: "You nap a minute, Ra, I'll call US Air on their 800# from the hotel here and see what they say." That's the last I heard. When I awoke, he told me that the airlines could add her to the ticket for the $75 fee; there were only certain times they'd do this and the fall was one of them. Otherwise it might be too hot or too cold down in luggage. If she was small enough we could put her in a carrier under our feet – but this was no Chihuahua or miniature poodle. Pete stressed, however, that this still left us with what to do with her for the rest of the trip. Tomorrow we left for Chinle for our two days in Canyon de Chelly.

"Well, why don't we call up there and see if we can find a hotel that takes dogs?" I said through my post-nap fog: "We have the AAA tour book. Let's call the hotels in Chinle and find one that does."

The Wop looked over at me and said, "It's your turn. You're awake now. I'll kick back and listen to your pleas. But I've got to warn you, my cell phone won't work. I've tried."

I gave him a look and said, "Fine. Fair enough. Where's the AAA book?" I sat back against the headboard crossed-legged with the phone in my lap. He handed me the tour book on New Mexico/Arizona. I squinted hard a couple of times, trying to get my sleepy eyes to focus on the words. "Pete, hand me your reading glasses, will you please? I can't be*gin* to read this fine print right."

"So much for your eye surgery. You're supposed to see like a hawk now."

"A hawk at a distance. They said I was on my own with these forties-eyes. Most times I'm okay, but not at the moment." I put his reading glasses on. Instantly the fine print focused. "*Voila!* Let there be words!"

I cut to the chase and looked in the index to find Chinle, AZ. There were three hotels there: a Best Western, a Holiday Inn and a Thunder-bird Lodge, where we'd stayed with the kids last summer. None of them said whether or not they accepted pets, but we knew a lot of hotels on the rez didn't. So I checked the numbers. The Holiday Inn had an 800#. So did the Best Western. The Thunderbird Lodge did not. I used the hotel phone to call the first two. No, no pets were allowed at these hotels. *Damn. That left the Thunderbird. They'd allowed children last year. Often our pets were better behaved,* I thought impishly ... *maybe I could suggest that as a counter if they, too, said no. Just thinking ahead...*

"Okay, Pete, where's the long-distance calling number? Let's see if it works yet. We'll need it here. The first two are duds, pet-wise." Pete fished that out of his wallet. "Holy Smokes! *Look* at that string of num-bers!" I dialed the access code, the hotel's phone number, and our home phone number... all in the sequence they showed, very carefully pushing each key in the dial pad, so as not to have to start over. A sugar sweet female voice came on: "I'm sorry, your long-distance is not connected. Please try again." I saw crimson instantly. "Well, double damnit, *any*way, Pete! It's *still* not working, and there's no 800# to the Thunderbird Inn. *Now* what?"

"Maybe it's a 'sign,' Razza." He raised his eyebrow at me, turn-about being fair play and all. "Maybe she goes to the kennel and we get on with our trip. They'll find her a home and she certainly won't starve there."

"Pete, that's a roll of the dice as to where she'll go. I'll always wonder who adopted her. But mostly I'm worried about her picking up Parvo or distemper in those crowded cages. Maybe we just take our chances with the Thunderbird? This place was very good about taking her. In fact, they've been great."

"*This* place isn't on the rez, Laura. You know they usually have an altogether different policy there."

"I don't know that. I'm learning. I can't believe *all* the hotels on the reservation don't allow pets. I still say let's take our chances."

"I say we go to dinner. I'm famished and we're not getting anywhere. The pup's sound asleep, so let's leave her while we can."

This made sense. "Okay, only we're *not* eating at McDonalds. Where else can we eat that's close by?"

"I don't know. Let's put our jackets on and take a walk. We'll find something."

"Sounds good. I'll be out in just a sec." I made a stop off in the bathroom. Little Dingo was curled up and snoring on my denim jacket. I quietly put plenty of food and water down for her, if she woke up before we came back. I brushed my hair and got fixed up a little and then pulled on my maroon fleece jacket with the Hoop Dancer pin we'd found in Santa Fe. The symbol that meant, basically, 'Dance to your own rhythm.' I put on a pair of sneakers and joined Pete by the door. He wore a heavy, lined windbreaker.

"You may want to put your windbreaker on over that, Laura. It's probably gotten pretty chilly by now."

"Okay." I pulled it on as we left, hoisting my backpack over my shoulder as we strolled down the hallway. I peaked over the balcony to see if Marcos or Scott was working tonight. Nope. Two ladies that I didn't recognize were on duty.

"You know, I think I saw a little restaurant across the way, by the hotel next door, when I crossed the street last night with our McDonald's fare. You want to try that? It's close and I'm starved." Pete threw a companionable arm over my shoulders.

"Sounds fine to me. I like that it's close. We can get back to Dingo sooner."

"Yup. 'Foot Loose & Fancy Free.' That's our anniversary trip. Can't wait to tell my friends at work what a time we had…"

We walked under the overhang of the Holiday Inn Express next door. Across the parking lot was a place we'll call the Canyon Café. A lot of people were sitting at the tables inside; this was always a good sign that the food was decent. We went in and stood, looking around, waiting to be seated. It was nothing fancy, but it would certainly be a step up from fast food.

"Two?" A blond lady with a cheerful face approached. "Smoking or non?"

"Non, please." We followed her. I asked spontaneously, having rehearsed the line all day, if she knew of anyone that might be interested in a puppy. We'd asked so many people the words just tumbled out of my mouth, but my heart was not behind them.

"Not right off," she said, "but I can check with some of the wait staff. They might." She smiled. "How's this?" she asked, pointing towards a booth across from the kitchen.

"Fine. Thank you." We slid into the vinyl bench seats.

"That surprised me. I thought you wanted to take her back with us." Pete looked over the table at me quizzically.

"It surprised me, too, Pete. It just came out. Habit, after today on the rim, I guess. But I'm torn – when we brought her off the rez, I said we were only going to find her a home. You've been a really good sport…" and then I thought a minute of all of his derogatory remarks, "Mostly," I added. "But we have four more days ahead and the Canyon walks have been nixed. I know how much you wanted to go down in. I don't want her to screw up Chinle for you, too. But I *would* like to keep her. I *am* torn, Pete."

A man came over to our table. The hostess had been talking to him. He smiled at us. "Hello, I am Ricardo and I will be your waiter tonight. I understand you have a puppy you are giving away. I would like her."

Pete and I did a double take. He hadn't even seen her. He knew nothing at all about her. This was too weird. I studied him a moment. He was a small man, very thin. He had sparse black hair streaked through heavily with gray, an exuberant mustache, and spoke English carefully with a thick Hispanic accent. His nose was extraordinarily small, and his face looked worn and leathery. But his brown eyes were kind, under their heavy brows. "Listen… Ricardo? We're in a dilemma with this pup. We're on the fence about a home for her. We may decide to keep her, ourselves – we're getting attached, you see. We found her just yesterday" (*Just yesterday, that's all? We'd had her with us now for all of maybe 30 hours and we felt this close? Maybe that was a 'sign'…*) "starving in Monument Valley, up on the Navajo rez. We meant only to bring her out and find a home, but we like her. *But,* we're also out here on our anniversary and she's changing all our plans around."

Ricardo had been listening intently, thinking.

Pete said, "Enough with the dog, already. I'm starving. We came to eat. What's good?"

Ricardo smiled and said, "Everything. Especially the roast beef pot roast." He told us the rest of the specials today. Pete chose the pot roast and vegetables. I wanted a salad. I hadn't had a good salad in what felt like weeks. I chose the cob salad with blue cheese on the side. We ordered a couple of iced teas and the man was off to put our orders in.

"Okay, now what, Ra? This Ricardo fellow wants her. You've found her a home. Congratulations, kiddo, you did it." Pete said, with a smile and certain relief in his voice, which strengthened my resolve even more.

"Now I plan to ask the man a *whole* lot of questions as to how he'll care for her." My chance came quickly; he was heading over with our teas now with slices of lime in them, as we'd asked. Good. "May we please also have a couple of glasses of water with lime?"

"Sure. How old is this puppy?" he inquired, looking down at me.

"We're guessing about 4 months old, max. She's just a little thing, but very smart. She's survived up there all this time, after all. But she was well on her way to starving."

"She's lucky you found her. She could have starved or been eaten by coyotes. There are lots of them in the desert, you know." We hadn't thought of prowling packs of coyotes. *Criminy! She* was *a lucky little thing… She could have been torn to shreds, simply have been a desert hors d'oeuvre…*

"No, we didn't know there were coyotes up there. Or I guess we did, but hadn't thought of that." I commented and grimaced, then returning to the possibility of a home, I added: "Have you had dogs before? What kind of a home would you give her?"

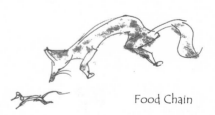

Food Chain

"Oh, yes. I have had a lot of dogs. I used to be married, and my wife and I had a big Dalmatian dog, but she got him. She got the kids, also. He sure was a good dog, though."

"Have you ever had a puppy?"

"Oh, yes. Many. I train them well."

"Well, Ricardo, if we *were* to give her to you — and believe me, our feelings are mixed at this point about letting her go — but *if* we did, would you be sure to have her vetted, get her shots, and have her spayed when it's time?"

"Oh sure, sure I would. I would take very good care of her. I would do whatever the vet said I should do. I would have her spaded. I live alone in a little trailer park called 'Tinkerville,' in Valley, south of here. She would be good company for me." He glanced around, knowing he needed to keep working. "Let me get your waters and I will check on your food."

"Well, does that make you happy yet?" Pete asked, as Ricardo walked away.

"I don't know. A part of me says 'Great, now we'll get our trip back and I'll stand by my word to you' and another part of me screams '*Forget* your word! *Keep* the dog — it's meant to be!' I just am not ready to seal the deal yet, Pete. I'm sorry."

Ricardo came back with our waters. "Your food is almost ready," he smiled. "What does this puppy look like?"

"She looks like a small yellow dingo-dog. In fact, we're calling her 'Dingo.' She's got this crazy corkscrew tail and the markings of a yellow lab. Her face has a husky-like look to it. She's real cute, too, but she was *so* skinny when we found her yesterday." *Yesterday,* I thought again. *Scheisse. It couldn't possibly have been just yesterday... So much had happened since...*

"Well, if you give her to me, I will give her a real good home," he said. A bell rang behind him. "Your food is up! Let me get it for you." He smiled and turned.

"Well?" Pete asked, as Ricardo walked away.

"Well, what?" I felt like I was in front of a firing squad.

The waiter was headed back over with a large plate and a big bowl of salad, the dressing resting in a cup on the side. He set them down carefully. "Looks good, does it not?" he asked Pete. "That pot roast is always a special here. It is delicious."

Pete closed his eyes and inhaled the scent of slow-cooked beef, the rich gravy, the pungent onions, his hands resting on the table on both sides of the plate. He let out an "*Aaah... Smells* delicious, too. Thanks." It did look good with the potatoes and carrots nested in the gravy beside it. My salad looked tempting, as well, with a mix of lettuces, chunks of red apples and English walnuts, blue cheese crumbles, bacon and avocadoes.

"I will bring out a plate of hot rolls." Ricardo said and left again. Pete had dived into his dinner, a deep look of satisfaction on his face. Poor guy *had* been famished. I took a bite of salad mix. The waiter came back with the rolls.

"What did you decide about the doggie?" he asked. "Are you going to give her to me?"

"Not so fast, there, fella'," I said, trying to swallow the salad and talk. "I think maybe we need to sleep on this. The problem is that we leave here tomorrow, heading up to Canyon de Chelly – you know, up in Chinle?" Ricardo nodded. "And so far the hotels up there don't take dogs. But our airline has said we could fly her back home on our tickets. We're just not sure about the rest of the week."

"Well, I am off tomorrow. How about we meet here in the morning, say, about 10:00? Is that good for you? You can let me know what you have decided to do with her."

Pete had been eating, too busy to talk, absorbed in his meal as he was. "That sounds reasonable." He nodded, chewing.

Now that I opened that can of worms I wanted to close it again. Tightly. Here was what we'd been looking for, but a little voice inside said 'Not so fast – don't go there, don't do that.' "We'll sleep on it, and then we'll meet in the morning. Okay. But *if* we did give her to you, Ricardo, do you have a yard, some-place for her to play?"

"Oh yes, yes. I have a fenced-in yard right around my trailer. There is plenty of room for her to run, and I would walk her every day. Believe me, I would give her a very good home – trust me." I looked at him closely. He seemed to be kind. He seemed very sincere in that he truly wanted her and would take good care of her. *Still...*

"Okay then. We'll see you in the morning, about 10:00." Pete con-firmed.

"Okay. Let me know if you would like anything else. You ready for more tea?"

We said yes; he came back with the pitcher, poured our refills, smiled again and left.

Pete's dinner was almost gone. My salad was almost untouched. "Looks like you'll have to have coffee and maybe dessert, while I eat there, friend. I dunno', PeterWop. 'Be careful what you ask for,' and all. Now that we've got a home for her, I just don't want to do it. I don't know *what's* going on..."

"You went and got yourself attached, *that's* 'what's going on,' Razza. You can't *not* care. But here you've done everything you said you would: you saved her from starving; she's not eaten by coyotes; you've found her a home. I'd say that's a pretty good days work. Great going there, kiddo." He raised his iced tea in a toast, nodded his head and smiled.

I just looked at him quietly, kind of miserably, and began picking away at my salad. I was hungry, but sidetracked. Pete called Ricardo over and asked for a cup of coffee and a slice of apple pie a la mode. He sure was going all-American on dinner tonight.

"I'd like to swim after dinner, Pete. After we walk Dingo, I'd like to go out and swim. Unwind. Think."

"You're nuts, Laura. Baby, it's *cold* outside – and the pool is outside. This is October in the high desert. You're insane."

"The pool is heated, remember? And," I said enticingly, musically, "*there's a* hot *tub in the corner...*"

"Well, *that* sounds like a possibility, but I'm sure not going to swim."

"I didn't think you would, but it's been a couple of days since I've been in the water. I'd like to do my exercises; I'm stiff. Besides, my mind needs it as much as my body."

"Okay, I'll bring blankets and booze to warm you up, after rigor mortis sets in."

"Pete, talk about a nut – that's for when you're dead. This is just a swim. I want to do *some*thing under the full moon, if we can't hike down into the Canyon."

"Oh, *I* can think of things..." he grinned wickedly.

"Yeah, now that you're fat and full, I'll just *bet* you can. But *first*, I'm swimming."

We finished our dinner, left Ricardo a hefty tip and told him we'd see him in the morning. As we left we stood outside huddled together, looking up at the brilliantly clear western sky, full of stars and lit brightly by the rising robust moon. While we watched, our arms around each other, we saw an absolutely amazing shooting star blaze across the heavens. It was *huge*, and it was slow, as if carrying that size added a drag on its momentum. We collectively caught our breaths. I quickly made a wish.

"Pete, it's in*cre*dible! It's the most incredible shooting star I've ever seen! Surely, this is a 'sign'! What are the chances that we'd be here, *right at this instant*, to watch it pass? It's divine intervention. But I don't know if it means that *we* keep the puppy, or if *Ricardo* should keep her..." I looked up at him, my brows furrowed, questioning.

"Laura, save your breath. That wasn't a shooting star. It was way too big and slow. It was space junk, that's all."

"It was *not*. It was a shooting star, daggonit, Pete, and it was a 'sign'."

"Space junk." He insisted. "Come on, let's walk the dog." As we passed under the overhang to the Holiday Inn Express, I looked up and saw their logo on the wall: a shooting star lay emblazoned there, as if cementing the fact.

"Okay, smarty-pants, if you didn't believe me when the real one past as we watched, what's this?"

"A logo." Pete said immediately.

"*You* know what it is; you just don't want to eat crow. It's time to make a wish. I already have…"

"And I'll just bet I couldn't possibly guess what it is, either."

Dingo was whining a little when we came in. I went to her imme-diately; she wagged her tail at me and came over, very happy to see us. She'd eaten some of the dry food, lapped or spilled her wa-ter all over the place – and she'd 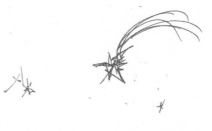 nailed bin Laden with a good bowel movement. I congratulated her and made a big deal of it. She was thrilled.

"Okay, kiddo, let's take you outside and see what other contributions you can make. I'll clean that up when we get back." I attached her leash to the purple bandana, zipped up my two jackets and joined Pete, who was all ready. He was always all ready.

"Well, she finally hit Osama square in the face," I shared with him.

"Good for her. She's earning her keep. Let's see what else she can do."

We walked out into the starry night, Dingo sniffing her way around, thrilled to be outside. After a good walk with Dingo around the back of the hotel we brought her back and settled her in again in the bathroom. She walked over to the denim jacket, circled a couple of times and lay down contentedly. I cleaned up her messes from earlier and then went into the room and found my camera, taking the lens cap off and check-ing the settings as I returned. She lay there quietly watching me as I took three photos, one with her head up, staring directly at me, fully alert. Another with her head down on her paws, rolling her eyes up at me, one ear cocked to the side and tipped over, the other straight up, and a final one with her eyes closed, ready to drift back to sleep. She looked totally at home.

It had been hard to enter, I'll have to admit. This night *was* chilly, but I'd never swum outside on the 1st of October before, and never ever in the Grand Canyon. It was a challenge and a thrill. I threw my kickboard ahead of me and decided to dive on in. Pete sat in the hot tub adjoining the pool, a plastic cup of wine beside him, another waiting for my madness to end. Our luscious moon sat full and bright overhead, waiting to watch the game, accompanied by a throng of tiny curious glowing stars. The heavens, too, doubted my intentions. I could do this. I inhaled deeply, looked at the still black blanket of water before me and dove on in. An icy jolt met me full-force as I carved an arc through the glistening pool. I pretended I was a seal; this was my haven, my heaven. I did a happy spiral under the water before bursting out with a splash and a large expulsion of air as my body spasmed with the cold.

"Chilly in there?" Pete asked me calmly, laid back in the hot bubbly suds, wine in hand.

"Nope," I lied, my teeth clinched so as not to chatter, "It's heavenly. I'm totally enjoying this – you should join me. Work off some of that pie."

"Oh, I am. And I walked the pie off, earlier."

"Ha!" I said, started to tread water, eventually warming into the exercise routine. I did my full workout, starting to thoroughly enjoy the movement, and thinking of all the calories I was burning just to keep warm. By the time I pulled myself out, I had long acclimated to the chill and was very glad not to have listened to the waterlogged naysayer cooking in the hot tub. "Did you drink my wine?" I asked, leaning down over him and shaking my hair out like a dog, spraying him with icy water beads. Pete ducked down lower and mocked a chill.

"*Augh!* Get in the water, woman! Warm up! You make me cold just looking at you!"

The nippy night enveloped me as I made my way into the hot tub to join him. I slid down beside him, letting the bubbling warmth pulse around my shoulders and back. It felt wonderful. I was handed my wine, took a sip and closed my eyes. Heaven. I could sleep here.

"Well, soon *I'll* need to get out. I'm all shriveled up like a raison now, waiting for you, LauraWop. I've been waiting for you all night. First the salad, now this… *Not* a good omen." He smiled knowingly.

"I'm sleeping here tonight, PeterWop. This is just way too comfortable. Goodnight."

I winked at him and closed my eyes again, starting to feign a snore.

He hoisted himself out and sat on the side. I opened my eyes a bit and watched steam coming off his wet body to evaporate into the frosty night air. Pete had had a build like Michelangelo's marble statue of *The*

David when he was younger. Now he was a softer, kinder version – The David in middle age – and I still loved his physique. He sat there a couple of minutes, braving the cold on his upper body, his feet still in the pool. "Betcha' won't fall backwards into the big pool…" I challenged him with a smile.

"Betcha' I won't, either." He said, not rising to it at all. "Betcha' I'm getting back in here." And he slithered back in, sitting close to me. "Let's go in soon. I want more wine. And I *don't* want to waste that moon up there." A hand slipped over my knee, as he pointed to the sky and he gave me a heh-heh kind of PeterWop smile.

I wandered through a neon checkerboard jumble of paths, entangled together, interlinked, but not. I was lost in a labyrinth of loose ends. Lakota appeared, then hid behind Osama bin Laden's face, that smiled benignly as he watched me wander, searching again in vain for my beloved wolf-dog. I called along these walkways, tearing at vines that clung to my arms and legs, trying to hold me back, and then dear George was beside me, walking along in his blue jeans and white tee shirt, his gentle aura surrounding me, saying it was okay, we could still make that dolphin ring. He had thought about it, and he liked the idea of the diamond chip as the twinkling eye; the blowhole would remain open for oxygen. Only I wasn't getting any – Mary and Galen revolved around and through the checkerboard. They laughed and ran gaily, kicking up autumn leaves and then I saw images of electric red pumping amongst the fragments of their faces. And there was Lakota again, bowing down before me, asking me to play with him, his blue eyes dancing. I want to, 'Kota – I want to! Let's walk. Let's walk together and out of and away from this madness… And then a rumble of noise and clouds of black smoke as huge towers fell down upon themselves, screams and cries and pleas of help and bin Laden was laughing now, this maniac's laughter echoing in my ears. I thrashed and spun in the neon maze, trying to find an exit -

"Laura, Laura –s*shhh*… it's okay – you're dreaming. Or having a nightmare – something. Here now, wake up, it's okay…" Pete's voice penetrated the swirling fogs and his arms enfolded me. I fought to be clear of this awful prison of thoughts. I climbed hard out of the nightmare, tears streaming down my face, shaking and trembling, still grasping for Lakota and signs of George. Images of Mary and Galen faded away as the walls of the hotel room formed around us.

"Where are we? Pete, what's going on? It was so awful; I felt so lost. So terrified. Lakota was there…" I mumbled to him… and, in a shaken voice, "and George was there. We walked through the maze, he wanted to make our dolphin ring – to finish it. He was so *real*, and then he was gone, too. And, oh God, goddamned bin Laden was there, like a madman, laughing at us all, laughing at love, and all that's good..." Pete held me close to him; I was talking into his bare chest.

"Heh, it's okay now, Razza. It was all just a dream. Or a nightmare. Wake up and get out of it. I'm here, it's okay." He stroked my hair gently as he spoke to me softly. "It's 5 AM, time for you to go back to sleep and try to relax and rest. Really, it's all okay, baby." His voice was so soothing. I was so sleepy. I snuggled into the safety of his arms, but couldn't yet dare to return to sleep, to fall again into that god-awful maze. Soon I could feel his breathing level out and soft, gentle snoring began. He'd talked himself back into a good sleep.

I lay there close to him, trying to be still but my eyes wandered the hotel room as I tried to reorient and do a reality check. The pounding of my heart slowed. Okay, we were in the Grand Canyon. This was the Red Feather Lodge. We were still on our anniversary trip, out west. This was Monday night, October 1st – no, no... this would now be Tuesday morning, early, October 2nd... just after the anniversary of the attack on Mary, Galen and Sean. And then it hit. *Oh yeah, this is the morning we decide the puppy's fate – whether or not she stays with us or goes home with this Ricardo fellow.* I was waking up now; it was all coming back, tuning in with vivid detail. I slowly took in a great lung full of air, trying to relax and be still while Pete slept. My mind was now churning with the fresh memories of the bizarre nightmare and Dingo's fate.

I felt the quiet rise and fall of Pete's chest, my head still on it and in the crook of his arm. I could smell his scent, the underarm odors beginning to mix with his deodorant. I thought of Ricardo, how he lived alone in his trailer, somewhere south of town. *He said he'd been married, but his wife had left him, took the kids, took the dog. Poor man. That's got to be lonely... No wonder he wanted the pup, sight unseen. But still, that was weird... if he was so lonely, why hadn't he adopted one of the local strays or gone to the Grand Canyon Kennels and adopted a dog? Maybe he just hadn't made the time...* My thoughts drifted along. *Good grief, Lakota had seemed so real... we'd almost gone on a walk again; God, I missed him so. And a chance to talk with George again, to hear that laughing voice... There was no closure of Mary and Galen, just this spinning of images of the two of them in my head, amidst that electric red.* I took another slow, deep breath, trying to get a lung full of oxygen in the stuffy room without waking Pete. I peaked up at the glowing digital red numbers of the clock: 6:13 AM... There was time to turn off the thoughts and sleep.

I eased out of Pete's arms and snuggled down with my bone pillow, getting comfortable under the covers, my leg in contact still with Pete's. But my mind would not quit. Images of Dingo's face now appeared. I saw her lying calmly, watching me with that questioning look, on my denim jacket in the bathroom. I closed my eyes. *We'd found her a home; I'd promised Pete we'd find her a home. We'd done it, go to sleep. And then Lakota reappeared, kneeled down, asking the golden puppy to play. They were bookends of each other, facing one another like that – he older, gray and black, she tiny, all yellow and soft – but bookends, nonetheless. I remembered whispering to Lakota so often: 'I wish I'd had you as a pup, before the abuse, fella'. Started you off as a puppy... You wouldn't have been so shy or devastated the rest of your life... One day I'll start over.' And here the two were playing... What did this mean?*

Rest, Laura, rest. Today will be a long one; you'll be up soon enough – rest... And there was Dingo's sweet, calm face again, watching me intently. What will you decide? Do I go or stay? Her head tilted a little, waiting for the answer. "We have the rest of the week ahead – we can still ride and hike, you know..." Pete's voice told her, me. Anyone who would listen. "But Pete, I changed my mind. I lied. I can't give her up... We've gotten so close..." "But Laura, you promised; keeping her was never 'in the deal'." "I know, I know..." Oh damnit!, God, for the decisions you make us face. All the trials and tribulations... I sucked up a deep breath and tears rolled down my cheeks. My body tensed.

And so it went for the next two hours, until 8:04 AM, when the alarm jangled and Pete rolled over to silence the timepiece. He stretched and yawned, then rolled over to hold me in his arms. I felt his sleep-warm body against mine. I let him envelop me, breathing in his scent, breathing in the moment, still trying to quiet my sleepless mind.

But my mind, like the labyrinth, was a jumble of tangled thoughts, none of them finished or laid to rest. Tears were still warm on my cheeks at the thought of parting with our winsome pup. In just a couple of hours we were to meet Ricardo and decide. My teeth and jaw ached from clenching them these past few hours, and I hadn't even realized it. It was time to stretch now, myself, to get ready to face the day. We'd need to gather our things, to pack up here within the next few hours, regardless of whether the pup came with us, or stayed with Ricardo. Today we were to head to Canyon de Chelly, in northeastern Arizona, up close to the Four Corners grid. 250 miles away. *Ugh.*

"Hey, Ra, did you go back to sleep okay?" Pete whispered, still holding me.

"I tried to, Pete. I snuggled beside you and tried to get my mind to stop racing but I kept thinking of Lakota and Dingo, George, Mary and Galen. I refused to think any more of bin Laden. But I couldn't sleep any longer – too many ghosts. But you slept – even snored a little. That soft, whistling kind you do." I kidded him. *Such* a musical snore.

"I did not. I do not snore. You dreamed that, too." He smiled over at me. "It's all just your imagination, and you *cer*tainly don't lack that."

"Sometimes, my friend, I wish I had no imagination, no visualization, no nothing of the sort. I'd just carry on through life, nary a care in the world…"

"Yep. And you'd sleep better. But you wouldn't be as interesting or eccentric."

"Oh, I'd be interesting – just not as colorful. Or maybe neurotic. Sleep helps even all that out…"

"It sure helps me!" He smiled. "Shall we get up and walk the dog? Before you know it, it'll be time to meet Ricardo at the Café for our breakfast."

My heart thudded down my throat. Reality hit again. It was 8:20; in just over an hour and a half we'd have to make our decision…

We dressed and took the back road behind the hotel where Pete had met all of his 'babes' yesterday morning. Today there was no one in sight, which made me think that I wasn't the *only* one with a vivid imagination. It was a crisp and gorgeous fall day; the sun shone brightly in a Robin's egg blue sky, but we were thankful for our jackets, nonetheless. Dingo, wearing her purple bandana as a collar, strained the blue leash to its maximum at every opportunity, delighted to have both of us along and to experience all of these great scents.

She was changing. For one, I could see her filling out just a bit and her coat didn't feel as dry, but the real change was in her demeanor. She wasn't nearly as timid. The night before I'd made playful overtures to her in the hotel room and at first she had looked confused and unsure, just as Lakota had. (What was it, anyway, in teaching these poor pups to play?) But she had caught on quickly, her eyes dancing, bowing down to me, her round tail wagging in joy. Today this newfound playfulness was evident. She looked and acted much more like a young exuberant puppy than a timid and scared little stray, trying to live by her wits in the wild. She was learning to trust us. Her burden had been lifted; she had allies;

she was breaking through the chains of sheer survival to now celebrate her life. And on this beautiful morning she did. I would romp around her, kneeling down and clapping my hands, saying, *"Dingo! Dingo!"* and she'd yelp in delight and bound to me or away in play. Pete knitted his brows, an old fuddy-duddy not interested at all in the game. "You two behave, damnit, she's romping all over the place."

"That's the point, Pete. *Duh*. She's finally breaking free – enjoy it. Watch her be happy!"

"Just walk, like a normal person, will you?"

"Poor baby, you're missing all your babes this morning. *That's* why you're grumpy. Well, you've got a gorgeous young blond right here, dying to play with you. Open your eyes, man."

He just glared at the two of us.

By the end of the walk young Dingo was bounding high in the air, a butterfly on a string, delirious with happiness and the vitality of youth.

By the end of the walk, however, the wind had blown out of my sails. It had been great to see Dingo's metamorphosis, but my own psyche had taken a backslide. The nightmare this morning had left me shaken up pretty badly, and although this walk had been a carefree unwinding, reality was quickly closing in. It was now close to 9:30. We'd be meeting Ricardo in half an hour with a decision, one way or another. My mood took a rapid nosedive.

"You've grown awfully quiet," Pete commented as we headed back to our room.

"Bet you can't guess why," I responded glumly.

"Laura, *what* are we going to do with her in Chinle?"

"I don't know, Pete, but we're good at winging it. We'll figure out something."

"Well, we've got to decide soon. We meet the guy in half an hour."

"Don't I know, Pete. Don't I know." I said nothing more on the walk.

We came back to our room where we'd done a lot of packing up earlier. We had loaded some things in our car on the way out for the morning walk. We'd take another load when we left for the Canyon Café. We'd leave the pup in the bathroom again, unknowingly awaiting the verdict. That thought made me catch my breath. Here, she'd come to place her total trust in us, had followed along with anything we'd asked of her, proving herself to be a very adaptable little dog, indeed, and here we might leave her cold-turkey with a stranger. There were so many changes in just a couple of days for this poor puppy, already. Tears welled up in my eyes and I fought to keep them at bay. But the interrupted sleep from the night before, the intensity of the wicked teasing dream, September 11th magnifying the haunting ghosts of fall, and the clock ticking away like a time-bomb were all too much. Emotions and exhaustion collided. I burst into tears.

Pete looked up from his packing. "Laura, what's wrong?" I just stood there numbly, overcome with these emotions. I couldn't talk; I tried and choked and turned my head away in humiliation, shoulders heaving. Tears streamed down my face; I felt so damned *help*less. "Laura, Laura, it's okay. We'll figure something out." He came over and turned me around and held me close to him. I just stood in the safety net of his arms and sobbed.

In a bit we pulled myself together and I went into the bathroom to run fresh, cool water over my face.

Dingo lay on the jacket, beneath the sink. I knelt down and she wagged the end of her tail and inched over to me on her belly. I lay my head against her, trying to fight off a return of the tears. I said nothing, just stood and looked in the mirror at my red eyes and damp, sad face, my hair a mess. I half-heartedly ran a brush through it, then laid it on the sink quietly and turned to leave. She lay watching me intently as I closed the door.

We walked out to the car with our suitcases and odds and ends and put them in before passing the shooting star nailed to the wall, there at the walkway. We went under it and over to the Café. It was a few minutes after 10AM. Ricardo was inside, waiting for us. He smiled as we entered. Pete nodded a hello and I tried a weak smile as I slid into the booth across from Pete. Ricardo sat down next to me. A waitress came over. "Coffees?" she asked us. "Yes, but make hers a decaf, please." Pete requested. She left menus and Ricardo looked at us both. "I can see it was not a happy night. I am afraid to ask what you have decided to do."

Today Pete did the talking, because I could not. I was in a state of shock, numb, just this side of breaking down altogether. I tried to keep my mind in some soft, neutral place. Pete thanked the waitress when she set our coffees down, then looked at Ricardo, who said: "I think, from the looks of your red eyes, that you should take this puppy with you. I think you should fly her home."

That's all it took. I burst out in tears again, feeling like a blithering idiot and excused myself, trying to feel the way to the bathroom like a blind woman. There, in the cocoon of a closed stall in the cold and empty room, I just let the heavy emotions tumble out. Glimpses of George and of Mary, Galen and Sean, poured out with the tears. Lakota was there and Dingo was there. So much love and so much loss. And Osama bin Laden emerged from nowhere and sat there on the toilet, laughing his head off at the level of human emotion over so much pain.

I became angry and roughly wiped the tears away. *You bastard!* I whispered fiercely to myself and to him, *you have* nothing *to do with this — go back to your goddamned cave! Get* out *of my head!* He vaporized. I stood there now, enclosed by the silence, alone, my head resting on the cool gray walls of the stall, feeling like I was losing my mind. *Okay, kid, pull yourself together. It's okay; all of this will work itself out.*

I opened the stall, not recognizing the haunted face in the mirror. I tried to become presentable and then went back to the table. The men looked up; Pete was worried, Ricardo, not quite knowing what to think. I smiled anemically as Ricardo rose and I slid into the booth beside him. Pete reached over and took my hand. "I asked the waitress to bring you a cup of hot coffee and a plate of fruit for your breakfast. You okay, Ra?"

"Oh yeah, just Jim Dandy there," I responded weakly.

"You know, I have an idea I was thinking about last night that will work for everybody." Ricardo piped up. "What if I take the puppy this week while you travel. I will 'babysit' her for you. You go on up to Chinle. If you decide you want to keep her, why then you call me here at the restaurant and I will bring her back in to you. And if you decide you do not want to take her with you, then *I* will keep her. That way, either way, she will have a home. And you can go on with your trip. My next day off is Friday. You can let me know by then." He smiled at us hopefully, his dark eyes looking earnest and sincere.

Pete visibly perked up with the promise of our trip picking up as he had originally planned. I squirmed. I didn't feel right about it. "Come on. I will take very good care of her." Ricardo said. "Here," he wrote down his name, a P.O. box, and a phone number. "This is the number of the Canyon Café here. I do not have a phone at home. Leave her with me, and call me here if you decide you cannot live without her."

The waitress came over and smiled at me very kindly as she put a hot cup of coffee and a beautifully arranged plate of fresh fruit in front of me. "You okay, honey?" she asked, genuinely concerned.

"I think so," I smiled up at her wanly. "We've just got a great big decision to make and I'm not handling it too well."

"Well, take your time with it, honey. Listen to your heart." She said and smiled at me again. She was so motherly and sweet.

Pete worked on his oatmeal and toast. He looked thoughtful, as he sipped his coffee. "Laura, you know this might work real well. We could leave Dingo with Ricardo here, go on over to Chinle today, do our hiking and riding tomorrow, and think about her. We'll have until Friday to decide. If we decide to keep her, I'll come back, I promise. I won't even complain," he looked so eager and hopeful. I felt like a heel, a party-pooper, sitting there so sad and torn.

I turned to Ricardo, who had his coffee midway to his lips. He stopped in midair and cut his eyes towards me. "You promise to take *very* good care of her? Feed her well, walk her and not lose her?" I made my list.

He finished sipping his coffee, put the cup down and turned to me. "Of *course* I will take very good care of her – as if she were my own little doggie."

"Okay," I said, entirely half-heartedly. "We have dog food and a leash we can leave with you. We couldn't find her a collar, so we're using a bandana. But you won't need to buy her anything unless we decide not to keep her. You'll have what you need for a few days."

"That's okay, I will find her a collar," he said. "Don't you worry. Now eat. Eat your fruit. *Do not worry.*"

Pete smiled at us both, looking as if a huge weight had been lifted off his shoulders. "Well then, we've got ourselves a deal." He grinned and reached over to shake Ricardo's hand.

Ricardo walked back to the hotel with us, past the shooting star, and up the hallway to our room. We went in and Dingo whined. I opened the bathroom door and knelt down to her. She came out into the hall and crawled up into my lap with her front paws – the first time she'd ever done this – a gesture of complete trust. I burst into tears, feeling like Meryl Streep, in *Sophie's Choice*.

"Oh no, not again." Ricardo rolled his eyes good-humouredly.

"She'll be fine," Pete told him. "Laura didn't sleep well last night, and it's hard for her to let go. She has gotten very attached to this little dog."

I was miserable all over again as Dingo looked up at the men and hovered in my lap, pressing herself against me. I untied the purple bandana from her neck. For some reason I would not leave this with this man. I took the long blue leash and pulled it through the wristband and around her neck, tying it off securely to make a makeshift collar out of the end of the leash so it'd be a two-in-one. This man was not tall; he wouldn't need all the length. And he said he'd find her a collar. I felt like being obstinate.

Finished, I gave the little desert dog a last big hug, burying my face in her neck a minute, letting her coat wipe away the tears. And I stood resolutely beside the two men. Ricardo looked her over and said: "She sure is a pretty little thing. I will have her fattened up in no time." What he didn't see yet was the corkscrew in her tail. It was listlessly down behind her back, as she stood there looking confused by this hallway tête-à-tête and the uncertainty in the air.

"Okay, we'll walk you out, Ricardo, and say our goodbyes. And we'll call you in a couple of days, one way or another, with our decision." Pete spoke so calmly, no catch at all in his voice. *How could he walk away from her so easily?* My mind was absolutely numb; I couldn't think; couldn't talk. It was then I knew what a zombie must feel like. There was hardly any feeling to it at all.

We left, Dingo for the last time in Pete's arms, not nearly as frightened as before. When we got outside he set her down. "My van is over in the other parking lot, beside the Café. I will take her from here." I quietly handed him the bag of dog food I'd brought from the bathroom and knelt down to say one last goodbye to our small desert find. She wagged her tail and licked me in the face enthusiastically, expecting to go on another walk, just like this morning, butterfly-mode, free as a bird. I choked and swallowed. Ricardo pulled on the leash, "Come on, little doggie, come on. Thank these good people." He said and he tugged. She stood her ground, looking up at us, as he pulled her to him. She relented and halfway followed, was halfway dragged, as he coaxed her along. He disappeared with the little yellow pup under the Holiday Inn walkway and the shooting star.

I broke away from Pete and ran to follow them, a glutton for my own punishment. I watched him put the dog food down on the ground and lift her up carefully, her ears out to the side, her tail hanging down limply, looking totally lost and confused, into his old two-toned green van. He put the dog food into the van behind her and closed the door, moving around to the other side to get in, himself.

I stood there, leaning on the stone pillar and broke into fresh tears, the war of emotion inside slamming me like a tidal wave. I staggered back to Pete and into his arms, my head buried in his chest, lost. He stroked my hair, "It's okay, Laura, it's okay. We have an arrangement. He's only babysitting her. We'll come back and get her if you want. Now let's get on with our trip."

"But Pete," I blurted out, "I can't help it and I can't explain it, but this just does *not* feel right. I don't want him to take Dingo. I don't know *what* we'll do in Chinle, but we'll think of something. I want to go get her. I want to take her with us *now*."

Pete pulled back and looked down at me, exasperated. *Women.* "Good grief, Laura. Make up your mind!" I pulled away and turned, running back under the overhang. The van was gone. My heart sank to my knees.

"Let's get in the car quickly, Pete. The van is gone, but maybe we can still find him!"

"Laura, for Christ's sake, we have it all worked out. He's *gone!* Let her go."

"*No!* Give *me* the keys then!"

"Damnit, okay, I'll drive, you're in no mood." We went to the Camry and he unlocked the doors. "We'll see if we can find him."

Pete and I drove back and forth along Tusayan Village, peering into parking lots where he might have gone, but the old green van was no-where in sight. Pete shook his head. "Let it go, Laura, damnit, *let it go*. I told you, I'm willing to come back and get her. Give it some distance."

I sighed deeply in resignation, feeling absolutely hollow inside. She was gone. "Then I guess we'd better finish packing, check out, and be on our way."

There wasn't much left to pack up. A few personal supplies back in the bathroom and loose ends around the room. I picked up my denim jacket off the bathroom floor and held it to me, inhaling her scent. I gathered up her food/water dish – we'd forgotten to give this to Ricardo – and started to pick up all the newspapers when Pete came in. "Why don't you go down to the lobby and check us out, Ra," he said gently. "I'll gather all this stuff up and load it. It won't take me long at all."

I felt distant from him and still simply numb. I had no energy to argue. "Okay." I went downstairs and found Scott behind the desk with a man that I didn't recognize. "Where's Marcos, Scott?"

"He comes in tonight, Laura. I see you're leaving us." He looked at me more closely. "Hey, you look like you've had a rough time. Are you okay?"

I gave him a small smile and shook my head. "We found a 'babysitting solution' for the puppy. We left her with the waiter next door – Ricardo?

At the Canyon Café? – and Pete is thrilled with it, but I'm not. I miss her, already. But Ricardo said to call him if we want to keep her and we can come back for her. Which I'm hoping we'll do."

"Well, that's a good deal. Here, let me get you all checked out." He was very adept at his job and had us finished in no time. I signed the agreement, noticing that they had returned our $40 security deposit.

"Scott, thank you for everything. You two were very good to us about the puppy – very understanding. Please thank Marcos again when he comes in, and tell him goodbye for us. Hopefully, we'll see you all again in just a couple of days." I tried to be cheerful.

Scott gave me a big smile. He had such a sweet face. "Hey, it was our pleasure, Laura. It was a good thing you did in saving that little puppy. It'll all work out – and I bet you'll come back and take her home with you."

I smiled again, took my copy of the hotel invoice and said, "You take good care of yourself, Scooter, okay?"

"I will, Laura. You, too. Have a safe trip now."

"Okay." I turned and went back to the room. It was empty.

TWENTY

(The Hopi) Over Three Mesas to Canyon de Chelly

"In the final analysis, our most basic common link is that we all inhabit this small planet. We all breathe the same air. We all cherish our children's future. And we are all mortal." John F. Kennedy

Pete was waiting for me in the Camry. Everything was all packed in neatly, ready to go. I slipped in quietly beside him, letting him know that Scott had refunded our security deposit. Pete suggested that we stop by the Tusayan grocery for another bottle of wine to take with us to the hotel tonight as there would be no chance of a purchase, once on the rez. I nodded "okay." We stopped and he went in to make a selection. I stayed in the car, remembering how Pete – just the day before – had been standing outside this market holding Dingo while I spoke with Barbie about the pup's fate. *I thought back to meeting Jama here, over a year ago with the kids, and how we had hit it off and how she had copied that long letter to Mary – my travel log. How time changed so much and how relative it was. Here we were at another crossroads, or maybe just a rest stop. In any case, a decision hung in the air and would be made within the next 3 days. A decision that wasn't even on the drawing board just 3 days before. Crazy.*

Pete returned with a large bottle of Shiraz and a 6-pack of Corona for the rest of the week's travels. I rallied and tried to give him a welcoming smile as he got in. "Looks like we're set for the week. If the Indians see this they'll think we're a couple of drunks passing through. We'd best lay low."

"Of course we'll 'lay low,' but I wanted to get it while we could. You still have those empties you refused to throw away?"

"Yes. They're down behind my seat. We can recycle them at one of those recycling bins at the Canyon pull-offs as we leave. It's no big deal."

"LauraWop, must I remind you we're on vacation? You can resume your dedicated recycling as soon as we get home."

"Pete, you just now said it. A 'dedicated recycler' finds a place to recycle even on vacation. The Canyon makes it easy with their drop-off bins. And we'll save *these* future empties for our return for Dingo, okay?" I nodded to our new purchase in the back. "Not that we'll drink them all in the next couple of nights." I paused, reflected, remembering something I had read, and added: "Do you realize that by recycling *one* aluminum can enough energy can be saved to light a *100*-watt bulb for *3½ hours*? Imagine if it's only a 60-watt. Maybe it would be *4½-5* hours or more. That goes a long way, in itself, in cutting the umbilical cord on our oil-dependency in the Middle East... There are all kinds of ways to conserve energy. Recycling is just one of them. Reuse is another."

"Where did you hear that statistic?"

"I didn't hear it. I read it in one of *Natural Resources Defense Council's* newsletters, or maybe it was *Environmental Defense*, or *The Sierra Club* newsletter. I've seen the statistic more than once. *3½ hours of electric per can.* That kind of info sticks with me."

We had been driving out of Tusayan Village, headed to the canyon rim and overlooks up 64/180 on the South Entrance Road. Soon we turned right on 64, or Desert View Drive, that would parallel the rim and take us out of the Canyon. We were driving along what they called the Coconino Plateau, in the Kaibab National Forest, which is all found in a wide diagonal swath of mountainous terrain that runs a northwest to southeast belt through the state, called the Arizona Highlands. The lower southwest Sonoran Desert area of Arizona was called the Basin and Range Region. Now that Dingo wasn't sprawled over my lap, I could open a map of the Canyon area and study all of this in fascinating detail.

Soon we pulled into the Moran Point overlook, named not for Thomas Moran – the incredibly talented 18th Century English artist and naturalist whose paintings helped persuade Congress, under President Woodrow Wilson, to establish the Grand Canyon National Park in 1919 – but for his brother, Peter.

This day that had started out so clear and beautiful was clouding now and turning gray, as if rain were pending. Dry as it was here this would be a blessing, as the area was in an extended drought. But the low gray sky set veils over the view; the infinite layering of the inner canyon walls disappeared in monotones of mists.

We dropped off the glass beer bottles and our one wine bottle in the outside recycling bins and peered over the edge of the canyon. Each day would be entirely different here, dependent upon the season, the mood of the sky, and incoming wind patterns. Pollution drifting in from major cities hundreds of miles away from this national treasure, from all sides, impacted views regularly. Over the last centuries, with the Industrial Revolution, the scope of distance one might see this magnificence had gradually diminished, like an older person's vision gradually fading and their not even being aware of the loss.

I shook the thoughts away. The sky was gray enough and my mood was blue enough that I didn't want to think of this at the moment. I'd pull a Scarlett and think of that tomorrow — or some other time when I could actually do something about it. Like send a check to one of the many environmental groups I believe in so. There are so many fine ones out there, fighting for our National Parks, for the air we breathe and the water we drink, for the last of the habitats for our wildlife, for the health of the great oceans. The list is endless. And more and more, it seems, they are fighting the national government, itself, to keep these precious gifts alive. Even crazier, as the federal government had established the parks, in the first place, by past presidents with a *much* grander vision to the future than the one now running the show.

Pete and I loaded up and headed on over to Desert View for a quick visit. This was my favorite 'man-made' point of interest in the entire park. But a woman had designed it, and she had done an incredible job. Mary Jane Colter, one of the very first female architects in the United States, was asked to design several structures in the Grand Canyon area. The Fred Harvey Company hired her in 1904 to design an 'Indian house' across from the El Tovar Hotel on the South Rim. She modeled her project after Old Oraibi, the ancient Hopi village of which we would soon pass through. This became known as the 'Hopi House.' Hopi crafters lived here and it became an outlet for their arts and crafts. Hopi legend believes that somewhere in the bottom of the Grand Canyon lies the original sipapu, that hole from which humans emerged from the underworld to the earth plane.

The Hopi House was followed by another commission in 1935, in which Mary Jane Colter designed the Bright Angel Lodge located on the 'peninsula' of land taking one to Bright Angel Point, on the North Rim. One sees the North Kaibab Trail from this point, as it meanders to the bottom of the Canyon and to the famous Phantom Ranch. In the Bright Angel Lodge's History Room stands a 10'-high fireplace built with stones from the Canyon, arranged in geological order as they vertically ascend.

In 1932 she was commissioned to design a structure that looked as if it rose from the rocky rim of which it overlooked. Desert View sits on the easternmost official overlook of the South Rim; it rises triumphantly, a 70'-high tower, from the high desert sands and rocks. Built by the Hopi Indians, the tower favors those built by the Ancestral Pueblo people. It offers panoramic windows overlooking both the Canyon and the park on two levels, with smaller windows here and there as one climbs to the top of the tower. Murals painted by Hopi artists depict rituals so sacred that Hopi children are not allowed to see them until they have reached certain rites of passage. When we brought the children here in the summer of 2000, all of us were fascinated by the huge depictions of Hopi legends lining the inner tower walls. Some looked aboriginal in their simplicity; we were aware of being in the midst of something sacrosanct to another culture. I photographed Natalie sitting on a bench at the base of some of these murals, and wondered as I focused about some Indian's belief that photographs stole the soul.

At the top of the Desert View Tower, on a rare perfectly clear day, one can see the inner sweep of canyon walls go on for undulating endless miles. Looking down one sees a huge soapstone lookout built in a large circle atop the round gift shop below. Tourists of all nationalities mill around, cameras and camcorders in action, absolutely astounded by the deep inner earth, eroded by iota's over the millions of years of its existence.

Inside the circular gift area are more huge rectangular 'eyes' to the Canyon and desert landscaping surrounding this ancient-looking structure. Here one finds an array of tourists souvenirs, from tee shirts, magnets, jewelry, Indian pottery, dream catchers and other arts and crafts. It is beautifully decorated with the Native American influence permeating the atmosphere. Today a Navajo elder sat at her loom painstakingly weaving a blanket, using long threads of naturally dyed wool. She wore a purple velveteen blouse over a navy skirt with tiny white flowers. I stepped back and took a photo of her, trying not to interrupt her work. As I turned away to look at colorful Indian rugs draped over a triangular wooden display she reamed me out about not paying her for the photograph and pointed to a small sign over a basket of wool beside her. It said: **"Photographs of Navajo crafter $1.00"** *Geesh. Had I known.* I fished a dollar out of my backpack and put it in the waiting receptacle. I guessed she had never heard of Belagaana's saying that 'honey catches more flies than vinegar.'

Peter joined me, holding tee shirts for he and Jared. He asked if I'd like to look at some for the girls, so I joined him in a gift search. We lingered a little longer, buying a few Grand Canyon magnets, post cards and small gifts for family and friends at home. As we left, I took a shot of him leaning against the solid rock tower outside; Pete was dwarfed. He took a shot of me on the steps, and we made our pit stops at the neighboring visitor's center before leaving. I noticed an American flag flying solo, tall and proud, outside of the visitor's center, against the neutral gray sky. There seemed to be a unanimous vote that by this point in time Old Glory would again rise to full height, like Americans standing tall and defiant, in the face of this assault on our homeland.

"You feeling any better?" Pete asked, as we loaded the car with our gifts.

"I'm distancing myself, Pete – trying to get on with the day. It helps to know that we can come back for Dingo, but I miss her. I'll be able to write in my journal, though, when we travel today – something I haven't been able to do with her on my lap."

"See, there's a bright side. And we'll be able to actually hike and ride down into the canyons when we get to Chinle. You'll be glad we left her with Ricardo for a couple of days. You may even decide it's all for the best, Ra."

"Now you're stretching it there, friend. I haven't gotten *that* far in this distancing thing."

"Oh well. One can only hope."

We passed the entrance station to the park, shortly beyond Desert View. This left us still with another 16 miles of open road, after our 45 mph leisurely stroll through the park. Although we had our cornmeal ready and waiting, we saw no more fox or coyotes crossing our paths. As we neared the Little Colorado River we came upon signs saying: **"Stop Ahead! Friendly Indians!"** Soon we saw Chief Yellowhorse's Tourist outlet. **"Handmade Authentic Indian Arts & Crafts – Don't Miss It!"**

"Oh, what the heh, PeterWop. Let's stop. Maybe we can find some jewelry for the kids."

"Okay, but let's make this short, Razza. We're not getting off on a very fast start and we *do* have a lot of miles ahead."

"I know it, Pete – and I've got my camera all ready," I gave him a smile and a wink, trying to crawl out of my funk. He gave a resigned groan, put the left-hand blinker on and pulled in front of the long row of gaily-painted red plywood buildings. "**Open**" was printed in bright horizontal yellow letters at several entrances and a happy life-sized dancing Kokopelli figure hoisting his flute decorated one of them. Pete walked over and stood beside him, in his khaki pants and denim shirt, and hoisted his own imaginary trumpet to play along with the native music maker. I called for him to hold that pose and took a photo of the two music men playing their tunes, as both American and Navajo flags snapped in rhythm above their heads.

Inside were displays of pottery and blankets, dream catchers, knick-knacks and tables of handmade jewelry. I found matching necklace and bracelet sets for each of the girls to hold for Christmas and another for Mary, as a thank you. I bought several chokers of turquoise, a white shell, and hematite for the girls to give their friends as birthday gifts. While looking, I came across a lone choker made with bits of turquoise and a soft brown stone. In the center hung a large silver teardrop pendant of a little desert coyote howling at a quarter moon in a turquoise sky. Bits of coral gave additional color. If this wasn't a 'sign' I didn't know what was. Only the one of them, and it was waiting for me – a good luck omen to keep the faith. My day just jumped a couple of notches skyward. I showed it to Pete with a big smile and he said, "Well what can I say? How can I argue with *that*?"

We purchased this array of gifts, my necklace, and a piece of Navajo pottery for Jared for Christmas, and were soon on our way again past the fairly incredible depths of the Little Colorado River Gorge canyons to soon pick up highway 89 at Cameron and head on up to the turn just before the 'Dinosaur Tracks' display. Mounds of warm Painted Desert mesitas greeted our return. Here we would travel on to Tuba City on 160 to head for 264, which would take us through Moenkopi and over the Three Mesas in the Hopi Indian Reservation, on through Keams Canyon and eventually we would intersect with Highway 191, a 30-mile run north to the town of Chinle, entrance to Canyon de Chelly National Monument. A day of roughly 250 miles of travel to this beautiful destination. Time to buckle one's belts and roll on...

The Hopi

The Hopi Indian Reservation sits in the midst of the huge sprawl of the Navajo rez in what resembles an upside-down shape of the state of Arizona. It encompasses roughly 500 square miles of territory, which is about a quarter of the vast lands allocated to the Athabascan descendants.

The Hopi people (from 'Hopitu,' or the 'peaceful ones') are thought to descend from the Anasazi (the Navajo call the Anasazi 'the ancient people who are not us' or 'those that came before us'), the Sinagua and the Mogollon cultures. The Hopi say that their ancestors are the Hisatsinom (their word for Anasazi), meaning 'people of long ago.'

The Hopi are a gentle people that farm this arid land quite creatively, using a method of planting called 'dry farming.' They long ago taught this to the Navajo. They learned to plant at the base of areas that will receive maximum runoff from the minimal rains in the region; they plant seeds deeply and they depend on the underground aquifers to help nourish the roots. With this dry farming method they have been able to grow corn – a revered staple – squash, beans, pumpkins and peaches – successfully for many centuries.

They, amongst the multitudes of Native American tribes throughout the United States, have fought to keep their culture and rich heritage alive and apart from other tribes and Bahana's ('White Man' to the Hopi) ways. Whereas the Navajo are an adaptable people that readily absorb the cultures and ways of another – and indeed this trait has helped them survive and thrive as an Indian Nation – the Hopi guard their old ways and customs as sacred and apart from the rest of the world. Indeed, they ask no more than to live their lives in peace, free to practice their old and sacred teachings to the next generation to carry on, as their elders did. But after this younger generation of 'progressives' have gotten a taste of Bahana's ways – running water, electricity, yearnings for material gain – the youth then clash within the family, yearning to expand beyond the Old Ways. This concept is nothing new, but it flies in the face of Hopi traditionalists. This latter group of Hopi continually struggle with the encroaching Navajo tribe, missionaries that attempt to convert them to Christianity, the federal government's insistence that the Indian children be taught in government schools, and the lure of 'wage-jobs' – instead of the Old Way of living off of the land – that lure many into a more modern and material way of life. This friction has divided the Hopi culture into the old villages of Old Oraibi, Shungopovi, Hotevilla and the more modern villages such as Mishongnovi, Walpi and Polacca.

For a time the Hopi lands included the Grand Canyon and the San Francisco Peaks, near Flagstaff. About 60 miles from Flagstaff lies the ruined Hopi village of Wupatki. The San Francisco Peaks are one of the four sacred mountains to the Hopi, as well as the Navajo, and it is from these mountains that the Kachina (Ka-chee-na) – the supernatural beings who dwell in lakes, mountains, and sacred springs and bestow their blessings on the Hopi – come. The Hopi believe that the Kachina are the ancestral spirits of all things, living and inert. (The Zuni natives call these same spirits 'koko.')

Past the small towns on Hotevilla, Old Oraibi, Shungopovi and Mishongovi runs the 264 Highway through Third and Second Mesas. The 'Three Mesas' are fingers of land masses encompassed by a much larger land area called Black Mesa. The Black Mesa mass is a 5,500' tableland, a sacred female mountain of the Hopi. Its multiple village-states lie in the southern edge of this steep-walled plateau in these three finger-mesas that fan out from this strange landscape. This is an intensely complicated and undeniably ancient land full of twists and turns of canyons, rocky arêtes, broad sweeping dry washes, lonesome buttes and far-flung mesas. In centuries before, these three southern prongs of this larger land mass provided the Hopi, and their predecessors, with natural protection from their enemies, as the villages were on higher ground. Driving from the west, one first enters Third Mesa, where the ancient Hopi towns of Hotevilla and Old Oraibi stand, between Third and Second Mesa. Old Oraibi is thought to be the oldest continually occupied settlement in North America, vying possibly with the village of Acoma, in New Mexico, for this distinction. Both were established around 1,100 A.D. The traditional Hopi live further west; the progressives tend to live closer to Keams Canyon and the world of Bahana.

Peter Matthiessen writes of the Hopi and their history here on Black Mesa in a chapter he calls "Mesas" in his book, *Indian Country*, for anyone looking for further information on this fascinating culture. I would highly recommend it to understand the Hopi way of life, or any number of the Native American tribes that once civilized this wild vast country, in those days long ago before Bahana ever laid a foot on the North America continent.

*See top of map, page 409.

"Navajo Time"

As we headed back to the Navajo Indian reservation we set our watches forward an hour. *Hmm.. .We had forgotten that in our planning.* The state of Arizona is one of the few in the nation (Hawaii and most of Indiana are others) that do *not* observe Daylight Saving Time. The Navajo Reservation – extending through much of Arizona – does, however. On the other hand, the Hopi Rez – encompassed by the Navajo reservation – also does not, which further confuses the concept of time in Arizona. We came to know this as "Navajo Time."Another concept we came to know about Navajo Time is that these Indians live calmly and at their own pace, not bothered too much by a ticking timepiece.

I enjoy this concept very much. It drives Pete nuts.

So we drove past the rolling layered gentle sands of the Painted Desert, entering now the Colorado Plateau that encompasses the upper northeast part of Arizona, the upper northwest part of New Mexico, the lower southeast part of Utah, and into southwest Colorado: all right smack in the Four Corners area. We drove on through the tiny Hopi town of old Moenkopi, which lies 40 miles west of the mesas and is a farming community outside of their reservation. Just before passing the itty-bitty town of Coal Mine Mesa we crossed over from Coconino County into Navajo County. On the eastern-most edge of the Hopi rez Apache County would start; Canyon de Chelly lays in between the Black Mesa tableland and the Chuska Mountains, with the Lukachukai chain of mountains running directly north; Chinle Valley lies at the base of these mountains. It was confusing, as Coconino, Navajo, and Apache Counties all lay within the vast Navajo Nations spread, subject to their tribal law. But then, the Hopi have their own sovereignty. Go figure... The Bureau of Indian Affairs must be in a state of constant red tape over these overlapping counties within two larger reservations.

Huge open spaces divided the endless gray ribbon of road. One looks out over the vastness and suddenly notices that the land has caved in, giving way to a huge canyon amidst these tabletop plains and mesas. It's as if the land were stretched out tautly and then laid back over itself, so that the mesas would then be inverted and fit down into the canyons, a custom fit. Like a key in a particular lock. Perfect. And thus we leave the first finger of Third Mesa, heading on to Second Mesa.

A long low mesa to the west lays stretched out and golden against a deepening blue sky; it looked like rain in the distance – always a sweet promise. Pete stopped so we could get a photo. As this dynamic scene was on his side I gave him the camera to shoot from his window. The bottom of this mesa was a soft pastel of moss green creeping up and melting into the tremendous base. The colors here are so varied and subtle I could stay west and be lost in paintings for months on end. This land is a stark contrast of open and lonely, hard and harsh, then swiftly changing to breath-snatching spiritual beauty. An "**AmeriGas**" business lies amidst the small houses and signs hung for "**Hopi Indian Arts**," in the small old town of Kykotsmovi, between Third and Second Mesas.

We pass this village and, once again, the infinite lands surround us. Now we are swimming through rolling hills, canyons and mesas dotted with piñon pines and stunted, wind-twisted junipers. Seeing these green mounds rolling off in the distance, it is easy to believe they are buffalo grazing afar. And now the tops of these rolling hills dotted with scrub pines and dry grasses remind me of the beach. One could easily imagine the great ocean, instead of these sprawling plains, rolling away down below us, I muse as we pass.

At Second Mesa we stopped in to see Weaver and Alberta Salinas, where we bought our silver Hopi bracelet and Kokopelli earrings in June of 2000. Funny, looking back, I wear the bracelet constantly on my left wrist. It is 'Coyote' running with the great wind and rain symbols. It's so ironic to me now, as if it were a preview of the year to come, only it would be Dingo as the wild desert dog and not the coyote, at all.

Weaver Salinas was not there today but Alberta Salinas was. She told us that Leonard Phillips (the "LP" initials inside my bracelet) had been the man who had made it; he had just past away from 'too much drink.' She said another fellow from her clan, Antelope or Snake, named Arthur, was sitting in the back of the jewelry studio working away on silver over-lays, the Hopi trademark. The corn designs were intricate and delicate. Each of the symbols used in the jewelry had a specific meaning sacred to the Hopi. In a cabinet was a collection of hand-carved Kachina dolls, representing the supernatural beings integral to the Hopi culture. They carve these only from the root of the cottonwood tree, she explained; she told us of the many clans of the Hopi. I reminded her how she had shared apricots, from her small orchard behind the building, with us last year when we had visited. We didn't purchase anything today, instead just 'oohed' and 'aahed' and listened to her fascinating stories before leaving. These were gentle, good people from a faraway world.

We left the Salinas' and in a while Pete pointed to the top of a very long low mesa tabletop to our left. Perhaps this was Second Mesa at a distance? Or Third? (It's very confusing here without a guide, as the land falls so strangely and unpredictably.) He'd noticed antennae atop these square buildings that blended into the mesa, itself. I suggested to him that these homes might be considered modern-day cliff dwellers.

We passed First Mesa and the town of Polacca and were coming on to Keams Canyon, which was named after Thomas V. Keam, an Englishman who had opened a trading post here in 1878. It was Keams who named these mesas, in the opposite of the way the Hopi referred to their ancestral sites. Before entering Keams Canyon, we passed the Hopi Law Enforcement Agency on our right, a fairly large and modern facility, much of which was surrounded by barbed wire. Serious business, that. Just past this was the high school. Okay… A sign read, "**Keams Canyon Hopi Indian Agency**." Soon we'd be driving through a small triangular-shaped Navajo rez lying inside the Hopi rez, like Russian dolls stacked inside one another. All of this was part of the "patchwork reservation" of which Hillerman writes.

This road over the three mesas is *so* much easier to travel than Pete's bushwhacking over the dusty old washboard roads, back on the inner reservation, in the Ford Aerostar van we'd rented with our family last year. We had bumped along in the sand and the dust, trying to read tiny battered road signs or route numbers, feeling totally lost on another planet. Free-range beasties were everywhere. The kids were grumbling about the jarring ride and 'when are we *ever* going to get there'… They were tired, hot, and fussy. *What* a memory. We had found our way to Second Mesa, finally, and met the Salinas' who had strongly urged that we take 264 on to 191 to reach Chinle that way. God Bless them.

The road was also awesomely scenic in many places with the land unfolding before us like panoramic postcards of the west. This one of canyons; that of buttes; now here we have plains… these are the tiny villages reflecting Third World poverty, so often found on the reservations, in the midst of this wealthy country. These are not postcard shots.

It is not at all uncommon to see hogans nestled next to the small put-together homes. On two occasions Pete and I have seen death-hogans, where all the windows and doors to the east are boarded up. Upon death, a door to the north is knocked out to let the evil Chindi (spirits) escape – or this is how Pete explained it to me from his Hillerman reads. For the sake of multiple-hand sources, I think I would prefer to learn just how this is done directly from a Navajo. I didn't think hogans *had* windows; many I have seen out here, the little earthen ones, did not. But I have learned that the entrance is always to the east, meant to greet the rising sun. I do know that when someone has died in a hogan the Navajo will no longer live there, and that when it is originally built, the hogan is blessed with corn pollen so that "the home will be happy."

We have also seen many tiny corrals for horses and woven wooden sheep pens. Huge gorgeous 'cubes' of alfalfa hay – which luckily grows well in dry soils – feed this livestock. They weigh 700–800 pounds *each*. The living green of this rich fodder is a luxurious contrast to most of what is out here to eat.

Soon we turned left, and north, on Highway 191, our last leg on up to Chinle. A right would have taken us to the historic Hubbell Trading Post, just down the road. Straight on ahead would have taken us to 264, on east to Ganado (where Cynthia was born) and on into Window Rock, the Navajo Nations headquarters, just west of Gallup, where Pete had originally hoped to be by the end of the week. It was late afternoon by now.

To our left, in the controversial Black Mesa direction, a stormy steel-gray cloud hovered over the golden length of a long, low mesa. The clouds split above this mass of rock, like an inverted canyon in the air, and blue sky shone innocently through, illuminated by soft silver clouds backlit by the sun. Because of this spectral illumination, the whole scene glowed. I asked Pete to stop the car. This time I got out and breathed it in deeply in full wonder, before slowly undoing my lens cap and taking the photo of this awe-inspiring late day land- and skyscape.

By the time we reached Chinle dusk had fallen hard. We stopped the car again to capture photographs of the sun sinking behind distant slate-blue mountains, leaving a deep goldenrod glow that merged to mauves and smoky lavenders above. And then it was dark, just like that. We were there.

TWENTY-ONE

Trail Ride in Antelope Canyon

*"We sleep, but the loom of life never stops and the pattern which was weaving
when the sun went down is weaving when it comes up tomorrow."*
Henry Ward Beecher

Chinle

The tiny Navajo town of Chinle reminded Pete and me of Kayenta.
Basically you were there, and then you were not. The Navajo word for
it, Ch'inlí, means 'the mouth of the canyon where the water flows out.'
Chinle began as a trading post in 1882. It lies 3 miles west of the beautiful Canyon de Chelly, one of my most favorite places on earth. Chinle
hosts the three hotels of which we had called, to shelter travelers coming
in to visit this national treasure. We stopped by the Thunderbird Lodge
and found that they did not accept pets. Pete and I decided to stay at the
Best Western and, on a hunch, I asked at the front desk about their pet
policy. It surprised me when they said they would; someone had given
us erroneous information on that 800#. We could have brought Dingo
with us, after all – but our hiking and riding down into the canyons
would have been nixed here, too, as dogs are not allowed down in, even
on a leash, and we wouldn't have wanted to leave her in the bathroom or
the car for hours on end.

Pete and I unpacked our bags and went to the adjoining Navajo-run
restaurant, called The Junction, for dinner. We were beginning to feel
very comfortable amongst the Diné. They are an industrious, pleasant,
and polite people; we enjoy their company and they enjoy our tourist
dollar. We ate a good meal, then went back to the room, closed the cur-

tain and opened the bottle of Shiraz. We felt a little wicked, as we weren't supposed to have it here, but we drink moderately and would haul the proof out with us.

From here we called home on our 800# and spoke with the kids a while. They knew the whole puppy saga and were eager for Dingo to come home with us. We explained our 'baby-sitting' agreement with Ricardo to them and then we spoke with Jean and Al, discussing return plans a little. It was hard to think that our time in the Southwest was coming to an end.

After the call, leaving the wine in the room, we decided to check out the pool area. They offered an enclosed pool with a beautiful painting of Spider Woman Rock at the bottom, shimmering mysteriously through the sparkling water. Spider Woman is a legendary figure to both the Navajo and the Hopi. It is believed that she taught chosen Holy People to weave on her magical loom, made of sunrays and lightning bolts, and the Holy People then taught chosen individuals this art, as they gently guided the weaver's hands. Weaving is so important to the Navajo that legend has it that infant female's hands are rubbed with spider webs to make sure this gift is passed along. Her spirit is said to live in Spider Woman Rock, a lone 800' red sandstone spire standing between the junction of Canyon de Chelly and Monument Canyon.

A hot tub awaited us in the corner and tables and chairs were placed around the perimeter. Plants graced the tiled floors. I could have stayed in here for hours, writing in my journal, but tonight we opted to swim. Even PeterWop joined me in the big pool.

After our water workouts, some frolic time, and a leisurely soak in the hot tub as a nightcap, we returned to our room for another glass of wine and a good snuggle together, books in hand. Pete was closing in on finishing Nevada Barr's *Ill Wind*; I was getting back to Hillerman's *Hunting Badger*. I had been too busy writing letters, journaling, and working with the newfound pup, to read. It took some pages to find my place again.

We planned to turn in early that evening, so we could get a fairly early start for a good long ride the next day down into Canyon de Chelly. We had passed a sign for a stable on the way in; we'd stop off there in the morning, check them out and see if we could find a Navajo guide and spend the day on horseback.

I rubbed my leg up against Pete's under the covers. "You know, I was thinking about Dingo in our travel today…"

"There's a surprise," Pete interrupted, looking at me over his reading glasses and laying his book over his stomach.

"Of course I was, but now that she's not with us *what* I was thinking was about finding her. About putting my Kokopelli belt on her as her first collar/leash combo. And then I was thinking of the timing of her birth. You know, Pete, she was born roughly the time Lakota died. What does that tell you?"

"I don't know. That it's quite a coincidence?" He wasn't biting.

"Sure. Quite a coincidence, but look at all his mannerisms that I see in her. *That's* no coincidence. I think Lakota is in there, Pete. Heck, I've *seen* his soul in her eyes. I think he managed to reincarnate himself into this puppy and I think we were meant to find her – *destined* to find her – under that sagebrush, just waiting for our arrival."

Now I had his attention. He took his reading glasses off, put a marker in his book, placed it beside him, and rolled over to look at me. "So you think Lakota was reincarnated?"

"Yes. Yes, I do." I said firmly, totally convinced of it, myself. "His spirit is in that pup. I should have seen it earlier, but I was too busy saving her to make the connection. Oscar came back to us through Whiskey Cat. Ruffian did through Stinky. Why not Lakota? He wasn't ready to leave the family – and Lord knows we *certainly* weren't ready for him to go." It made more and more sense to me. "And you know what else, Pete –"

"I'm afraid to ask…"

"Well, *she's* our 'Kokopelli.' *She's* the husky or husky-cross we've been trying to find in the shelters back home. Only, of course – *duh* – to find the *real* Kokopelli one would have to come West. We did, and there she was, waiting for us. We even put the Kokopelli belt on her. If *that* wasn't a 'sign'! But I was so mad at the time having to fight you to save her it made me dense."

He rolled his eyes. "God, why did I ever marry a *woman*. You all just don't think like we do. Maybe you really *are* aliens, from – what did the guy say? Venus?…"

"Yeah. Rhymes with 'penis' – and what would Martians ever do without us? You'd be lost. Pete, you *know* this makes sense. To me, it's as plain as day. We go back for our puppy – for Lakota – and we fly her home with us. And we change her name from 'Dingo' to 'Kokopelli.' *That's* what the images in the dream-thing meant, when I couldn't get back to sleep yesterday morning. Life has these strange twists and turns, if you'll stay tuned to them. This is most definitely one of them."

He groaned. "Damn. Why'd you have to be an artist, sensitive and all to these 6th sense musings? Here I was hoping distance would have you forgetting about her. I guess there's not a chance of it now." He looked over at me hopefully.

The determined look on my face, and the hope therein, must have answered him. Pete just shook his head and said, "Come here, you. *You're* the Kokopelli spirit around here, creating all of this trouble and mischief with your imagination." He wrapped me up in his arms in a big loving embrace. *Ill Wind* rolled to the floor. "And you're irresistible in that convoluted logic of yours." So much for our turning in early tonight.

Canyon de Chelly Trail Ride

The sun rose over a beautiful day that Wednesday, October 3rd, promising warmth and a need for sunscreen. We breakfasted at 8:30 at the restaurant, eating heartily, as we knew it might be quite a while before we saw food again. We continued our discussion of the night before and I reminded my husband again of the irony of finding her. We easily could have passed her by.

"You know, Pete, if we had ridden at El Capitan that Sunday afternoon we wouldn't have found her at all. But some little voice told us to change our plans. Remember? And then we almost left Monument Valley. We passed on by that overlook and decided to back up to get the photograph of the elder with her jewelry in front of the distant butte. Remember that? I'm telling you, it was divine intervention. We were *absolutely* meant to find that little desert dog and to bring her home with us."

"Okay, okay, I'm beginning to really believe you, Razza. We'll call Ricardo tonight and let him know. I did tell you I'd take you back to the Canyon and not fuss about it. Or at least not fuss too much." He crossed his arms over his chest and leaned back in his chair, "But let's have our fun and freedom today, alright?" Pete didn't look so excited. In fact he thought and then said, "Well, if we'd *kept* the pup with us, we could have skipped the ride. I probably wouldn't have complained too much about that. Not like I'm going to complain later, anyway, after we've been in the saddle on a horse for hours..."

"Oh, I have secrets that'll take care of being a little saddle-sore, Peter-Wop," I winked at him mischievously.

"Oh yeah? Like what?"

"Well, for starters, we walk the horses in the last half an hour and stretch out those thigh muscles that have been abused for so long. And then we clean up and soak in a hot tub awhile... *then* we rub some Arnica in our poor beat-up thighs and *then* we…" I smiled.

"I get the idea. It's not sounding too bad now. Let's go find those Indians and saddle our steeds."

We found the stable set back under the shade of cottonwood trees in one of the entrances of the canyon. Several Navajo men were there to help us. They asked how long we'd like to ride. An hour? A few hours? All day? We looked at each other and said, oh, maybe four or five, max – we hadn't been in the saddle in a while. Two of the men put their heads together, discussing something quietly and one looked up and said, "We can take you to Antelope House on a 6-hour ride. 3 hours there, and 3 back. There are beautiful old pictographs painted on these walls, there are the Anasazi ruins down at Antelope House, and many more sights on the way."

Pete and I looked at each other, put our own heads together to discuss this quietly and see if we were game for 6 hours in the saddle. We decided that would be the very maximum and we'd walk it out a good while on return. "Okay." We agreed. "Six hours then – but that's all. *That'll* kill us."

"What kind of ponies would you like?"

"I'd like a quiet one that has power-steering and power-brakes." Pete quickly piped up.

I smiled and turned my head. *Yeah, and a CD player built in.* I told the man I'd like a responsive pony with some spice and personality. We walked over to the pens where they kept the horses in tubular corrals in the shade. They looked well fed. There were water troughs in each pen and mounds of hay. Their feet were all in good shape, kept naturally trimmed by the treks through the sand. All were barefoot, as there was no need for shoes. Most were paints, with a sorrel or two and a few bays mixed in the herd. Our guide, Jacko, brought out two brown and white geldings and handed the reins of the taller, slimmer equine to Pete. "This is 'Rainbow.' He has power-steering, but no brakes." Jacko grinned widely, enjoying his joke. Pete looked at me, asking me silently if he was kidding. I shrugged and smiled.

"Well, look at it this way, Wop; the landing'll be soft." I giggled. Jacko gave me the reins to 'Chili Pepper.' "He's gotta' lotta' fire. You'll see." He smiled again at his own joke; he was playing with us. I was curious to see what he was up to. 'Chili Pepper' looked like his fire had been all put out with the gelding of him. Jacko brought out a couple of blankets, western saddles and nylon bridles, and we tacked them up. Then he went to another corral for his personal mount, a rangy buckskin he called 'Rambo;' Rambo was already tacked up.

I had forwarded saddlebags and my chaps all the way from Virginia for this opportunity. We had had them sent out by UPS to the Comfort Inn in Santa Fe. We put water bottles and a couple of apples and carrots for the horses in the saddlebags. I zipped up my chaps and pulled my Safari hat off my shoulders. "You have everything, Pete? Sunglasses? Hat? We'd better take the sunscreen with us." Pete looked like the Virginia Cavalier (UVA's sports mascot) crossed with the Marlboro Man, in his blue jeans and jean shirt, topped off with his dark goatee, mustache and high-cheeked facial structure. The ball cap and sunglasses he'd just put on gave him a sporty look.

"Yes, I've got all that. Can we put the sunscreen in your carry-on luggage?"

I gave him a smile. "Toss it to me." I caught the sunscreen and turned to our guide, "Jacko, do you want to be paid before we leave, or do you want a deposit or anything?"

"No, no. We trust you. Pay us when we get back." He and the other Navajo exchanged looks. "Okay, let's mount up."

"Hang on, Pete; let me check your girth." I had this thing about girths and cinches after one broke on me in mid-gallop when I was exercising horses as a teenager, on a big black gelding named Brass Tacks. The leather was old and the stitches had dry-rotted and had simply fatigued. The next thing I knew, the saddle and I were *sailing* through the air as the horse galloped out from under me. It was a very strange feeling. The reins had ripped through my hand and sliced the soft area between finger and thumb; I'm lucky that was pretty much the extent of my damages – it could have been much worse, but gravity was kinder and gentler back then. I hit the ground rolling, with the reins being torn away as the horse continued on his merry way. My right hand still has those scars to tell the tale.

These Navajo were using colorful braided cotton cinches. They looked good; the stitching looked strong, new, and tight. I eyeballed the condition of the nylon bridles and checked the hardware and the fit. These were typical western curb bits. They fit well, but these ponies looked like a snaffle would have been overkill. "Okay, looks good, Pete. We're set," I said, as I gave my own cinch a quick run-through. Jacko was holding Rainbow as Pete put his left foot in the heavy wooden stirrup. He bounced on the ground several times, like a basketball, getting the momentum to swing up. I smiled to myself. He looked like Billy Crystal, aka 'Mitch,' in *City Slickers*, mounting up. We had our own horses, but they were never Pete's 'thing.' This was stretching it; this was pure love. PeterWop much preferred keeping both feet on the ground, especially having been just told his horse had no brakes.

When I saw that he was mounted up safely, I made sure Jacko was checking the stirrup length to fit Pete's long legs. Jacko had the build typical of a lot of Navajo: a barrel chest and strong upper body, small waist and short sturdy legs. He ran the stirrup down several notches and I walked over and patted Pete's thigh, looking up, "They feel good? You don't want too much bend, but you'll want enough to lift yourself and brace if this fellow's trot is a little rough." He grimaced. More fun. "Okay, just checking. We sure want you to get through this all intact." I smiled up at him warmly.

"Thanks, Razza. That makes me feel *so* much better."

"And having your stirrup lengths even makes the ride a whole lot more balanced." I added, referring to our deal early in our relationship of trading riding lessons for lessons in German.

I went over to Chili Pepper. Jacko had been holding him for me. I said thanks and gathered the reins. I didn't remember these chaps being this tight. I had had them made about thirty years ago, as a teenager, and they were supposed to last forever. Last, they did; what I *hadn't* accounted for was the change in me over the next thirty years and three children later... *Hmm...* I put my left foot in the stirrup, stretched back to loosen the chaps, then swung up, trying to land easily on the horse's back. I'd always tried to ride as if I were the one being ridden. And I wouldn't want some damned fool landing hard on my kidneys or yanking around on my mouth. Generally, I'd found horses responded well to a light touch. Especially the more sensitive ones – but I think these poor fellows might long have been desensitized, as trail ponies become over time and with many different riders.

"Does he neck rein?" I asked, looking down at our guide.

"A little. You'll like him a lot, I'm sure of it."

"Jacko, I'm not convinced this poor fellow, despite his name, has a whole lot of get up and go left in him."

"None of 'em do. It saves us law suits." Oh yeah. That. But we had already signed the leases.

As we headed out a flock of crows on the ground beside the tubular corrals rose in flight, circled behind us and landed in the limbs

of the cottonwoods. A raucous cawing followed us as we rode away. I turned around in the saddle and looked back curiously at the racket, and then shook my head to shake off the uneasy feeling I'd just gotten. Silly. Here we had this beautiful day ahead of us, in one of the most beautiful places in the world, with a guide that was perfectly capable – it was time to turn around in the saddle, look foreword and enjoy the moment.

We followed Jacko out of the stable area to the vast entrance of Canyon de Chelly, where it would branch out into deep fingers, like a hand stretched open wide. This was a labyrinth of hidden passes lost under sheer vertical rock faces. The White House Ruins trail, which we had hiked down into with the kids last summer, was the only one where tourists could go without a guide. Even then there were strict rules to be followed to respect Diné lands. We had emphasized that to the teen's last year. Treat this land respectfully; it is truly a privilege to be allowed to share in this beauty.

Now here we were, on a picture perfect day over a year later, riding into the depths of these beautiful sacred canyons, with a Navajo guide that I couldn't quite get a handle on, on very quiet Navajo ponies that probably too often faced these deep sands. Pete had several Kodak one-time cameras in one of the saddlebags and I had pulled my Canon out of mine, to wear around my neck for the ride. Life was fine.

We meandered through these golden sands and deep gorges, marveling at the walls, the bases of which were softened by Russian olives, coyote willows, cottonwoods and tamarisks growing in and around streambeds. The soft yellows and blue greens contrasted against the red rock colors. I noticed several horses in the distance grazing at the base of one wall. Jacko said they let the horses out to give them time off. They looked beautiful and wild as they chose to ignore our little group. We rode on. In a while Jacko suggested we stop for a chance to rest, as he maneuvered Rambo up a series of flattened rocks. Rambo was surefooted and able. Jacko tethered the trio in the shade of a couple of Russian olives. "Why do we need to rest so soon, Jacko? We're only half an hour or so into the ride." Pete asked.

"I wanted to show you this area. Besides, it's been a while since you've ridden, you said. This will give you a break. This is where you come if there is flash-flooding in the canyons, a higher place like this. Otherwise, you could get washed away and drown." It didn't look as if we had a chance of that today. I remembered Andersen and Johnny's story of getting the Ford stuck down in here a few years ago and shared that with him.

"Yeah, I know those guys. I remember that. That's a really funny story. We still laugh about it around here." *Small world*, I thought. We sat for a while and talked of life down in these canyons.

"How far in is this Antelope Ruins, anyway, Jacko?" Pete asked in a bit.

"Oh, it's a right good ways. Guess we'd better go. It's on the way down to Canyon del Muerto and Massacre Cave. You know about that?" We mounted up as he talked.

"Yeah. I've been doing some reading about it. It sounds like the Spanish got tired of the Navajo raids and things got out of hand. Times when your cultures were clashing big time." I looked over at him.

"I'd say so. It was back in 1805. A bastard named Antonio Narbona trapped more than 100 of us Navajo down in what is now called Massacre Cave. They stood at the top of the canyons and used us for target practice. By the end of that day, most were dead. Over a *100* men, their women and children, all shot in cold blood. Our rifles could not reach the distance of their stronger guns. In Narbona's report to the 'governor' of Santa Fe he said he had killed mostly warriors – because that's what the governor would want to hear. The son of a bitch actually sent the governor *ears* from the dead to brag of the kill. The filthy *bastard*." A very hard edge had crept into Jacko's voice; history still haunted the man.

We were quiet for a while after that. Somehow saying "I'm sorry" sounded so trite. I could visualize the angry and terrified Indians trying to find cover from the bullets raging down from above, as they watched their loved ones fall victim to this genocide. It was not a pretty sight. No wonder they called this finger Canyon del Muerto: Canyon of the Dead.

We rode on through the beautiful maze. I saw a few crows land ahead of us and thought of the dead and then shook my head to clear the sight. I clicked Chili Pepper to ask him to trot on up to Pete, and, when that didn't work, I kicked his sides a little; my pony's shorter legs kept falling behind. "How are you doing on your wild thing there, PeterWop?"

"I'm realizing that I don't even *need* brakes with this one. He rarely leaves first gear. So I'm fine; how 'bout you?"

"I think mine ranges between 'idle' and 'low'… The poor pony has these short little legs. I sure wish I had Tequila down here. She'd set the place on fire." Tequila was my black-bay thoroughbred mare at home. She was *definitely* a firecracker; I updated my insurance policy before each ride. She'd come off the track and ended up being trained for two years to play polo, but had never actually played in a game. Del had said she had all he had wanted in an ideal polo pony: the smarts, agility, speed, everything. Only one thing was missing – she didn't like the contact – she'd kick the bejesus out of anything that got too close. Of course polo is a contact sport. I had grinned at Del and said, "Shows me she's got too much sense to play the game." And, after a lengthy test drive, I'd handed him a deposit. Only her name had been 'Annie' back then. I had changed it to 'Tequila Mockingbird,' or T-bird for short, as a tongue-in-cheek attempt to lighten up after all of the autumnal deaths. I was trying to live by Oscar Wilde's sage comment: **"Life's too short to be taken seriously."** When I'd 'test driven' her she'd been a push-button sweetheart – ideal, I thought, for trail riding, which is what I love to do. When I'd brought her home and fattened her up she had become the firecracker she now is. But she sure would be fun down in these canyons today. In these deep sands she'd settle down soon enough. And her neck reining responsiveness would make this ride a joy. You thought it and she was there. A shift of your weight in the saddle... a tiny movement of leg... This poor fellow acted as if he'd taken a big swig of tranquilizer before we left.

The further into the canyons we rode, the steeper the reaches of sandstone cliffs. The slick rock faces were gorgeous; they looked as if they had been varnished. Colors ranged from deep red rock to wet sands to the palest of peach and vanilla tones. Swirls of textures and cut outs abounded. Our giant had had a field day creating these complicated

canyons. Jacko would take us close into some of these areas to show us pictographs or petroglyphs of images on the rocks that might go back centuries. There were names like Echo Ruins; Big Hand Ruins (handprints, upright and upside down were imprinted here); Little Cave Ledge Ruins; the Ute Raid Panel. There were Kokopelli figures dancing on the walls, triangular petroglyphs, and one area called Newspaper Rock, where all sorts of figurines shared history in a time without words. Another they called 'Sleeping Duck Ruins.' Jacko pointed out how this could be so and added wryly: "We call it 'Cold Duck Ruin.' Get it?" he grinned. He was quick and had a dry sense of humor; we were enjoying him as a trail guide. Jacko explained to us that that the Navajo name for this area is 'Tseyi;' the word 'de Chelly' was a Spanish corruption of the word 'Chegui,' meaning canyon.

Much further in he pointed out pictographs of stick figures astride depictions of primitive horses. Jacko then explained that this was the Spanish invasion, when they came with their horses and their guns to conquer this area. "The '*Conquistadores*'," he said with contempt. He pointed to figures of stick people falling dead. "That was us." We rode on further into Canyon del Muerto. Soon it was time for another break and pit stops in the deep shade of a rock structure dotted with many shrubs at its base. There were outhouses there, to our amazement. "We aim to please." Jacko said. "No, really, this is where we bring tourists for overnight campouts. We have the fire over there –" he pointed to an open area in the corner, "and sleep at the base of the cliffs." He waved a hand to the right. It was a beautiful protected encampment. If the Spanish weren't around.

We made our stops, drank some more water, and sat on a log to rest a bit. The horses nibbled at grasses they could reach. A few more crows flew in and landed several yards away from where we sat. *Were they looking for handouts? Following us? What?*

"Are there always so many crows down here, Jacko? I haven't seen a lot of other birds." I asked the guide.

"No, not really. This is unusual today." He looked baffled.

Pete looked at his watch. "Jacko, how much further to Antelope House? We've been riding for 2 hours. We're close then, right?"

"No, not really. I'd say another hour and a half, maybe a little more."

"Remember we only want to ride for the six hours. That's all we signed up for – and all we're paying for." Pete told him. We were beginning to understand that exchange of glances between those two characters. With that we were on our feet and on our way. The pace picked up and our leisurely guide grew a little gruff. Perhaps we weren't going to be the easy marks he'd pegged us for.

We heard a low grumble coming from the bowels of unseen gorge ahead. Pete and I exchanged our own glances. Jacko caught the look and told us, "That's one of our tourist trucks. We can haul whole groups down in here. Lots of people don't like to ride horses."

With that the rumbling increased and a big army-looking vehicle appeared loaded down with an array of tourists in brightly colored clothing, brandishing cameras and camcorders. The side of the truck read

"**De Chelly Tours**" with the phone number. Jacko neck reined Rambo around and cantered off to join the driver in shooting the bull, without a word to us. While they talked Pete and I rode on, enjoying the beauty and solitude.

We came upon a verdant basin in the lower reaches of canyon, with a grove of Mormon teas, tamarisks, and a small peach orchard off to the side. Sweeping up above this pastoral setting were a swirl of rocks capped by distant red rock walls rising to enclose this valley. Soft powdery clouds spun through the pale blue skies. It was breathtaking. I reined in Chili Pepper, who was always glad to stop, and took several shots. Pete was off exploring the peach trees, looking for ripe fruit. Jacko came galloping up, exclaiming, "You two can't ride off without me – I'm your guide. You were supposed to wait!"

"Where's the harm?" I asked him. "We're just enjoying your scenery. It's so beautiful here." I smiled at him and he gave us a forgiving smile in return; no damage was done.

"Let's pick up the pace then." Rambo was already lathered, but our paints had barely broken a sweat. Jacko's navy blue tank tee shirt had big sweatstains under his arms.

"We'll try," I responded, "but these fellows might have other ideas."

"Okay, then I'll get you switches; that'll convince them." He rode over to one of the Mormon teas and came back with a couple of small branches. "Show that to those lazy things."

We did and they picked up the pace a little, but neither was duly impressed with our 'threats.' They'd seen this before, and probably much worse.

The deeper we rode into Canyon del Muerto the higher the height of the sandstone walls that swept above our heads. This was a fortress, a tricky maze of rock structures, deep sand bottoms, and greenery of varying types.

We continued as I hummed America's "*I rode through the desert on a horse with no name…*" I stuck my foot out to the side; the shadow did the same. I got a photo of myself reflected in the sands against Chili Pepper's neck. I looked down and laughed at my shadow so clearly following along under Chili's feet. I waved my hand; the shadow waved back. My abstract, hat-wearing, featureless alter ego had come along for the ride. Pete looked around and called, "Laura, stop fooling around with whatever that is you're doing and look up." I did. Ahead of us sat a dense thicket of pale sea green Russian olives against towering rounded red canyon walls. Along the tops of these walls were huge holes that ran horizontally around the edges, as if they had been strategically cannonballed. A sandy path created by the plethora of tamarisk led into deep shade created by the trees. It looked very mysterious.

"Isn't this *beautiful*, Pete? Maybe we're close." Once we cleared the trees, Pete and I held our breath. Our mouths dropped open. Ahead of us the sandy road continued leading directly under a massive sweep of swirling rock that leaned out and over us, creating a drastically sloping roof over our heads and deep shadow beneath. This was truly a phenomenon of nature. Jacko was turning around with his hand on Rambo's rump, watching us for our reaction with a big ole' grin on his swarthy face. We didn't disappoint the man. "This is *amazing* down here, Jacko! What do you call this place?!"

"Rooftop Ruins." Of course. "This is where we come when it rains," he kidded. "Of course, not in male rains; you'd be drowned by the flash flooding." We just shook our heads in disbelief as we rode under and through this bosky enclosure. Jacko pointed out more pictographs of the Spanish invasion, by now well blended into the shadowy walls. Soon we were riding into Antelope House Ruins.

We tethered our horses to a hitching' post under the deep umbra of three tall Mormon teas. Behind these a massive buttress of round-edged sandstone rose above our heads. The trio stood there with hind legs cocked lazily, switching their tails. They knew the routine; this was rest time. We stretched and twisted our saddle-worn bodies as we walked over to a shady overhang of trees. We could see Antelope House sandwiched beneath the huge sloping walls above it and the sandy canyon floor beneath. A well-built wire fence kept visitors from getting too close to this Indian archive. Walls crumbled, but I could see the intricate sandstone's blocks still lodged into place for time eternal.

A sign to the side said: "HANDMADE HOMES: THESE WALLS ARE TESTIMONY TO THE BUILDING SKILLS OF THE ANASAZI. THE 'CUT-AWAY' DRAWING SHOWS HOW THE ROOMS IN FRONT OF YOU WERE BUILT. SANDSTONE BLOCKS [A], SHAPED TO FIT, WERE CAREFULLY SET IN A MIXTURE OF MUD MORTAR AND SMALL STONES CALLED 'SPALLS.' LINTELS [B] FOR WALL OPENINGS SUCH AS DOORS OR VENTS WERE MADE OF SHORT STICKS. ROOFS WERE SUPPORTED BY BEAMS [C] 6-8 INCHES (15-20CM) IN DIAMETER, LAID ACROSS THE NARROWEST DIMENSION OF THE ROOM AT ABOUT EVERY 2 FEET (.6M). A LAYER OF SMALLER POLES [D] WAS PLACED ATOP THE BEAMS. THESE POLES WERE COVERED WITH REEDS AND FINALLY AT A 6-INCH (15CM) LAYER OF PACKED EARTH [E]. WALLS WERE OFTEN PLASTERED. THE MORTAR AND PLASTER LINES ON THE

CLIFF ABOVE THE STANDING WALLS INDICATE THE LOCATION OF FORMER ROOMS WHICH FORMED A MULTI-STORIED TOWER PROVIDING ACCESS TO THE UPPER LEVEL."

An illustration, showing loin-clothed Indians hard at work demonstrating these building techniques, along with the appropriate alphabetical letters, was above this plaque.

A second sign described the Anasazi in "THE PLACE CALLED RUNNING ANTELOPE: PREHISTORIC ANASAZI PEOPLE LIVED IN THIS SPECTACULAR SITE FOR ALMOST 600 YEARS. THE EARLIEST PIT-HOUSES DATE ABOUT AD 700. BY AD 1050, STONE DWELLINGS WERE BEING CONSTRUCTED. SOME OF THE WALLS YOU NOW SEE WERE BUILT AS LATE AS AD 1250. THROUGHOUT THIS TIME, THE LIFE STYLE OF THE ANASAZI CHANGED IN MANY WAYS. THEY IMPROVED THEIR SKILLS IN MAKING POTTERY. THE ANCIENT THROWING SPEAR WAS REPLACED BY BOWS AND ARROWS. GRADUALLY, THEY INCREASED THEIR RELIANCE ON CROPS CULTIVATED IN NEARBY FIELDS, AND FLOCKS OF TURKEYS KEPT IN THE VILLAGE. THEY ALSO RAISED COTTON AND MADE FINELY WOVEN COTTON CLOTH."

This illustration was an aerial perspective showing Antelope House from above "as it might have appeared about AD 1240." Both plaques were very professionally done and very descriptive, giving the viewer that had gone that extra mile to come down to the recesses of the canyon a real appreciation for "those that had gone before." Pete and I studied these faded ancient ruins and thought of centuries ago when the Anasazi had lived here in utter simplicity, living off of the land and at the mercy of the elements – and eventually, other Indians. I wondered how long our softened, but technologically adept, culture could survive in the empty reaches of these meandering canyons. We photographed the ruins and the signs and turned to study our surroundings.

Two Navajo children, a little boy and a little girl, were playing in the sands. She wore bib-overalls and was riding a small bicycle, of which the little fellow, in his tee shirt and sweatpants, wanted a turn. I thought back when our trio had been this young, only 10 or 12 years ago. Time did fly with wings. I smiled at their antics. Beside them their parents had a display of cool beverages laid out on a table in bottles. Pete and I bought a couple of fruited teas and wandered around, continuing to get the kinks out. An old Navajo woman sat behind her display of jewelry, exhibited very precisely on a table. I walked over to look. There were some beautiful pieces there: necklaces, earring sets, and a few bracelets. I saw a little sign saying that she would take VISA or MASTERCARD. I asked Pete if he had our credit card here with us and he nodded a 'yes,' with a smile. Each artisan had their own style and this elder knew her craft. I especially liked her work with hematite, the highly polished soft gray stone, said to be healing. She had these stones separated with beads of turquoise. I chose a necklace for me, and one for my little sister, Marcy, that I thought she'd like. This would be for Christmas. I found one with Skye's name on it. The older woman carefully wrapped them in individual plastic bags, then again with tissue paper in a larger bag. I handed her our MASTERCARD, marveling at making this transaction at the bottom of the Navajo canyon 'Tseyi.' We seemed so far removed from the reaches of any form of real civilization that this just seemed absurd.

I smiled at the gentle old woman and told her we would enjoy these necklaces very much. She told me "They will bring you much luck and many blessings," and gave me a big toothless grin. May the Great Spirit watch over her. I guess she would make this her livelihood until arthritis completely locked up her hands or her eyes could no longer focus. I fished deeply in my pocket, past the straps on those damned tight chaps, and fished out a rumpled-up $5 bill that I'd put in there for some kind of reserve. "Here, this is a little extra thank you for being down here, and for making such beautiful jewelry."

Her eyes danced and she grinned again, nodding her head at me. I walked away from her, wondering what her life had been like all these years as a Navajo Indian woman, living here in America.

Jacko was at the horses, untying them. We'd all made our pit stops and left our iced tea bottles off in a recycling container they had beside their table. (I had looked at Pete directly and meaningfully into his eyes and smiled, but said nothing.) Jacko asked us if we were ready to ride hard going back. Pete looked panicked; both of us were feeling the first 3½ hours in the saddle; we'd been here about a half an hour; I guess this meant that Jacko wanted to condense 3½ hours into 2 on the way back in order to make our 6 hour limit. I guess this meant we wouldn't be stopping for leisurely breaks and chats in the shade. I guessed right, too. Pete was doing his bounce-&-hop-mount-thing and I laughed at my husband and got a photo of his antics, as poor Rainbow braced himself for this gringo to climb aboard. I then put my package of Navajo necklaces carefully in the saddlebags and checked both of our cinches before mounting up, myself. Jacko held Chili Pepper for me as a courtesy and I thanked him. He mounted up and we were on our way back through this astounding Canyon of Death.

We started out at a trot and then rolled into a canter under the 'Roof-top Ruins.' The horses suddenly had more energy on the way home. Funny how that is. I enjoyed the wind in my face and the feel of really riding again, discovering that little Chili Pepper had a scat-gear and could move along right well, when he was so inclined. I reined up next to Pete and cantered beside him, "Pete, relax your hips, put some of your weight in the stirrups and feel the motion down through your legs. Loosen up your shoulders and just roll with the ride; you'll get the feel of it!" I called to him, watching him relax a little. He glanced over at me, concentrating hard, "Like this?"

"Yeah – *roll* those hips, man! Relax! *Feel* the motion! It'll be easier on your pony, too!" I called to him. We cantered along for a good little ways, but when the horses tired Jacko raised his hand.

"We'll walk 'em out a ways. There's a watering hole up here in a quarter of a mile, or so. We'll give 'em a good drink." As we walked along, the six of us, Jacko looked over. "You all ever hear of the 'Long Walk'? How we Navajo were forced to leave Canyon de Chelly?"

"We know a little something about it, Jacko. This time it was the federal government in this country after you all for all of your raids on the settlers coming into the area, right? The Cavalry sent in their big guns. And Kit Carson was involved, if I remember correctly…" I looked over at Jacko, questioningly.

He nodded, looking glum. "Yeah, that's right. Our lands, and the federal government wanted them all. It was 1863 and this time – you're right – it was General 'James Henry Carleton'," he said with contempt. "The big man sent in Kit Carson 'to kill all the Navajo men wherever you find them. Take the women and children prisoner,' Carleton said, so Carson collected all these volunteers to help him out, you see, and these people included some Spanish and even other Indian tribal members. The Hopi, Zuñi, the Utes – they *all* turned against us to help out the damned troops!" Jacko angrily spat on the ground.

"Did the Navajo and Apache raiding tactics on these tribes have anything to do with that?" I asked Jacko, trying not to smile.

He was indignant. "Of *course* not! They'd been bought. Turn coats." Right. The Navajo, Apache and Comanche in these parts had all been Saints.

We rode up to the water hole at the base of a sandstone abutment down in the gorge. The horses eagerly waded in to take big drinks. "So anyway," Jacko continued, swinging a blue-jeaned leg up over the saddle horn and hooking it there to rest, while he talked. "On the way here to the canyons these men were ruthless; they burned our hogans, rampaged through our fields, killed our livestock. They called it the *'Scorched Earth Campaign'.*" *Hmm*, I thought, *code names, even then.* Jacko again spit disdainfully. "After that, any who didn't surrender and end up in Fort Defiance had taken refuge with other tribes that might take them in. And a bunch of us came to hide out down here, in Canyon de Chelly. But would they stop? *No…*"

Chili Pepper started to paw the water vigorously. I knew this meant he was about to lie down and roll in the cool waters, so I quickly gave him a kick in the sides and reined him around and out, "Oh *no* you don't there, boy! We're heading back to dry land!" Rainbow looked up calmly and turned his head, watching us, his muzzle dripping. "Sorry there, Jacko, for the interruption…" I called to our guide. Pete neck reined Rainbow around and followed us out. He had been listening intently to the story.

Jacko went on without missing a beat, now fully astride again and bringing Rambo out of the watering hole. "Okay, so now it's January of 1864. The winter. Carson and his men are instructed by Carleton to come in and get us out. They camped down in here, rooting us out and taking us prisoners, when they could find any of us. They burned our peach orchards, down in the canyons here, to the ground. By spring they had gathered as many as *8,000* Navajo – men, women, and children, can you believe it? – from around the Four Corners area and they forced us to march *all the way* to New Mexico, on foot, to Fort Sumner. That was about 250 miles, beyond all our four sacred mountains. Many of Diné died along the way. This is why they call it the 'Long Walk.' The new reservation where they put us all – those that survived the walk," he added contemptuously – "was called Bosque Redondo – the 'Round Grove' – named for a few cottonwood trees out in the middle of nowhere. There were no trees, 'cept these, like we'd been used to, no canyons, no shade of any kind. Just the blazing hot sun. Many of my ancestors died of exposure, and others died of Belagaana's diseases and dysentery. We stayed there for four long years of hell, trapped like animals, dreaming of one day returning to our lands."

He shook his head, a deep sad look on his face. I noticed that Pete was still listening, but looked cramped and uncomfortable. The ride was getting to him. "Excuse us a minute, Jacko. Pete, bend around in the saddle, twist your torso and stretch out your thigh and buttocks – your muscles will all feel better. Then do the other side." I was doing this now to show him and to stretch out my own tight muscles. It felt really good, like a long deep yoga stretch. "Go ahead, Jacko. We're just stiff. We haven't been riding and we'll be paying for this! We're listening…"

"That's a good pointer — looks like a good stretch. I'll have to remember that one." I smiled to myself: *I'm down in the bottom of Canyon de Chelly teaching Indians yoga on horseback. Cool…* Jacko grinned. "Okay, where was I? Oh yeah. Bosque Redondo. There's not much more to say. We were there for the four years until the government realized the error of their ways. They got a lot of flack from a lot of people around the country who heard of what had happened, and we — those that survived Bosque Redondo — were allowed to come 'home.' Back to what had become the reservation and to Tseyi, thanks in good part to one of the Navajo leaders named Barboncito, who said when the feds asked them to go to a rez in Oklahoma, 'We do not want to go to the right or left, but straight back to our own country.' Legend says that, aided by the Great Spirits, he held a turquoise stone under his tongue that had been brushed with the pollen from a coyote's coat. Barboncito spoke wisely and well, winning support for Diné to return to their homelands. This is one of the areas that has been our home for over a century now. But we learned some things from the White Man. One, not to trust their treaties."

"I'm really sorry about all that, Jacko. I think what our government has done to the Indians around this whole country absolutely stinks. We call ourselves a 'Democracy,' but Native Americans weren't really a part of that big picture, were they? Immigrants, by the boatloads, yes. But you who were here weren't part of the overall plan. Belagaana were like locust rampaging over lands throughout the U.S., taking over all of this great country in their quest for 'Manifest Destiny.' Where did the government get that sense of entitlement, *any*way? Look what they did to Mexico, in 1848, with the 'treaty' of Guadalupe-Hidalgo — basically they wanted that land down to the Rio Grande, so they took that, too. Guess it wasn't just the Indians that were screwed. But it gave the government sovereign power over the Southwest Natives then, too. I don't even want to *think* of how many treaties have been broken, how many lies have been told…"

I shook my head sadly as we rode along quietly, and then began again, "The same thing as your 'Long Walk' happened with the Cherokee Nation and what is now called 'The Trail of Tears,' where they were forced to leave the mountains of North Carolina. President Andrew Jackson wanted the 'Injuns' out of the east, so he and Congress conjured up the 'Indian Removal Act of 1830' and the Bureau of Indian Affairs to 'handle' them. The U.S. 'assumed dominion' over Indians throughout the country. The Cherokee actually took this to the Supreme Court and fought off the – what I guess was inevitable – 'eviction' from their lands for almost a decade. They actually *won* the case, but were ignored. In 1938 they were forced to go. The Cherokee were forced to leave their ancestral lands, as you were forced to leave yours, and walk all the way to Oklahoma. *All the way to Oklahoma,* that's *800 miles,* where over *4,000* Cherokee died on the way! It was *despicable!* And it was government-condoned. Our young 'Democracy' at work. These will forever be blackmarks on this good country's history, just like slavery was, in the South… and I'm *from* 'the South.' I would have been considered to be a Confederate. My, how things do change." I smiled sadly over at Jacko and played with a wisp of Chili's mane, reflecting. "Sorry I got so long-winded there, guys. All this really just infuriates me."

"Oh?" Pete asked me, smiling gently. "We would never have been able to tell."

Jacko just smiled over at me, but with a look that said I'd probably never really understand, even though I tried.

"Hey, but look at the bright side there, Jacko! Now you Navajo have this gorgeous canyon, and now *we* have to ask *your* permission – and pay big money – to come see it. I'd sure say 'turnabout is fair play,' wouldn't you?" His smile got bigger.

"Speaking of 'big money,' you gringos had better pick up your speed if we're going to get back in 6 hours!" We started cantering again. The water, the walk, and the promise of home had refreshed our mounts and the trip back was much faster than going in. Pete had loosened up and gotten the feel of the motion and we were ready to rock and roll a while.

We were trying so hard to get back by 'curfew' that there had been no time to lead our ponies in that last half hour – or to stretch out our own kinks. We'd gotten back in somewhere between 6¾-7 hours. Two men waited to take our mounts for us as we rode into the corral area. I fished a couple of carrots out of my saddlebags first and gave broken-off pieces to all three horses as a tid-bit of gratitude before they were led off for unsaddling, cooling down and their evening feeding.

A couple of men were holding a dark bay thoroughbred mare that reminded me very much of Tequila. I had to go over and check her out, so I excused myself from Pete and Jacko. She was beautiful, probably 16½-17 hands tall, stately and proud as an eagle. Tequila was just shy of 16 hands. I joined the two fellows. "She sure is a beauty. Doesn't look like your Navajo ponies, though. Where did you get her?"

"Off a track in New Mexico. She's got a bowed tendon. We're doctoring that up, and we'll ride her down in the canyons when it's healed."

"That's because they race them so bloody young. Most are just two and three year-olds." I hated that part of horseracing.

"Yeah. That is too young. Their bones and tendons and muscles are all still growing. They're babies."

"Um hum. Horses mature at around five years old. This is like racing your teenagers hard. When the horses break down many of them aren't as lucky as this mare, here. A good many end up at the meat market. It's horrendous." I scowled.

The men laughed with one another. "You don't feel too strongly about this, do you?"

I watched one of the men squat down and carefully rub liniment into the bowed tendon. A mass of wetted-down greens was at his side, probably some sort of poultice to follow.

I shook away my anger over racing the youngsters, willing myself to return to the good mood I'd ridden in on. "I have a thoroughbred out east. She started out as a racehorse. She got sold around, ending up being trained for polo, but she'd kick. Sure would have loved to ride her in these canyons today. These are beautiful lands you live in. Very spiritual."

"They *are* very spiritual. Many people come here for this. So where do you come from?"

"Virginia. We'll be coming back to learn more about the canyons… Maybe we'll do an overnight camp ride. Maybe I can ride your mare next time?" I smiled. The two men looked at each other and winked. Maybe.

"Good luck with her. I hope she heals completely for you."

"Thank you, lady. Please do come back to these canyons. They are very healing. Bring *your* mare."

"Maybe I will." I smiled and waved. Anything was possible.

I rejoined Pete and Jacko. It was time to settle up. The man from this morning – Jacko's 'partner' – was talking to the two of them, saying that we'd ridden 7 hours, not 6. Pete was explaining that 6 hours was all we'd signed up to ride and we'd been told we could get to and from Antelope House in that time, so that's what we were paying for.

Jacko turned to the other fellow, "Leonard, it's okay. They reminded me a couple of times they'd only signed up for 6 hours. They're good people – forget it. It was my fault we didn't get back in time – not theirs. Let it go." Leonard looked at Jacko questionably, but apparently didn't want to argue with the man. "Okay… Let's call it a straight 6 hours then." He turned, but shot another look at Jacko over his shoulder as he stalked off.

"Travelers checks will be okay in payment, won't it? Or we could give you a personal check." Pete offered our guide.

"Travelers checks will be just fine. I enjoyed riding with you gringos. You were lots of fun." Jacko gave us a broad grin.

"We enjoyed you as a guide – and thank you for the history lessons, Jacko. They added a whole new dimension to these canyons." I told him. Pete had pulled out and signed several of the checks and handed them to the Navajo, then gave him a $20 bill on top. "That's for you. Thanks for sharing your land and your life with us." He smiled.

Jacko grinned in return. "Anytime. You two come on back anytime – and ask for me."

"Oh, we will – and we'll send you some photos, care of the hotel, okay?" I called over my shoulder.

"No, no, let me give you my address. You can send them to me direct." And with that he wrote down his name and P.O. box on a piece of legal paper from the office.

We slipped it in our pockets, put the saddlebags, chaps, and our hats in the second seat, and waved our goodbyes to the cluster of men standing around the corral. It had been a day we would long remember.

TWENTY-TWO

Janus Presents Himself

"Good judgment comes from experience, and a lot of that comes from bad judgment." Texas Bix Bender

After our long day in the saddle, the Wop and I went back to the restaurant at our hotel for dinner. Pete ordered mutton stew, a specialty on the reservation, made with mature sheep, potatoes, celery and such, in a clear broth; I ordered a Navajo taco, another specialty. When in Rome, and all... The Navajo taco is a staple in the west, made with homemade native fry bread surrounding a mixture of ground lamb (or maybe beef?), beans, cheese and salsa. It was huge and very filling. Time for another doggy bag, and *this* time we had a dog to carry it home to – tomorrow. It would keep well in the cooler.

Pete leaned back in his chair and stretched his long sore legs out in front of him. We had made a point of walking around Chinle a while on return to stretch our muscles out, as we hadn't slowed to walk our ponies in. But six hours in the saddle for unprepared muscles was tantamount to running the Boston Marathon with only weekend sprints as training.

Later we'd used the Arnica gel, after a shower and a good soak in the hot tub. We'd just gone back to our room to wash our hands and freshen up after the walk, not taking time to shower, as we'd been so famished. I had a memory from *City Slickers* of Mitch and the boys sitting in the ranch house after their first days ride, holding ice bags over their tender vittles. I had to grin. This sure would endear the Wop to riding, forevermore... "You going to be okay there, Pete?" I leaned forward; being saddle sore again actually felt good to me. It'd been far too long. "Remember that scene from *City Slickers*?"

"Oh yeah. The icepacks on the privates? Oh yeah; I can relate." He grimaced.

I smiled, "But it was worth it, right? Down in the midst of all that beauty? And with the history lesson from Jacko's perspective…"

"Well, yeah, that was plenty interesting. But it would have been as interesting on foot."

"We wouldn't have made it in to Antelope House."

"We would have in the truck."

"Yeah, like a bunch of colorful cattle, and that wouldn't have been 'on foot.' I *much* preferred this. And being a little bit saddle sore is a small price to pay. It's like bringing back a souvenir."

"Speak for yourself. You're not a guy."

"And thank God for *that*." I winked at him. I felt jubilant, knowing we were returning for Kokopelli the next day.

The waitress brought out our food with a big smile. This woman was my age — middle-aged, whatever *that* meant — wearing jeans and sneakers, a long-sleeved tee shirt with an Indian motif and 'Canyon de Chelly' written on the front. "All nice and piping hot," she said in her sweet singsong voice. "Ready for more iced tea?"

"Oh, yes. This food looks *so good*." I smiled up at her. She left and we leaned into our meals. All that fresh air and sunshine and the hours since we had last eaten anything substantial had stoked our appetites. "I'll be taking back half of this for the puppy. Since you did agree to go back," I looked up over a big bite of taco; he was busy with the stew. "It's strange not to be calling her 'Dingo' — but 'Kokopelli' is so fitting. *Look* at all the trouble surrounding her, already. We can call her 'Pelli,' for short."

"Don't talk with food in your mouth. Didn't anybody ever tell you that?" Pete asked, as he chewed the mutton in his stew.

"Nope. So, we calling Ricardo after dinner?"

"Yup. I suppose. A promise is a promise. But you get to make the call."

"Gladly." I gave him a big smile. The waitress brought more tea and lime wedges.

"You're looking for a big tip," I teased her. She smiled shyly and left.

"You know, Pete, the only thing that bothers me right now are the crows."

"The what?" he looked up from his food.

"The crows." I put my fork down, opened and put a sweetener in my tea and squeezed a lime, then stirred. "The crows we've been seeing all day. They spell trouble ahead and I can't quite put my finger on it. But they're always a bad sign. In fact, there's a nursery rhyme, or children's story – or something – about crows. We have the book at home. What seeing just one alone means – that is that someone or something close to you is going to die – what two means, and so forth. I can't remember what '2' is, or '3' means, but I do know that a group of them together spells trouble. I mean, look at Edgar Allen Poe's *The Raven*. And we've been seeing them all day. Like they were following us…"

"They're just birds, Laura. Big, black birds. They don't mean *any*thing. Crows are everywhere. Remember how many we see at the beach, hanging around with the gulls?"

"Sure I do. But that's there, and this is here. And there were no other birds in sight. I'm telling you, it's just been giving me a strange feeling all day." I cut off some taco to finish tonight, and signaled the waitress. She came right over. "Would you please bring me a container to take some of this back with me, when you get a chance?"

"Sure will. How about you, sir?" she turned to Pete. There was nothing left in his big bowl. "Was it good?"

"Oh, yes." He smiled, rubbing his middle, as he leaned back. "I really enjoyed that – thanks."

"Dessert? Coffee?" She asked us.

"Two coffees," Pete said. "Make one decaf – You want anything else, Laura?" I shook my head no, "and our check, please."

"*…Life is fired at us point blank.*" José Ortega y Gassert

Back in our rooms we closed the big curtains for privacy and poured a couple forbidden Coronas. "Okay, Pete, do you think your cell phone will work from here?"

"We can give it a try, but we haven't had much luck out in these parts." He unhooked it from the recharger. "Where's the Café's number?"

"Let me find it." I went through my journal and a page of names I'd been collecting. Here it is," I read it off to him, as he dialed. Nothing, nada, no signal at all. "Well, I guess we try that damned long-distance phone number. Maybe a miracle has happened and they've connected us today, like they promised about twenty times."

"Guess there's not much of a choice." He pulled the card out of his wallet. "Here, Ra, I'll read the numbers off to you and you dial." I took the room phone over to our bed, sat on it cross-legged to stretch my aching inner thighs, and dialed as he spoke. *The phone actually rang! We had our phone card long-distance service! And it was about time, too.*

"Hot damn, PeterWop – it connected! – it's ringing, and no syrupy operator is coming on –"

"Hello, Canyon Café, may I help you?" A young man's voice answered.

"Yes, hello. I'd like to talk with Ricardo Santillan, please."

"He's with a table. If you can wait just a minute, he'll be right with you."

"Okay, I'll hold. Thank you." Why not, I'd give this card a test-run… Soon Ricardo's voice came on. "Hello?"

"Yes, hi there, Ricardo. How are you? This is Laura Giannini – my husband and I left 'Dingo' with you yesterday morning…"

"Yes. Oh yes. What can I do for you?"

"Well, Pete and I have had lots of time to think about her, and we've *defi*nitely decided to come back to the Grand Canyon tomorrow for her. We're going to fly her back home with us!" I told him, my voice full of excitement and anticipation. The line was eerily quiet. "Ricardo?"

"Yes. I am here. I was just thinking. I do not know how to tell you this… but you see, I have made her things. I have bought her things. And I have gotten attached to your little doggie. I have decided," there was a pause and then, " – you cannot have her back."

Now my end of the line was silent. I sat there, stunned. Had I *heard* the man right? "Excuse me? Would you say that again, please?"

Pete said "What?" watching my reaction. I put a finger up, telling him to be still.

"I have decided to keep her, myself. Her name is 'Lucky.' Or maybe 'Sunshine' – I have not yet decided which. But I like her a lot."

"Ricardo, *excuse me*, but we have a 'babysitting' arrangement until the end of the week. This is only the *next day!* Remember that? This was your idea. You called it that, yourself, just yesterday morning, when I couldn't talk. This was *your* idea!" My voice rose. This was unbelievable… I raised my eyebrows at Pete in exasperation, held my hand over the phone and whispered fiercely, *"He's gone back on his word!"*

"What?!" Pete exclaimed –

"Excuse me, but the boss is giving me the 'evil eye.' I have been on the phone too long. I must now go. Call me back in an hour, okay?"

"Ricardo, listen, we *are* coming back to the Canyon tomorrow to pick up our dog – please bring her back in with you."

"Call me back in an hour, please." The phone went dead.

I sat there quietly, not believing what had just been said. My elation over the prospect of talking with Ricardo and arranging the reunion with Dingo/Kokopelli (now Lucky/Sunshine!) had turned in a heartbeat to bitter disappointment and incredulity at the man's gall. *The liar. The two-faced lying little bastard. Had he intended this all along? Had we been that gullible? Had he not cared a whit about the emotional anguish that I had obviously been in over the decision to leave her or to entrust her to his care?*

"Laura, what exactly did he say?" Lost in these thoughts and reeling from the conversation I had simply tuned out Pete, who was sitting beside me now, his face full of questions.

"He said, and I quote: 'I have made her things. I have bought her things. I have gotten attached and you cannot have her back'." I looked at Pete, disbelief still ringing in my ears.

"I'll be damned. That stinking, lying, little bastard. That two-faced *scum*bag…"

"Keep talking, Pete. I'm agreeing with everything you're saying."

"What else did he say?" Pete asked me angrily.

"He said that his manager was giving him 'the evil eye' and to call him back in an hour." I looked at the bedside clock. 9:10 PM. (8:10 PM, Grand Canyon time.) That'd be about 10:00, our time, to return his call. "Now what?" I looked at Pete.

"Now we wait. But not here. Pour what's left of your beer in a plastic cup. We're going for a little drive."

The moon shone brightly down into the deep canyons, highlighting various areas and leaving others in shadow. Pete had finished his Corona back in the room; I had sipped on mine on  the way over to White House Ruins and finished it as we parked. No one else was there in the lot. No one at all — we were totally alone here above this mystical haunt of switchback trails that led one deeper and deeper into the soul of these ancient ruins.

"Here's a flashlight, Ra. I knew we'd be needing them at some point in this trip." We had shipped these out with the chaps and saddlebags, as well a few other bulky odds and ends that would be useful on a trip such as this, but were too cumbersome to haul with our regular luggage. He handed me the smaller of the two. "It's smaller, but the bulb is brighter. Watch your step carefully now. We're not going to think too much about what Ricardo said. We're going to go for a little walk down into the canyon, while we can. I'll keep my eye on the watch."

I followed Pete quietly, glad to have something to do with the hour, glad to be moving. Despite the moon, the trailhead was dark enough for the footing to be tricky, and any fall from the trail could prove treacherous. I was certainly glad of Pete's foresight to bring the flashlights along.

"Here, give me your hand, Razza." Pete reached back to me. "Be careful now."

"Why would he have gone back on his word, Pete?" I asked quietly.

"What?" He hadn't heard.

I raised my volume a little and repeated the question.

"Oh. I have no idea. The little bastard. This was yesterday morning. This was his idea. I have *no* idea, Laura, except maybe he is that lonely."

"Then why didn't he adopt a local dog, then? Lord knows there are enough of them around, from what we heard about the strays – and what we saw at the kennel."

"I can't tell you, Ra. I'm not in the guy's head." He stopped, "*Shhh...* cut your light."

I bumped into him, then switched off my light and realized what he had seen. Far down below us, in the bottom of the canyon, a fire was flickering and then it burst higher. Soon after we heard drums faintly echoing up through the canyon walls. Chanting followed behind the drumbeats. It was mesmerizing.

"Well, I'll be. This is right out of the movies," Pete's voice was hushed, reverent. "Listen to them – some sort of ceremony."

"Our timing couldn't have been better. It's awesome, Pete." We stood there in silence, holding hands and listening to the Navajo chants in the valley floor below us. Years rolled away from us then, in that snapshot in our Belagaana's view of time. What we were privy to hear, as the ancient music reverberated off the omnipotent canyon walls, were voices from time eternal. The clock had been turned to centuries before, as when these chants were common place and no White Man's ears were anywhere near the Native American lands.

We stood entranced in our reverie, there on a switchback trail on the way down into the Anasazi ruins. We listened to the steady drumbeats and saw the flames leap occasionally, the sparks flying high. I had written several poems a year before, while lying in bed half delirious with fever from a vicious flu. Thoughts and ideas had poured out of my head and through my hand, flying over the paper from another place in time. I'd been listening to the Dave Matthews Band playing "Two Step," "The Dreaming Tree," and the like. I wrote the poems to become songs to be put to the music of DMB – not the loud, raucous ones they did, but the fluid, flowing energy that were mercurial and alive, that touched the soul. This scene below us was exactly what I'd envisioned, in my near-hallucinatory state. It was eerie. It was déjà vu.

"Firedancer"

Drumbeats beat like a heart in motion
beat down low, a primitive moan
quicken the blood, awaken ancestors,
quicken the blood, awaken emotions,
Firedancer, celebrate this dance,
this Dance of Life, forevermore.

Flames of life climb the sky
lick at heaven with their fiery tips
spit, spark & flicker bright
dance around the well-worn ground
spread-out low, bursting high
spread-out low, bursting high
flames of life climb the sky.

Firedancer, dance this rhythm,
celebrate this dance,
this Dance of Life.
Primitive, eternal, all-sustaining –
Firedancer, dance this rhythm
celebrate this dance,
this Dance of Life.

We are together, yet each alone –
A lone eagle, lost in flight
soaring higher, ascending heavens,
ascending to heavens magic throne.
Looks down at the raging fire
reaching high, to heavens door –
sees the dancer, the lone Firedancer

296

Celebrating
the Dance of Life....
Spirit dancer, forevermore...

Laura Cockerille Giannini © 2000

As we stood there, becoming part of the canyon in our trance and in our silence, I thought of Carlos Castaneda's writings. I thought of Henry David Thoreau and of John Muir and my friend, Ed Clark, who dreamed up the Wildlife Center of Virginia to rescue wounded and injured animals and return them to the wild. This had now become a model of veterinary technology and a teaching facility to launch young veterinarians into the world. I thought of Gary and Cynthia, whose work everyday brings them into the vastness of nature, and then teaches them to be still and listen, so they might learn, and this they had done. So they, too, might peel back the centuries to uncover fragments of secrets of the earth gone before.

There were tiny sounds behind us in the rocky ledges at our heads, as small nocturnal animals became comfortable enough with our presence to resume their evening lives. Stars shone sweetly in the western sky. Our beautiful moon reigned supreme over all, completely ripe and resplendent in her golden robes, as she watched the dance below and witnessed our eavesdropping. We were caught in a net of magic.

It was Pete who broke the spell. "Ra, he turned and whispered, "I don't know what time it is, and I don't want to cut the flashlight back on just yet, but I'm sure it's time to turn around and head on back, if we're to call Ricardo in anywhere close to an hour."

"Okay, you're right," I was torn away from this enchantment, back to reality. *Back to the reality of another White Man breaking his treaty*, I thought wryly, *even though Ricardo, technically, was Hispanic.* "I'm ready to turn around I guess, PeterWop – but if it weren't for this phone call, I could stand on the edge of this canyon all night with you to witness this. Watch it become day."

"Don't tempt me, RazzaWop," Pete responded. "This is the kind of thing we came out here to do."

"The Canyon Café. May I help you?"

"Yes, please. May I speak with Ricardo Santillan?"

"I'm sorry, but Ricardo has gone home for the night. He left about forty-five minutes ago." Came the man's voice over the long-distance phone. I looked at my watch: 10:17. He had left around 9:30, our time – a half an hour after our call. He'd said to 'call him in an hour.' "But he asked me to call him in an hour. I am."

"I'm very sorry – really. But we got slow and he left for the evening. Is there a message that you would like to leave him?" *Not anything I can say to you*, I thought angrily. *The little weasel.* "Did he leave a message, maybe?"

"No. He said that he was tired and that he was going home. That's all."

"Well, is there any way that I can get a message to him, then?"

"He works tomorrow. Let me see," I heard papers rustling. "Yes, here is the schedule. He comes in tomorrow at 2:00 and works until 11PM. He closes tomorrow night. Would you like to leave a message for him?" The young man asked.

"Yes, please. Just let him know we *are* returning for our puppy. He'll know what that means. Thanks and goodnight."

I hung the phone up quietly, simmering inside. The magic of earlier had gone up like the smoke from the massive bonfire. I didn't need to repeat the conversation to Pete, as he'd been listening intently and it was certainly self-explanatory.

"So the son-of-a-bitch slid out the back door and went home for the night, did he? Not only is he a liar, he's a lily-livered coward, as well." I looked up at Pete. He seldomly got this mad, but he was seething. We'd both been had. "Well, let's skip the hot tub – or do you want to go? They close it at 11:00, I think."

"Let's get in, Pete. It'll be good for our thighs. And then we'll rub the Arnica into the muscles and call it a night. We can't change anything now. The man doesn't have a home phone – he said there was no connection down there. We have a long drive back to the Canyon tomorrow, so we may as well try not to hurt. Physically, anyway."

We half-heartedly got into our suits, then into our jackets, wrapped towels around us and brought the room key. We soaked in silence and bitter disappointment for who knows how long. The only thing said as we sat in the cheerfully bubbling water was: "Now I know what all those crows meant."

October 4th

We arose early that Thursday morning, packed our things, loaded the Camry and then went back to the room to call the Café again. On the third ring a woman answered:

"Hello. Canyon Café. May I help you?"

"Yes, please. I would like to speak with a manager."

"I am the manager here this morning. How may I help you?" she asked pleasantly. I told her the story and how we'd called Ricardo the night before, telling him we'd be coming back. I told her his response.

"Oh? You're willing to make the return trip from Chinle for this puppy? And Ricardo told you he wasn't giving her back to you?"

"Yes we are, and yes he did. He asked us to call him back last night – and we did – but he had conveniently left, so we never spoke with him a second time. But I *did* tell him we were coming back for her."

"Oh. Okay then. Well, I'll tell you what. Ricardo comes on at 2:00. If I'm here then, and it's slow enough, I'll ask him to go home and get her for you, if he doesn't bring her to work with him. How's that?"

"That works for us. But we do have an appointment with a veterinarian at 5:00 in Flagstaff. He said he didn't live too far away. Somewhere south, in a place called 'Valley,' I think."

"Yes, that's about 15 miles south, down on 64. If I'm here, I'll have him do that. But the evening manager might be here then. His name is Crandell. But I'm warning you, he's not as lenient as I am. So I suggest that you get here as soon as you can." This manager's name was Denise; I thanked her for her (potential) help and hung up, relaying to Pete our conversation.

"Well, let's skip breakfast at the restaurant this morning and get something to go at the Burger King, then."

"Fine by me. And I guess we keep the veterinary appointment in Flag for now, as – hopefully – we'll have a pup to vet."

"I guess so. You check the room for loose ends, Ra? Get all our empties?"

"Yup. They're behind my seat, ready to recycle."

We pulled into the Burger King at Chinle. Pete and I smiled at one another, used to this sight by now. Outside of the restaurant, grazing on grass clumps on either side of the highway, were several free-range Hereford cattle, eating away, like they did everyday. This was nothing unusual in their book; one just got used to driving slowly and keeping one's eyes open around here.

We parked the car and I noticed a few dogs over by the dumpster, scrounging around for anything at all. I looked at Pete.

"Laura, *don't* even start. Look at the trouble this has caused already. Close your eyes and follow me inside."

"You go on in, Pete. Order something for me; I'll be right there. Kokopelli is going to sacrifice her doggy bag for that nursing female." I nodded at one bitch that obviously was feeding a family of pups somewhere. Her ribs protruded above her swollen teats. I couldn't 'close my eyes and walk away.' "*Go*, Pete. I *prom*ise I won't stash any of them in the car while you're inside." He gave me a long and dubious look.

"Okay. But I'll be watching from inside."

"Fine. *Go*." He did, reluctantly.

I got out, fished through the cooler and located the Styrofoam container with the remnants of Navajo taco. Taking it out left a good portion of new space in the cooler.

I closed the door and walked carefully over to the group of dogs, trying to signal the hungry female. They milled around and I waved my hand away, wanting to feed them all, but knowing I'd have to pick and choose on this one. She got a whiff of the taco and circled back around, her tail between her legs, her head hanging low.

"Come here, girl. Come here." I called softly. "It's okay – this is just for you." The others didn't think so. They circled around, just behind her. I felt like the cub on *The Lion King*, with the hyenas skulking.

"Come here, girl." I opened the top and set the tray on the ground. She gingerly inched over, more enticed by the promise of food than fearful of my presence. I knelt there, trying to be non-threatening. The other dogs were right behind her, but kept a respectful distance, eyeing me. The bitch engulfed the taco, much as Dingo had engulfed the Breakfast Burrito. She licked the Styrofoam vigorously, willing there to be more. "Sorry, girl – I was hungry last night, too. If I had known I'd be meeting you, I would have eaten less – or ordered a second one." She looked up at me, wagging the tip of her tail.

"You're welcome. Good luck, kiddo. Now I've got to go, before I get myself in trouble again with my husband." I looked at the hungry animals and fought back the tears. *God, I'm a sap. There's something about hungry little kids, starving animals of any kind, and old people in need that nails me every time. I needed those blinders that Pete kept talking about. Some sort of dark glasses that blocks out this neglectful world.*

I picked up the spotless Styrofoam as I arose. The dogs scattered, but hovered, hoping I'd magically produce the 'loaves and fishes,' as Jesus had purportedly done. *Sorry guys, I ain't him.* I found a garbage can and threw the container away. The dogs headed to the receptacle.

Pete emerged from the Burger King with a paper bag and a cardboard container holding coffees and juices. He looked at the dogs, as if counting them, then bent down to look inside the car. "You didn't check the trunk, Wop." I kidded him. "No, they're all out there. They're a family – I couldn't divide 'em up."

"Given enough provocation, I'm sure you could. Open the door for me, please – we're all set." I did. He put the food in on the seat and leaned over to put the coffees in the console.

"Pete, I'll be right back – I'm going to make a quick pit stop and get my hands all washed."

"Okay. I've already taken care of business. We'll be ready to roll when you get back."

I ran in, ordered four Whopper Juniors off the Value-Meal, heavy on the mayo, hold everything else, then took care of my own business and washed my hands while they filled the order. I returned with the bag. I opened the papers and threw a burger to each of the dogs with a sweeping motion of my hand. The food barely hit the ground before each dog was on top of this manna from heaven, the each of them devouring the burger without a taste. *This is my version of the loaves and fishes, guys,* I relayed to them.

I got in the car with Pete. "There. Now *I* feel better about eating breakfast, myself. Let's go." He rolled his eyes and backed the car out of the Burger King lot, driving carefully past the cows grazing calmly alongside the highway, all part of the food chain here.

"Well, I guess I'll call that a compromise, Razza. *You* got to feed them, but *I* get to drive away."

We left Chinle about 10AM, and made good time going down 191 to where we took a right at the Ganado High School. I wondered if Cynthia had gone there. *I wonder how she is doing. I*  *hoped her life was full and that all was okay. I sent her a little prayer.* We passed scenery now becoming familiar, as we backtracked across Highway 264.

This land area was mostly flat and sparsely vegetated, with long low mesas off in the distance. Here and there a canyon ripped open the earth.

Pete looked over at me. "We're on the rez now, so our watches are correct. But when we get off we leave Navajo Time and gain an hour. Which is great for us today. So you set your watch backwards one hour and I'll keep mine on reservation-time for now, okay?"

I smiled at my husband – always the planner. The keeper of time. "Okay. I can do that. That's cool getting an extra hour back in the day. It means we have an extra hour out west." I smiled at him. "I wonder why all of Arizona doesn't use Daylight Saving Time?"

I'd read somewhere that the government had implemented this in World War I, as a way to save energy, back in March of 1918, in the 'Standard Time Act.' It was a controversial concept and hadn't lasted. But in World War II it had been reenacted, again to save energy. After 1945 it was hit and miss, as Congress reestablished it in the 'energy crisis years' around 1974. In 1986, Daylight Saving Time had become law and was passed permanently, stating the starting date as the 1st Sunday in April (I always considered it a birthday gift from nature) and the ending date as the last Sunday in October. Somehow Arizona, with the exception of the rez, most of Indiana and Hawaii had opted out...

Pete interrupted my thoughts to point out the Keams Canyon Campground, off to the right. We'd just been through the short stint of Navajo rez within the Hopi reservation that nested within the balloon of Navajo rez around it. The two cultures were vastly different, yet they shared sacred mountains, such as Big Mountain, Black Mesa, and the San Francisco Peaks. Both Native American tribes believed in the legend of Spider Woman, the Hopi's believing that Spider Woman was the magical link between the human world and the world of the divine. There was most definitely a clash of cultures and differences amongst the two, and both vied for the same lands, each claiming their ancestors had been there before the other. But there were plenty of similarities, as well. Each wanted their respective 'Old Ways' to remain respected and intact, even as the world spun madly into the 21st Century, threatening to leave their deep love of Mother Earth, and that simplicity and spirituality, in the dust.

Our return to the Grand Canyon hung ominously with the question of whether or not Ricardo had brought Kokopelli to work with him. He had left us distinctly feeling that he had no intention of standing by our agreement. For whatever his reason(s), he had back-pedaled completely and in only about 30-36 hours time. That's about how long she had been in our care when we were thinking seriously of keeping her. What was it about this pup that made the caretaker not want to give her up? We discussed this and the possibility of his being so lonely that here this precious pup had breathed life again into his dull existence so much that he hadn't wanted to part with her. It never occurred to us then, from that one short phone conversation the night before, that there might be other motives.

We arrived in the Canyon about 1PM, by now both of our watches were in synch and off of Navajo Time. I was back in Pete's world. Ricardo had not yet arrived. Pete sat on a bench outside the Café to check his voice mails from work, while I went over to the Red Feather Lodge to see if Scott or Marcos was there. Marcos gave me a big smile when he saw me walk in.

"Welcome back, Laura! You came for your puppy?" he asked in that wonderful accent of his, that I'd now established to have originated in San Diego.

"I hope so, Marcos. We're here for her – yes. We have definitely decided to fly her home. Only Ricardo isn't cooperating. He told us last night that 'he had gotten attached, you cannot have her back'."

"*Nawwww…*," he drew out the w's in disbelief. "He didn't. The *weasel.*"

"That's what we said, and a bunch of other things that I can't pollute your young ears with – but he's changed his mind."

Marcos shook his short-cropped head. "The shmuck. The lying little *shmuck* – and after you all saved her from starving in the desert." The phone rang and he held up a finger in the air. I whispered "I'll see you later…" and went back to join Pete.

We watched Ricardo drive his battered two-toned green van into the lot. Both of us sat there on the bench to catch his expression when he saw us. He got out, whistling and oblivious, heading into work. He saw us and did a double take. "Hello, Ricardo. We're back – like Laura said we'd be last night, before you hung up and took off. Did you bring the puppy to work with you?" Pete asked. In 25 years of marriage I had never heard that icy tone in his voice.

Ricardo diverted his head a second, looking for an escape, and then looked back at us. He smiled. "I really did not think that you would drive all the way back here from Chinle just for that little doggie. No, I did not bring her with me."

"Well, we told you we would. It's not quite 2:00, and the Café is not that busy – we checked. Maybe you could go back to your home and get her for us, because we *did* drive all the way back from Chinle, like we said we were going to do, last night." My pent-up frustration and anger at this dishonest man was not well contained. "Our agreement was that if we decided to fly her home with us, then we would come back from wherever we were in Arizona to claim her. Here we are." Today I could talk; the emotional milk toast of two days prior was gone.

"Ricardo shook his head, with his gray-streaked thinning hair. Now it did nothing but remind me of a molting skunk. "No, I cannot do that. I live too far away and I must start work now. I work all afternoon and all evening. Please go now. I told you I changed my mind. You cannot have this puppy back. She is now *mine*. You let her go."

"We did *not* 'let her go.' We had an agreement. These were your words. You and Pete even shook on it, remember that? You called it 'baby-sitting.' We're prepared to stick around, Ricardo. We've made an appointment for a vet down in Flagstaff to have her checked. We've called the airlines. We're set to take her home. All we need now is for you to stand by your word and return our puppy, or does your word mean nothing?"

He looked at his watch. Pete looked at his. Dueling watches. Five minutes until 2PM. The place was practically dead. Ricardo slipped by us into the sanctity of the Café.

"Well, *that* went well." I sat down beside Pete and obstinately crossed my arms. "But I'm not giving up. I'll pester him to death."

"I know you can do *that*." Pete said to me. "While you pester him, I'm going to spend a little more time answering my voice mail, Razza. It's stacked deep. I've let it go too long."

"Don't they ever pretend you're actually *on* vacation – and off the clock – when you vacation, Pete?"

He shook his head emphatically. "You know better than that."

"Well, I'm going inside to get busy with weasel-breath."

"Good Luck…" and then Pete was back to pushing a button on his cell phone and leaving a return message in one of the Mike's voice mails. This could go on a while. Ricardo had better be stubborn.

And he was. We spent the next 2½ hours there, my trying to be reasonable with this little man who made big promises that he had no intention of keeping. Manager Denise had left before we had arrived and been replaced with Manager Crandell, who was a balding, pudgy skeptic who also wished very much that we would just leave. He muttered to us that, "People should leave the damned reservation dogs on the damned reservation, where they belonged." Clearly this man was in Ricardo's camp. He and Barbie Doll would make a fine cynical couple. I really should introduce them.

Ricardo came outside to light up a cigarette, one of about ten he smoked in the course of that afternoon, as he wished us away. I hadn't realized he was a smoker – and hadn't thought to ask. That would have been the clincher for me in keeping her. While he stood outside, inhaling deeply while trying to ignore us, I told him of the fully-grown female that we had seen at the Grand Canyon Kennels. She looked just like this puppy, but as an adult – *and* her name was 'Sunshine.' It was perfect. It was a 'sign.'

"No," he said, "I want to start with a puppy, and I like this one. I like her personality. So I bought her lots of things. And I even spent big money in having my yard mowed and cleaned up so that she can run and not be hurt." He flicked an ash on the sidewalk and glanced over slyly for any response.

"Ricardo, you did *not* have to spend a dime on anything for her, except maybe a collar. And we would have reimbursed you for that. We left you with plenty of dog food for the week and a new leash. We called you the *next* night – when in the world did you buy her all these 'things' – or have your yard mowed?!" I was exasperated. He was lying again. Now I didn't trust anything the man said.

"Do you believe in 'fate,' Ricardo? Or reincarnation?" I'd change tactics and actually confide in him. "Well listen – when we had some time and distance away from this little dog and I could think clearly again, it occurred to me that we were meant to find that pup when and where we did. Our husky, Lakota, died suddenly in July, about 6 weeks before the terrorist attacks. It left me reeling. And call me crazy – I don't care – but I think he's reincarnated through that puppy and that we were sup*posed* to find her. Subconsciously, that's why I had such a hard time parting with her on Tuesday morning. I just needed some distance to figure it out. And then it hit me, like it had always been obvious. That's why we are back for her, Ricardo, and why she means so much to us." There, I'd laid my heart on the line. Let him think me a nut, or a fool; I didn't care.

He had been listening, inhaling deeply in thought. He let out a big exhalation of smoke and stomped my exposed heart hard. "Yes, I believe in 'fate.' I believe that I was fated to have that puppy. Which is why you came into my life with her. And this is why I want to call her 'Lucky' – because she is such a '*lucky* little doggie.' But I cannot decide," he shook his head, dropped the cigarette and squashed it absentmindedly with his foot, "to call her 'Lucky' or to call her 'Sunshine,' because of that pretty golden coat. You know, she will make very pretty puppies with that golden coat and cute, curled-up tail."

The *bastard! Another lie!* "Ricardo, first of all she is such a '*lucky* little doggie' only because Pete and I made the effort to bring her out of Monument Valley. She would have starved, otherwise – or been eaten by coyotes, as you, yourself, pointed out. And secondly, just two days ago you were promising us that you would have her vetted and spayed if you kept her. Remember *those* words?"

He turned to me with a calculating look. "I remember, yes; but I changed my mind. And now that she is my dog, I can do what I want with her." We were getting nowhere.

"I must return to work." He went back inside.

I walked over and sat next to Pete again, fuming, and listened to him leave a message concerning rolls of plastic and fractions of sizes. He finished his call and closed the phone. "Any luck?"

"No luck at all. This guy is stubborn as a jackass. *Now* he intends on making 'pretty little golden puppies' with her. And he can't decide between 'Lucky' and 'Sunshine' for a name. There are two originals. Why doesn't he just call her 'Curly'? We're going in circles, Pete. I think the man has a hidden agenda – there's something else I'm picking up from his innuendos and body language."

"Yeah, like money. *And I'll be damned if I'll pay the man to buy back a stray dog!* Not what he'd be looking for. The guy's a weasel. And you know what, Laura – I've *had* it with all this puppy nonsense! She has colored this entire second week of our vacation and turned it inside out." Suddenly he was mad at me again.

"*Whoa* there, Nelly! That's just what this man wants to do. Divide the two of us in this. We had an agreement on coming back for her, Pete. We just hadn't counted on this bullshit."

"That's what I mean, Laura – we should just be able to pick her up and go. We have hours and hours of driving ahead of us to make it to Albuquerque by tomorrow, to get packed up for our flight out Saturday morning. We don't need this bullshit holding us up." He looked at his watch. 4:15 PM. "*Damn!* We were supposed to be at the vet's office at 5:00!"

"Pete, we need to call the vet and cancel this appointment. That's an impossibility, *especially* with no dog. Maybe they'll have something early tomorrow and miraculously this guy will change his mind."

"Yeah, miracles do happen." He said sarcastically. "I'll call the vet. Give Ricardo one last shot, but then we have to go."

I walked to the doorway and then turned to look at my husband. He was explaining to Dawn, at the Canyon Pet Hospital, that the dog we *thought* we had was with us no longer. But we were still trying. Might they have something for the morning?

I saw him sitting there, still trying to work it out – he'd tried so hard this week to go with the new flow. I looked inside and caught Ricardo staring at me intently. He turned away and walked over to customers, giving them a big smile. *Bastard. Weasel. Lowlife.* I sucked in a deep breath and went inside. *Pete was right. We were getting nowhere – this man had no intentions of giving this pup to us or honoring his word.* I waited for him to come over to me and then said to him quietly, as Crandell looked on:

"You greatly disappoint us, Ricardo. We thought you were a man of character, which is why we left the puppy with you in the first place, but we now see that you have none. You lied to us about returning the puppy, if we came back to the Grand Canyon for her. You lied to us about having her spayed. God only knows how many lies you have told. And you now have us in a bind because of our schedule to return to Virginia. We have no choice but to leave this puppy here with you now, because you have our backs up against the wall, but this is *not* over." I said it, but had no idea what I meant by the words.

Ricardo said nothing, and he acted ashamed, but he must have felt he had 'won.' As I turned away to leave this small man I could swear that I saw a tight thin smile of triumph as he walked back into the restaurant depths.

I resolutely went back to the Red Feather Lodge and said goodbye to Marcos. I let him know how Ricardo had entirely backed out of his word. Marcos had looked so sad, so disappointed in our story ending this way. I thanked him again, and asked that he say goodbye to Scott for us – and we left.

We left the Grand Canyon and Tusayan Village, picked up state Highway 64 to head south towards Flagstaff, and we left this small, crooked man behind us. And with him, the chances of our returning to Virginia with this winsome starving puppy that had stolen my heart. I shook my head; the numbness was returning. Something akin to shock was settling in around me, something surreal that it was ending this way. It was crazy – here we were, practically fighting over who was to keep this little stray dog that only a few days before no one in the world had wanted. What a perfectly odd way to end this anniversary vacation of our dreams.

Pete and I passed a small sign at an intersection at 64 and 180 that said 'Valle.' *So the word had no 'y'; so this is where Ricardo lived.* **Hmm**... *Maybe his trailer park was in sight. How many could there be?* "Pete, if we see a trailer park around here, let's drive through and try to spot the one's with yards. We could peek in... and if we see her..."

"Laura, I know where you're headed with this, and the answer is **no**. We're not looking all over the place for trailer parks, and I'm *not* going to break into somebody's yard."

"I'm not talking about 'breaking into a yard.' I'm talking about looking in to see if we *see* her. And, if we do, opening a gate – and reclaiming our puppy. Ricardo can find his own damned dog." My jaw set. *The little two-faced weasel.*

Pete looked over and smiled. He'd 'heard' that thought. He put a hand on my knee. "Cool it, kid. Take it easy. It's over. We're headed home – and we have a long haul ahead of us. You found her a home. It's settled."

"Not a good one, Pete." I knotted my brow; my head was beginning to hurt from the tension. "The longer I talked with the man this afternoon, the more I realized what a poor home this is for a young pup. First of all, as we saw ourselves, he's a heavy smoker – so she's got to breathe all that. Secondly, he works, counting his travel back and forth, like ten-hour days, five days a week –"

"Honest labor," Pete interrupted.

"I don't have a problem with someone working long hours. That's certainly commendable. I *do* have a problem with the puppy having to be on the waiting end of that. A young pup needs contact – lots of love, training, discipline, more love, and housebreaking. They're like young children. And, speaking of that, he has no children or other pets for her to play with. She's *totally* alone while she waits."

"He has a yard."

"She's still alone. It's just not a good home. It's simply a home. She won't starve. At least not physically. But emotionally and spiritually she will."

"*Spirit*ually, for a dog? LauraWop, come *on!*"

"Sure, why not? Dogs are full of karma."

"Whatever you say..." he sounded skeptical.

"Wish you'd said that two days ago."

"Let's not start that, okay? What's done is done. Everything happens for a reason, as this did. Let it go. If you *really* want a puppy, when we get back to Virginia, you can check out the shelters again."

"No, Pete. It's not the same. I found my pup." I picked my backpack off the floor and started fishing around in it, found an aspirin bottle at the bottom and popped one out. "Killer headache starting," I explained. "Want one?"

"No thanks. But I will take a mint or a chocolate, if you have one stashed down in that cavern of a bag of yours."

"How 'bout some pistachios? I've got them on top of our dry goods, in the box on the seat."

"Okay – but you get to crack 'em and feed me. Be my slave, woman. I'll stop up ahead."

"You're dreaming on that slave-part; but maybe I'll crack open one or two for you… *especially* if I can persuade you to turn around when we see a trailer park…"

"*Lauraaaa…* Don't even go there! We're *not* looking back. Now behave." He signaled his turn at a pullover and I got out to find the pistachios and chili powders. We were now surrounded by aspens, birches and evergreens, the tops all golden and on fire in the late day sun. Shadows were deep and ominous at the base of the ghostly slim trunks. The contrast was somehow very fitting for our trip. We had entered into the Kaibab National Forest again and would have a spectacular drive as we threaded southeast, past the mystical San Francisco Peaks, which included Humphrey's Peak at 12,643', the highest peak in Arizona. I poured a couple of waters with a few ice cubes, to go along with the pistachios and chili powder, and climbed back in, buckled up, and began cracking the colorful nuts, trying to think of anything other than the absent puppy.

TWENTY-THREE

Empty-Handed to Albuquerque

"This is the assembly of life that took a billion years to evolve. It has eaten the storms – folded them into its genes – and created the dawn that created us. It holds the world steady." E.O. Wilson, the Diversity of Life

The long lonesome miles passed us by as we closed in on the end of our two weeks in the great American Southwest. The closer to the Arizona border we came, the further away was our little desert pup, and the further away from the shining star of that second eventful week. I tried not to think like that, though. I told myself that Pete was right, that my original mission was accomplished – we had saved her from starvation and we had found her a home. Our goal was achieved. But although my brain registered this information, my heart was in mutiny and refused to be appeased. The only way to quiet it was to think of something else.

We decided to aim for Holbrook for the night, a little over thirty miles from Winslow, or about an hour and a half east of Flagstaff. In the morning we would take the 'scenic loop' through the Petrified Forest and the Painted Desert before buckling our belts on real kick-ass travel to bring us into Albuquerque and close-out our trip.

We arrived in Holbrook about 8 PM, checked into a Ramada Inn and unpacked essentials before looking for a place for dinner. We called home, making return arrangements with Al, and left word for the children that Ricardo had kept the puppy. We did not go into details; we would do that Saturday night, in person.

It was close to 9:00 by now and five places in a row must have closed down as we parked to eat; Holbrook seemed to shut down at 9PM sharp.

"Well *now* what do we do? They must not like our faces in this town," Pete turned to me, as a flat-topped Southwestern-flavored establishment turned its lights off inside as we pulled in. A neon sign blazed above us with **"ME A RESTAURANT"** in yellow on red. It was actually called **"MESA RESTAURANT,'** but the **'S'** had burned out. It was pretty funny.

"Look at that, will you? They *adver*tise it as a restaurant… Well, I guess we could head down the Old Rt. 66 and see what we find." I pointed to an intersection leading deeper into town and showing the Historic Route 66 highway symbol.

"Guess it wouldn't hurt. We're out of options, here on the strip. Let's see what we find." The Wop backed out of the lot.

Traveling down Old Route 66 that evening proved to be quite entertaining. It smacked of 50s Main Street America with small old shops hosting large glass-fronted windows surrounding recessed old wooden doors. **"SLEEP IN A WIGWAM"** was lettered on a bold sign we passed and we rubbernecked around, not believing our eyes. A number of huge white teepees rose to the sky – individual 'room' units. The office was a regular building with a large sign overtop that called itself the **"WIGWAM MOTEL"** and underneath it asked: **"Have You Slept in a Wigwam Lately?"** Vintage Chevy's straight out of the 40s and 50s were parked in front of these conical contraptions. It was surreal, some automotive Indian twist on *Alice in Wonderland*. We must have swallowed little magic pills.

"Too bad we're already registered for the night," Pete kidded me. "That would have been a hoot."

"It would be fun to see what they look like inside. Wonder where the bathroom is?"

"They don't have one; they're *tee*pees." Pete joked.

"Very funny. *Tech*nically, they're 'wigwams.' Oh well, I'm all for conventional housing tonight, Pete. I'm travel-weary. Let's just find a place to eat."

"How about that place?" Pete pointed ahead. We were still tripping. A long low shake-shingled building stood before us. It was fronted in what looked like upright cedar planks, with a salon-door kind of an entrance and perched above this was a stagecoach that looked as if it might have landed in some recent windstorm. We'd changed channels from *Alice* to *Dorothy*; *Wonderland* had become *Oz*. Crazy. A sign said **"BUTTERFIELD STAGE CO. & STEAKHOUSE."**

"If it's open, it works for me." I told Pete.

There were few cars parked out front. Apparently Holbrookians ate much earlier in the evening. We parked and tried the doors. Open.

Good. We ventured into the dark interior and were greeted promptly by a manager-type in his late 30s. He was tall, had slick-backed hair and was neatly dressed – and he was *very* glad to see us. Guess it had been slow all night.

He seated us in a booth close to the salad bar, which seemed somehow out of place in this very western motif. Radicchio, olives, and pepper wedges seemed sissified when it came to Porterhouse and T-bones steaks, smothered in onion, gravy, and topped off with A-1 Sauce, with fat wedges of steak fries on the side. *Really.*

The heavy wooden booths separated seating groups around round tables in the inner sections. Steer skulls adorned the walls beside western art and daguerreotypes of Old West characters: Wyatt Earp; Bat Masterson; "Doc" Holliday; John Wesley Hardin; "Wild Bill" Hickok; Billy the Kid and Sheriff Pat Garrett (the latter was later killed by the former); Butch Cassidy and the Sundance Kid (and not portrayed here by the Paul Newman-Robert Redford version) were shown in one very old tintype. A photo of Kit Carson, in his fringed buckskin jacket, bridged the 'Cowboys' and the 'Indians.'

Daguerreotypes of Indian chiefs also hung around the rooms: the Chiricahua Apache, Cochise; Navajo leader, Manuelito; Oglala-Brule Sioux, Crazy Horse; Nez Percé, Chief Joseph; Chiricahua Apache, Geronimo; the Tewa, Popé – a shaman of the San Juan Pueblo – who was instrumental in the great Pueblo Indian Revolt of 1680, in which a coalition of Indians throughout New Mexico drove the Spanish out of Santa Fe and all of New Mexico, sending them packing for twelve years south of the border. The Oglala Sioux, Red Cloud; the Hunkpapa Sioux, Sitting Bull; Comanche Chief, Quanah Parker and Cheyenne Chief, Black Kettle....

The Indians and the Cowboys, the faces and ghosts that haunted these walls – staring at us from weathered and wrinkled and soulful gazes out of the multi-valued ancient black & white or sepia-brown photographs – echoed through these rooms. Looking at them closely and reading the captions peeled the year's away and brought history to stand there before us. These were the men who had brought the western legends alive to this day, even as they lay in their graves, or their bones lay scattered over the windblown omnipotent desert sands. Their spirits drifted around us in this room, whispering those secrets of their turbulent past in our ears.

All of the other restaurants had closed so that we would find this one, as our visit neared its end. It offered a chance to unroll before our eyes – like a slideshow recapping our trip – some of the many names and faces of the glorious, vibrant, violent and rambling Old West. These were a few of the characters that had shaped the colorful past. I found post cards of Wild Bill Hickok and Buffalo Bill Cody to send to friends and to add to our own album. On one of these I'd write to Johnny Lewis and the boys, wishing them all well and hoping they had safe flying out of Albuquerque tomorrow. These weather-toughened, sun-soaked cowboys and Indians were the closest thing we'd seen to the originals since we'd been out here. May the Great Spirit of the West, and all their ancestors, watch over them. Our waiter came over to return us to the 21st Century. Our dinners were ready.

We returned to the Ramada Inn and had a beer together as we packed up a couple of boxes that we had scrounged up for our UPS returns. Tomorrow we'd locate a UPS outlet in either Gallup or Grants to send the larger items on ahead of us, to arrive after us; it sure would lighten the load at the airlines. Anything to make the fiasco of air travel, post 9/11, easier.

I carefully folded my chaps and packed them in the bottom of one of the sturdy low boxes, reminiscing of our ride in the bottomlands of Canyon de Chelly. Saddlebags went on top, with the flashlights wedged in around. "Why don't we go ahead and send our hiking boots on, Pete – we won't be needing them for a week. Sneakers would be a lot more comfortable on the flight." We had worn our hikers on the flight west, to lighten our packing, but ensure we had them with us. By the time we'd arrived in Albuquerque, our feet had felt as if they were ensconced in lead.

"Good idea, Ra. And let's send on any of the gifts we can. Also the blankets, okay?"

"Sounds good. In fact, we can pack the blankets around the boots in the second box. I'll wash them when we get home and put 'em on the line. We can put all our wool-weight socks in there, too. Just put the used ones in a plastic bag. But I'm *keeping* the jewelry we bought on me. I don't want there to be a chance of that getting lost."

"Fair enough. That's relatively small and light."

And so it went. We stuffed the two boxes with our larger items and wedged odds and ends in and around them and then I neatly wrote up two contents-lists for each – one to put inside with our names and address and one to keep for our records and insurance purposes. We taped them up tightly and this mission was done. We switched from our beer to a glass of wine, showered and called it a night. Time to snuggle up and read a couple of chapters before shut-eye.

Friday, October 5th

Morning came quickly. This would be our last full day on the road. Today we'd be in the arid Southwest; tomorrow we would fly some 2,000 miles over the diversity of sprawling intercontinental states to the now arid East coast. It still amazed me how that could happen. How long had it taken the pioneers to traverse these untamed lands? First, they had had to build the roads. Before that they'd had to clear the virgin forests and figure out how to cross the mighty rivers. This was only a little over a hundred years ago. And Lordy, oh Lordy, just look at what the pioneer's progress had done to the landscape now… I didn't want to think about what another century might bring.

We turned on CNN as we packed up to leave. News was that a fellow in one of the tabloids had succumbed to air-borne anthrax. It was speculated that he might have picked it up in Georgia, on a recent camping trip. It was pretty eerie, after all of this recent talk of biological and chemical attacks since 9/11. And here was a case of anthrax, out of the blue. My father had used to inoculate his cattle against this disease; he had dreaded it like the plague, and the man was a chemist – he would have reason to know what he feared.

Strange, I thought... *I had just mailed the letters to the kiddos from Bluff on Monday with the pinches of red desert sand from Valley of the Gods in each. They'd be arriving about now. One of the possibilities of this man's exposure was also from the mail – this was too coincidental, too strange for words.*

Pete and I ate breakfast, gathered up our UPS boxes and luggage, gassed up the rental, and ran it through a car wash to wash away the last traces of Monument Valley before we hit the road, heading south on Highway 180 to pick up the lower entrance to the Petrified Forest National Park. Pete had been here in his après-college ramblings over a quarter century ago. He told me of seeing these trees and stumps that were literally millions of years old and turned-to-rock. I visualized forests of stone, their trunks glistening in the desert sun. Imagine my surprise – as we drove through the park and stopped at overlooks – of seeing stumps and logs and ancient pebbles. Although, I have to say, they were most certainly solid rock. When one examined them closely, we could see the growth rings and bark textures beneath what looked to be layers of shellac.

Overlooks with names like Agate House, Long Logs, Giant Logs, Crystal Forest, Jasper Forest and the Agate Bridge led us through the Petrified Forest. I read some of the brochure to Pete as he drove: *"fossils of some of the earliest dinosaurs, plants, fish, and giant reptiles have been found at the park since 1981… Supported by donations, fossil research continues to reveal life in Triassic Period forests of 225 million years ago.*

"… Evidence of early human occupation is readily visible on the landscape. Sites throughout the park tell of human history in the area for more than 10,000 years. We do not know the entire story, but there were separate occupations, a cultural transition from wandering families to settled agricultural villages — pueblos — and trading ties with surrounding villages. Although evidence of these early people fades about 1400, their story remains through their dwellings, pot shards, and petroglyphs.

"In the mid-1800s, U.S. Army mappers and surveyors exploring this area carried stories back East about the remarkable 'Painted Desert and its trees turned to stone.' Next, pioneers, ranchers, and sightseers made their way into the area. After a period of using the wood for souvenirs and numerous commercial ventures, territorial residents recognized that the supply of petrified wood was not endless. In 1906 selected 'forests' were set aside as Petrified Forest National Monument. In 1932, 53,200 more acres of the Painted Desert were purchased and added to the monument. In 1962 the area became Petrified Forest National Park, and in 1970, 50,000 acres within the park were further designated for preservation as wilderness. Research continues to unlock the geological and human stories set aside for present and future generations…"

We continued north up through the park, passing the Blue Mesa and The Tepees pullovers, lost in the vastness of opens spaces through this barren desert country, to go on to Newspaper Rock. We got out, stretched, and took photographs of the multitudes of pictographs and petroglyphs on the huge rock facings. All sorts of primitive insignias were covering the rocks, some much more visible than others, but all of them spiraling back through the centuries. Soft winds caressed our hair and faces as we stood in time. The striated mesitas here were tones of taupes and browns and chocolates, looking as if they had been steeped in teas or petroleum products.

The reaches of the Painted Desert were huge. It started just south of the Kaibab Plateau, which lay northeast of the Grand Canyon and sprawl of the Kaibab National Forest, stretching up to the lower reaches of the Glen Canyon National Recreation Area and Lake Powell, across the Utah border. From there, the Painted Desert swept down across the western reaches of the Navajo rez, and south of the Moenkopi Plateau, below the Hopi Reservation, on to the I-40 Interstate. The striated mounds behind Mexican Hat had, indeed, been part of the Painted Desert.

The Petrified Forest lies within the southeastern end of the Painted Desert, on the southern side of I-40. To 'technically' enter the loop of Painted Desert, Pete and I crossed I-40, going north. Signs read: Lacey Point, Whipple Point, Nizhoni Point, Pintado Point and Chinde Point (Restrooms closed in winter).

The Painted Desert offered panoramic views of desert rolling away from the overlooks in layers of mesas and mesitas softly created by our giant in colors from his pastel selection. Hues of striated colors lay powdered over the lands in the distance, introduced by sweeping strokes of rolling sands and texturized by scruffy sages, rabbitbrush, and hearty grasses interspersed through the lonely lands. There was a feeling of eternity here, as if this land had always looked just like this and would always look just the same. Neither the wear of years, nor wind, rain or sandstorms, or even the weight of mankind, himself, could change the scene before us. Yet in its etched look of eternity lay fragility.

Between Kachina Point and Tawa Points sat the Painted Desert Inn & National Historic Landmark, a beautiful stone building that emerged from the desert sands, blending in beautifully. Beyond this was the Tiponi Point and the entrance (or exit, depending on which way one traveled) station, with the guards asking if you had collected any of the petrified wood in your visit. If so, it was a federal offense, subject to a fine, imprisonment, or both. We pleaded innocent and continued on to the Painted Desert visitor center for bathroom stops, visited the gift shop, found a CD for our travels east today: Karen Therese's *Warrior of the Heart*. We bought a few gifts and lemonades in Petrified Forest motif travel mugs to take home, and then we left to continue our journey.

As we headed out and on towards Navajo, Chambers and Houck, we passed crazy dinosaur statues stalking the edges of the Interstate, remnants of 225 millions ago. A water treatment plant rose high to the left, sporting a roadrunner image. I thought glibly that I would love to hear a song that Mark Knopfler might devise of the old cartoon of Wile E. Coyote and his swift nemesis, that roadrunner. Knopfler, although an Englishman like Elton John, loves our great country. He'd do a fine tongue & cheek rendition, I was sure.

This land was vast and low. Buttes and mesas lay in atmospheric layers off in the distance, as if seen through a mirage. The Santa Fe Railroad continued to parallel our path eastward. Here and there a lone windmill or small oilrig would offer a vertical relief to the horizontal lowlands. A dry arroyo would appear, and as quickly disappear, leaving a jagged wash of sands leading the viewers eye astray and then away from the infinite gray ribbon of road. The sky today was but a tint of days before, rung out and all used up.

And so it went, as the miles west piled up behind us. In Gallup we took a break and drove into the town to find a UPS outlet. It took us a while, but we found it deep into town, with Pete grumping about the time we were wasting. I told him it was a trade-off; we'd be relieved we had done this tomorrow, when our heavy load through the airport was considerably lightened. Even then, we'd have a tremendous amount to pack up tonight, once we got into Albuquerque.

As we left Gallup we noticed that Jim Chee's U.S. Highway 666 would be a straight shot north directly up to Shiprock, and from there only twenty miles, or so, to the Colorado border. If we had just a *little* more time we could add a stopover in Durango, in our Fourth Corner state, and maybe take in the Mesa Verde National Park with Gary and Cynthia, Cori and Gordon. But not on this trip; our sands had run dry. That was just wishful thinking.

So we hit the road again for the last long haul through western Arizona on to Albuquerque. By now it was about 4 PM. We had had a late lunch in Gallup; we would get dinner after we'd settled into our Comfort Inn by the airport. We'd listened to Karen Therese's *Warrior of the Heart*, loving the upbeat title song and others, like "Wohenge," "Peyote Love Song," "Wings of Faith," and "Love Like a River." After we listened to the music twice, we slid in Eric Clapton's *Pilgrim* CD to serenade us through the open desert lands, as we watched dusk gradually settle around us and the afternoon came to a rest. He had written the songs for *Pilgrim* after his young son had tragically died; in this music he had tried to find a reason to carry on. We could relate to this so well with the murders in our past — so tragic, so senseless, so final. These surroundings, and our leaving Arizona without Kokopelli, somehow fit this melancholy mood and heartfelt lyrics.

Pete and I rehashed our trip, remembering, reminiscing, and wondering how little Kokopelli faired in this new place we had begrudgingly left her. As soon as we began this conversation I pretty much wanted to end it. It got us nowhere and served only to drag me down low. I wanted to focus, instead, on all the animals that awaited us back at our small farm in Virginia, and how eager we were to see our teenage trio. Absence certainly made the heart grow fonder. We weren't thinking of the noisiness of adolescents, the bickering of siblings, the loud music of deaf young ears. No, we missed their personalities, their smiles, the gangly bodies eager to see us home, but reluctant to express their emotions in words. Not a spore of moss had grown on us this trip, but all good things must come to an end – and all that – as this was doing now, and *that* was a good thing, because we were homesick. Yes, homesick, plain and simple, especially with the craziness of having traveled post September 11th, with the ensuing chaos of a world like we'd never known, laid out as a crazy carpet before us.

Up ahead we saw that traffic on the Interstate had come to a crawl. It looked like the DC Beltway at rush hour, which was an oxymoron in itself, as not a thing 'rushed' on the Beltway to or from work in Washington, Monday-Friday. Pete gave an audible, massive groan. His forward motion had just come to a grinding halt. His brow furrowed and his body tensed. This was *not* on his itinerary. I had been working on a letter to his folks that would double as a trip journal. I stopped writing and looked up at my usually patient husband. "Pete, it's okay. We've made really good time. Ease up there, buddy, before you bust an artery, or something."

He glanced over at me, tapping the wheel. His adrenaline was cooking; this is the last thing in the world he wanted to be doing. A sarcastic, *"Great,"* was all he could muster.

"Listen, PeterWop, so it's cutting into our time a little bit. Big deal. Think of the people involved in the accident up there. Hopefully no one is seriously hurt, but think of *their* day – it's pretty much shot."

"Yeah, yeah, Doc. I hear you." He tried to take a deep breath, but by now automobiles and Mack trucks flanked us in; we were going all of *may*be 6 mph. It looked like we'd be here for a while. One of those little light bulbs appeared in my mind. I rolled down my passenger-side window and motioned the driver of a light blue minivan beside us. He looked to be Navajo. The man turned to me, a little startled out of his secluded world there in the vehicle, but curious.

"Excuse me, sir, there's an exit a quarter mile, or so, up to the right. If we take that, can we wrap around this traffic and pick up the Interstate further east?" I called to him.

"Sure. Sure you can. In fact I'm going on back in there. If you can cut behind me here and follow us, I'll show you the way." His slow singsong voice was followed by the wave of his hand.

Pete nodded to the man and smiled, putting his blinker on. As traffic crawled on ahead the Honda behind the van eased back to let us in. I waved them a thanks. It took another ten minutes to just get to the exit but, once on, we started making good time again.

I continued writing to Jean and Al, sharing this experience with them, too, as we followed the van deeper and deeper into the winding intermeshing roads. Looking on the map we appeared to be on the Laguna Indian Reservation, driving down through Acoma and an area called "Enchanted Mesa." I guess this man was not Navajo, at all. Now Pete was starting to grump about how far in we were going. Did the guy understand what we were trying to do? Or was he intentionally trying to get us lost? I told him to hush, at least we were moving, and if not exactly paralleling the Interstate, probably we were going in somewhat the right direction. Suddenly the van stopped ahead of us at a small intersection in the road. The gentleman got out and walked to the Camry. Pete rolled down his window and the man leaned down and smiled at us.

"Now I am turning right here," he said carefully and pointed the direction, "but you will take a left. Just stay on the main road. It will wind a little more, but soon you will be back on the Interstate and you should be beyond all of the traffic."

Pete nodded as he listened. I leaned over and thanked the man for his help and his time, and Pete thanked him, as well. We were two grateful travelers, beholding to another's kindness. He just smiled and wished us a safe journey.

We followed the road and soon saw the stretch of lights clustered to our left: a string of white Christmas lights were still entwined around themselves and plugged in, but someone had forgotten to unravel them. To the right, the dark and empty highway yawned and stretched, inviting us aboard. It was now soft, velvety nighttime. Pete shook his head and said, "Thanks. This makes up for all our lollygagging with UPS in Gallup. You did good there, RazzaWop."

I just shook my head at the man, a little exasperated by his lack of imagination and his condescension. "Try talking with people sometime, Pete; they're usually happy to give you a hand, if you ask them nicely. By and large, people are generally pretty decent."

With that, we were back on I-40, the road wide open in the eastbound lane again. We switched CD's to some old Bob Dylan tunes, singing to

"Tangled up in Blue," "Silvio," "Shelter from the Storm," "Jokerman," "Gotta' Serve Somebody," "Lay Lady Lay," and "If Not for You." We were singing the lyrics from "I Shall Be Released"…

"I see my life come shining, from the West down to the East…
Any day now, any day now, I shall be released…"

And soon we saw the landed stars that had fallen to the earth ahead of us. Like a fairytale's volume of gold dust and sapphires, turquoise and rubies, all aglow from within and scattered across the dark desert floor, Albuquerque welcomed our return.

We arrived at our hotel a little after 9PM, checked into the Comfort Inn, poured ourselves Coronas with a fresh squeeze of lime from the cooler, and carried everything into our room, intending to untangle the rest of our luggage, paraphernalia, and collection of gifts and trinkets to repack for tomorrow. Reload, condense, neaten up. We looked at the collection of this night's 'to-dos' and decided we'd have dinner first. The job could wait.

"Pete, except for last night, when we were so tired, we've been eating at fast foods and Mom & Pop restaurants since Taos. Let's dress up in some of these fancy duds we've been hauling all over the place and find a nice restaurant as our last dinner on vacation. Kind of a 'Last Supper' thing, before we return to the real world. Lord only knows when we'll have our *next* date."

Pete looked up from some tee shirts he was folding. He was tired from all the driving; I could see this in his eyes and the drawn look on his face. He could use a good dinner and some downtime before we started into all the packing. "Okay," he answered, "but we can't get too leisurely on this dinner thing, Ra. This isn't a 'dinner and a movie' kind of night, you know. We have a lot to do yet, and we'll need to get up early to return the rental and get to the airport two hours before departure, like they're requesting these days."

I smiled at the Timekeeper. "I understand all that, PeterWop — but let's take a break before diving into all this. We'll find a nice place close by, enjoy a good meal, and come back to this. Sound good?"

"Twist my arm," he returned my smile. "A break sounds better and better. But it's a *com*promise kind of break, just remember."

We donned some of the nicer things we had packed. I had been touting around a black pleated skirt, a pair of low black heels and tights the entire trip, to wear with a black velvet turtleneck. I had worn the outfit once in Santa Fe, and again in Taos, for our dinner out with the cowboys. Then I had felt like a peacock in a chicken coop. Blue jeans – the more faded and worn the better – were the dress for *that* evening. But the cowboys had seemed to love the change of scenery.

By adding some of the new Indian jewelry to this simple and somewhat elegant outfit, I indeed felt all dolled up and ready to go play – even if on borrowed time. Pete put on his dress khakis, trying to smooth the wrinkles out, and wore the one maroon dress shirt and matching tie that he had brought, along with his scuffed penny loafers. We topped off our outfits with fleece jackets and walked into the night to locate our culinary destination.

We found The Yacht Club, a very nice seafood restaurant a few blocks away. We found the entrance, where large aquariums filled with soft aqua lights and exotic fish graced the windows, enticing one to come inside. This would be just the ticket for a little bit of magic in a travel-worn day, on the eve of our departure of this adventurous trip.

We had a lovely evening of fine seafood by candlelight, delivered by a handsome and attentive waiter, there for our every whim. I saw Pete visibly relax as the meal progressed. After coffee and a shared slice of cheesecake the man was regenerated.

We returned to the hotel… *and?*

We returned to our hotel and changed into our nightclothes so that we could pack everything else, except our travel clothes for the next day. I turned on CNN to see if there was an update on the anthrax case. A man named Bob Stevens, who worked for American Media, Inc., had succumbed to the dreaded disease. Reports touched on this, but little was known. Florida was in a flurry of activity, as well as the Center for Disease Control in Atlanta, as they tried to establish its origins.

Additional major news tonight was pending war. The United States was on the verge of pouncing on Afghanistan, in retaliation for the hijack attacks of September 11th. We were in search of the illusive Osama bin Laden and plans were to bust open al'Qaida and the Taliban in that mission. Our military was in place. The grim reality of upcoming warfare lay suspended in the air: a hammock full of apprehension, retaliatory anger, military muscle, and raw determination lay ready to explode itself over the rocky roads of this strange and faraway Middle Eastern land. Until recently, many in America had no idea where Afghanistan lay on the map. Now, thanks to ceaseless media reports, not only were we versed as to *where* it was, we knew of Kabul and Kandahar, Jalalabad and Mazar-e Sharif. This was but the deafening, nerve-wracking, gut-twisting silence before the storm.

America had not seen itself in war in ten years – not since the last Bush administration, in Operation Desert Storm – and that, too, was in the Middle East, saving Kuwait from Iraq's intrusion for oil and power. Once again, although it would never be admitted in polite society, crude was the bottom line. When was the last time America's might went to bat on this scale in Africa over a country's takeover?

This upcoming war in Afghanistan – Operation Enduring Freedom – was not for crude. It was in retaliation for the most horrible affront ever committed on our soil by fanatic men without souls. But their hatred and bloodlust against America, against democracy, and against the Bush politicians, had grown and festered in that war. It spawned the venom that would poison the next decade: an unadulterated, vitriolic, fundamentalist fanaticism that had festered and spread to become the cauldron that would produce the impassioned men who planned their lives around their own deaths, in order to devastate America in broad daylight on national TV. It was an amazingly brilliant and sadistic plan. It was madness, and it was happening. The 'eye for an eye' approach to 'justice' – their jihad against our country – had begun. Were we to begin an overseas version of the Israeli-Palestinian madness?

Pete and I packed and packed, finishing off the last of our wine as we did so. We had our suitcases, camera case, gifts and odds and ends, all standing by the door of the room. We would leave the cooler, with its ice packs, as a nice tip for the maids. Finally, about 1AM, we fell into bed, wrapped in each other's arms, trying to will ourselves to sleep before the alarm sounded – like the buzz from a starting gate – to signal our departure from the warmth of our bed and, ultimately, our vacation. Time to return to reality, as we knew it.

The Camry was safely returned, with no dents in sight (but definitely some red sands deep in the crevices, despite the run through the car wash). We gathered our worldly goods and loaded them in a shuttle for the airport. A kindly black gentleman with a broad, warm face greeted us.

Reality hit us smack between the eyes upon entrance to Sunport. People milled around in long lines like ants on parade, one after the other after the other – first to have one's tickets checked, then to empty our bags of all of their contents so they could be riffled through with magnifying glasses and fine toothed combs. People that were trying to be cheerful about their new job responsibilities now repacked all of our careful packing; we stood aside, pretending this craziness didn't bother us at all. Finally, stamped and approved as good American citizens and not terrorists intent on blowing the plane to smithereens, we had arrived to the 'clean side' of the airport. And we still had forty-five minutes before boarding.

Pete remembered the balloon festival and ran to the windows, looking for the fanciful air-filled flyers. I remembered the Painted Ponies and tried to locate as many as I could, getting a photograph of each for a keepsake of this bittersweet trip, and for Natalie's collection. The "Dream of Flight" bronze welcomed us back with open arms. We felt right at home.

Pete came back to me, as excited as a young boy, exclaiming that he'd located a cluster, come see. We both ran to the windows and watched maybe fifteen balloons rising at varying heights, off in the far distant sky. Colorful, weightless ovals of flowers aimed for heavens heights. Perhaps Johnny and Rocky and the boys were in that bunch. We laughed, feeling a kinship with them now, and – in a whispered prayer – wished them all a safe journey, as so many had wished us. With this we felt a closure upon leaving Albuquerque. With the exception that Kokopelli stayed behind, like an open book not yet completed, our trip was done. We could go home now, back to our everyday lives.

Part III
Return to Reality

"You're not a realist unless you believe in miracles.
Anwar Sadat, former Egyptian president

TWENTY-FOUR

Reality Check/Reality Rethink/ Readying to Return West

"God created memory so we might have roses in December." Italo Svevo

Saturday evening, October 6th

Pete and I arrived at the Charlottesville/Albemarle Airport about 6 PM Saturday night, October 6th. Jean and Allan had arranged to have a car waiting for us there. Al was at home with the kids, all dressed up, looking smart and with somewhere to go, as he was headed to an evening out with the Charlottesville Symphony with Jean, Pete's older brother, Jim, and Jim's good wife, Connie.

Our homecoming reminded me of Dorothy and Toto blowing into the Land of Oz, after the tornado blew through. The airlines had 'lost' our luggage; because of this, I was relieved that Pelli hadn't flown home with us, as I would have been frantic. They assured us we'd have it by 10 PM that night, and yes, indeed, they would bring it to our house.

The farm was a mass of confusion. Jared and Natalie were there, happy to see us in their teenage ways – hovering, not too exuberant, Jared teasing Nattie at any opportunity – looking for what we might have brought them. And 'what we brought them,' of course, was in our wayward luggage. Skye was out that evening with a friend at a concert. Nothing had changed. Al stayed long enough to give us a run-down of activities and let us know that the ceiling to Natalie's room was dripping downstairs, apparently from a leaking toilet or sink upstairs. Trey and Amanda were delirious, vying for our attention, and Whiskey Cat climbed atop the cars, crouching in wait, hoping to be scoffed up and given big loves by either of us. In the confusion and waiting, he lost his balance and slid down the back window of the Taurus, claws screeching as he went. Welcome home…

An eerie event occurred within the school system in the week following our return. Thank God it hadn't hit one week earlier, when the grandparents would have had to handle the madness – this would have been above and beyond the call of duty. I say 'eerie' because this disease had been one of those almost unheard of – in the United States, anyway – since childhood inoculations brought it to bay. In Third World countries it is still prevalent, where vaccinations aren't readily available. Whooping cough emerged, as if out of nowhere, to prey upon unsuspecting students. Before anyone realized what the deep and persistent coughing was all about, the sickness had spread via classrooms, lunchrooms, athletic buses and activities, visits to friends, and the like. Apparently, immunities had worn off.

Parents were contacted that week following our return, if a child had been exposed in any way, to one diagnosed as having the dreaded cough. If so, they were told to stay at home, go into immediate quarantine, and proceed to take a special antibiotic for ten days. We had one teen started on medication, when we got a call about another. Within the course of that first week all three were in quarantine, but I refused to put Natalie on the antibiotic, as her exposure had been on an open soccer field. I had the medicine; if she were to show any symptoms, I would give it to her immediately. She never did. And within three days 'rules' changed. If the child was showing no symptoms and was on the med's they could return to school. All three returned by the beginning of our 2nd week back, with my eye on Natalie for any sign at all of the sickness. She stayed chipper and full of beans, her usual precocious self. Of course, her vaccination was also the freshest.

The local health department, the Center for Disease Control in Atlanta, and the school system were stretched. School administrators, nurses, guidance counselors, and teachers went above and beyond the call of duty, working long hours – intense and trying – to contain the infection. Several neighboring counties had bouts with the cough as well and went through the, now-practiced, quarantine procedures. Although I seriously doubt this strange and frightening incident was 'terrorist induced,' it was an eye-opening situation for all involved, and served as a dry run for any truly serious biological threat. The school board and health agencies did a fine, organized, round-the-clock job on containing the whooping cough. I am quite sure they combined notes to share what they learned in controlling what could have been a statewide epidemic. This experience might be considered one of those 'blessings in disguise,' in getting a jumpstart on more serious threats in the future – natural, or terrorist induced. But, in light of the anthrax letters circulating and the case still unsolved, nerves were stretched tautly and speculation ran rampant.

All this was quite the reintroduction back to our parental responsibilities. I ran ragged that week picking up first one child and then another at school and stressing to them the importance of isolation. Right. Tell a teenager they're cut off from their friends for a week or ten days, and see the reaction you might get… And then I was off to the drugstore – where certain antibiotics were no longer available, due to demand. So we needed to change their prescription – but first, we needed to run a background on allergies, and if this drug would in*deed* work against the whooping cough, as this disease had not been a pharmaceutical contender in years. Yes, that first week back splashed cold water all over the sweet memories of our recent anniversary trip, placing it in a 'dream status' (did it *really* happen, or did we both just simultaneously dream of having this wonderful fantasy vacation?…)

The war in Afghanistan – Operation Enduring Freedom – officially started on Sunday, October 7th, the day after our return to Virginia. And the little desert dog was placed firmly on the back burner, for the time. Only later, after that dust settled and we regrouped with catch-up mail and phone calls, homework, tests, my studio work, work around Pete's schedule, an unexpected funeral, and the aftershocks of our country now at war, was I able to refocus on Kokopelli.

And so it went. One day blended into another like this, full and overflowing, with our farm full of critters to feed twice a day, kids to feed and get off to school, after school pick-ups and activities changing on a daily basis, my catching up in the studio, and Pete's nonstop schedule with Kendrick (although his busy fall travel ceased; the company wisely placed a moratorium on business travel, after the terrorist hijackings, for the safety of their employees).

The anthrax scare hung like a toxic cloud over everyone. People warily circled their mailboxes and opened their daily correspondence wearing latex gloves – some even microwaved their mail. The horses stayed at the vineyards, for the time being, while we waited with bated breath for fall grasses to grow *just a little bit*. As we had received next to no rain while gone, they didn't. It would be another winter of stocking up on any hay we could find. There was nothing left to graze in the fields. Orchard grass (1st cutting only this year, as there had been no 2nd with the drought) and alfalfa would be their daily fare, along with a hot mash of feed in the evenings in the late fall and the winter months.

A few days after homecoming I faced the third anniversary of my mother's death, which had fallen on October 10th, 1998. She had had quintuple bypass surgery at 80 years of age, the year before George's death. She had died just over a year after George's murder — almost exactly a year to date of his Memorial Service. She died at the Augusta Medical Center, at 82 years of age, following a stroke brought on by a blood clot after carotid bypass surgery. After the stroke she had lived long enough — by sheer willpower and strength of spirit, I am convinced — for her family and beloved cousins to gather by her bedside and say goodbye. Although she could no longer talk, Mom realized we were there, I'm sure of it.

The surgery, itself, on her left carotid artery in her neck, was successful. A blood clot following the surgery triggered the stroke. Bambi and Elizabeth had been there with Mom during the operation and had called the family with the tragic news.

The stroke was on a Thursday evening. Pete and I had hurriedly made child- and farm- care arrangements with neighbors, then left for the Shenandoah Valley Friday evening. Bambi and Elizabeth went home to get some rest; Pete and I took over, spending that last night with Mom, rubbing her head, trying to soothe her, feeling her soft, transparent skin and thin, silky white hair. We sadly realized that her age-shrunken and feeble, pale body and useless right side were indicators that there was little fight left in her. Mom's eyes could not focus, try as they might, and she could not talk, though she wanted to. She was trapped inside her own body and frantic; I could see this in the body language she had left. Her mother, too, had died of a stroke, but had spent years suffering the after effects of many smaller ones. This had become my own mother's worst nightmare of old age. It terrified her. I had talked with my mother through that final night in 1998, rubbing her head, massaging her feet, assuring her we would all see this through.

Pete had been dear, taking turns with me, talking to his mother-in-law gently, holding her hand and stroking her head. The two of them had been close over our many years together. Indeed, Mom had thought of my husband as the ultimate Prince Charming. Between the two of us, we did not leave her side until the wee hours of morning. I finally asked if the young male nurse on duty might not give her some morphine to help ease her mind and calm this agitated state, allowing her to rest for incoming family the next day. It was obvious she could not or would not relax to sleep on her own. He did, and we watched Mom finally become calm, her eyes settled down, her body relaxed and she slept peacefully for several hours. Pete and I curled up on hospital chairs close by, trying to do the same.

Looking back, I know my mother willed herself to live to be able to say goodbye to those that mattered most. My brother, John, arrived from Ft. Lauderdale, and Marcy, our youngest sibling, came to her bedside from her home in Chester, Virginia. Pete and I had had to return to the care of our children. Mom died later that afternoon with the two of them beside her – two of her favorite people in all of the world – a look of peace at last on her stroke-stricken face. John and Marcy swear they saw her spirit gently rise from her frail, spent body when she breathed her last breath; they assured us all that she had found peace.

As hard as it is to lose a parent, this transition is much easier to come to terms with – indeed, to understand – than the loss of a loved one through murder. A well-lived life is a gift; old age is but the end of this physical sojourn on earth, and the transitional phase to the hereafter. It was a blessing and a relief to be able to see her transcend her ailing and aching body. We, her family, were relieved that she did not live to suffer the indignities of this stroke – as this would have been her version of hell on earth. Nonetheless, the loss of a parent is devastating, even with all of the intellectual reasoning in the world. Mom's death became another anniversary of the fall to feel coming and to brace myself to bear.

"The comfort of having a friend may be taken away, but not that of having had one." Seneca

As this anniversary settled upon us, after our return, we also received word that my friend, Emily Couric, had weakened tremendously with the return of her cancer. She was at home, surrounded by her immediate family. I had met Emily at a friend's home and studio several years ago. Fred and Beth Nichols – he, an artist, and she, his agent and wife – hosted an introduction party at their gallery one evening, as Emily was running for the Virginia General Assembly. Emily and I talked that evening and simply hit it off. We planned to get together at a later date and have coffee, which we did. Lunch soon followed at Mono Loco's, on the downtown mall in Charlottesville, where we walked from her office, close to the mall. Over the course of the next few years that Emily and I came to know one another, our friendship quietly grew.

She and I would sneak away from our busy lives and take a break for such a special visit. There was always much more to talk about than there was ever time. And then I heard – Charlottesville heard, Virginia heard – of her cancer. Cancer of the pancreas. By this time, Emily had been elected to the Virginia Senate and was doing an outstanding job. She was a smart, bipartisan, respected and capable woman in a good ole' boys world. Her soft voice and carefully chosen words were heard by all. She used to tell me that she prided herself in listening to as many opinions as she could – Democratic, Republican and Independent – before making an informed decision. By doing this, she learned so much about the issues, and volumes about human nature. Emily Couric was a role model for me, a mentor. I do not put many people on a pedestal – I've seen far too many feet of clay – but Emily was one that I freely admired and thoroughly enjoyed and respected: as a woman, a mother, a friend, a fellow citizen – and as an elected official. She held herself to such high standards that she helped breathe life and hope again into my jaded view of politics. This fine lady wore many hats, and she wore all of them well.

It was generally thought that with the respect that Emily held with her constituents and fellow office holders in the Virginia Congress, and with her bipartisan approach to politics, that the sky was the limit. There was talk that she might run as Virginia's first female governor. This was entirely possible. But then came word of her cancer: pancreatic cancer, with practically no chance of a cure, much less remission. The kiss of death. Virginia, collectively, wept.

But dear Emily, with her typical optimism and never-say-die attitude, gamely faced the diagnosis with an upfront: *"Okay, so let's gather all our facts, get the best doctors on board, and fight this thing"* approach. And she did. Her husband, George Beller, a fine cardiac doctor at UVA, knew the crème de la crème in the medical field. For months longer than the medical establishment, statistics, or logic might dictate, Emily gamely gave it all she had. She underwent the rigorous treatments, lost her hair and wore a stylish wig, managed that famous Couric smile throughout the ordeal, and all indications were that she had managed, *some*how, to beat the odds – once again.

When I heard the news of her cancer I wept. For Emily and her family, her sister Katie, who had recently lost her husband to colon cancer, and for all of us in Charlottesville who knew and loved this courageous woman. My heart simply broke for all she stood for – and I prayed alongside thousands in Virginia that a miraculous cure might be found.

I wondered what I could do for her... her church and friends would send food and flowers and cards of good wishes. I thought and thought and thought and then I knew... I would share with my friend my love of music – that that tamed and soothed the savage beasts, what*ever* they might be. I knew she regularly drove to Richmond for her sessions in the Senate. I decided to make her several customized cassettes of favorite, soothing or upbeat music. I thought of musicals, but so many ended in death: *Camelot; Romeo and Juliet; Don Quixote; Phantom of the Opera*... No, I would concentrate on life, instead.

I taped for her *Echoes of the Andes* with the soundtrack from *Medicine Man* – lively, lyrical Peruvian instrumental sounds. I taped *Mozart at the Movies* and *Strauss Waltzes*. I made a mix of Rock n' Roll from the 60s era – our era – and taped a medley of *Enya*, to soothe or caress a wounded spirit with her gorgeous haunting Celtic voice overlays. I made 5 or 6 cassettes, wrote on the covers the contents, wrapped them up in beautiful paper, and sent them to my friend with a cheerful card of support. Emily called soon after receiving the collection of tapes, telling me how touched she had been and how much she was enjoying listening to them in transit. She suggested lunch again. We set up a date at Hamilton's, on the downtown mall, in June of 2001.

Emily arrived even later than I had, a lady after my own heart, on a busy version of Navajo time. She had lost the wig, and – her treatments behind her and promise of remission before her – was sporting a short and stylish cut of her own new growth. She looked so vulnerable and frail, but had a precious pixie quality to her iron-like fortitude. I was so relieved and happy to see her, I gave her a big bear hug, trying not to hurt her in my exuberance. Each visit now was precious, a blessing; she was a walking testament to the gift of life.

We talked nonstop for the hour and a half that her secretary had allotted her for this lunch break. Emily ordered a carefully crafted lunch of the food that she could easily digest on her specialized diet, thanking the waitress for going that extra mile, and apologizing for any inconvenience. She told me of the medical procedures that she had undergone and how hopeful the prognosis looked. I told Emily of our upcoming anniversary trip, of our endless plans and revisions, how excited we were, and she asked that we have lunch upon return – she wanted to hear all about it.

Only there was no lunch upon return. At a Basha market in some remote location between Chinle and the Grand Canyon – as Pete and I returned for our futile reclaiming of Kokopelli – we saw a tabloid headline: **Katie Couric Sits by Her Sisters Deathbed**, or some such blasphemous news. One never knows what to believe with a tabloid. But this one proved to be true.

Upon homecoming, we learned that Emily's cancer had indeed taken a turn for the worse. The cancer was back with a vengeance. Amidst the whooping cough scare and slew of domestic catch-up, I read and heard this in the local news. Her family had gathered – her devoted husband, her brother and sisters and loving sons – she was in a near comatose state. There was nothing anyone could do now but wait. And so we did. I did not even try to be in touch with her then. I heard that she was so weak and spent; this was strictly family time. Instead, I paced the floors and sent prayers of peace for Emily, for her family, and for a gentle passing. My precious friend died on October 18th, 2001 – 3 years and 8 days after the death of my mother, and 4 years after George's murder.

A service was held for her at St. Paul's Memorial Church, across from the University of Virginia's Rotunda. The church and Parish Hall overflowed with her family and friends, loyal constituents and members of the Virginia Congress. Pete and I arrived early enough to sit in the Parish Hall, where we watched a screening of the services in the main church, officiated by the Reverend Wayne Arnason. On the 1st page of the Memorial program was Emily's beaming face, the columns of the Virginia Assembly, in Richmond, behind her. Mary Chapin Carpenter, a Charlottesville resident and friend of Emily's, somehow sang "Morning has Broken" and later, Jackson Browne's "Late for your Life." The family spoke with courage and shared wonderful memories: Clara Couric Batchelor, one of Emily's sisters, and Katie Couric – the famous one – spoke, along with her brother, John Couric, who made us laugh with memories from a brother's perspective. And her beloved son's, for whom she should be tremendously proud – and for whom she was, I know from our talks – Raymond and Jeff Wadlow — spoke. They told us of their mother, of her lessons and her convictions, of her bravery and her triumphs and her goofs. They spoke with awe and the deepest of love, a reciprocal gift that will forever sustain them in this continual testing of our life on earth. Her voice will be forever in their ears, a personal Emily Cricket's of conscience thought. God Bless this fine and decent family, one and all.

I wept through most of this service, *try*ing to understand how it was that such a fine person, again like George, be swept away from us all so early. She was only in her early 50s — George's age. I came to think, over time, that God simply needed another good angel by his side, this one a diplomat with political experience. But that day in October, the condensed month of such death, this was no consolation. I was raw, cut to the quick in pain and denial. Pete sat beside me, tearless and brave, handing me tissues and holding my hand once again, an anchor in a storm-swept sea.

Emily's Memorial service closed with all of us singing — or trying to sing through tear choked voices — "Amazing Grace":

"Amazing grace! How sweet the sound
that saved a wretch like me!
I once was lost, but now am found;
was blind, but now I see.

"Twas grace that taught my heart to fear,
and grace my fears relieved;
how precious did that grace appear
the hour I first believed...
The Lord has promised good to me,
His word my hope secures;
He will my shield and portion be,
as long as life endures.

Through many dangers, toils, and snares,
I have already come;
'tis grace hath brought me safe thus far,
and grace will lead me home.

When we've been there ten thousand years,
bright shining as the sun,
we've no less days to sing God's praise
than when we first begun."

After Reverend Arnason read his closing words, together we all read **The Prayer of St. Francis –**

"Lord, make me an instrument of your peace,
Where there is hatred, let me sow love;
… where there is injury, pardon;
… where there is doubt, faith;
… where there is despair, hope;
… where there is sadness, joy;
O Divine Master, grant that I may not so much seek
… to be consoled as to console;
… to be understood as to understand;
… to be loved as to love;
For it is in giving that we receive;
… it is in pardoning that we are pardoned;
… and it is in dying that we are born to eternal life."

We returned home to our chock full lives, our wonderful family and our overflowing Cornucopia, and we continued living after Emily's death. We had planted butterfly bushes when George and Mom had died, in their honor. Now I ordered a rare blue wisteria, to keep potted and alive in this drought, to plant when our arbor was ready in our back yard. I would plant this in Emily's memory, and another, a lavender one, on the opposing pillar. Together they could grow and intertwine – and I would look up from our arbor upon these intertwined branches and flowers with amusement and pretend one plant was a Republican and the other a Democrat, and somehow the two had found common ground – in deference to Emily's ability to having done so, so often.

336

We continued hearing of the war in Afghanistan and of our hunting down the Taliban; we listened to updated news about the anthrax letters that had been sent to Democratic Senator's Tom Dashle and Patrick Leahy.

And in the midst of so much death, one must gravitate to the goodness in life, to the living, or go over the edge to bleakness and despair. In the midst of this gray, I would think of Kokopelli again. A lone starving puppy in the middle of this high desert symbolized life. That golden ray of Hope. Meaning. Lakota's beautiful spirit renewed: A new beginning in the fall of life, where of late it had just symbolized so many ends.

Reality Rethink

October drifted on by, a beautiful month, except for the drought. Dry forests had us all praying for moisture from any source (i.e. God, please bring us a hurricane…) to decrease the fire potential. We were so busy catching up with our lives, and recovering from the deaths, keeping up with the kiddos schedules and my early Christmas commissions in the studio, there was little time to think of Dingo/Kokopelli. But then I would catch myself looking out the studio bay window, drifting in thought, and suddenly there she would 'be,' romping around the backyard with big old Trey. I blinked my eyes. No, Trey was there, alone. Another time I looked out, daydreaming, off-guard, and I'd 'see' Trey and Natalie cavorting through the yard, Kokopelli jumping up and around them in joy. I'd shake my head to clear the vision and get back to work. But the vision stayed in my mind while I worked. I would try to concentrate and get on with our lives.

No good. Another day, I would be busily working away in the studio and glance down, where Lakota used to lay on hot days while I painted, and there was Pelli, laying there quietly watching me, curled up on his rug. *What* was going on? Was I going *nuts*? Maybe … but the feeling that she was destined to be at our farm, living this full life of ours, was getting stronger and stronger. My feeling early on that Lakota had been reincarnated and that we were meant to have found that particular puppy under the shade of that sagebrush out west grew.

The clincher came as I drove down Rt. 29 to Charlottesville in late October, minding my business and listening to Margo Timmins, of the *Cowboy Junkies*, sing "2000 Years." I glanced over and started. There again was Kokopelli, curled up and riding in the car beside me, going where

I was going. She looked up at me as if asking, "Well, what have you decided to do?" I shook my head. *Maybe this is crazy*, I muttered to myself, *but daggonit — it sure seems like you're to be with us. Maybe this isn't over at all?...* She looked up, her pert young face intent on mine, those golden brown eyes interested in what I was saying. After all, it did have to do with her future.

The rest of the way into town, and throughout that day, my thoughts changed to not *if* but *how* could I rewrite that fateful day that left her in Ricardo's hands, when he had insisted on not returning her to us. The past few weeks whirlwind return, the whooping cough 'crisis,' then confronting the constant responsibilities and decisions to be made, facing the memory of Mom's life and the reality of Emily's death, reading about the war raging in Afghanistan and seeing the death and uncertainty there, as we searched for bin Laden and the Taliban, had somehow emerged into a gradual metamorphosis from 'acceptance of 'Kokopelli's fate' to the slowly emerging knowledge that I did not *have* to settle with this and accept it as unchangeable. We had found that pup there for a reason. She, indeed, had symbolized renewed Hope.

Over those last few days, as these visions of Kokopelli being there on the farm with us became more real, I grew more and more restless. I had a hard time concentrating on *anything*. I went through the motions, but my mind was in turmoil, subconsciously putting in the data to process, then spitting out fragments of 'what-ifs.' These became tangible possibilities. A game plan was in the process... I began to become more and more focused — my mind solidly made up. Indecision and uncertainty were replaced with a new conviction to change fate.

This became a quiet feeling of empowerment. I did not *have* to 'live with this home' we had so quickly found for her and, as quickly, found unsuitable. I did not *have* to 'live with' this man's going back on his word. I would take the fate of the desert pup into my own hands, once again, and shape it anew. As the young lady had said, on the rim of the Grand Canyon our first full day with Dingo, she thought this puppy was to become a Virginian. Well, I had come to think so, too, and now planned to make that happen. I would go *back* to Arizona for my puppy. I came home the day of 'seeing' Kokopelli on the seat beside me and shared with Pete the good news.

Pete had told me, exasperated, "Laura, you are certifiably insane! Why would you go *back* to Arizona for a stray puppy, when you could adopt *ten* dogs at a shelter here for what this will cost!" His voice rose in disbelief as he spoke.

I had countered, "If we'd just kept her with us, originally, and taken her to Canyon de Chelly, this never would have happened. Entrusting her to Ricardo – believing both of you *men* – was the problem. Now I'll have to undo it, myself. Lakota – I mean Kokopelli – is out there waiting for me, and I am going back to get him. Her." I corrected myself.

He had shaken his head incredulously. He had long thought this to be just an interesting blip on our anniversary trip. But then he had come around that evening and realized how dead serious I was about returning for her. He'd lived with me long enough to know my convictions, so his head shaking became planning, instead. We looked at the calendar and decided that Sunday, November 11th, would be poetic and prophetic as a return date. I would stay a week, to allow enough time to retrieve the puppy and to visit Santa Fe and Taos again – if time allowed – on the back end.

Readying to Return West

Days slipped on by. The first few weeks of unquiet, unacceptable acceptance had slowly, gradually, hardened into a quiet and steely resolve. My game plan fell into place with my calling the law in Coconino County, explaining to them what had happened and enlisting a very understanding man named Deputy Dick – I kid you not – to help reclaim our dog.

I then called the Red Feather Lodge, where we had stayed in Tusayan Village, and talked with Marcos and Scott. Scott was there when we checked out, after we had entrusted Dingo to Ricardo; he had remembered the babysitting agreement and how distraught I had been, despite it. Marcos remembered Ricardo going back on his word, when we had come back to the Canyon to retrieve her; he volunteered to help locate Ricardo; he would find out just where he lived and the exact days he worked. Dates had been chosen, the airline called, and these dates were booked on the last of our frequent-flyer mileage. The plans for my return to rescue this puppy from her trailer home imprisonment, by a man who left her alone for 10-12 hours at a time at least 5 days a week, now were pretty much written in stone.

Before returning west for Kokopelli, I had been reading Robert Ludlum's novel, *The Bourne Identity*. I had read it what now seems centuries ago, but the story is so fascinating, it was an excellent reread. Full of espionage, danger, intrigue, subterfuge, and deep covert operations – just like the one upon which I was about to embark. Although I felt empowered by such reading as makes one think they can melt into new environs, blend, establish their mission and accomplish 'it' with as little commotion raised as possible, in all actuality, in Ludlum's world, I would be but a simple sacrificial lamb: snuffed out in Chapter 1. *Who was I kidding?* But then something still *has* to be given to a mother of three teenagers, at any given time. This job calls for mental prowess, at all times, and nerves of steel. One will have unforeseen verbal combat explode in one's face in the course of a seemingly normal conversation, and still must keep one's wits about them.

The job requires the leader of this pack of ravenous beasts to forage for vast quantities of food that may be consumed night or day (mostly night, often after midnight, like wolves). Such a job as parenting a teenager also requires one to master X-ray vision that will cut through the layers of make-up, blemish plasters, protruding facial rings and neon hairstyles to see to the soul of the youth beneath the surface, fighting to find his or her way clear.

This job also requires the ability to balance on a high wire a rapidly shifting mix of friendship, understanding, respect and discipline, enough to convince the typical skeptical adolescent that their role-model knows something about which they speak. And such an all-encompassing task as parenting a young person, about to emerge from their chrysalis into the expansive world of the adult, requires tactics in maneuverability. Yes. The raw ability of balance, the sheer physical agility that allows a mother, with an armload of clean clothes, to wade hip-deep through the jungle of the typical teen's den, through unseen and unforeseen chaos, to make the drop. All the while carefully watching her flank for burning candles, unattended, incense wafting through the air that actually might be a cover for – dare I say it? – *cigarette* smoke?! And for tiny slips of papers encoded in numbers of potentially dangerous influences…

Seriously, this is a jungle as dangerous as any Jason Bourne has traipsed, and now it hits me. Right between the eyes. I could probably make it through Chapter 2. I was ready to go west and bring my puppy home.

Part IV
"Going Back In"

"If you think you're too small to have an impact,
try going to bed with a mosquito."
Anita Roddick, Founder of The Body Shop

TWENTY-FIVE

Return for Kokopelli/Laying the Groundwork/Veteran's Day

"Do not go where the path may lead – go instead where there is no path and leave a trail." Ralph Waldo Emerson

Kris Kristofferson long ago wrote a song called "Sunday Morning Coming Down." This could be said of the Sunday morning I left for the Charlottesville/Albemarle Airport with Pete as my chauffeur, in the 'wee, wee hours' of dawn, as Bruce Springsteen likes to say. We arrived in the dark, found a place to park down in the lot, as one could no longer be dropped with their luggage, curbside. Precautions were still very much in place for any 'evil doings' – so we lugged my luggage through the lot, up the elevator, and into the airport, braced for the inevitable frisk and search. We were not disappointed. Discreetly told by one of the attendants en route, frequent-flyers were red-flagged in the computer, es-*pecially* if the name was different from the person that had accumulated the mileage. This made good sense, so I tried to be a good sport.

I undid my gray photography vest, full of metal zippers, and put it on the conveyor belt, then turned to Pete to say goodbye. I was still sleepy, trying hard to put up a brave front for my husband, and trying to maintain a sense of humor about all these search tactics before dawn. I knew, like most of us flying now, not only were we, by and large, not terrorists, but place one in our midst and we would storm and seize them, as was later done with Richard Reid – the would-be "Shoe Bomber" – in his airline flight from Paris, the following month, at Christmas. In trying to light the fuse in the tip of his shoe (*how the hell did this man pass through surveillance,* anyway?!!) he was besieged by two heroic flight attendants

– Hermis Moutardier and Cristina Jones, who was bitten severely on her hand by this monster – and several passengers. In a twist that normally would have been funny, if it weren't so deadly serious, bottles of Evian water were poured over Reid to douse the fire he might have started in his explosive-rigged shoe. I read that one of the passengers was a doctor who sedated the man with Valium, and another a prominent sports figure, a *big* guy, who sat behind this varmint, hanging on to his ponytail throughout the flight. It gave Americans a sense of empowerment, of championing a great cause – something we are very good at doing. It was a nerve-wracking flight for this courageous crew and their passengers, but they rallied together and safely landed American Airlines Flight 63 in Boston, instead of the intended destination of Miami. The terrorist was so bound and gagged with duct tape by those on the plane that the incoming FBI spent some time cutting him loose just to arrest the man.

Only I wasn't thinking of this particular event, as it hadn't yet happened. I was just thinking: *give us the chance to apprehend any of you bastards, thwart your cause – we're just looking for the opportunity. But how does one translate all these brief and transient thoughts to the individuals, whose job it is at these post 9/11 moments, to distrust us all? So smile, joke a little, be friendly – go with it, kiddo – get to the 'clean' side of the airport and don't look back*, I told myself, as my suitcases and camera case were opened, contents unpacked and thoroughly inspected, my vest rummaged through, pocket by pocket. A rounded-tip fingernail file was removed from the vest and placed in the suitcase, with a stern reprimand. *Oh yeah. This was certainly a most dangerous item.*

Pete must have by now realized I was dead serious about this return mission. He held me closely to him and whispered: "Good luck, Laura. Be safe. Be*have*. I love you, you crazy free spirit, but I *still* don't believe you're going!"

I looked up at him with a sleepy smile, and told him, "Yeah, I'm a little hazy on that, too, but I've got the ticket here in hand, and I'm packed, so I may as well follow through. It's just a week." And then, after a real kiss, I kissed his cheek with the weekend's stubble and breathed in his natural scent and closed my eyes. It was real – I was headed out, and it was time to leave. A huge pang of homesickness swept over me like a cold wave in the face. I braced against it. Time to square up the shoulders and go face the great unknown. A sweet silly puppy with multiple names awaited rescue and this was the plane to take me to Cincinnati, the first step of those 2,000 miles… "Auf Wiedersehen, PeterWop, Iche liebe dich. And thank you, again, for your support in this mission," I whispered to him and looked up into his warm chocolate eyes. With that, we gave one another a last big hug and I turned to walk on through the metal detector to the other side.

As my suitcases were repacked – funny how things don't fit as snuggly the 2nd time 'round – and reclosed, my vest rezipped around me, camera case closed up, San Diego safari hat slung back over my head to ride on my shoulders, and my fuzzy bone pillow under my arm, I turned around to wave one last farewell to Pete. He stood there in his jeans and maroon chamois shirt, a mixture of pride, doubt, and apprehension on his face. I turned confidently and headed up the escalator with my camera case and carry-on bag, hat, and pillow – and a security woman promptly stopped me. Okay, short trip. "Lady, you're on Delta Airlines, and that's not upstairs – that's behind you, down below." *Well, hells bells first thing in the morning, I didn't know there* was a *'down below'!* I smiled at her sheepishly, came down the other escalator, grinned over at Pete, smiling reassurances at him and waving again – like I knew what was going on – and headed down to the Delta waiting area. There it was; I saw it now. It was just too early in the morning to think for us night owls.

And Pete stood there, shaking his head, probably wondering: *"How in the hell is she going to make it through three more airports, and drive through two huge states – with her sense of direction, no less – and get this dog, if she can't even find her plane?"* The looks on his face changed like clouds before an incoming front: now apprehension and worry replaced that look of pride. *"I hope she knows what the hell she's doing – God, be with her, please…"* I could hear him thinking it, as I disappeared.

When I arrived at the Delta waiting area and sat down, rearranging all my paraphernalia beside me, I breathed in deeply and planned to relax. That lasted about 3½ minutes. Someone over the loudspeaker announced: "We need to do a random check of the carry-on bags of the following people…" Of the three, my name was included. Oh boy, I got to get frisked and searched all over again! My sense of humor instantly evaporated, and I marched over to their tables, unloaded my stuff before them, and told them I hoped they were having a very good time making a lot of people miserable the very first thing in the morning. The lady, looking like female Gestapo, looked up at my angry face and said: "And a good morning to you, too." *Humph.*

Upon leaving Charlottesville, headed for Cincinnati, I thought again of Cat Stevens' song, "Morning Has Broken," as I watched the darkness of deep dawn give way to the awakening day. I rested my head against the cool window, the bone pillow supporting my neck. The light out the window of the small plane was magical. The horizon was soft, there way above the lower cloud mass, and brilliant, an odd mix of intense warms, as the sun awoke in the lower sky. The cool blue cloud layers stretched before me, a soft pale blue sea of eternity. The endless sky above was a soft neutral gray, leaving just the prism spectrum of intense, yet soft-edged, pastel lemon, apricot and a lively shrimpish tone, blending into the cumulus clouds, glowing and separating magnificently the upper and lower skies. I thought this a preview of what to expect in Heaven. The sight of this spectral wonderment of nature made the intense security checks, the frisking and repeated bag searches, bearable. It seemed another 'sign': Hope: a promise that this would all be fine, that I was right on course. I thought of a line from Emily Dickinson that I had seen on a greeting card: *"Hope is a thing with feathers that perches in the soul/ and sings the tune without the words/ and never stops at all."* I had to believe it; what else was there?

The sun was ready to burst through this pastel skyscape and reign supreme, claiming another day her own. 7AM in the infinite skies, in the middle of nowhere... *and what awaits this day?* I wondered. I thought of St. Jude, the Patron Saint of Lost Causes, and decided to think of something else. I thought of the Roman god, Janus – the son of Apollo – and his two faces that looked in opposite directions. The god of gateways and doorways: beginnings and ends. Janus, the god of past, present, and future – so apt for this short period of the last several months – his opposing faces might symbolize for me either success or failure in my mission to retrieve that which was not returned: our puppy. The month of January was named after Janus; January 1st is symbolic as celebrating a new beginning, and looking nostalgically over the year gone before. So I was a couple of months early. The point of this trip was to ensure the safe delivery of Kokopelli into our loving home, thus ensuring that we could look back, and have good reason to celebrate.

I was just planning ahead.

During the flight from Cincinnati to Atlanta, a flight attendant inquired about my attire. In fact, two of them were asking me about the trip, as I hiked to the back of the plane for a pit stop. A young brunette, and a little older woman, with short, blond hair, were sitting in the rear of the

727, taking a break. The photo vest and safari hat had them thinking I was a photojournalist, or some such. We started talking and before we knew it I was telling both the ladies the whole story, up until this return. I even confided my "Plans A & B." Plan A, in working with the law and cooperating completely; Plan B, in wearing dark clothes and doing whatever it took. They were laughing and supportive, downright cheering squads, remarking on my making the trip back solo, and how brave this was, all for a stray puppy, how truly lucky she was, etc. In all the chaos of the trip, I hate to admit that I don't remember these kind ladies names, so I'll call them Betty and Paige, for two of my friends at home, also supportive of this adventure. Betty and Paige had me promise them to leave word of whether I was successful or not with the flight attendants on duty the Monday of my return, if they weren't working. They were dying to find out how the story ended – and if, indeed, I would get my puppy back. I told them that I was kind of curious about that, myself. Time would soon tell.

During the long flights back across the country I continued planning how to go about the next couple of days, as I would head from halfway across northern New Mexico into the depths of northern Arizona. I used the time to continue in my journal, as well. I wrote long pages of free associations of thought and unlocked the door of the subconscious, letting these images – suppressed by the constant needs and responsibilities of our crazy daily lives at home – pour out and roam the pages, at will. The canvas of blank pages and unchained consciousness prompted my writing to flow like wine into a crystal decanter, catching pinpoints of refracted light: highlights of reflected thoughts.

Laying the Groundwork

Delta Flight #1125 from Cincinnati to Atlanta was ready to land in Albuquerque while I wrote on this solo return west, on this mission of mercy, or whatever it was. Call it Love; call it Principle; call it Insane. It has been called all of these – and more. I planned to rent a generic-looking vehicle, leave Albuquerque in the afternoon and head for Gallup for supplies at a Wal-Mart: a pet carrier, other items Pelli would need, and a pillow for my neck. Sometimes a hotel has a comfortable one, sometimes not, but it makes all the difference to a good nights sleep. And sleep would be important for a successful coup. Ludlum swears by it. By evening I planned to be at least in Holbrook, midway back to the Grand Canyon, and back to Kokopelli. And "If the Lord is willing and the creek don't rise" – and I don't end up in jail – I'm bringing this puppy home.

And so, my friends, the next phase of this adventure begins. It was sunny in Albuquerque, cool and promising. We landed at 12:39 PM Mountain Standard Time. A porter helped me hoist my luggage to the 2nd level of the Albuquerque International Airport, where I had a hearty lunch in a Southwestern restaurant, buying time so that my rental car for the week could be returned later the next Sunday afternoon, enabling me to stay in Santa Fe even longer – providing the mission went well.

I took the shuttle from Sunport over to National Rental Car to choose my wheels for the adventure and ended up getting an 8-day rental, so the lunch 'layover' had been unnecessary, but the lunch had been good. On the flight out there had been time to think about my 'shopping list' for the appropriate rental car. A tall, heavy-set fellow with light brown hair, glasses, and a sun-tanned face under a ball cap walked with me to the fleet of cars. "Daryl" was the name on the badge on his blue shirt. "What sort of car are you looking for?" he inquired. "Small, mid-sized, a larger model?"

"Oh, probably a mid-sized sedan, something that will not look too touristy. I want it to blend. I'm looking for a gray or sand-colored vehicle with good gas mileage, a drivers-side-only airbag, but none on the passenger side. And I'd *love* to have one of those models with a tape/CD player combo. I brought both out with me. I'm a music junkie."

"Oh. Okay. No specifics then, I see." He laughed. "That's a lot of specifications for a single driver. Why don't you want a passenger-side airbag? Usually that's requested."

I looked the man over carefully. Pete kept telling me to be secretive about my mission – not to keep telling people the story. But I found it easy to share; usually people were very interested and very much on the puppy's and my side. They wanted to see her rescued. So I told Daryl why I was there and what my mission was, including Plans A & B. He bristled. "Well, all I can say is, lady, I'll be happy to help you in any way I can. We'll search the lot for the right car for you. I know how it feels to have your dog stolen. Just a few months ago someone stole my prize German shepherd right out of my home. I love that dog and was able to follow the trail through friends and people who I *thought* were my friends. I found him only recently – he'd been nearly starved, the bastards. I found out somebody had been using him solely for breeding purposes. I took the bastards to court – and had my dog neutered. I'm *still* hopping mad at what some people will do! So, yes, lady, I'll help you find your car, and I hope to God you find your puppy. Ask for me when you come back, okay? I'd like to see her."

I smiled at him and thanked him. I don't know why Pete kept telling me to "rein it in." People were happy to help. We walked around the lot, looking for nondescript sedans. No reds or bright blues for me — and the black ones were too damned hot, especially if and when I had a dog in the car. We checked the sound-systems, as well; Daryl was a downright Saint. In roughly forty-five minutes we were looking closely at a Malibu sedan, sand-colored to blend into the desert landscape. It had a drivers-side only airbag, for some reason, but only a CD player, no tape deck. The tags were Nevada; I took this as a 'sign' — I chose it in honor of Nevada Barr's mysteries and my favorite feisty, diminutive ranger, Anna Pigeon. I also thought glibly that if I had to resort to 'Plan B' and flee the state of Arizona with my pup, why the law might think, if they only got a glimpse of my tags, that I had gone the other way and not to New Mexico, at all. This worked for me. Daryl helped me load up my collection of suitcases, camera bag and loose ends. Suddenly I groaned. Something was missing.

"What's wrong?" he asked. "You change your mind?"

"What? Oh, no. Not that. No, I can't find my fleece jacket — the one I was wearing on the plane…" My mind flew back several hours. "Damnit, the one I was wearing on the plane, and put into the overhead compartment. I must have overlooked it in getting off. Double, double dastardly *damn!!*" I exclaimed under my breath. I'd have to backtrack now to the airport and track it down. "More fun," as Jean, Pete's dear mother, likes to say. "I wasn't paying much attention on the shuttle coming over here, Daryl — can you give me the quickest directions back, please?"

"Sure. It's easy…" He told me, and then how I'd find my way from there to the Interstate to finally head west. Pete would be bonkers by now if he were with me, with all these delays. Hell, he'd probably *be* in Arizona by now.

I got into my little Malibu and checked the seats out. Comfortable. Nice lumbar support. Good. There'd be an awful lot of miles ahead. Daryl showed me the controls: wipers, lights, hazard lights, stereo specifics — all the important stuff. I pulled out the map I had copied, enlarged, and spliced together back home of both states with the Interstate and key towns and cities highlighted and then I'd covered it in clear contact paper. Daryl whistled. "Organized lady!"

"Not if you knew me. No, more like a determined one — or, as my sister, Mary, and I say: a 'dē-ter-mine-did' one. It's all in where you place the accent. I want to be able to glance at this thing, get my bearings, and not be unfolding and squinting at two different state maps."

"Impressive. You can be my navigator anytime."

"Funny, that's what my husband always says. And with *my* sense of direction, that's a joke – we both get a charge out of the idea. Nope, *this* trip I'm at the wheel." I grinned up at him. "Daryl, thanks for your help and your patience with car shopping. Wish me luck."

"Hell, may I call you Laura? I'll wish you more than luck, lady. You've got gumption. You go give that son of a bitch a swift kick in the balls for me." Immediately he grimaced. "Sorry," he apologized, "I'm still smarting from anger over my own dog."

"Listen, Daryl, I understand. Believe me, I've had some of the same thoughts. I'll look you up when we get back, okay?"

"You got it. You rock, girl!" He called after me as I eased over those lethal-looking teeth that stick up out of the exit of the rental lot, found my way back to Sunport, paid dearly for a half an hour of parking, raced in, found my maroon fleece jacket with the "Hoop Dancer" Indian pin on it that Pete and I had found in Santa Fe two months earlier. Delta personnel were holding it for me. I thanked them all heartily and raced back to the car. Time to get *in* the Malibu, get *on* the Interstate, and make tracks for Arizona. It was now about four in the afternoon – and I hadn't even left Albuquerque.

The small desert towns to the side of I-40 rushed past as I tested the little car on the Interstate. 85 mph was a piece of cake. Good. Now cool it, kid. The Malibu handled well and the sound-system was great. I thought about the sand-colored car, with its neat black trim. It had all the markings of Costner's buckskin, "Cisco," from *Dances with Wolves*. That's what I would dub this little car for this trip: "Cisco." There, it now had a name.

Sarah McLachlan's *Fumbling Towards Ecstasy* played. *If I could actually sing, I'd like a voice like hers,* I thought, *or maybe Margo Timmins, from* Cowboy Junkies. *Or Kathy Mattea's…or perhaps K. D. Lang's vocals – what a powerhouse!* I continued my musings. *And then there is Enya. Daggone, what a talent* she *is! Or maybe Sarah Brightman's glorious soprano… Or a voice like Laura Light, my singer/songwriter friend at home, such a sweet, clear alto…* These fragments of thought raced in and out of my mind, like the haunting monoliths rising from the barren desert. I took a deep breath, trying hard to come back to the here and now, to realize I was really back in the Southwest, this land I was so growing to love. *It felt so comfortable, another home somewhere in my soul from another time and place. Perhaps I, too, had been reincarnated. Perhaps I* really *did have Indian blood pulsing through my Caucasian veins. It had always felt like it. And wouldn't that be something…*

As I got closer to Grants, my thoughts shifted to the war going on in Afghanistan, of how America had been in "Operation Enduring Freedom" for just over a month now, starting the Sunday of our return to our family and farm. *The military was tracking down the Taliban, searching under rocks and in caves for the illusive Osama bin Laden and his key operatives, Khalid Shaikh Mohammed, Ramzi Binalshibh, Mohammed Atef, Ali Abdul Aziz Ali... all those names that rolled or tripped all over the tongue... Despite our big guns and impressive technological equipment, Afghanistan was a rugged country of mountains, caves, and hiding places that defied description. This, of course, was all to the advantage of those trying to hide and escape America's wrath. This knowledge of the land and the language barrier were strong suites for al'Qaida and the Taliban. Few Americans spoke the Afghani tongue. It'd be a tough war. I thought then, okay, if they can have a code name, then so can I for my covert attempt to relocate and free my little desert pup. She was like a prisoner, just like the mixed group of young Christian missionaries being held hostage by the Taliban.*

"Operation Enduring Freedom..." Hmmm... How about "Operation Desert Pup's Enduring Freedom?" That had a certain ring to it. And I didn't have to go through any committee. I could cut straight to the chase. Okay, I shifted in the seat and turned up Sarah's "Good Enough." *My mission now had a covert name. Cool. It'd be "ODPEF," for short.*

The afternoon deepened. Grants was getting closer now. Clouds sat low and brilliant over the flat desert floor, illuminating the buttes magnificently. I just couldn't get over how haunting this land is for the starkness of it. *What is it about this place that calls to the soul? It has the same magnetism for me as the sea. But is hasn't been the sea for millions of years. What is it? This land had so many secrets to tell and she was in no hurry to divulge a one.*

I thought of the date. *November 11th. Two months, to the day, since America lost her sense of being isolated and protected from the 'restless forces of the outside world...' Two months since our anniversary. Good grief, so much had happened in this short span of time. Our 25th Anniversary. A quarter of a century. 'Celebrating' it from here on in would certainly be bittersweet. Our joy would be tempered in prayer for too many good people, both living and dead, plunged into that horrendous day of infamy.*

We were at war. It had been ten years since "Operation Desert Storm" – our war with Iraq over Kuwait – ironically with Bush, Sr. at the helm. History seemed to be repeating itself. My thoughts shifted. Tomorrow will be the 12th of November, Veteran's Day. Again in the midst of war, I wondered on a daily basis how my young nephew, Will, fared on the USS Peterson in the midst of the Mediterranean Sea – and how those stalwart young men we had seen on our original flight from Atlanta to Dallas/Ft.Worth two months ago might be faring. I said a quiet prayer for all of them. They, their families, perhaps some of them had young wives, left at home. Young children. And, of course, there were plenty of courageous young women who would be leaving their own loved ones and families behind for this war. These (hopefully) soon to be veterans were the fine young people to be celebrated tomorrow, both the living and the dead, right beside the heroic veterans of other wars past. So many people, so much unrest, so much of it based on religious differences. Might not we focus, instead, on how many similarities we have? Find common threads? Look for creative, nonviolent solutions. Personally, I prefer the pacifist outlook of Henry David Thoreau, predecessor to Martin Luther King, Jr., and Mahatma Gandhi. The pen is mightier than the sword, as Froissart said. I remember a bumper sticker I had seen recently that said: **HONOR OUR VETS; WAGE PEACE.**

But tell that to the bodies lying under one stark white headstone after another in the Tomb of the Unknown Soldier in Arlington, Virginia. Tell that to all the boys that became men, ready or not, and in that instantaneous threshold of manhood were killed or maimed in foreign lands, fighting for our country's causes, some never to come home at all.

I thought of a poem by one of my favorite poets, ee cummings. Often one needs to read his poems several times to decipher the content, for his mind runs deeply into the soul of mankind. It reads:

Thou in whose swordgreat story shine the deeds
of history her heroes,sounds the tread
of those vast armies of the marching dead,
with standards and the neighing of great steeds
moving to war across the smiling meads;
thou by whose page we break the precious bread
of dear communion with the past,and wed
to valor,battle with heroic breeds;

thou,Froissart,for that thou didst love the pen
while others wrote in steel,accept all praise
of after ages,and of hungering days
for whom the old glories move,the old trumpets cry;
who gavest as one of those immortal men
his life that his fair city might not die.

I cannot think of Veterans Day and not think of my own grandfather, Charles Franklin Henkel, my mother's father. He fought in Germany in World War I and survived to come home to Virginia to his beautiful young wife, and (almost) two-year-old daughter. But fate had other plans. On the train home he caught the Spanish flu – the infamous influenza that spread like wildfire around the world – a pandemic that felled over 22 million people worldwide, more than the 5 years of the war, itself. My siblings and I, of course, never knew my grandfather, but what is so much more difficult to accept is that my own mother never knew her father. She had vague memories of him from her early childhood, probably formed by descriptions of loving and bereaved adults. To have survived the awful war and then succumbed to a virus. How utterly tragic.

My grandfather is buried in the Riverview Cemetery, in Waynesboro, Virginia. His tombstone reads Charles Franklin Henkel: 1891-1918. My grandmother, his wife, Bessie Kingsbury Henkel Wilkins, is now buried with him. He lived to be all of 27 years.

Each Veteran has a different story to tell, or to be told, of his or her efforts in whichever war they fought. Those that lived have their own memories of witnessing atrocities no human should ever bear witness to – and, too, of valor and steely courage in the face of these atrocities. One of the Veteran's groups I support, The Blinded Veteran's Association, sent me a letter requesting another donation recently. This is an excerpt from that letter. It is written by Graham Williams, "an ordinary serviceman faithfully serving his country during the "War to End All Wars." Graham described this holiday experience as the "most beautiful Christmas I'd ever seen." The holiday season that year found Graham in the thick of World War I's trench warfare. His comrades and he were separated from their German counterparts by a few scant yards of abandoned turnip field commonly known as "No Man's Land." Death was as close as raising one's head at the wrong time. Fear was a constant and unrelenting companion.

"A moving incident took place along that Western Front battlefield in 1914. I'll let Graham describe the extraordinary sights he experienced during his Christmas Eve sentry duty: 'I was standing gazing out and I thought what a different Christmas this was going to be from what I'd ever had before. At exactly midnight German time, I suddenly saw lights appear in front of me all along the German trenches. I was wondering what was happening. They (the German soldiers) started singing Stille Nacht (Silent Night). I thought what a beautiful tune it was.

'That was the start of an unofficial truce along the Western Front during which time soldiers from both sides exchanged cigarettes, food and even buttons, from their uniforms. They showed each other pictures of their families and posed for photographs standing with arms embraced in the dreaded No Man's Land.

'The unofficial truce wasn't to last for long. The commanders on both sides ordered

their soldiers back into their respective trenches so the battle could resume. Soon the rifles on both sides spat forth death across the shell scarred turnip field. The spirit of war returned to the site where the spirit of peace had triumphed just a few hours before'."

Good God Almighty. Imagine this. Stop the war. Stop killing one another long enough to form a truce at a sacrosanct time of year. Meet one another, become names and faces. Bond. Care. Give a damn for the human reality behind the madness of the abstract principles that take on a life – or death – of their own. How can one then go 'back to the trenches' and resume the bloody carnage? It's all insanity to me. Simply insane.

I decided it was time for a pit stop and a good long stretch, so I pulled off I-40 at Grants. There were many hotels and restaurants along in here. I found a Taco Bell, took care of business, got an iced tea and did a series of stretches. It'd been just 75 miles, or so. I looked at my spliced-together map with the Interstate highlighted in yellow. My own yellow brick pathway leading to the Grand Canyon and whatever awaited. From Grants to Gallup looked to be another 60 miles; I'd make it that far and see how my energy was. This would put me just east of the Arizona-state line, a good jumping-off place to begin the next day. By now it was fairly dark. I sipped the tea and studied the map closely, now both navigator and pilot of this solo trip. I pretended to be Pete. The little town of 'Thoreau' was just over mid-way. I wondered how it had come by that name and if it had to do with Henry David. South of here, be-tween Gallup and Grants, lay the Zuni Mountain National Forest and a Zuni Indian Reservation that was bordered both north and southeast by the Navajo Rez. I was very much back in Indian Country, back on the 'Checkerboard Reservation.'

I hit the road again and watched the desert go dark around me. Mack trucks whizzed past my little car; I braced the wheel to keep it steady. *If I was going 75-80 mph, what were they traveling?! Hope those boys stayed awake… it'd sure be one big mess if they didn't.* I listened to a soundtrack that I'd burned of *Moby*, a techno New Age artist Jared had introduced me to before leaving. Some of his music was too loud for my tastes, but some I liked very much – it certainly had a sound all its own, with searing, haunting rhythms and lyrics that somehow matched this land. *Moby* sang me into Gallup, where I found a Comfort Inn with a nice indoor pool. I'd call it a night here; so much for Holbrook – there were still too many deeds left to do tonight to continue. Close by I was told there was the 'largest Wal-Mart in America,' a dubious honor, but hopeful for locating puppy supplies. After dinner and before my water workout, I'd go and take a look.

Indeed, this Super Wal-Mart was gigantic. It consisted of a huge main store connected to a large grocery store to the left of it. Good. Tonight I'd get the puppy supplies, of which I had made a list at dinner, and in the morning I'd get foodstuffs before leaving. Perfect. I made my way to the pet supplies section and found an adjustable collar that I thought would fit Pelli well. It had a purple and turquoise zigzag pattern, edged in black, very Southwest. Great. I found a blue harness to use to secure her to the seatbelt in the front, beside me, so that I could talk with and visit her as we traveled. This is why I hadn't wanted the passenger-side airbag. That could kill her if it deployed. Or it did deploy and didn't kill her, she'd likely never recover from the shock. But I doubted that she'd ever set foot in a car again... Just thinking ahead... Okay, next on the list...

I found a plastic food and water dish combo, some rawhide dog chews, some Purina puppy chow in a 5# bag. Good. Anything else? Oh yeah! *Of course!* The travel carrier. I looked around; the unassembled boxed kits were on the top shelf. I found an employee who helped haul a couple boxes down. We discussed sizes and I figured a medium would fit her by now, sure she'd grown in the last two months. Okay, I had a leash I'd brought from home. We were set in this department.

I moved on to the sports department and found a small Playmate cooler, a couple of ice packs and a thermos. I looked at the list – oh yeah: the clean-up brigade. On to the cleaning department: I loaded into the cart Marcal paper towels (again,100% recyled), a small bottle of ex-tra-strength Febreze spray, a can of Lysol disinfectant and a pair of latex gloves. Okay, we were set. I could now get out of here, put all of this in the trunk and – with a promise and a prayer – have actual use for them in the next few days. Better keep the receipt.

As I shopped around the Wal-Mart, I noticed that it was filled to overflowing with flags to wave and tee shirts of every type, promising pride and retaliation. Even diapers were emblazoned with the American flag, so that every infant in America could display their loyalty and pa-triotism for this great country. Patriotism had sprung up in America as mushrooms might after a soaking rain. The red, white and blue trinkets fresh from China were everywhere one turned, as a symbolic show of our outrage. But patriotism came with a price. It was canned, bagged, wrapped, stamped and sealed with a dollar-mark that the country was only too willing to pay. God Bless America. Somehow this in-your-face commercialism for a cataclysm of this magnitude had me sadly shaking my head and heading for the exit as quickly as I could get out of the store. It would be a good time to go for a water workout – my stiff back and jaded mind were looking forward to that.

After a wonderful forty minute 'swim,' with my trusty little kickboard and downtime in the hot tub for dessert, I settled into the room for the night, poured a glass of wine (I'd gotten that much from the grocery store) and called Pete about 9 PM. 11 PM his time – reasonable. We had a good phone visit; all was well at home with the kids and critters; he missed me and wished me continued good luck and we said our good-nights.

I had a good nights sleep, after writing a while in my travel journal. The alarm went off about 8:00 and I dressed and mosied next door to a farm breakfast before heading back to Wal-Mart's grocery store for the list I'd just made: cheese, a half-gallon of milk, a small jar of Stuckey's raspberry jam, and the inevitable Skippy's Super Chunk peanut butter. I put a small loaf of rich multi-grained bread in the cart and a package of Wasa crackers, some fruit, and a six-pack bundle of pre-packaged short-cut carrots. Perfect, a pack-a-day to snack on. A six-pack of Corona, a couple of limes and a church key to open the bottles… some chocolate, and I was set to hit the road. The hotel had frozen my ice packs last night. Life was good.

I purchased the goods with a travelers check and was leaving the store about 10AM, when I noticed a vendor set up outside. He was selling all sorts of colorful items that could be in scripted there on the spot. Among them were bone-shaped dog tags. Lord, it was a most definite 'sign' – thank you. I looked them over and chose a magenta one. "Will you please engrave 'Kokopelli' on this one, with this phone number? On the back you can put 'Laura Giannini' as owner. He did, saying he didn't recognize the area code. "Oh, that's from back in Virginia," I said. "Long story." I thought a minute. Amanda, our elderly beagle, long had had an identification placket on her collar, but we were missing one. "Will you please make another one on this gold bone tag? This one I want to say 'Trey' with the same phone number, and on the back, the 'Gianniny Family'." *The boy had no tag yet on his collar, and he certainly deserved one. Gold would fit both his markings and his personality. Perfect, I thought. I felt like the guy had been waiting for me here. Another bit of kismet. Sorry, Ricardo, the stars just aren't in your court, I feel it in my bones…*

I thanked the fellow for his tags and for being there, went out, packed the items to be chilled in the cooler, settled in the rest of the stuff and slipped in a *U2* mix. "With or Without You" played. Appropriate. Time to hit the road and head on to Arizona. I didn't get too awfully far, however, before stopping over the state-line at the visitors center for a rest stop and to checkout a Chief Yellowhorse tourist shop, set at the base of an awesome carved-out sandstone cliff. Placed strategically on ledges above it were statues of elk, a black bear stalking a cougar, and an eagle with its wings spread wide. All were symbols of the wildlife in the upcoming mountains of Flagstaff. A large yellow sign with red letters read: **"Indian Arts & Crafts. Jewelry. Pottery. Blankets. Kachinas. Southwest Souvenirs."** Below it was a long sprawl of colorfully painted buildings with a series of shops. A tourist's Mecca. A huge white tepee with zigzags painted around it sprouted beside the shops. The kids would have loved this. I took a couple of photos for them.

Jared had asked me to get an Indian blanket so that he could make a poncho back at home. I found one in blue and brown stripes I thought he'd like. I found another in red, white and blue tones to take to Art and Carole, in Santa Fe, in honor of his being a veteran of World War II. I found one in warm apricots and turquoises for Cindy; I'd hope to get together with her in Santa Fe or Taos. She didn't even know I was back. I'd have to call her and see what we might work out. Now, one for Kokopelli. Here was a purple, gray and black striped one; purple would compliment that golden coat. Perfect. I gathered them in my arms and headed over to the pleasant Navajo woman in her traditional clothing behind the counter. "Will this be all?" She asked in her soft singsong voice.

"For today, thank you. I love these blankets. We got some on our last trip out. They're so warm and versatile. And the best part is they're machine washable."

"That's always good. I'm glad you like them," she said simply.

I left, laughing at the thought that these were called 'Indian blankets.' Who were they kidding? Real hand-woven woolen Navajo blankets would cost hundreds of dollars, some going into the thousands. They'd become a collector's art form. These cotton ones were up from Mexico and machine produced, which made them so reasonable. But I still loved the darned things and they made a nice gift. Everyone could use one or two.

Okay, time to really hit the road now. Bono was singing "I Still Haven't Found What I'm Looking For." Good grief. Give me a break; I was certainly trying... The pale desert flew past me. I'd aim for Holbrook for the next pit stop and hoped my bladder registered that. The little towns of Manuelito and Houck came and went. Chambers was next; Navajo on the far horizon. Buttes, mesas and canyons flashed on by, not as grand or distinct in this area as they had been in New Mexico and eastern Arizona. The long stretches of highway loomed forever on. Bono now sang "Pride in the Name of Love."

I breathed in deeply, trying to relax and get into the present moment, to stop projecting myself ahead. The driving force of music wired me too much. I needed something calmer, so switched CD's carefully, putting in a mix of Enya favorites I'd burned, and I breathed in deeply again. Good. Now relax… It's all in God's hands now, and he's been whispering in my ear all the way. Have faith; everything will be just fine…

TWENTY-SIX

George and Connie: Travel Reflections

"God made the world round so we would never be able to see too far down the road." Isak Dinesen

Driving down these endless stretches of Interstate, where I've come to believe one mile in the east translates to ten in the west, allows hours of 'gray space' thinking time to unfold. Gray space is to thought what white noise is to sound: subtly intense and constantly there. Gray space allows thoughts long gone into hibernation a chance to unfurl themselves from these deep recesses in the mind and re-emerge, renewed. Driving meditations, these thoughts become. I treasure long solo drives just for this gift.

At such times as these, I find myself thinking of George again. Part of it is the time of year, here in the fall. The rawness of his loss has eased, as has the anger at his senseless death; those emotions are futile. I have come to realize with time the story has been told. I know the ending and know it cannot be changed, not for all the King's horses and all the King's men. I think of Connie, and wonder how or if she has recovered in these years passed. It's been some time since I've seen her; I heard she had moved to the northeast. I'm sure September 11th ripped open her old wounds, as it did ours, causing her to – once again – seriously appraise humanity.

George met Connie in a t'ai chi class in the Spring of '97. He was attracted to her delicacy and her intensity immediately, but she would have nothing to do with him. She had been in two abusive marriages, was free of them and doing quite well in her life now, thank you. Men were not on her menu. Still, George persisted until ever so slowly he broke down her massive walls of distrust in men with his patience and quiet charm. Months passed. They dated and then fell madly in love in their midlife years; both were around fifty at the time. George, too, had been married, but long ago. He had dated many women since then, but had now found the love of his life, and it was mutual. George and Connie were like teenagers in wild, pure, unadulterated love. The world was their oyster.

Connie would tell me later how she regretted all those months when she had ignored George's advances. This was precious time when they could have been together – but then they had their whole lives ahead, didn't they? They planned to be married by Christmas, would move into her beautiful, spacious 'California style' home in Ivy, with high, vaulted ceilings and breathtaking views of the woods and mountains beyond. The Christmas tree would be huge, there in an alcove by the stairs. They had it all planned. George would keep his little home of umpteen years in the Belmont area of Charlottesville, for the time, as his jewelry workshop and gallery. Georges' godson – my son, Jared – would visit them both at Connie's and get to know them as a couple. Life would be grand. Yes, they had it all planned. But just ask any New Yorker these days if life doesn't turn on a dime...

George and Connie's last big hurrah was a trip to the Outer Banks of North Carolina that August: a wonderful week, just the two of them, caught in the magic of sparkling new love. Connie later gave us two photographs she had taken of George, the beach his backdrop; he looks blissfully happy. I treasure them and have one of these photos now in my studio office, as I write these memoirs. I wish I had one of the two of them together.

By September they had returned from this trip. George had ordered two expensive diamonds for Connie to choose the one she wanted for her ring; they would design it together. And the countdown began to George's murder, all the behind-the-scenes planning by Dorian Lester, and his Bulgarian 'countess,' had begun. Like the invisible threads woven to create the madness of September 2001, these threads for September 1997 were being sewn. But who amongst the hundreds of us who knew and loved George – our dear, sweet, shy jeweler friend, collector of Samurai swords and Japanese artifacts, gentle spirit in this crazy world – had an inkling?

George had called Connie on Saturday, the 27th, and told her that he was working late, but would be home for dinner. He did not come and he did not call, which was completely unlike him. She became worried and planned to go to his home on Leonard Street, just to be sure he was okay. She left a note for him, should they pass in transit. Lord, that that should have happened.

It was Connie who found George, lying in a pool of his own blood. This person she had come to love more then life, who had gently taught her to trust in a man again… Now her trust in mankind, itself, was instantly shattered. In the beat of a heart, from love to loss, her life exploded in madness. Police and detectives and George's neighbors surrounded her that night that his death was reported. Momentarily, she was a suspect and then a key witness. There was no time to step back, run, hide, crawl into a cave and work through any of this, reflectively. From the moment Connie found George slain amidst his creations, through the trials and after, she was in the spotlight. How she survived, her mind intact, I will never know. There were times, she admitted to me, that she wanted to end this insanity and join George in the hereafter.

Connie, and several of his/their close friends, were instrumental in putting together a Memorial Service for George in the University Chapel, on the grounds of Thomas Jefferson's University of Virginia, in Charlottesville, eleven days after his death, on October 8th, 1997. The church filled and spilled over mourners into the entrance and out onto the stately lawn. Several of us who had known George well, from different aspects of his life, spoke that afternoon. The service was a testament in the enduring, unfathomable depths of the human soul. Eve Waters, a renowned harpist/singer, and a dear friend of George's, sang and played as an angel amongst us. It was both an incredibly moving afternoon, and an incredibly draining one.

I will never know how Connie managed to pull this together, unless the sheer necessity to do this for George, to offer these remembrances – which is all any of us had left – was what saved her own sanity. George's friends leaned heavily on one another during this first month; we were all in massive shock. It was this being there for one another that saved us all. When one buckled in grief, he or she was caught by someone that – for the moment – had it more together. And then they, in turn, would be strong when another person's grief became too much to bear. Our memories and stories, anecdotes and photographs, kept/keep George alive and with us to this day.

Connie had even seen to it that miniature Snickers bars, George's favorite candy, were available beside the Memorial programs upon entering the church, and that he was buried with them, along with one of his festive Hawaiian shirts – his 'dress-up' attire. We still have an old battered Snickers bar, to this day from that day, by the second of his beach photographs upstairs. I keep everything of sentimental value.

All of these thoughts of George and Connie, how they met and fell in love, intended to marry but were torn apart by the 'fates,' for lack of any better perspective, reminded me, too, of the poem that she had included in his Memorial program. Not, of course, that I remembered the poem verbatim. Just fragments, the gist of it. But this is how it reads:

"The Going," by Thomas Hardy
(1840-1928) English novelist & poet

Why did you give no hint that night
That quickly after the morrow's dawn,
And calmly, as if indifferent quite,
You would close your term here, up and be gone
Where I could not follow
With wing of swallow
To gain one glimpse of you ever anon!

Never to bid good-bye,
Or lip me the softest call,
Or utter a wish for a word, while I
Saw morning harden upon the wall,
Unmoved, unknowing
That your great going
Had place that moment, and altered all.

Why do you make me leave the house
And think for a breath it is you I see
At the end of the alley of bending boughs
Where so often at dusk you used to be;
Till in darkening dankness
The yawning blankness
Of the perspective sickens me!

You were he who abode
By those red-veined rocks far West,
You were the swan-necked one who rode

Along the beetling Beeny Crest,
And, reining nigh me,
Would muse and eye me,
While Life unrolled us its very best.

Why, then latterly did we not speak,
Did we not think of those days long dead,
And ere your vanishing strive to seek
That time's renewal? We might have said,
"In this bright spring weather
We'll visit together
Those places that once we visited."

Well, well! All's past amend,
Unchangeable. It must go.
I seem but a dead man held on end
To sink down soon... O you could not know
That such swift fleeing
No soul foreseeing -
Not even I - would undo me so!

This poem is so apt, too, for all the families and individuals who lost loved ones that simply went to work that fateful day in the Pentagon, or The World Trade Center, or boarded one of the four fateful airliners, used as bombs.

It is also dedicated to any of the many heroic souls, as Willie Nelson put it in singing his sweetly intense post-September 11th rendition of "America, The Beautiful," for inclusion in *A Tribute To American Heroes*. This was a fund-raiser immediately organized by many altruistic and talented souls in the music and entertainment industry. It was aired Friday night, September 21st, the night before we left for our anniversary trip. We were so busy packing that evening we didn't watch it, but both the video and the CD were on my Christmas list for 2001. Many of Hollywood's notables were also part of this generous event, answering phones in a telethon to raise money for the families left behind. What an incredible effort, so quickly pulled together, where the giants of the music and movie industries became simply fellow Americans, united in tears, patriotism, and compassion for their fellow man. I don't know this for certain, but I have a hunch that Bruce Springsteen was a powerful influence behind the event; it would be just like him.

("America, The Beautiful" *lyrics, continued:)*
"America, America
God mend thy every flaw
Confirm thy soul, in self control,
thy liberty and all...

Oh Beautiful
For heroes prove
In liberating stride
Who bore themselves a country's love
And mercy more than life..

America, America
May God thy gold refine
Till all success be nobleness
And every gain divine...

America, America
God shed his grace on thee
And crowned thy good with brotherhood
From sea to shining sea..."

From Willie's lips to God's ears, this is for the firefighters, policemen, and -women, and for the medics, who fearlessly ran into the inferno of the Twin Towers to try to save these strangers' lives, and thus lost their own. Or those of you who came away physically, and/or mentally wounded, now living with memories of that apocalyptic day. These words are also for all the people that innocently boarded the American and United airliners that day, like any other, to never set foot on the earth again. And for all those working at the Pentagon to protect American lives... These words and *"The Going"* are for you and for your families. God Bless and be with you, one and all.

TWENTY-SEVEN

Grand Canyon, First Night: Marcos

"Often in the stillness of the night, when all nature seems asleep about me, there comes a gentle rapping at the door of my heart. I open it, and a voice inquires, 'Pokagon, what of your people? What will their future be?' My answer is: 'Mortal man has not the power to draw aside the veil of unborn time to tell the future of his race. That gift belongs to the divine alone. But it is given to him to closely judge the future by the present, and the past."
Simon Pokagon (1830-1899) Potawatomie

The highway rolls away through these vast and bleak western lands. Often the interstate parallels the Santa Fe Railroad. I see the train off in the distance and reminisce about "The City Different." My mind wanders a little here, a little there. Such are the thoughts that return to visit on such a drive. And with each visitation over that hallowed ground of remembrances, the next journey back is a little easier. Time now to shake off these reflections and work on my game plan for recovery of our sand-colored pup. Then I think of Snoopy's cousin, with his suave mustache and hard luck, stuck with only a cactus as a friend in the desert. Poor kid.

The law knew I was returning. I had spoken to Deputy Aaron Dick in the Coconino County Sheriff's Department several times from home, explaining the whole story and I had left my telephone number with him. Upon reaching the Grand Canyon, I was to call the deputy to arrange a time to deliver to Ricardo the letter from John Slate, my attorney in Phoenix. But I did not yet have the completed letter. Friday evening, before leaving, I had faxed the pertinent information to Mr. Slate. He would use this to write the necessary letter and have it ready by Monday. Only Monday, November 12th, was Veterans Day and likely his office would be closed – or close early. I hadn't thought of this in the grand scheme of things in my arrival in the Canyon that afternoon/evening.

I made a point of stopping in Winslow, Arizona, about 3 PM that

Monday to try to get through to Mr. Slate. No luck; the switchboard was down. The letter might be ready, but I could not get to it. This would have to wait until tomorrow. Oh well. So I called Marcos at the Red Feather Lodge to get an idea of how much travel lay ahead. He gave me a reference from Flagstaff and told me that he'd found out exactly the trailer park where Ricardo lived, giving me directions to find it north of the Valle intersection, off of 180.

I decided to make it to Flagstaff, get a good cup of coffee and let it get dark, so I could go into the area and scout around. *Maybe find Ricardo's trailer on the way to the canyon! Maybe – if the Lord be willing – I'd see Kokopelli tonight! Maybe even be able to take her with me, somehow... Now I was getting ahead of things. One step at a time here, kiddo. But the weeks since I had seen the small desert mutt had stretched out so and had seemed so endless. I was anxious to reunite. I had to calm my pounding heart and keep a cool head. This was enemy territory – no one at this trailer park would know me. On one hand, I'd be an intruder, a stranger; on the other, in being a stranger, I would be unidentifiable – at first. Long enough to snag my dog and leave? I don't know! But Ricardo would certainly not welcome my return with open arms – maybe in pure disbelief, yes – but once over the shock, he would return to his stubborn self, I was quite sure of that.*

Coming into Flagstaff I could see the mystical San Francisco Peaks off in the distance. The sky was dynamic, striated by layers of steel gray and deep golden clouds running horizontal stripes over and under one another. The late afternoon sun tried its best to blaze through an upper layer of mackerel clouds. The intense combination over this sacred mountain promised exciting times ahead.

The coffee at Starbuck's was scrumptious, even if it was decaf. This Starbuck's had a couple offerings of Fair Trade Coffee, but none in decaffeinated. I picked up a *USA Today* and a fund-raiser CD for hunger relief, biding my time until the light faded. On leaving, I spoke with a young couple leading a gorgeous wolf-hybrid. We traded dog stories there in the parking lot and they wished Kokopelli and me the best of luck on reuniting and returning home safely. A sweet young couple they were; another time and place and we would probably be good friends.

I threaded through Flagstaff and then entered the Coconino National Forest towards the San Francisco Peaks, heading north through this huge park, the last leg of the trip that would complete the closure on my incredible circular escapade. A part of me was still in disbelief that I was actually *out* here, carrying through on these questionable plans. Another part was steely determination on getting my dog back. *One way or another,*

366

Ricardo. One way or another. When you dealt with that emotional milk toast the morning that Pete and I entrusted "Dingo" to your care, you did not have an inkling of the flip side of this coin, did you there, buddy? Nope, you thought this chapter closed. Well, amigo, Janus is alive and well; get ready to start the story over again, because a new chapter is about to begin. How it will read only time will tell...

Mark Knopfler's *Sailing to Philadelphia* CD serenaded me as I sailed through the parkway at dusk. "What it Is" played, better than caffeine at revving me up. Marcos scolded me later for driving so fast, telling me that elk came out to feed at dusk and a bull elk crossing a road would hit at about the top of their legs, sending their huge body – and head and antlers – crashing over the hood and through a windshield in a heartbeat to render a car – and perhaps its contents – useless in a heartbeat. This area was full of elk, I came to learn, and many a nasty accident had been caused by ignorant touristos, such as myself, in a hurry to 'get there,' never to get there at all. In my excitement and impatience to see Kokopelli again, I was being stupid. I didn't remember the elk then, but in Virginia deer feed at dusk – and their small bodies can wreck havoc. Not to mention what all this does to the poor animal's day. That night God put an angel in the backseat to compensate for my foolishness. Later, after Marcos explained all this to me, my vivid imagination created a bloody enough encounter in my mind to sober up the rest of the drives through these parks considerably. *Accomplish your goals, Laura – but in one piece.* Knopfler's "Prairie Wedding" came on, calming me. *Breathe deeply, kiddo, breathe. Think Lamaze...*

It was only about an hour from Flagstaff to the trailer park at the speed I traveled, but like a thoroughbred chomping at her bit before the Derby began, this seemed forever. It was truly dark upon arrival. I slowed where Marcos had said the pavement darkened, followed his markers to a tee, and turned right, in the middle of nowhere it seemed, heading up some Godforsaken washboard gravel road for a mile or more. A wall made of rocks rose to the left; beyond this were lights from many homes. *Just as Marcos had said! I was there! But which one?* I slowly turned in, driving down the main road of the large circular road through the mobile homes. All was fairly quiet. I came to the end of this road, where the choice was to turn right, through another rock wall enclosing a courtyard and a home back in there (I came to find out later, let's say in a round-about-way, that this is where the security guard lived) or take a left, by a tree, on to where the road wrapped left and back around to join the original entrance way.

I had to eliminate that Starbuck's java in the worst way, so I slowly drove as far back off this road and parked as unobtrusively as possible. Now, some of my friends say I have balls to be doing this. (I prefer 'Chutzpah.') But it's not the balls that I want. *This* is where I have to admit that I actually have that Freudian concept of "penis envy." That portable, bendable, hose-like contraption sure would come in handy, with my enthusiastic bladder, at times like this… So first things first. Pelli had waited this long; she could wait a little longer. I took care of business there in the dark of the trailer park, while listening to Hispanic music coming from the nearest home and wondering if this was where Ricardo lived and if he planned to walk outside anytime soon.

In driving through the trailer park looking for, but not seeing, his old beat-up green van parked amidst any of the homes, I called it quits for now. Time to head north and catch up with Marcos. At least I knew fairly well where Ricardo lived, thanks to my young friend, and I hadn't even arrived in the Canyon yet.

Marcos and Scott were at the front desk when I got in about 8 PM. They had a room waiting and Marcos said he'd come up when he got off at 9:00. I told him I was famished, so would eat while waiting for him. He suggested The Grand Hotel across the street, where I enjoyed a spicy Southwest dish while watching Native Americans, in full buckskins and head-dress, demonstrate a ceremonial dance. Fascinating. What an exciting way to begin this new journey! But I watched the watch (for once), leaving in time to take the important things on up to my room and unpack enough to get dressed in my dark 'scouting' duds. I joined Marcos downstairs to head back to the trailer park. He'd gone back to his place, while I was getting ready, and changed into his dark clothes. Marcos had donned everything black or navy, including a heavy hooded sweatshirt, and then wore white shoes. *Hmm….* I'd have to give this boy a Ludlum to read.

Traveling south in my rental was when Marcos reprimanded me for driving up here so fast. He told me of some bone-chilling tales of dumb newcomers, such as myself, doing Interstate speeds through the parkway and making a mess of everything when they encountered elk. Once I was properly chastised, my young accomplice lightened up and told me about himself. I found him to be an entertaining comrade in arms and was extremely grateful for his so willingly wanting to help recover the puppy. Marcos just said simply that it was wrong of Ricardo to have gone back on his word, especially as we had saved her from starvation, and he wanted to help. Besides, he added, he was bored and this kept him out of trouble. *Well, maybe… I'm not sure if he had figured out this dark clothes thing, or not...*

We drove the 15 miles south to Tinkerville. As we drove slowly through the area looking for Ricardo's trusty old vehicle I found myself again antsy and excited. *What if she was in the yard that Ricky had spoken of? Just running free... Would she recognize me? Jump the fence in her excitement, right into my arms — no law against* that *— and we would drive off and away. It sounded like a fairytale, and it was. Too easy. Oh well.*

Sure enough, rounding the corner at the top of the 'tee' close to where I'd parked earlier when nature dialed me direct, was Ricky's two-toned green van. It was parked beside a trailer with a fence around it, a camper trailer off a ways beside it, and a tall pole directly in front, spilling light down over the whole scene. *Damn. About three lights in the whole bloody trailer park, and one had to be directly in front of Ricardo's place. What? Did he know I was coming?*

When Marcos realized the location of Ricardo's trailer he directed me to drive on past and park across the road from the next one down, by a dumpster. His buddy, who was to have been looking out for the exact trailer, and who told him the trailer park where Ricky lived, lived there. Marcos was frustrated that he hadn't told him they were next-door neighbors!

We got out, the two of us in our spying duds, and sauntered nonchalantly over to where our waiter-friend lived. We could hear the TV on inside, covering any sounds we might be making. I held my breath, hoping the puppy would be in the yard and — playing out the scenario I'd just envisioned — I called her quietly. Nothing. Marcos nonchalantly stayed on the road, looking around, while I walked silently around Ricardo's home, in between it and the camper trailer, hoping to hear Kokopelli inside. Still, nothing.

Suddenly, out of the indigo blue and starless night, a jeep raced around the corner and slid to a stop. A lady jumped out, confronting Marcos. I wondered if I should just stay put in the shadows or join Marcos, deciding on the latter, to give him moral support. This was my gig, after all. This woman was petite and mad, reminding me of a feisty terrier that had been perturbed. She identified herself as the security guard of this establishment. I glanced up at Ricky's light and sure enough, sitting up high and pretty above it, there were security cameras. *Well, double-damn, anyway — who would have ever thought this sleepy little Arizona trailer park, in the middle of nowhere, USA, would have* security *cameras?! My Ludlumesque edge was slipping — better get more observant here if this is to work out.*

The security lady demanded: "*Who* are you, and *what* are you doing around here? I don't recognize either of you!"

Marcos' reply was comical: "We're not from around here and thought we saw a wild animal. I've never seen a wild animal before, so we decided to follow it." Yes, this is what the fellow said. I turned my face, smiled, and rolled my eyes. *Sure, she'd buy that. Next, she'd be calling the law on* us.

Just about then the door to his friends trailer opened and two young girls stuck their heads out, as if on cue, exclaiming "Hey, it's Marcos! Whatcha' doing out there, dude? Come on inside!"

Marcos glanced at the stern authority figure, and told her "See, I know these people." I just grinned like a fool, figuring enough had been said without my two-cents worth.

The security guard looked pretty darned dubious, but said: "Go ahead. Go on in. But 'wild animals,' my foot…" She was mumbling, as she got back in her jeep to go.

Two young women and one young man, all in their late 'teens or early twenties, invited us to sit down and join them in smoking the biggest bong I had ever seen. They were fairly well flying without wings. Poor Marcos walked over and sat down, beet red, looking at me and wanting to fade into oblivion about then. I was old enough to be his mother and here they were offering me marijuana. I smiled and politely declined, telling them that I was looking for something and had to keep my wits about me, but thank you, anyway. Indeed, I found the whole evening – from our round with the security lady to this grand party – extremely amusing. I asked if any of them knew if Ricardo Santillan lived in the trailer next door, and they asked if it was the Ricky that worked in the Canyon Café? Yes, yes, that's who it is. Well, does he have a small yellow dog over there with him? They looked at each other, in their general fog, but none of them could remember Ricardo having a dog. *Hmm... Either these kids don't go out, or the puppy doesn't go out. This was too weird. She's been there, one lot over, for 5½ weeks and they know nothing of her, even with the "Beware of Dog" sign on his gate?* One young woman got all fired up, ready to march over there *right now* and demand to know if he had my puppy, after she heard a little of the story. We settled her down, assuring her that we would take care of it, but thanks. Shortly after this, we left.

"Marcos," I asked, as we headed out of the trailer park, "you don't think those girls are going to go over there tomorrow and talk with Ricardo about the puppy, do you? And inadvertently let him know I'm back for her – before I have the letter in hand, and Deputy Dick there with me to deliver it?"

Marcos looked at me and shook his head no: "Listen, Laura, those girls are stoned out of their heads. They're not going to remember that we visited, much less what we talked about... Don't worry about that. Besides," he added, "they hardly ever leave the trailer. They're always stoned like that, and they haven't even finished partying tonight. *Don't worry.*"

I wasn't quite sure what to think of that. I was beginning to wonder if perhaps we had made a mistake about coming down here tonight. If Ricardo found out I was back from Virginia for my dog, I was pretty sure he'd see that she disappeared into the wild blue yonder and claim ignorance when I did show up with the big guns. But what was done was done, and Marcos reassured me they wouldn't remember a thing. Oh well. It was just one more day, anyway. Tomorrow, Tuesday, would likely bring some answers.

As we drove up the road watching for elk Marcos opened up to me about his life. This fellow had lead a remarkable twenty-two years. His mother was a missionary that worked in prisons to help convert inmates to Christianity. It was in a prison down in Mexico that Marcos' mom met his dad. When he was released from jail down there he married her and moved to the United States, in California somewhere, now a legal citizen. Shortly after this, and before Marcos was born, he left. Marcos said that he had met his father only a couple of times in his whole life, and had neither love nor patience for him. His mother, on the other hand, he adored; this went without saying. Any time he spoke of her it was with respect and reverence. She had raised Marcos on her own, working long, hard hours in doing so — like millions of single working mothers all over the world. My hat surely went off to her; she had done an excellent job. It was good to have the opportunity to know him better.

He was telling me that he had grown up in San Diego, not in the best part of the city by any means, but had managed to stay out of trouble. He had worked hard, kept his nose clean, and had taken a form of karate — the type he told me, but I've forgotten — and gone on to Black Belt with it. That was how he had handled his aggression. *Hey,* I was thinking, *I've got a legitimate bodyguard here!* Marcos was a big fellow, not to be taken lightly (except when talking with security guards...). I told him of our trip out to San Diego in June of the prior year to see my nephew, Bill, marry his lovely bride, Rochelle, who had worked with him in the Environmental Protection Agency. I remarked on how beautiful the city was, and how much we had enjoyed the San Diego Zoo and Wildlife Park, both of which are truly spectacular, both in flora and fauna. In fact, it had been confided to me by a security guard at the zoo that the vegetation there – the astounding array of plants that landscape the grounds, both indigenous and imported, and the plants (like bamboo) that feed the animals – was worth more than the animals, themselves. I found this to be dumb-founding, having just seen the multitude of creatures from around the world, many of them endangered, on display in this huge compound. I had been feeling like we had visited the Ark, years after it had landed on Arafat, and procreation had had a chance to flourish.

I told Marcos about my son, Jared, who had taken Myo Sim Karate for several years, working his way just shy of a Blue Belt, then quit, feeling that he wasn't getting anywhere. He had wanted to start playing soccer and do other things. It had been frustrating for me to see him quit like that but, like a horse at water, he had to want to drink. Our conversation was easy going up the road. This was a nice young man here. I found myself telling Marcos about my older daughter, Skye, thinking maybe I should somehow introduce them. But then he tells me he has a girlfriend. Oh well. I was thinking that dating might be a problem, anyway, considering geography. Marcos then went on to say that he had been working in San Diego, in one of those places that sell five-gallon jugs of bottled water, when they sent him on a delivery, in his own truck, to one of the rougher parts of town. He knew where he was going, felt comfortable enough driving into that area, but one just never knows when that day will be the fateful day that turns your life inside out.

For Marcos, this was his. As he was returning to his truck, a street gang accosted him at gunpoint, demanding that he give them the truck. Marcos tells me he thought back on his karate teacher's advice, and the man would have told him to always keep your maximum advantage when facing the opponent. In this case, it was getting in and staying in his truck, keeping that between him and the punks. So they shot him sitting there in the vehicle, right through the windshield. He said when the bullets hit he became like a raging bull, roaring in pain, and gunned the truck at the gang, then through them, as they jumped aside. Luckily just down the road a ways was a street officer, giving someone a ticket. Somehow Marcos stopped his truck before he lost consciousness; when he woke up he found himself in the hospital, heavily bandaged. The bullets had broken ribs, punctured his left lung, and destroyed his spleen. There is a bullet in his back that will be there forever.

It took some time to mend from the wounds. The water company paid his hospital bills and gave him a cash settlement. Marcos lived on the money for a year and a half, until he could become independent again. He ended up giving his grandmother some of the cash, to help her clear up some debt. He gave some cash to this mom. Marcos didn't want the rest of the money, saying that he had had a chance to think while being bedridden like that and watching his life come so close to an end at such a young age. He wanted to leave the San Diego area, go somewhere where drugs and violence weren't everywhere, and so he ended up starting a new life at the Grand Canyon, working at the Red Feather Lodge. I asked him if he had ever watched the movie called, ironically, *Grand Canyon,* with Kevin Kline, Mary McDonnell, Danny Glover, Steve Martin, Alfre Woodard and Mary-Louise Parker. He hadn't, had never heard of it. I suggested that he watch it and think of this conversation.

Marcos went on to tell me about the drug problems that a tourist place such as this has. Here is all this magnificence, surrounded by pockets of civilization and temporary help, who are left with nothing to do after work. He said bored people get into trouble, and so, the drugs; he had seen situations like this before. I asked him how old he was again? Marcos gave me a sad smile. I had seen a lot of life at a tender young age; so had this fellow. But he had his head on good and straight. Whatever he chose to do, he'd be okay. Right now, because he had given all the money away, he was saving to go back to school, likely back in San Diego.

Marcos and I returned to the hotel. We decided that our mission, although not completely accomplished, was partially done. Now we knew exactly where Ricardo lived. Tuesday was supposed to be his day off – Marcos would check in the morning and see if Ricky was working the breakfast shift. I would continue trying to get in touch with my attorney, John Slate, finalize the letter, and reach Deputy Dick – see what his hours were. Now we knew just where to deliver this letter, tomorrow should be 'the day.'

By now it was close to 11PM. Marcos went on over to visit his girlfriend and I went up to my room to call Pete. *Criminy. I had forgotten about this time zone difference, in all the excitement – I'd have to do better about this in the upcoming week. It was 1AM on the east coast!* I gave the Wop a quick call to let him know I had arrived at the Canyon just fine, and that Marcos and I had located Ricardo's trailer, but hadn't had a chance to see Kokopelli yet. Hopefully, that would be tomorrow – for him, today. Pete wished us good luck, sleepily, albeit, and told me to behave myself "out there."

Pete was glad to know we had found the trailer, but reminded me to "be good" and to "work with the law. Remember, they're on your side in returning her, just be patient."

Sure. He was telling that to an Aries. Patience is not an Arian virtue; he had to know that after a quarter of a century together... I reminded him to give the kiddos a hug in the morning and tell them I missed them. I hung up, keeping the conversation short, as it was so late. Pete was tired and work came early for him, especially in the dual role of being Mom and Dad while I was here. I was worn out and wound up, still high on adrenaline from our clandestine evening out, and having been so close to seeing Pelli again — yet so far. Although physically and mentally exhausted, it was not a restful night.

NON SEQUITUR © 2002 by Wiley Miller. Dist. By UNIVERSAL PRESS SYNDICATE. Reprinted with permission. All rights reserved.

TWENTY-EIGHT

Plan A in Action; Tinkerville with Deputy Dick

"The good road and the road of difficulties, you have made me cross; and where they cross, the place is holy." Black Elk, Oglala Lakota Medicine Man

Grand Canyon – Tuesday morning, November 13th

The next day was absolutely gorgeous in the Grand Canyon. The weather was brisk and crisp, garnished by a clear cerulean blue sky with silvery clouds drifting lazily through it. It would have been an excellent idea, in retrospect, to take a timeout from this game of cat and mouse, to go hike the rim, or go down into the Canyon a little ways. To just take my camera and a backpack and change the station awhile. Take a break from this intense planning, clear my head, fill it with oxygen and astounding natural beauty. As it turned out, this would have been the only opportunity to do so. Imagine, coming as far as Tusayan Village from 2,000 miles away, and not going a *little bit further* to again see the breathtaking, goosebump-raising, awe-inspiring beauty of one of nature's miracles. But no, I got up and went back to work. I was myopic when it came to seeing his puppy again, and the sooner the better. I started calls to John Slate's office. The man was gruff and a little curt with me, as if he had a desk full of much more important things to do and this letter was a trivial interruption to his important day. But he was kind enough to humor me with the 'corrections.'

I took a break long enough to cross the road – looking for signs of Ricardo's van at the Café next door on the way out – to get breakfast and bring it back to my room to work. The hours passed as the letter got faxed from the downstairs desk, back and forth, cleaning it up to read 'just right' for full impact. I kept looking longingly out the window, wishing all of this could be done outside. Outside is where my heart belongs.

There was a knock at the door. I was sure it was Marcos, checking in at 11AM, as he'd said he would. But no, it was one of the maids wondering if I planned to stay on another night. *Hmm... Good question.* Looking around the room, one queen for sleeping, the other a desk covered in pertinent papers to 'the case,' the phone laid out upon it ready for communications, as necessary, I just nodded my head and said I thought I would. The idea of packing all of this up to go only God knew where would interrupt all forward progress. I went down to the front desk and renewed my key for another night in Tusayan. I was renting a hotel room, and an office, in one package.

(Later.) Frustrated. Ricardo's not working at the Canyon Café today – there is no sign of his van, and Marcos said he wasn't there for the breakfast shift. Apparently, the overtime he has been working does not infringe on his Tuesday/Fridays off. This is speculation on my part, but what really is concerning me is that once I have the letter in hand, and Deputy Dick by my side to "serve" Ricardo, he may not be home. And I don't know who his girlfriend is, or where she lives – yet. Would he be there? And would he have the puppy with him?

What just galls me is that if I could only have been in touch with John Slate in the afternoon yesterday, as I tried to do from Winslow about 3: 15, I could have had him fax the letter to the Red Feather Lodge, and gone down to Tinkerville last night, with Deputy Dick in tow. Ricardo was home then, with his old van and his fenced-in yard with the "Beware of Dog" sign on the gate. (Yeah, she's a real dangerous animal there, buddy. A real killer.)

So here I sit, amongst my piles of papers and notes, with faxed drafts of letters to John Slate, and the like. I wait for his response; the phone sits there, ominously. I stare at it; it stares back, silently. It's time to re-establish my game plan and get a fresh perspective on the potential reading in the proverbial crystal ball...

Plan A is totally legal: *the letter, deputy-delivered, hand-her-over-route. All up and up. You went back on your word, scum, therefore you essentially stole her, and I've come back for my dog. Hand her over there, you double-talkin,' back-stabbing piece-of-shit and be glad-you're-not-going-to-jail type route. Which keeps me from having to* *re-steal her (only, I ask, how can one steal something already rightfully theirs – and it all goes back to the old point of law about possession being 9/10th's of the law... Oh, yeah.) Anyhoo... This Plan A will keep me out of jail.*

Plan B. Okay, I admit, this one is still in the developmental stages. If Plan A doesn't work, it's my fallback plan. *Say Ricardo isn't home this evening, when Deputy Dick and I deliver the bailment letter. Maybe the deputy and I should just go see the security guard, ourselves, and explain to her that this Ricardo-character is an out-and-out dog thief. Yes, ma'm, living in her trailer park. Get her in on it; maybe she can help us figure something out. She not only looked feisty, she seemed pretty quick on the uptake. This also may be where the dark clothes fit in.... The 'do whatever it takes' option that comes into play...*

I glance around at my mess. The 'desk bed' holds luggage and the clothing that I have not unpacked and hung up, there at the bottom. My camera sits ready and waiting for gorgeous shots of the canyon that may not ever become a reality on this trip. *Unimaginable!* Flowers sit on the dresser, beside the TV. Newspapers, with current updates on the Taliban fiasco and news of al-Qaida, wait to be read. So far, no bin Laden in sight. But they're all on the run; bombing has begun. Kabul and Kandahar have been hit. Afghanistan is in a state of chaos. I can relate.

My "Kokopelli file" sits open, with various drafts of letters and all the legal papers collected thus far. I have spoken with John Slate several times this morning, as we worked on our "bailment" letter, saying, essentially, that Pete and I entrusted this puppy into Ricardo's care, at his word, and that he would take full responsibility for her and see that she came to no harm. It was very much like a babysitting agreement. I want it to have a kick-ass, I-mean-business closing and have faxed the revision back to him. I now await, what I hope to be, the final copy. 2 PM. The beautiful day calls to me. It beckons me to come play... those wispy clouds drift lazily in the carefree sky... it is extremely tempting....

I have been kicked into over-drive for days with planning, anticipation, airport travel that now fries my nerves with stringent security and repeated bag checks; there have been changes-of-plans, and long, long drives over huge sprawling states, waiting for any sort of hope to even see the puppy. I am tired and ready to see some results. *All sorts of snafus might lurk, I remind myself. Practice patience – a skill that is not a strong suit. I remind myself that 'Murphy' is alive and precocious... keep an eye on the little punk and stay centered there, kiddo. This will all work itself out, give it time. Breathe.*

Excellent! I've now been able to get through to Deputy Dick. He comes on at 3:30; I will meet him at the Grand Canyon office. He's given me directions. My last trip to the front desk was fruitful: Mr. Slate has faxed back the final draft and it looks good. Ends are pulling together here, time to sew this up. I called his office and said this letter was good to go, and asked if they would send a hard copy, on their legal letterhead, directly to Ricardo, giving them his P.O. address that he'd given to us, when we had traded addresses, back on October 2nd. I gather the legal information that we would need, my small photo album with Lakota's picture and those we had taken of 'Dingo,' when we first found her, our rim walk with her on October 1st, and the second night in the hotel. There were other photos in it, too – some of Pete and me from the anniversary trip before we had found her, and some of the children, from home. I would show this album of Dingo to Deputy Dick, as proof of ownership.

I make a pb&j sandwich to eat on the way over, grab an apple, some milk, and my camera and equipment. And then I dress in my dark clothes – for whatever reason, perhaps they empower me, maybe this is subconsciously a part of Plan B – and take along Jared's navy lined windbreaker for the inevitable evening chill, making sure my black riding gloves and the navy stocking cap are in the pockets. I gather Kokopelli's leash, brought from home, and her new collar and harness, fresh out of Wal-Mart, a couple of rawhide chews, and other doggy whatnot, in anticipation of our reunion. I had even brought from home a pair of knotted-up old socks, remembering that Ricardo had said that she liked these as toys. Looking around the room, I try to think of anything else that I had forgotten. No, it seems this was everything one would need in our reunion. It is out the door, and into that beautiful day, and on to the great unknown... With a prayer and a promise, by the end of the evening Kokopelli and I will be together again.

It takes me a little bit of driving around the airport to locate the law office, which is in a trailer over to the side, hidden amongst the heavy trees. There sits a large white truck with the proper legal insignia on the side of its door to make it official. I am there. I knock at the door and am greeted by Deputy Aaron Dick, himself, a man in his thirties, about my height, fully decked-out in deputy duds, including gun and badge,  with "Deputy A. Dick" on his nametag. I can only imagine the ribbing he must have gotten in high school years. He has the short haircut that seems to be required with law enforcement, a pleasant face, and glasses. I had spoken with him several times from Virginia, when arranging to return to recover Kokopelli; it was good to now meet him, in person.

We exchange pleasantries and I show him the small photo album of our anniversary trip, proving to him how we had found the puppy. I am hoping to get him emotionally involved, but a man and a woman see these photographs differently, I think. He is all business, wanting a copy of the letter from John Slate for their files. So I set my manila folder down, containing all of my legal jargon, along with the small photo album, pull out this letter and give it to him to Xerox.

Deputy Dick gets the copy he needs, I pick up my folder, and we leave for Tinkerville. He suggests that he follow me in his truck, as he might be called off on a more pressing matter at any point. As we are leaving, he turns to tell me that he is only there to keep the peace between Ricardo and myself, as this is a civil matter, and that if Ricardo were to ask if he had to hand the dog over to me, he would have to tell him no, he didn't – that the whole thing could go to court, possibly be appealed, while Ricardo kept the pup. *Well, damn*, I'm thinking, *what are you good for? You didn't mention anything about this when I was still back in Virginia! Ricardo could just take off with Kokopelli and disappear, or have* her *disappear, in the meantime. I also don't live in Arizona – what am I supposed to do while this inches its way through the legal system? Move* here*? Temporarily desert my family to work all this out? This won't work, at all. I've spent all this time and money, traveled 2,000 miles to retrieve my dog, go to the trouble to go in with heavy ammo – with the law and the letter – and here you take the bullets out of my gun?! Damn! I am watching Plan A evaporate before my eyes.*

Deputy Dick must see the frustration on my face. He tries to be reassuring about Ricardo's returning her to me without all that hoopla, but he doesn't know how stubborn the man is with whom we are about to visit. I remembered well that Thursday afternoon, when Pete and I had returned from Chinle, driving back 250 miles to pick up our pup, and Ricardo had totally refused to stand by his word. *Humph.* 2½-3 hours of persuasion, pleading, anger, etc., and we had gotten nowhere. (I later found out he was absolutely holding out for money). No, I do not feel hopeful any longer.

So the good deputy is following me down 180 in his big ole' truck, and I'm thinking: *Great, he now knows the make, model, color and license plates of the car I'm driving. It'll be ingrained by the time we get there. I can't speed ahead, so he won't get a clear shot, or I'll get ticketed for all the wrong reasons. Ugh.*

As we drive along, the afternoon light deepens and the artist emerges.

I start to go into my enraptured state of watching magnificent scenery unfold, with the dramatic play of warm red light and shadows bringing the park to life; it is beautiful. *Heck with the speeding ticket, now he can nail me for reckless driving,* I think, grabbing my camera from the backseat and try to focus, shoot and steer as we drive south. I figure he wouldn't be too patient with my pulling over and repeatedly asking him to wait a moment while I clicked off a shot... My memories of driving through such beauty with Pete were fresh enough in my mind, and my husband knows this weakness. Here is a total stranger; his job is not to cater to the artist, but to uphold the law. *Okay, behave,* I tell myself and continue clicking away, taking one of Deputy Dick following behind me through the rear view mirror.

We manage to get there intact. No elk, no running off the road and no tickets, at all. I signal the left turn into Tinkerville and we drive down the long, dusty, bumpy old road to the trailer park entrance. This is like driving those backcountry, washboard miles over the Indian rez. We arrive, my heart pounding madly as perhaps 'the moment has come'... all these weeks of emotional roller-coastering, and I might soon be seeing the precious little mutt that for weeks has been the center of magnificent chaos.

I drive directly to Ricardo's trailer, with the deputy behind me. There is no van parked here today. Great. Last night Ricky was home, van was there, dog was there, but no Deputy Dick. Today, legal papers in hand, deputy beside me, dog in the trailer (I hope), and no Ricardo. *Double dastardly damn! Calm down, pounding heart, we'll work this out...*

Deputy Dick gets out of his truck and looks around. He knocks hard on the side of the trailer, as one has to go through the gate to get to the 'front' (side) sliding entry door. No response. He says, okay, we can go through the gate and up to the door and knock. We do. I hear the puppy inside, whining frantically on the other side. I kneel down, only a pane of glass between us, ecstatic to be this close to her again after so long, and call her – " 'Dingo!'...'Lucky!', *'Pelli!'*... Come here you confused little dog!" The whining is closer and she is clawing away at this lacy curtain Ricardo has in front of his door. I'm calling louder now and knocking; it's just killing me that she's so close, yet so far! And then she manages to nudge the curtain aside. *There she is! It's her!* Her pale golden coat, her perky, foxy face nosing against the door, leaving wet marks on the glass, that crazy corkscrew tail... It's her, she has grown, and she definitely recognizes me. Her whining grows louder, as she is trying to get 'through' the door, frantically pawing at it and then she bounds aside and disappears. I notice she is now wearing a large red collar, as well as a red bandana. *Not only did you steal our dog, you're using a bandana on her, too. That's insult to injury there, Buster.*

I turn to Deputy Dick now, frustrated that we can't do more. He is standing behind me quietly, giving me time with her and waiting for Ricardo to return home. I notice that the lock on the sliding door is just a small padlock that the man has devised to secure his trailer. I see another door, an old brown thing, further down, past the woodpile. It is secured with nails toenailed in, ancient and rusted. *Hmmmm.... Laura,* Behave...

Okay, time now to follow up on my idea of approaching the security guard lady that came barreling down last evening to question Marcos and me. She lives over in the trailer, kind of at the top of, and to the right of the loop, fenced-off from the rest. Deputy Dick agrees to go over and talk with her, and so follows my car. *He really is a pleasant fellow, and he is trying to be helpful.*

The lady is home and she knows Deputy Dick. I introduce myself, and she tells me her name is Debbie and her husband is Tinker; they own/manage the trailer park. Now that I am seeing her with light left in the sky, and the pressure is off, I can focus on the woman, not the authority figure appearing out of nowhere. Debbie is petite, with a lively, pretty face and is very keen on what is going on – she doesn't miss a thing. She is crowned with a mane of dark, wavy hair. Debbie asks if I am "Teresa," from the night before? Well, I had never heard myself called "Teresa" last night in all the excitement, and so deny it. She looks dubious. We explain to her that Ricardo stole the puppy, by reneging on his agreement with my husband and myself, almost six weeks ago. Debbie tells us that she had only just seen the pup about a week ago, when she saw Ricardo walking it. She asked him where he had gotten the puppy, and he had told her "some tourists gave her to him." I said "*Ha!* There's a *whole* lot more to the story than that!" Yet I found it extremely interesting that Dingo had been with Ricardo for this amount of time and Debbie – with her stringent security – is just now seeing the pup. I thought: *Apparently his yard remains empty; the poor dog must have stayed in his trailer night and day, except for those rare occasions when he opted to walk her. What a stink must rise from that place. Egads! What a wonderful life, to go from starving but free in the wide-open desert, to being fed and 'cared for,' confined to Ricardo's smoke-filled quarters 24/7. Criminy, was I glad I had followed my heart and come back here to finish the rescue. My resolve deepened to bring this puppy back home with me, with room to run, attention and loving from an entire family – people and critters, alike –being her new destiny.*

Deputy Dick is called off on a "domestic," but again reminds me that he is only here for the delivery of my letter and to keep the peace, something called a "Civil Standby." Basically, I think he is worried that I am ready to punch the guy's lights out, grab her and run. He is beginning to know me. Before he leaves I ask him, only half in jest, "This *is* the West. Can't you just pull your gun out and demand that Ricardo give her back to me?" He gives me a stern look and says: "No, I can't do that. Now be*have*." *Damn.*

As Deputy Dick leaves, he tells us that if Ricardo were to come home, to call him and he would get back up here as soon as he could. Debbie invites me to come in and I follow her through an inner gate into the courtyard. My attention is riveted on her beautiful wolf/shepherd there in the yard, a gorgeous, slim gray-toned creature with the intelligent and graceful bearing of a wolf. I fall for him instantly, and start making playful overtures, which he promptly returns. "Gondo" is his name. Debbie tells me that they have had him since he was a puppy and that he is very special to them. It is easy to see why.

Debbie enters her cozy trailer, past a doormat that reads: **"Heck with the dog. Beware of the kids!"** I smile, relating, recalling and sharing with her a sign in a local restaurant back home that says: **"Raising kids is like being pecked to death by a chicken."** We laugh. Apparently their children were grown and gone. Debbie fixes tea for the two of us, while Gondo sniffs around me, curiously. I rub his head and talk with him, very glad for an animal fix. At her questioning, I go into detail about finding Dingo – now Kokopelli – starving in Monument Valley, in the middle of our 25th Anniversary trip. How we had brought her to the Grand Canyon to save her and then had fallen love with her, and had thought to take her home. How Ricardo had come into the picture, and in that morning of emotional weakness on my part, and because of our itinerary, we had let her go, trusting Ricardo to stand by his word about "baby-sitting." How we had gone on with our vacation plans, talked about it in Canyon de Chelly, definitely decided to fly her home with us, and how Ricardo had flatly refused to return her when we drove back from Chinle, after calling him twice. I confide that, indeed, it was me last night. I told Debbie who Marcos was, how he was trying to help, and how we were simply trying to identify just which trailer was Ricardo's. I try to show her the anniversary photos, but, after digging like a dog, find they are nowhere in the car. *Well, hells bells, I must have left them in Deputy Dick's office when we copied the letter. Scheisse!*

Debbie's husband, Tinker – thus the name "Tinkerville" – comes in for dinner. He is a tall and lanky fellow, with a kind, lived-in face, reminding me of Sam Shepherd. Tinker listens to the story in an abbreviated form and the two invite me to join them for a potluck dinner; I am famished, and gratefully accept the invitation. They then turn their security cameras on Ricardo's trailer, so that we can see when he comes home and thus let Deputy Dick know. Nope, he's not home yet. It is by now about 7:00 and pitch black outside, so we visit during dinner, getting to know each other, laughing and sharing stories. I tell them of our life in Virginia: our small farm, all the animals, our three lively teenagers, about Pete, and how dear he had been about my coming out to reclaim Kokopelli. The all of it. We have a fine time, as the night passes on by and we watch those cameras. When I mention something about how I feel about spaying and neutering, Tinker looks uncomfortable, saying that is hitting a little "too close to home," and excuses himself to watch TV. Debbie and I laugh and away he goes, a beer in hand and Gondo by his side. Debbie then fixes up a scrumptious mixed berry dessert and more tea. We glance at the security cameras.... Still no Ricky.

TWENTY-NINE

Night of the Heist (or Plan B in Action)

"Last but not least, courage — moral courage to see things through. The world is in a constant conspiracy against the brave. It's the age-old struggle — the roar of the crowd on one side and the voice of your conscience on the other."
Douglas MacArthur

After dessert, looking out at the velvety black night and then over at the cameras still showing no van, I look at Debbie. I am getting extremely restless, feeling I had been in the Canyon for two days and am basically getting nowhere. It is around 8:30. "Debbie," I say, "I can't stand it. She's in there, a glass door between us. I'm going over and pick that silly little lock and free her." She just gives me a knowing smile and disappears. I am not sure what is going on; maybe I've overstepped boundaries with her — maybe *she* is in there calling the law! No, here she comes, a grinning. In her hand is a bobby pin, a large paper clip, and a small, narrow screwdriver. Debbie tells me "You go, girl! I'm not going to notice the cameras." I give her a big hug and a huge thank you and tell her that if I *am* successful, I can't come back — we'll need to hightail it out of here. She knows. And I don't want to implicate them, or anyone else; this is my dilemma, my dog, and as far as the deputies know, I'm acting alone. Little did anyone know how many warm and caring souls were rooting for this small reservation puppy's emancipation.

I leave, grateful for the hospitality and support of this good couple. I drive back over to Ricky's road and, as I'm turning in, headlights are headed my way. *Great.* Now *he's coming home!* So I slowly and nonchalantly drive past the oncoming vehicle that turns out to be a big ole' truck, not Ricardo's van at all. The truck pulls into the trailer opposite Ricky's place. Okay, this isn't as bad, but now there is someone home and a potential witness to my escapade. I go down and slowly turn around, very aware now of the number of trailers around me, who seems to be home, and which lights are on, both inside and out. I park opposite of Marcos' friend's trailer, by the dumpster, and find the dome light to kill it, otherwise, this blasted rental car lights up like Christmas when I open the door.

Good. The dome light is out and now the outside lights won't come on when the door is opened. Once outside the car, I check all of my dark clothes and zip Jared's warm navy blue windbreaker jacket tightly around my neck, as the fall evening is chilling quickly. I pull out my black riding gloves, with one fingertip out (had meant to sew this up before leaving home...) and then pull the navy stocking cap over my hair. I stand in the dead quiet of the Arizona night in the sleepy little trailer park, breathing softly, watching my breath turn to frost, listening for anything unusual and watching for incoming vehicles. Nothing. The night is clear and dark. Time to unlock the car so – if and when I bring Kokopelli out with me – I can put her on the back seat, on her Indian blanket, and leave.

Okay. All is well. I stand beside the car with the key-fob thingy in my hand and hit the 'unlock' button, only in the dark of the night – for the first time since I've had the Malibu – I hit the 'horn' button, instead. **"Honk!"** it roars into the dead quiet night. **"Honk!"** a second time... Damn, damn, *damn! Where* is *the obnoxious thing?!!* **"Honk!!!"** a third time, **"Honk!!!"** Four bloody blasted blares of the blasphemous horn before I find the right button and kill the sound. Ah ... stillness again. Quiet. *Some stealthy thief you are, kid. Great way to get started here...*

I'm plastered up against the dumpster now, my heart just pounding in my chest – I'm sure 'they' can even hear this now – I'm trying to calm my racing pulse, waiting for the inhabitants to come pouring out of their long, rectangular homes, shotguns in hand. This *is* the West; the residents probably all have shotguns, and use them first and ask questions later... it's in their genes. I'll get my bloody head blown off for this silly pup...

But nothing happens. No one even peeks outside. *Are they all hearing impaired,* I'm thinking, *or is* everybody *stoned?!!* Still, nothing at all. *Well, thank you, Lord. You and Mom are up there having a belly laugh, aren't you, at my expense?...* I have to smile at the dunderness of it all – it is funny, knowing nothing came of the trip-up.

Cautiously I glide to the side of the dumpster and quietly start for the road, releasing my Indian spirit. Suddenly the door opens on a trailer close by and a man comes out on his porch. I duck behind a large cedar. *Of course, he heard the horn blowing and he's checking it out – it just took him a minute to load his gun.* But no, he's slamming something like an ice tray against the railing on his porch. I watch quietly, trying to figure out what the hell he's doing, because what*ever* he's holding is much bigger than the suspected ice tray, now that I can see it. He stops, whatever his mission was is accomplished, and now he returns inside. Oh well, it's not important; there is no gun involved. A quote by Winston Churchill passes my mind, *"Nothing in life is so exhilarating as to be shot at without result."* I'd just as soon take his word for this; I still had children to raise.

The moon is my accomplice tonight, my abettor and friend; she hides her warmth and magic behind the shadow of the sun, willing my mission to be completed, as she secretly watches from high. No one else is outside now, that I can tell. But there is a pretty good stretch of open grass between this trailer and Ricky's, with that blasted spotlight of his shining down; I duck further back, deeper into the darker part of the field, now questioning my own sanity, but not my resolve. *I came here to get my pup and bring her home. The Cherokee in me must now resurface. There is nothing virtual about this reality.... the time has come and this moment is real. Go for it!*

Still watching for any signs of life to be the ticket to become a statue, and seeing none, I let myself quietly in the gate, all the while listening for any vehicle coming up the road. Luckily, one can hear tires from as far away as the dusty entrance road. Now I'm standing in the wash of floodlight, peering at the small silver lock, wondering which implement to try first. I had always heard good things about bobby pins, so I opened it wide and start fishing around for whatever tiny mechanism inside that will pop it open. This doesn't seem to be long enough, so I try the elongated paper clip. No dice. Okay, then, the screwdriver. Nope. Holding the rejects in my mouth, I go through the process all over again, thinking: *some thief I am — honking horns and useless tools.... Where's Bev when I need her? She told me she's "good at this sort of thing." I won't press her on what she meant by that, but her expertise about now sure would be helpful.* All the while Kokopelli is whining on the other side of the door, and scratching away at it from inside. My thoughts continue: *is it against the law if she happens to paw her way through the glass and frees herself? It's a race! Who'll win?...* I try the screwdriver again, marveling at my own patience. *By jiminy! It pops open! I did it! I am now a 'criminal'!* I'm standing there, speechless, but only momentarily. *Gotta' work fast here, kiddo; don't push your luck...*

Little "Dingo-Kokopelli-Lucky-Sunshine" (*holy smokes, this mutt has more names than Elizabeth Taylor*) waits for me on the other side, looking confused now. She hesitates and ducks back into the living area, unsure, and then runs out into my arms. Sure enough, the little thing remembers me! I get enthusiastic puppy kisses all over my face as I hold her small, squirming, body. *Okay, okay, enough loving here, pup, we've got to get back to business.* I put her down a minute, and she darts all over the yard, ecstatic to be free. I close the lock, careful to wipe my 'prints' off, even though I'm wearing gloves, because of that fingertip being out. Besides, this is what they always do in the movies; it seems an appropriate time. I call her softly and she comes running. I gather the small bundle of constant motion into my arms, reassure her, and slip through, closing the gate behind me; we're on our way. I tell myself that I'm not stealing anything that wasn't mine in the first place. I didn't, technically, "break and enter." I "jimmied and opened" – I never set foot inside the trailer and I couldn't begin to tell you what it looks like, what color carpet he had, or anything, except this single guy's got sheer, lacy curtains. Kinky. And I had relocked his silly little padlock so that no one could come back and steal anything that Ricardo actually, truly owned. I feel absolutely no guilt – just a strange sense of exhilaration and accomplishment. This precious puppy that I had found starving to death weeks ago in the desert, and gravitated to like the North Star – in trusting that Lakota's spirit was in there waiting for me – is now back in the shelter of my arms.

Back to Tusayan

As I'm driving north again, back to Tusayan Village, back to my hotel and supporters there, I'm allowing myself to call "Dingo-Lucky-Sunshine" Kokopelli now. Poor kid will be so confused... She's in the back, on the purple and black striped Indian blanket that I had bought for her in eastern Arizona, on the way here. She is leaning over the back seat, whining, puzzled, and asking *what's going on?* I'm saying: "Dingo? *Dingo?*" No response. Okay, I'll give it a go: "Lucky?" Nothing whatsoever. She knows neither name. "Sunshine?" I venture... Again, nothing. *Great!* A clean slate for "Kokopelli," so aptly named for mischief-maker of the west. As the week progressed, I was to realize how true this would be... I'm talking to her, reassuring her (and me) that everything will be okay, wondering if it's true, myself. She is nervous and scared back there, totally unsure of what is happening. I just continue playing Mark Knopfler's CD, *Sailing to Philadelphia* – my partner in crime – which soothes me no end as I listen to the soft strains of "Silvertown" and "Sands of Nevada," hoping this will help soothe the pup, as well.

Before I return to the hotel I decide to walk her as she had been inside that trailer since Lord only knows when. I find a lonesome back road shortly before entering the village, not yet realizing there is a rapist/murderer running loose in this area, and this is no Rottweiler I'm holding. We walk and walk; she sniffs and sniffs, pulling me everywhere, *thrilled* to be outside. But she neither poops nor pees, instead just smells these wonderful scents to which I am oblivious.

I leave Pelli in the car, in the parking lot of the hotel, on her Indian blanket. She has a knotted-up old sock and a rawhide chew to keep her busy while I duck into the lobby to say "hey" to the guys at the desk. Marcos and Scott look up expectantly as I enter and ask excitedly: "Did you get her?! Did you get her?!"

I smile a yes at them, "I did, boys, but not quite as we expected. Ricardo wasn't home... I waited and waited after Deputy Dick and I went down to meet him. I even had dinner with 'our' security guard, Marcos — she's really very nice; her name is 'Debbie.' But Ricky never came home... so I went over to his place, picked the guy's lock, and got my dog back."

Silence. They look at each other and then burst out laughing. "Laura, you didn't, *really!* You're just joking, right?" Scott asks.

"No, Scott, I'm serious as a heart attack, which I almost had, but that's *another* story, altogether... No, I just got my dog back, which is *the* reason I came back west."

Marcos looks at me from across the desk, knowing I am dead serious. He laughs and says: "Laura, you've brought more excitement to the Canyon than we've had in the last year. But now we've got to get you out of here."

I walk over to the desk in my get-away garb, sans hat and gloves, my hair a mess. By now, he probably thinks I always wear black and blue. "No, Marcos, I've rented the room for the night, already. I'm dead-tired and not yet ready to face those lurking elk. I'm going on up to my room, pack up, call Pete, and try to get a little sleep before leaving."

"Okay..." he trails his words, not agreeing with me. "I'll be up as soon as I get off and see if I can give you a hand." Scott is just standing there in shock and awe; I'm not sure if he believed me yet, or not.

Leaving...

Back in my room, I stand in the entry, looking at all the 'stuff' to be re-packed and loaded up and just groan. *Why do I have to move into a place?* I call Peter, as I pull clothes off the hangers, semi-folding them and pushing them into the suitcase. The phone cord trails behind me, the phone, itself, wedged between my cheek and neck. The man answered – let's see, I glanced at the clock, it's about midnight on the east coast...

"Hey, LauraWop, I've been waiting for your call."(Who else would call at this hour?) "How did it go with Deputy Dick, today? Do you have Kokopelli?"

"Well, Pete...I *did* meet with the deputy. He was very nice, and tried to be helpful, but Ricardo wasn't at home. So we went over and talked to the security lady, Debbie. Deputy Dick had to leave but, before he did, he explained to me that Ricardo didn't have to give Pelli back to us." I went on to explain what the deputy had said. "So Debbie invited me to dinner and we watched the security cameras, waiting for Ricky to come home – "

"Ricky?" Pete interrupted –

"Yes, Ricky. Ricardo. That's so formal, I use both now."

"Laura, he doesn't even know you're *back* is what you're telling me. How can you know him *inform*ally?!"

"Pete, believe me, that's not the important issue right now. Please let me finish..."

I continue with the night's unfolding: "So anyway. Ricky never came home, and I decided to just take the matter into my own hands, after that talk with Deputy Dick," *Hmmm... let's see, how does one go about telling one's husband this next part? I guess, like* Nike *says, 'Just do it:'* (big breath) "So Debbie loaned me some tools, and I went over and picked Ricardo's lock and I've got Kokopelli."

Silence. For Pete, that's astounding. And then: "You're telling me that the *security guard* helped you? That you *picked the guys lock and got the dog back?! I told you to be***have** *yourself out there!*" His voice rose. And then: "Laura, tell me you *didn't*. Do you realize that you've now taken this from civil, on your side, to criminal, *against* you! *Damnit*, I told you to be *behave*. Now you've got to get out of there, and fast."

"I know. I know," I say, suddenly exhausted. "I'm packing up as we speak..." There is a knock at the door. I excuse myself for a moment to let Marcos in, telling him I am on the phone with Pete. Marcos goes to the corner chair, sits quietly, and watches me work.

"Listen, Pete, I'm going to load the car up and leave in the wee hours, but I've got to try to get a little rest – I've been too wired to sleep much. I'll get out of here early, and I'll call you at work in the morning to let you know how it's going, okay? Don't worry – everything will be all right. We've got our dog back, and that's *all* I did. I didn't even have to go inside his place to do that, as she remembered me and came running out. She's scared and lonely and confused, but, other than that, she's fine. He fed her well, apparently – she's no longer skinny."

"Okay, Laura. Try to rest – but you've got to get across the border as soon as you can, and remember – it's a *long* ways away. Drive safely, Ra, and good luck. I love you, but you're going to put me into an early grave yet..."

"Pete" – I couldn't resist – "I've always told you you should've married 'the girl next door' – maybe now you'll believe me. She would have had your dinner waiting; the house would always be neat. Heck, she might not even be an animal lover. All that."

"Laura, it's sounding more and more attractive. But somehow I do still love you, despite it all. But if I *had've* married that 'girl next door,' as you like to say, I would have *lived* a lot longer."

"Yeah," I wink at Marcos, "but your life wouldn't have been *nearly* as interesting..."

"Goodnight, Laura. Call me."

Marcos leans forward in his chair after I hung up with Pete, his hands are clasped together and a small smile is on his face from our bantering, but his expression is serious, as he says: "Okay, I've been thinking about this. First of all, I'm going to show you the back way out of the hotel, so you can load up your car easily. You can park around to the side." I continue packing up, stuffing my suitcase, listening. Then I start stacking and loading all those long hours of Plan A, at the legal end of it, in my satchel.

He continues: "Laura, you've got to know something that's going on around here that hasn't been publicized. They don't want it to impact the tourist industry, which is already off, since September 11th." (*Yeah, our 25th.*) "But knowing this could help you, if you do get caught. There is someone in this area of the Canyon that has raped and murdered several of the women workers here, in the past several months. They haven't solved it, or gotten many leads, and they want to keep it all hushed for now, until they do. Your case just can't be too important to them."

(Right. A case of rape and murder seems just a bit higher on the priority list here, as I'm thinking of Mary and Galen, a quick jab of pure anger in my heart.) "So remind them of this, if you have to. I should have told you sooner, with your driving around alone. But whoever is doing this seems to know his victims and party with them, so you probably weren't in any danger, yourself."

I stop my intense packing and look at Marcos, at this wise young man who had seen so much life in so few years. I study his unlined face; his heavy brows are now furrowed in concern. *Damn, I will miss my friend.* "Thank you, Marcos, for telling me that. It really does help put all this in perspective. I may need that information later — we'll just see how this plays out. Once I get all this stuff packed up and the car loaded, I'm going to try to rest a little before leaving. But I want to thank you again for caring about this puppy's welfare, and for helping us out so much."

He just smiles back at me, sitting in the chair, not knowing what else to do. "Well, let me help you carry some of that downstairs. And Scott is waiting to help you with checking out." Soon I found out what Marcos meant by that, but I won't write it down.

Later, with the car semi-loaded and Pelli freshly walked (still, no results), and me looking over my shoulder now for this unidentified rapist lurking in the shadows, I consider my predicament. I find a dumpster and get rid of "Sunshine/Lucky's" red bandana, but keep the big red collar Ricardo had gotten for her, intending to donate it to an animal shelter somewhere.

I think of the craziness in these last two months, the twists and turns and excitement surrounding our 25th, and the 9/11 madness. I think again of Janus, the Roman god of past, present and future... I think of all the 'signs,' leading us from one adventure to the next and of the poster Art had given us so early in our anniversary trip, way back when: **"Lost Dog: 3 legs, blind in one eye, tail broken, recently been castrated, answers to the name of 'Lucky' "**.... I have to smile at life's many ironies. Here, this somewhat closes the discombobulated circle to the here and now, Ricardo having named her "Lucky," because "she's such a lucky little dog." He had *no* idea.

That night – or morning – about 1AM, I finally lay my head down on the cool, soft pillow in my room, nestled under the covers, thinking about how comfortable this room is, how quiet. How inviting and safe – I would love to just sleep and sleep for days. I snuggle down into my favorite nesting position, there with my fuzzy bone pillow. The room certainly is conducive to a restful nights sleep. Only I couldn't find the switch to calm my mind, to let it rest. My body begged for repose but my mind lay there, turning over and over the events of the last few hours, endlessly shifting details and 'what if's.' And there, layered between rest and restlessness, in Springsteen's dark wee, wee hours before the dawn, I plan our escape. At 4:23 AM the alarm jangles beside me. I drag my weary, spent body out from under the warm cocoon of safety to begin the next chapter and our escape out of Arizona.

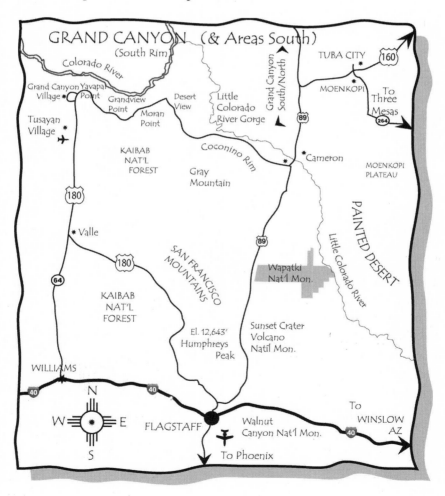

Part V
Wild West Woman in Action

THIRTY

Winslow, Arizona (enter Robert Redford)

"Speak your mind, but ride a fast horse."
Texas Bix Bender

Wednesday, November 14th

We had been up since 4:30ish. I was still 'high' from adrenaline as we left the hotel under the cover of darkness and drove down Highway 180, past the Valle intersection where 180 becomes highway 64, just on the edge of the Kaibab National Forest. I had watched the sun's earliest rays begin to caress the sky over the San Francisco Peaks – the northwestern most of the four sacred mountains – marveling in the quiet beauty of the area and grateful to have my freedom, with Kokopelli at my side. We arrived in Williams, a straight shot down from the Canyon, with the first light of day and found gas at a small station on the way into town. It was bitter cold that wintry fall morn; the attendant and I both commented on this fact, as I used my studio credit card for the last time. *(Fine, trace me here if you want, but from now on, boys, it's traveler's checks.)*

Crossing the railroad tracks I noticed a train with The Grand Canyon boldly written on its side. Guess this is also a straight shot to and from the Canyon down to this small town; I wondered how far south it went, and if it was meant for tourists, alone, or just what might be it's calling in the great scheme around here. I found a McDonald's and walked Kokopelli in the still morning light, taking in the wild mountains around me... There was lots of enthusiastic sniffing but still no results. Pelli seemed to be okay, but I was beginning to worry about some bladder dysfunction. I'd have to have this checked out with our vetting appointment. Wish we could somehow figure a way to blend our bladder capacities... from me, she would go more normally; from her, I wouldn't have to go nearly as often. And if wishes were horses...

Williams is known as the "Gateway to the Grand Canyon." Its elevation is 6,770 feet; it was first settled in 1874 and now has a population of about 2,500 people. Williams is also the headquarters of the Kaibab National Forest and is one of the few places in Arizona that all four seasons are seen. Downtown Williams is listed in the National Register of Historic Places, with most of the construction dating back to the early 1900s. Annual precipitation is 21.88 inches. (I read these tidbits of facts from the Fall 2001 *Williams Tour Guide* that I picked up at breakfast.)

After a hearty breakfast at the Golden Arches, Pelli and I found our way back to I-40 and out of Williams. As we drove along 1-40 towards Flagstaff I started getting sleepy. *Very* sleepy. These past few days of intensity focused on seeing Kokopelli again and then the attention to details and planning to recover her, had left me wired at night, making calls or writing in the journal 'til late – or watching CNN for terrorist updates. Sleep had not been a priority, especially last night as I lay awake, willing myself to rest but all the while planning my 'great escape' out of the area; it was taking its toll.

My eyes wanted to shut in the worst way, just for a *little* while, as we drove along the Interstate, amongst busy early traffic and Mack trucks. I would nod, then spring my eyes open, slap my face, roll down the window to that cold mountain air and breathe it in deeply. I fished around and found *The Doors* CD. Certainly Jim Morrison could wake me up. Still, with the car vibrating and gyrating along the fast open road, windows halfway down and the wind in my face, I struggled to put the miles behind us.

We passed all the exits to Flagstaff; my goal was to reach Winslow before stopping. There I planned to call Pete and give him an update, as surely he was worried. And I would call the law about the photo album I'd left with Deputy Dick the day before and find out what they now knew. I found a phone booth in the back of Denny's, in Winslow, conveniently located right beside the ladies room. First things first. When I could think clearly again I called the Red Feather Lodge, telling the young lady now on duty at the front desk that I'd left something yesterday with Deputy Dick and that if he brought it in later, would she please hold it until that afternoon, when I'd be back in the Canyon to pick it up. I planned to have Marcos just mail it to Virginia. She told me, as a matter of fact, that Deputy Isabella had called earlier, asking for me, but she had told him that I'd already checked out at 5:30 AM. *Hmm...* So the law is already looking for me? I guess this is no surprise...

After some digging around in my expanding notebook of many names and numbers and scribbles of notes, I found the number for the Coconino Sheriff's Department and dialed. I'm wondering things like: *Can an 800# be traced from a Sheriff's Department to a pay phone in Denny's? And if so, then how quickly? I don't know the answer to that – I need to read more Ludlum novels, but I had better not stay on long, just in case.*

While waiting, with all these thoughts running loose in my head, I was patched through to Deputy Isabella, whom I'd just heard about, but not yet met. Apparently he works the earlier day shift, with Deputy Dick relieving him mid-afternoon.

A man's voice came on the line, cutting to the chase immediately: "Ah, I've been looking for you. Where are you?" Gulp. *No "Hi," "How are you?" – nothing.*

"Why, I'm in Williams," I said, not feeling it prudent to com*plete*ly give away my hard-earned mileage. "I was just calling to see if you or Deputy Dick might drop the photo album I left yesterday in the Sheriff's trailer by the Red Feather Lodge – I'll be back up there later to pick it up."

"Williams, eh? Well, that's convenient. *I'm* in Williams. And I would *really* like to talk to you," responded Deputy Isabella, ignoring my request about the photo album altogether.

"Oh?" I asked innocently, all sweetness and light. "Why?"

"Oh, I think you know," the good Deputy responded.

"No, I don't. I haven't a clue. Why would *you* want to talk with *me*?" (Now all fluffy and blond.)

We played footsies on the phone a bit longer, and then he says, "I have this Ricardo fellow here, who is claiming a burglary at his home this morning. Claims he's missing something..." A long and dramatic pause, then Deputy Isabella adds: "...his dog."

"Oh?" I ask politely, the embodiment of innocence.

"You have the puppy, don't you?" Deputy Isabella now asks me, point blank. Well, here was the make or break moment, I later came to realize, but I'm tired, and tired of playing these silly little games about my own damned dog.

"Maybe. *Maybe* I do, and *maybe* I don't." I tell the man. Apparently, I'm a pretty good locksmith but a lousy liar.

"Okay, I'd *really* like to talk to you now. Where are you in Williams?" he asked, with deep authority in his voice.

"With my attorney. I'm seeing my attorney this morning." Now a flat-out lie. Maybe I could get good at this, under the circumstances.

"Oh, that's probably a very good idea. Let me give you directions to my office, here in Williams, and you can come see me afterwards."

"Listen, Deputy Isabella. Now's the time I think I should tell you that I should talk with my attorney first. *May*be I'll call you later."

"Please call me back, Ms.Giannini, I really need to talk with you about this dog. Two wrongs don't make a right, you know."

"Sir, in all due respect, I beg to differ. In this case, they definitely do; I have no doubt in my mind. I *may* call you later, depending on what he says. Goodbye." *Hmm...*

Think, Laura, think. First of all, he's not returning the album. Damnit. I mentally kick myself again for leaving it. *Secondly, how long was that call?... More than three minutes? And is it three minutes, or is it four, before they can trace it?... Didn't think to time the thing.* Later, months later, reading *The Bourne Supremacy*, by Robert Ludlum, I have this wonderful "ta dah" moment:

"...A trace! They had bounced him around, keeping him on the line long enough to put an electronic trace on his calls! Pay phones were the most difficult to track down. The vicinity was determined first; next the location or premises, and finally the specific instrument, but it was only a matter of minutes or fractions of minutes between the first step and the last. Had he stayed on long enough? And if so, to what degree of progress? The vicinity? The hotel? The pay phone itself? Jason tried to reconstruct his conversation with the operator – the second operator – when the trace would have begun. Maddeningly, frantically, but with all the precision he could summon, he tried to recapture the rhythm of their words, their voices, realizing that when he had accelerated she had slowed down..."

Of course, Deputy Isabella could also have Caller I.D. I leaned up against the phone and closed my eyes to think. Maybe I'd better move the car, and the evidence, just in case. I went out and joined Kokopelli in the front seat, warming the driver's side and waiting for me. "Time to move, girl," I confided. "Let's go to Wal-Mart." We did, driving around the huge structure and parked amongst many other sedans, over by the end of the lot. I lay my head back against the seat, mentally and physically beat. *How do Ludlum's characters keep going?* I'm thinking. *Four hours of sleep in three days time, shot up and generally mutilated, still they drag themselves through and save the day. Well, daggonit, if they can, I can, too. I haven't been shot (yet).* Kokopelli whines beside me, wants to crawl all over me, looking for answers, attention, anything. My thoughts continue: *Here I am, wanted in the state of Arizona for this crazy little trained-for-nothing mutt that won't pee for pleading. She's wild and wanting, and I've got to get her* back *to Virginia with the law on my heels. What have I done? Maybe I should just take her back to Ricardo's, put her in his yard, and be done with it. He can have the dog.* Then my old fire kicks into gear. *No, damnit, he* can't. *Not with what he's done with her. To* her. *I've got her now, and I broke the law to do it. I can train a dog. I didn't come this far, go through all this time, trouble, and expense, to go home empty-handed. She's going back with me, God and the Great Spirits be willing…*

Re-resolved to carry through on this journey of Janus I remember that, indeed, John Slate should be phoned. An attorney's advice would be good about now – and again, nature calls. So I trek into Wal-Mart to find the ladies room, which, in Winslow, Arizona, happens to be ALL the way in the BACK of the store, by lay-a-way. Bet in every other Wal-Mart in America it's up front. Not here. I came back from my hike and found the pay phone, just outside the door. I called John Slate, down in Phoenix, going through all the steps to make contact and talked with the receptionist, Destiny, (I will swear on the Bible that this was her name) a moment, and she then puts me through to the man, himself.

"Good morning, Mr. Slate, it's me – Laura Giannini. I've got some good news and some bad news. The *good* news is I've got the pup. The bad news is that I didn't wait for your letter to work, because Deputy Dick thought it probably would have to go through the courts, anyway. So I jumped the gun, picked Ricardo's lock, and got my dog back."

He laughed. "Come again. You did *what? You picked the guys lock?!*" He chuckled, his day just livened up. "You realize, don't you, Laura, that you've now taken a civil suit on your side of the law to a criminal suit against you? What is the deputy telling you?"

"First of all, Mr. Slate – or may I call you 'John' now, after all we've been through?" He chuckles again, saying 'Sure.' "John, that's what my husband said about the civil suit/criminal stuff, last night. I hate it when he might be right. Anyway, the law – Deputy Isabella – is telling me that he wants me to come in and talk to him."

"Sure he is. That's his job. And if you *do* go in, he's going to arrest you. As your attorney, I'm supposed to tell you to turn yourself in, but believe me, they *will* arrest you, and you'll probably have to hand the dog over until all of this is straightened out, which will likely be in court. If it were me," he adds, "I'd head for the New Mexico border as fast as possible. You have the pup, and 'possession *is* 9/10th's of the law,' as we say."

"That's exactly what I was thinking, Mr. Slate – John. I was heading in that direction when I stopped to make these calls. I don't plan to give up on this pup at this point. She's with me. She's safe. I'm training her, and now making plans to get her to Virginia safely – but I've got to get out of Arizona first! Wish me luck there, will you?"

"Laura, call me later, when you get yourself over the border. I want to know that everything went okay. *And* I want an update. Yes, I wish you good luck. And if you have any more questions..." He was still laughing as I thanked him and hung up the phone.

Back to the car, to Kokopelli, my wild thing. My head is back against the seat again while I talked to Pelli, rubbing her head, trying to get her to settle down while I start thinking along a very different line... It occurs to me *What would happen if they DO put out an APB (this is so cool, I know this means "All Points Bulletin," and it's so personal now, on li'l ol' me, for "puppy theft") and I don't have a dog? Now, this is Arizona, for heavens sake. We're in the West — sure, they put out APB's for horse theft and cattle theft, but for* puppy *theft? They'd be embarrassed; it's like these cowboys eating quiche, or something. But just in case, say they did... and here an Arizona highway patrol pulls me over, because they know my plates (when Deputy Dick followed me to Ricardo's yesterday for those fifteen miles — he was bound to have jotted down the plate #'s...) and there IS no puppy?! Can they arrest me without the goods?...*

Then I close my eyes, Pelli now calm and quiet beside me with my hand stroking her head and ears reassuredly. I then ask myself: *what would Robert Redford do?* What would *he* do in a pickle such as this, thinking of the old movie, *The Electric Horseman* that he made with Jane Fonda, umpteen years ago. My eyes spring open with renewed hope. I *know!* The answer is as bright as the desert in daylight... Ta dah!!! I turn on the ignition, telling Kokopelli we're on the move again, but now I have an answer. We drive around Winslow and, sure enough, there is a truck stop. I pull in between two huge big rigs, amongst a sea of these monsters, in fact — a patrol couldn't find us in here for months, unless they're taking an aerial perspective — and park. I walk up to several of these rigs and knock on the cabs, asking the curious fellows inside if they're going east or west? It doesn't occur to me until much later that this is what hookers do, when someone later calls this to my attention. Never dawned on me then. In any case, my attire was not that of a prostitute; I still wore my dark get-a-way clothes from the night before: black slacks, socks, practical black shoes and a navy thermal turtleneck. Hardly alluring, but they were warm, and I had donned a moss green fleece vest to waken-up the color scheme a bit. I wore the silver and turquoise choker with the coyote howling at the moon, that now represented Kokopelli and was meant as luck in this whole endeavor, as well as my beloved turquoise tear-drop earrings. The Navajo believe that this stone possesses benign powers that ward off many of life's hazards and calamities. This 'hidden power' might certainly be useful on this day. This was good-luck jewelry, to spiff-up my escape duds: feminize the get-a-way garb a bit...

Most of the truckers were headed west, but one older gentleman, sitting way up high with his rig idling, claimed he was heading east, as far as New York. *Great!* "Why?" he asked curiously. Above the roar of his engine, I tried to give him an abbreviated version of my predicament... He calmly looked me over, standing down there in my dark clothes, and shook his head. I don't know if he didn't believe me, or what. Then he said: "Your dog is shedding. I can't have all that dog hair up here in my cab. You got a kennel, or something?"

Hope! "Well, yes sir, I do, in fact. I got it at the Wal-Mart in Gallup when I first arrived – but I haven't put it together yet. It's in the trunk of my car."

"Well, we can fix that. I've got tools," he said and, bless his heart, he climbed down off his mountaintop, paused halfway down, and reached behind his seat for the toolbox. *Thank you, God! Another angel, sent to help!* This man was a very kind-looking African American fellow in his sixties, I'd guess. He had the gentle demeanor of Danny Glover and seemed as if he had seen about every sort of life there is to offer, etched there in his face. The calmness and wisdom of the ages radiated from his persona.

I pulled the travel kennel, still in it's packaging, from the trunk of the rental and laid it on the ground between us. We pulled off the wrapping and, as the two of us tightened the nuts and bolts and built the carrier into a secure 'box,' I told him the whole story. I grinned at him and told him he may be aiding and abetting a criminal, and he just grinned back, saying: "Honey, I'm a dog-lover, and what you've described to me is *no* life for a dog, especially a young puppy. I'm *glad* to be able to help you get her freed." He reached over the carrier and offered me his large, calloused hand: "My name is Gordie, by the way." I smiled back, "My name is Laura, and I thank you *very* much."

Gordie and I planned our escape convoy through Arizona into New Mexico. He asked: "What am I to do with this puppy if you do get pulled over on an APB? Not that I really think the law will go that far, but you never know. I can't take her to New York with me." *Hmm... Right.*

"I know. If I *do* get pulled, but have no dog, then they probably can't hold me. If you would wait for me in Gallup, just a little while, I'll catch up with you as soon as I can. If I don't show up, say, within an hour, then there's a friend of ours in Santa Fe, at the Comfort Inn, just as you enter the city. Could you drop the puppy, and all her paraphernalia, with Art?" I gave him Art's full name and number, there at the hotel.

Gordie agreed this would work. He'd planned to stop at Truck Stop 39, about 40 miles into New Mexico, anyway. He could wait that long. And Santa Fe was close enough en route that he could leave the pup with Art, if it came to that. What a sweet fellow! In the course of our conversation, I found that he had retired from the Post Office, was divorced and was looking for something to fill his time. As he loves to travel he started driving the big rigs to make money. I suggested that he plan on calling next time he was in our area and stop and have dinner with us, meet Pete, and see how Kokopelli had grown. There's a truck stop close to us; he could park up there and I'd be happy to come up and bring him back to the farm for a home-cooked meal. Gordie sounded like he might just do that. He told me of his favorite dogs, including one Great Dane he'd had, that had been a soul mate. Claimed he could understand English and then he shared some stories. Gordie also told me how to gently break Pelli from jumping on people. He said that a dog's chest is very sensitive, and if, when they're jumping up at you, you raise your knee firmly into their chest, telling them "No! Down!" they'll learn in no time. (I started working on this with Kokopelli at the next opportunity and found it works like a charm.)

I thought later, on the drive solo through Arizona, *it's funny: Here I come 2,000 miles across America to reclaim this puppy, thinking I'm all alone. But in reality I was surrounded by new friends ready to help, when the help was needed. Most of these friends were visible, tangible, flesh and blood, but a few were invisible spirits, offering their support and advice when needed. Looking back, sharing the adventure so freely with so many people all along the way, I never felt too alone. Or lonely. And never really threatened by anyone, other than the night in the trailer park when the horn was honking and I was flat against the dumpster, thinking my head just might be blown away. But then that was my own stupidity.*

With my invisible friends, it's as if I could pull mentors out of my pockets and ask them their advice. "Mr. Ludlum, how do I dress for this next move, where I might need to step outside the law a moment in camouflage?..."

"Ms. Barr, Anna Pigeon is always quick on the uptake, in a pinch. I need a little of that deductive reasoning of hers... and a shot of her toughness...got any ideas?"

"Mr. Redford, you've been my hero for years. How do we creatively wiggle past the law and get ourselves safely into the neighboring state over yonder there, my friend? How about back to Virginia, pup in tow? Hey, and while I'm at it, how 'bout going for a horseback ride sometime, like that gallop over the open spaces in The Horse Whisperer, *with Kristin Scott Thomas?" (I find it never hurts to ask...)*

Like that. And they — my imaginary friends — or the real ones I'd meet along the way when the time was right and they were needed, would appear. Just like angels. Or, as my dear cousin Paulette's husband, Tony, said to me later, when I shared the story with him, "Laura, this is kismet. Just like in The Arabian Nights. *When things fall into place, as if they were predestined, as if meant to be."*

"Yes, Tony," I had said. "It was exactly like that. Only it was like a divine kismet, from start to finish, beginning with our anniversary trip west. Everything as it was meant to be, we were all just actors in the play, with God the director. It was preordained — I've had that feeling all along."

Gordie and I had set up our plan. I left to go back to the Wal-Mart phones to call Pete and let him know what was going on; by now he'd be frantic. I called his direct line at work but voice mail picked up; he was probably on the phone. I hated to leave him a message and not speak with him in person, but we had to go and a message would be better than no word, at all. I'd minimize my trouble-potential as much as possible, keep it upbeat and all that: *"Pete, it's me. I'm on the lam in Arizona. Just talked with the law and with John Slate. Apparently, Ricardo came to the Sheriff's office this morning and reported 'his' dog missing. Ha! Deputy Isabella wants to talk to me, but I told him I'd need to talk with my attorney first. John — I can call him John now — suggested I make a run for it across the border, which is what I was already planning to do. I decided to get a trucker to help me get the pup into New Mexico, so if I am pulled over, there's no evidence. I'll call you later, when we're safely into the state, or maybe tonight. I love you — hope everything is going well out east. 'Bye."*

Okay, while there's a phone right here, are there any more calls to be made? *Think. Can't. My mind is mush. Hey! I can call Lori, my officer-friend—neighbor back home and ask for her advice.* I dial all the numbers to punch through, and her phone just rings into their machine, saying: "You have the right to remain silent. You also have the right to leave a message..." *Great. She's probably out on a horse right now, a place I'd like to be,* so I leave her a detailed message of what's going on, as she has already talked to Pete and knows the basic story. I gave her a summary of the latest developments, saying I sure wish I could get her feedback, a friend from that side of the law, and all. *Bless her, she'll be so worried when she get this, I'll call her from the road, as well, when there's an update. Okay, any more calls? Can't think of any. Time to hit the road.*

Gordie and I make our last pit stops before the long haul into Gallup, some 120 miles nonstop. Ugh. I decide not to have coffee to keep me awake or iced tea, or anything; we may be in our vehicles awhile, and I want my bladder to behave. My very worst-case scenario on this whole escapade would not be to be pulled over and hand-cuffed/arrested by the cops, but to be pulled over when I had to pee so badly and be asked to get out of my car and be frisked. Because my bladder is so damned out of control, I would wet my pants because I had to stand up before 'it' told me I could. Then the officer would think he had frightened me so much that I peed in my pants, when all the while it's this stupid incontinence. *This*, my friends, is what I dreaded the very most, and which is why I did not have a drop to drink of anything, except some orange sections, some 50 miles later. At this point I am praying mightily for Pelli's bladder control. And that New Mexico was a *whole* lot closer than it looked on the map, and thanking the Powers that Be in Arizona for 75-mph speed limits on I-40, which would get us all to the next pit-stop a *whole* lot sooner.

After we put all signs of 'dog' up into Gordie's cab: travel carrier with Pelli inside on her Indian blanket; puppy chow; dog chews and teething toys; dishes and bowls; her leash and harness, we compare notes. Guess that is it. There is no trace of dog in my car now except the hair on my pants and on the seat of the car. *What, are they going to do a DNA test?* As the kindly trucker climbs up into his cab, I ask him just what "Gordie" stands for. He looks down at me, quizzically, and says "Gordon O'Neil." I smile up at him, and say: "You know, I was destined to meet you. We have a nephew named Gordon, and call him Gordie, and my father's name was Frank O'Neil. This is just too much." *Then I relay to Pete, silently, hey – it's a sign. This is going to be okay.* As I turn to leave for my car, I hear Gordie calmly telling the scared little pup the same thing.

Up ahead is the rig with Gordie and Pelli inside. Outside reads "Landstar" and sports a huge blue star in the upper right hand corner. I grin and think to myself, *it's another sign, Pete – it's November, a month before Christmas – it's the Star of Bethlehem to follow, the star of the east, a whole month early.* And I slip a *Dire Straits/Steely Dan* CD I'd made for this trip into the player. Life is good. At this point I'm calling myself "Laura Louise" and laugh aloud at the whole insane situation. Wanted now in Arizona for restealing, like refrying beans out here, a puppy that at first was found starving, alone and unwanted, in the middle of nowhere. I basically allowed her to go from the frying pan into the proverbial fire, through none but good intentions. From starving, but free – or, as Kris Kristofferson wrote in Me & Bobby McGee: *"What is freedom, but nothing left to loose? Nothin' ain't worth nothin', but it's free..."* – to be fed and 'cared for' by being left completely alone in a smoke-filled trailer for 10 hours at a time, except for (per chance?) a walk a day, and back to the trailer 24/7. Which was worse? Frankly, if I were the dog, I'd take my chances in the desert. There's just something about fresh air and sunshine.

So here I am, following a semi down endless I-40 through arid Arizona, which is carrying this 'hot' innocent puppy that has managed to live more life in her short sixish months than many people live in a lifetime. I'm thinking *this has been* way *too much fun – the whole silly adventure – what an anecdote for the forties "same old routine." Break it up, turn up the volume mid-life – forget the red sports car and affair with a younger man. Hell, just go out west and break the law! Get wanted in some faraway place for a really good cause...* How *my mother would have loved this story and rooted for the underdog, living through it vicariously along with me!* How *Emily would have listened, enthralled, laughing, leaning forward, her lively face intent, making her wonderful comments... and how I missed the opportunity to share this adventure with the each of them.*

What a hoot! I have the strangest feeling that my mom is there in the seat beside me, having the time of her life. When she had lived, she had always loved the underdog, so to speak. She would have adored this whole story, and indeed, I think she was right there, living it, whooping and hollering with me. As bizarre as this situation is at the moment, I'm too happy to be singing the blues.

NON SEQUITUR © 1999 by Wiley Miller. Dist. by UNIVERSAL PRESS SYNDICATE. Reprinted with permission. All rights reserved.

Now Arizona is a great big wide-open state. Not only does it encompass the Grand Canyon, as a National Park and general all-around miracle of nature, Arizona also offers someone just about anything they might be looking for. Want mountains? Well, yes, they're here, and pretty spectacular, too. Want the desert, instead, or as well? Well, yup, we've got that, also, and miles upon endless miles of it, changing from the high desert country of the Colorado Plateau in Monument Valley and Canyon de Chelly, to the very different type of arid sands in the Sonoran Desert around Phoenix and Tucson, home to the magnificent saguaro cactus, further south and to the west. The sands, structures and vegetation all change dramatically. If it's water you want Lake Powell, bordering Arizona and Utah, is impressive. And there is always the Coolidge Dam, south of San Carlos, east of Phoenix. And, of course, there is the mighty Colorado River, but she has so many demands on her now that even her great bounty threatens to run dry. Want to see the ocean? Well, sorry, folks, but here you're quite out of luck. Once upon a time it 'twas here, but t'ain't no more — just the fossils and remnants of undersea life from 25 million years ago, if one looks carefully enough. George used to come west and look that carefully; he found amazing treasures in these vast deserts. God rest his soul.

Want to see real Indians? Arizona is full of them, as well as the history and lore of the Old West that goes with the heritage. There are reservations of Navajo, Hopi, Apache, Zia, Maricopa, Zuni and Pima, to name just a few. The Havasupai Indian Reservation borders the Kaibab National Forest to the south and west of the South Rim area in the Grand Canyon. Found at the bottom of this grand gorge, and only then by foot with a 10-mile hike, the Havasupai Indians have inhabited this sacred land for centuries. The name translates as "People of the blue-green waters;" they believe that the springs that feed this canyon possess supernatural, curative powers. Our friends, Scott and Debbie, were telling Pete and me that they had traveled down to the bottom of Havasu Canyon and had hired these Indians as their guides; they had to give up their U.S. sovereign rights when they were on this reservation. If they should break any of the Havasupai tribal laws U.S. courts could not help them — they would be 'tried' before an Indian council. So they were sure to behave themselves. To the west of this reservation lies the Hualapai Indian Reservation.

I am learning so much about the large number of tribes throughout the Four Corners area in traveling through these ancient lands and in writing this book, and the vast differences between them. Each has their own remarkable history, their own language and culture. Each has had to cope the best they've been able to with the limited resources found upon whatever land they were relegated to over a hundred years ago, when the almighty federal government claimed these lands as its own. But they are a hardy, resourceful people and adapt to the extreme conditions under which they live. Many of them, anyway. As with any culture within our society, some individuals adapt better than others.

And of course there is historic "Get your kicks on Route 66," called "The Mother Road," which turned 75 years old on November 11th, 2001, the day I returned to begin this chain of events. Formerly the only road west, John Steinbeck wrote of her in his classic tale, *The Grapes of Wrath*, when hordes of weary souls migrated from the Great Plains to California during the Depression years of the early '30s, to escape the Dust Bowl and to look for work. Williams holds the distinction of being the last town located on Route 66 to be bypassed by I-40. This current interstate highway system began in 1956, the year I was born. It took more than a decade and more than $355 million to complete this highway in Arizona. Interstate 40 sidestepped the last stretch of Route 66 in Williams in 1984, when my oldest daughter, Skye, was born.

Again, from the *Williams Tour Guide,* Fall 2001 issue:

"During the '30s, '40s, and '50s, vacationing Americans were treated to all the trappings of the Old West on Route 66. At its heyday in the 1950s, shop owners along the route vied for the traveling trade with roadside attractions such as snake pits, live buffalo and Indian dancers.

"Thousands followed the two-lane road in search of America. What they found were 2,448 miles of adventure from Chicago to Santa Monica, CA... In Arizona, one of the longest uninterrupted stretches of the old route remains intact, and some segments near Williams are in the National Register of Historic Places.

"Route 66 was officially designated in 1926 by the U.S. Bureau of Public Roads, marking the first time routes were uniformly signed from state to state. Called the National Old Trails Highway, it was rebuilt during the '30s as part of President Franklin D. Roosevelt's Employment Relief Program." Maybe some of those migrant workers didn't have to travel all the way to California in their old jalopies to find work, after all. And there you have it – your history lesson for the day.

I switch CD's to a Gordon Lightfoot mix I'd made for this trip, listening to his warm, honest voice and his silken guitar. This is music that I've known and loved since a teenager; it soothes away these endless miles over the flat open land. "Canadian Railroad Trilogy" comes on. I sing along, feeling the soul of this song touch me deeply, as it always does. *How timely, as we parallel the Santa Fe line, off in the distance. I think of how instrumental the railroad was to the slow crawl of progress from the east coast to the west coast, long before Route 66 existed, or the idea of Interstate travel was even conceived. How many lives were lost in the building of the railroad through these Indian lands. The backbreaking labor it took to lay the rails under the unforgiving western sun. These things we take so for granted now, in the age of the raging automobiles, racing from one destination to the next, and the swift, silver jets, leaving trails of vapor criss-crossing the skies. What nonsense it would have seemed then, some maniac's gibberish, if these brave men — the African American, the Chinese, the Irish, and the white men from distant lands, or born now of this young and bloody soil — had been told of such future means of transportation. And each of them, in their daily backbreaking stints, laid the groundwork, literally, for this to gradually come about, as civilization was introduced to the Great American West.*

As I drive down the road, the words from an old *Eagle's* tune haunt me. "*I'm standing on the corner in Winslow, Arizona... gotta' world of trouble on my mind...*" I could not, for the life of me, remember which song this was from. This keeps me busy awhile in trying to remember. Bits and pieces come back. Much later on, I dug out an old *Eagles* album after my friend, Cynthia E., reminded me it was from *"Take it Easy,"* written by Jackson Browne. I listened to it over and over one evening. *Good grief,* I thought, *I've* lived *this song! With a few changes of the lyrics, it is my time in Winslow.* I listened to the words and wrote them down:

Okay, with a few changes it could go like this:

Well, I'm runnin' down the road, trying to loosen my load...
I've got seven men on my mind -
Four that want to nail me, two that want to jail me,
an attorney that says he's a friend of mine....

Take it easy, take it easy...
Don't let the sound of your own wheels drive you crazy...
Lighten up while you still can, don't even try to understand...
just find a place to make your stand and take it easy.

Well, I'm standing on the corner in Winslow, Arizona
Such a fine sight to see - it's Gordie, my Lordie, that's a ten-forty!
And he's slowin' down to talk to me —

Come on, Baby, don't say maybe -
I gotta' know if your sweet helpin' is gonna' save me...
We may lose and we may win,
although we'll never be here again,
so open up, Kokopelli's climbin' in...

I watch the green highway signs flash by, stating how far away is the New Mexico border, Gallup or Grants or Albuquerque, and decide to take photographs of these signs. They would be placed in my album as a visual reminder of this day. So, with Gordon serenading me in the background, and Gordie driving on up ahead, I put my Canon on automatic action setting and aim away. As the mileage markers approach, I snap a quick shot framed by a stark desert backdrop. When I could frame it in time, I would shoot Gordie's big rig beside the signs, knowing that Pelli was safely ensconced behind all that steel and the huge blue star, cozy on the front seat beside this kind man. In the area of the Petrified Forest National Park, I even caught sight of a stealthy dinosaur prowling over rocks along the edge of the highway – and shot him, too.

When the sign loomed ahead, *finally*, of the New Mexican state border welcoming us as a jurisdictional haven, I flash my lights and honked my horn at the semi up ahead; Gordie's lights flashed in return. We have made it safely across the expanse of Arizona into a 'clean' state – or so I hope. I really have no idea how these APB's might work.

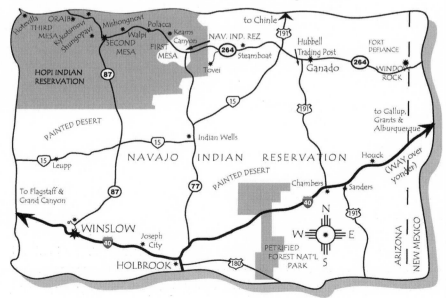

THIRTY-ONE

Gallup, New Mexico, on to Grants/ Dinner with Elena

"Well-behaved women rarely make history."
Laurel Thatcher-Ulrich (bumper sticker)

Gordie and I had a cup of celebratory coffee at Truck Stop 39, in Gallup, New Mexico. He told me of many of the dogs he had had in his life and some of his stories. He was an intelligent and kind man, someone who gave a lot of deliberation to his actions and would stand behind what he promised, unlike Ricardo. I immensely enjoyed our visit, but my energy – which had been kindled and rekindled by adrenaline from 'the chase,' and anticipation that at any moment a stern law enforcement figure might crystallize to arrest me – was dissipating like snow in the Southwest sun. I wanted to get back on I-40, Pelli and supplies safely back in Cisco, and head on to Grants for the night. The further away from the Arizona border the better, but my energy was not cooperating. Gordie suggested the energy drink 'Red Bull' to give me the kick to keep going. Leave it to a trucker.

It was now about 4 PM. Gordie needed to get back on the highway to continue his long trek to New York. I thanked him again for his going out on the limb to help with the pup's safe escape; he said it was nothing. Gordie was very happy to help Kokopelli reunite with me and wished us a safe return to Virginia. He told me it broke up the monotony of his trip in a major way. I reminded him of the invitation to join Pete and me for dinner sometime when he was headed our way; he said he'd call. He would like to know how it all turned out.

I walked Gordie out to our vehicles and attached the leash to Pelli's collar. I'd give her another walk and see if we might coax some results. The entry to the truck stop offered a good expanse of land beyond one of the parking areas. Across the road a pond reflected a long low range of mountains beautifully in its watery depths. I watched Gordie wind his way through the maze of roadway leading back to the Interstate and waved buoyantly to him as Pelli and I walked. A toot of his horn answered and soon I saw the blue star of the rig fading out of sight as he continued his journey east. I sent him a silent prayer for a safe trip and happiness in his nomadic life. Pelli and I continued our walk, she intent on sniffing at everything in sight, but indifferent to nature's demands. Finally I returned her to Cisco, frustrated by her refusal to eliminate as much as a burp.

Gordon O'Neil went his way and I went back inside the huge complex. There were fast food restaurants lined up one beside another and a large central area was filled with tables and chairs on which to eat. Potted plants added life to the dining array. To the right was a line of public telephones. To the left was a gift shop full of Indian wares. Behind the restaurants, off to the left, was an area that housed a large coin-laundry, complete with TV's to help pass time. The restrooms were also located back there. I made another stop, cleaned up, and decided to call Pete again to let him know that we had arrived safely in New Mexico. But first, I would call John Slate, in Phoenix; I had a couple of questions for the man, from someone new to being on the lam.

I found the quietest payphone amongst the lineup and dialed the long set of numbers. Destiny came on to direct my call; she knew me by now, although she was in the dark as far as the story went. Client-attorney privilege and all... She patched me through and the attorney's deep authoritative voice came on the line: "John Slate here."

"Hello, Mr. Slate – ah, John. It's me, Laura Giannini. I made it into New Mexico!"

A booming laugh came from down in Phoenix, "Somehow I'm not at all surprised. So you eluded the law, eh? How did it go?"

"Well, it wasn't too hard. I barely saw any police cruisers on I-40 at all; I'm kind of doubting they put an APB out. But, just in case, I found a trucker in Winslow who agreed to put the puppy, and all her paraphernalia, in his cab to haul her over the state line."

He laughed again. "Well, I'll be a monkey's uncle," he whistled. "You weren't fooling around, were you?"

"No, I wanted to be sure that she'd make it out and to safety, whether or not I was caught. Consider it a precaution."

"Well, technically, since you've taken this into the criminal element, I'm no longer your attorney." He chuckled again. " 'Prepaid Legal' doesn't cover escapades such as this. But if I can give you any more help or advice about the law, as a friend, you've got my number. And here, let me give you my home phone, as well." He did; I added it to my long list of numbers on my pad. We talked a good while longer, there on my Lowe's 100-minute card, left over from our anniversary trip. We had been shown how to use it, back at home; it certainly was proving useful now. John was telling me what an animal lover he was, and how many stray dogs he had taken in. He had even saved several horses destined for slaughter; he had two or three that he mucked and fed each day before cleaning up, putting on his lawyerly attire and coming in to work. This was not the same gruff-voiced man whom I had initially addressed; then he had acted as if he didn't have the time for something so trivial as an argument as to who owned some dog. But our relationship had done a one-eighty. Now I was talking to a man I'd never met, a big-shot attorney who worked in Phoenix and lived outside the city on his farm. He seemed to be a sensitive man, who hid his kind heart behind an armor of churlishness. And now here he was telling me in detail of mysteries that he had written, based on the legal profession, a la'Grisham; John Slate was in the process of looking for an agent and a publisher. My, how multi-dimensional people are when you come to know them…

John and I talked for half an hour or forty-five minutes, adding a major dent to those Lowe's minutes. He told me that in order for the law to track my credit card use – in order to pinpoint my location and travel route – they would have to get a court order to okay it. He thought that yes, it was possible that they might put out an APB over state lines, but he highly doubted it over a case this insignificant, in the great scheme of lawbreaking. Instead, he thought, they'd be laughing their heads off in good ole' boy moments. Sure, they'd put up a tough front when talking to me, *but…*

After our long auditory visit I thanked the man again for all his help and legal advice, wished him luck with his menagerie and the publishing of his mystery novels, and hung up. I stood there a moment and leaned my head into the cold blue impersonal metal of the payphone; I smiled and shook my head slowly at this insane predicament. For some inexplicable reason, Ogden Nash's silly little poem, that Pete would sometimes recite, came to mind: *"What a funny bird the frog are; when he stand he sit almost; when he hop he fly almost; he sit on what he ain't got almost…"* It went something like that.

I grinned again at the predicament and then decided to call Pete, using the zillion digits of our long-distance phone card to call him at work. *Please,* please, *PeterWop, pick up the phone this time, I don't want to leave another message for you on your voice mail...* three rings, four...

"Peter Gianniny here."

"Hey, PeterWop," relief flooded my voice, "It's your 'felon wife' calling from the northern depths of New Mexico. We *made* it!" I grinned, relief evident in my voice.

"*Laura!* Thank *God!*" Suddenly he was whispering. I had this crazy vision of his covering the phone and warily looking around his empty office. "Are you o*kay*? I'm so glad to hear your voice – I've been worried sick about you!"

"Sure I'm okay, Pete. I followed Gordie's truck across I-40. If the law stopped me, there would be no puppy in the car." I explained to him Gordie's and my plan if I was pulled over or detained. "Have you told anyone at work, or are you keeping all this good news to yourself there, friend?"

"Are you kidding? You're a *fugitive*, Laura – in Arizona. I haven't breathed a word to *any*body. I paced the floor last night after talking with you. I drank too much wine, trying to relax. I missed your call this morning, but got your message: 'On the lam in Arizona'! *Really!* I've been hovering by the phone since then, waiting for you to call back. Waiting to hear you're in jail somewhere out there over this damned dog." He ended his spiel in exasperation.

"Pete, Pete, it's o*kay* there, fella'. Really, Pelli and I are fine. We're going to get back on track here soon and head further into New Mexico, probably on to Grants, and find a quiet place for the night. Tomorrow we'll go on into Santa Fe. It's all worked out. Really. Take a deep breath – re*lax*. Okay?" I found myself relieved to have this distance between us, actually, else he might do me bodily harm, himself. The heck with the law. The man was strung like a new guitar.

He let out a long breath. "Laura, I don't think you have an inkling of the trouble you might be in. You're taking all this so lightly. It's not a game. You broke the law and now they're gunning for you. I suggest that maybe you change rental cars when you reach Albuquerque. But be careful – they may be waiting for you to show up."

"Pete, stop it. This sounds just like TV. You're making me nervous. I'm still standing behind my guns on this – I feel like I did exactly what needed to be done to reclaim the pup." Anger hardened my voice – "The man held her *cap*tive, damnit – stuck inside that trailer! Do you know, despite my walking her umpteen times, this dog has *not* gone to the bathroom since she left Ricardo's trailer?! There's something wrong with that! She has *no* manners. She's a fiend on the leash, she wants to jump all over everybody…" I blew my breath out. It was my turn to relax. "I'm apologizing to *no*body, Pete. This needed to be done; I just wish I'd gotten here sooner. I'll go down fighting for her every step of the way."

Silence. Finally, "Okay, Razza. I see where you're coming from. Just be careful, okay? You could be in serious trouble, *please* remember that."

"I know. I will be careful. We'll see about this rental car switch. I just spoke with John Slate a long time – he said he'd help, even though this is now out of his realm. He's really a very nice person, under all that gruffness. Turns out he's a bonafide animal lover, too. And, he's writing a mystery novel. A man of many talents. He said he didn't think the lawmen would bother tracking my credit cards – that if they do, they'd need a court order – for something he considers to be relatively trivial in the great scheme of lawbreaking out here. So that takes the cash crunch off some."

"You never know, Ra. I'd be careful how you spend your money. Don't be buying us gifts and things – this isn't a time for shopping. Remember your objective. And that's to get home with Kokopelli safely, in case you get sidetracked or anything else…" his voice trailed.

"Pete, I think my objective has been very clear this entire trip. And I think my mission is halfway accomplished. Or better. Now I've just got to get home. I'll take it all one day at a time…and I may buy a gift or two along the way, as Christmas *is* coming…"

"Well, God be with you." Pete sighed. "*And* his angels of mercy. Natalie and I are planning to meet you Monday night in Richmond for your homecoming. So come home."

"I dunno,' I think I could live in Santa Fe and all…" I teased him, then got serious again quickly, knowing the delicate state of worry he was in. "The Lord be willing, PeterWop, we'll be there with bells on."

"Call me when you get in tonight, wherever you end up, Ra, will you? Just a quick call to let me know you all are safe."

"Will do, Pete. And listen – everything will be *just* fine; I have a good feeling about it. I love you. And tell the kids that I love them – and miss them, too – okay?" We hung up our phones. Me, on my public pay phone at the Gallup truck stop; Pete on his office phone in small-town, Virginia. He had stopped whispering midway through our conversation and had resumed his normal voice.

I bought a bean tostada and an iced tea at the Taco Bell in the line up of fast food eateries and sat in the center area to dine. I then made a last pit stop before returning to the car. The one thing I had to be grateful to Ricardo for was that in the long days and nights in waiting for this man to return home, the puppy had learned patience. A blurb I'd read somewhere in my life, and had stuck like glue, flashed in my mind: *"Patience is the art of doing something else in the meantime."* Maybe it was in a Ludlum. I told this to the kiddos all the time. I wondered what the 'something else's' were this puppy had learned to do in almost six weeks time in waiting for Ricardo to come home…

I went outside to walk Kokopelli once again before we hit the Interstate, this time to travel together. Dusk was settling in; as I came out the doors towards Cisco, the western sky was brilliant in the golden glow of the falling sun. The setting clouds were afire in Mandarin orange and plum colors against a darkening backdrop. It was surprisingly celestial; the sky was celebrating. God and Mom and the Great Spirits of the West were congratulating us further for the good work done thus far, and saluting our journey on.

Dinner with Elena

"The world is but a canvas to our imagination."
Henry David Thoreau

Kokopelli and I arrived in the small town of Grants about 6:30; by now it was pitch dark. I found a Comfort Inn with an indoor pool area and checked in, paying in traveler's checks, just in case. Before unloading our overnight things I walked Pelli in a fenced area beside the hotel. Again, she sniffed and pulled, but neither peed nor pooped. I put her back in the car on her Indian blanket – which she deemed a sanctuary – along with a chew toy, and unloaded a few things for our stay. Then I decided to find some dinner.

A Denny's light showed high and bright across the street. I crossed to find the entrance, but apparently one had to drive *around* the block to the front of the building. A dirt road beside the Denny's seemed to be an obvious path to getting there by foot and – for my own sense of navigational abilities redemption – I wasn't the only one that thought so. Another woman was headed up my way, with a perplexed look on her face.

"Are you also trying to get to Denny's?" I asked her.

"I sure am, but there doesn't seem to be a way to get there from here." She pointed to a barbed-wire fence between the restaurant and us.

"There's *al*ways a way to 'get there from here.' Here, let me hold the fence for you and you can do the same for me. How 'bout that?" I asked her. "The strands don't look like they're strung too tightly." I walked up the bank and motioned for her to follow. She smiled and headed my way. "Okay, careful now, just slip on through. You're small; this won't be hard." She climbed through and then spread the wires carefully for me. I grinned with the memory of Pete's and my fiasco with the tautly stretched wire on the Navajo rez.

We walked up to the front entrance together. "Are you dining alone?" I asked her. "I am. Would you like to join me?"

She smiled shyly and answered, "Yes, I am. Sure, that would be fun."

We introduced ourselves. She told me her name was Elena and she was traveling solo from a visit with her family in Kansas. Elena was diminutive, a large doll that had come to life; she made Cynthia look tall. She had long straight auburn hair that fell to the middle of her back. Her face was heart-shaped and her eyes were round and a warm deep blue. There was a quiet sadness about her; she seemed to be looking for something she hadn't quite found. Nonetheless, I liked her immediately. Elena asked me, "So what brings you to these faraway parts, also traveling alone?"

"Oh, I'm not sure if you want to know. It's a very long and kind of complicated story."

"Well, we're here for dinner. So talk. I've got the time to listen." She settled into her booth comfortably, emphasizing this interest.

O*kay*... I took a deep breath. *Here goes*... I told her the story from beginning to end, paralleling our anniversary trip with the September 11th madness and changes in the country since. She listened intently, enraptured, stopping to ask questions or make interjections along the way. By the time I got to the here and now her eyes were alive and we both were laughing our heads off together.

"I don't know if I should have dinner with you now, or not. You're an actual *out*law, Laura! My mama always told me to be a good little girl and stay out of trouble. You could be a bad influence." She grinned impishly at me. I laughed. The waitress had brought salads in the midst of the story; she now came to take the plates and refill our drinks.

"Well then, now's the time to leave. I could be arrested at any moment," I leaned over conspiratorially and winked.

Elena laughed again and said, "No way am I leaving now. I've got to see what happens!"

"Well, the law might consider you an 'aider and abetter' if you hang around with me. But I'm enjoying the company. Usually I've been eating alone on this trip." The waitress arrived with our dinners and put them before us. Elena had ordered a fish fillet with fries; I had ordered broiled garlic shrimp – knowing Pete wasn't around to suffer my breath – and a baked potato. A side of broccoli was on each plate. The dinners looked wonderful and I realized I was famished. We ate quietly for a while before I queried, "Where do you live, Elena?"

"Down in Texas, close to Austin," she told me.

"You've come a long ways, then. We have friends – Cindy and Bruce – who moved from Virginia to Austin and built a beautiful house down there. Then they got homesick and moved *back* to Charlottesville within the last couple of years. In fact, Cindy and I were pregnant together with our first children – her daughter, Sarah, and my daughter, Skye. And *then* we were pregnant again with our second children at the same time, can you believe it? She had another daughter, Jamie, and we had our son, Jared. When we conceived Natalie, I pulled Cindy aside and warned her not to eat okra – that's what happened to us the third time. She knew our story and laughed her head off."

"Okra?" Elena looked puzzled. Our dinner had been so much fun I felt I was talking with an old friend. And our old friends knew about Pete and me and okra.

"Oh, sorry. You don't know about that. Every time Pete and I conceived, we had eaten okra. It was involved in each of our three children's conceptions. And here, everybody else claims it's sex."

Elena laid her head back and roared. When she had finished, tears were in her eyes. "You are unbelievably funny, Laura. How you think, all your escapades. Even your trouble with the law. It's so… so…" she looked for a word and settled on "insane." Her laughter was a bane for her mental state. When we had arrived she'd been quiet and unassuming, shades of shy and shades of sad mixed in. This laughter was a release for pent-up worries, freeing some sort of anguish I had sensed in her.

"I'm really not like this always, Elena. Believe me, this is my first run-in with the law. But I always figured I'd end up in jail, sooner or later, with the strength of my convictions. If this doesn't pan out, give me a few years…" I mused, just halfway kidding.

She laughed again and shook her head. We continued our dinner, visiting and sharing stories. She told me about her family at home in Texas – her husband and daughter and son. She had taken time from them to work through some midlife issues, thus her traveling alone. She, too, was an artist. She, too, was a gardener. We talked art and gardening for the rest of the evening. I was silently grinning inside, thinking of how serendipitous was our meeting on the dirt road in back of Denny's. Not an accident at all.

When the waitress came to take our plates she asked if we wanted dessert. We looked at each other devilishly and said, "Oh, why the hell not," and proceeded to order one of those hot fudge cake numbers, with heaps of vanilla ice cream and chocolate sprinkles, and two forks. We ordered fresh coffees. Live a little.

While we were waiting for our wonderful plateful of calories to arrive, I asked Elena, "Did you see that sunset tonight when you were traveling? I saw it in Gallup; it was spectacular, like God celebrating our safe arrival out of Arizona," I confided to her.

"Oh my God, yes! I was so intent on watching it, I almost ran off the road! It was *magnificent!* It glowed against the sandstone mesas like gold dust!"

"You do that, too?" I smiled at her, "I get so caught up in the scenery here that I'm a menace behind the wheel. Maybe that's why Pete always wants to drive. I actually take photographs at 70 miles an hour. Not *always* a good idea…"

"I do the same thing. All the glorious colors, the salmons and corals, the warm terra cottas; the taupes and adobe tans, the sienna's… the slates and azures and ultramarine blues… Oh, the nuance of color! I just go *zonkers*." *Oh, God in heaven above, thank you. You sent me an artist as a dinner companion — someone that goes just as nuts out here as I do and sees more than 'blue' and 'brown' and 'beige' in these fantastic lands…*

"Elena, I'm *so* glad to have met you. I think it was meant to be, our running into each other out back like that. I've had *such* a good time talking with you."

Elena smiled back and said the same. A cloak of worry had fallen from her. Our dessert came and as quickly went, as we continued exchanging stories of our lives amidst the laughter.

We walked back to the hotel together. Of course she, too, was staying at the Comfort Inn. Too bad we hadn't run into one another earlier or we could have split the cost of two queen beds in a room. I told her I needed to walk Pelli again. Elena said that she wanted to join us, as she was eager to meet this notorious and *very* expensive stray. I joked that I often thought of her as my 'Monumental Mutt' – the most expensive stray puppy in the history of homeless dogs. We walked and walked Kokopelli, who was thrilled with meeting someone new. To emphasize this, she sprang around us like a Mexican jumping bean, hurling herself up, as we put knees in her chest to coax her down, followed by stern *"No's!"* I silently thanked Gordie for this advice; it was working. Within a few leaps she had decided the game was no longer fun and went about her eternal sniffing, instead. But again, there were no results. Were her body cavities corked?

We gave Pelli every opportunity to relieve herself and she politely declined the chance. That is, until we came back to my room and I opened the door. We walked in and before I could point her to the bathroom, Kokopelli, my irreverent mischief-maker of the west, squatted on the entry room rug and downloaded two days worth of urine. I was mortified. Elena just laughed. "Well now, you can stop worrying about her urinary functions. They seem to work just fine."

I just glared at Pelli and ran to the dresser and grabbed the paper towels, starting the process of unwinding them on the way back. I put down a thick layer that immediately started absorbing the liquid mess. Elena brought the trashcan from the bathroom; I gingerly picked up one end and dropped the soaked wad into the plastic liner. I then added a 2nd layer of towels and unwrapped a bar of hotel soap and filled a glass with water. Pelli cringed in the corner by the door. I continued to glare at her. "*All* the chances I gave you to go *out*side, time and time again. Ricardo sure did you no favors, dog." Elena decided to stay quiet; it was safer. I was not in a generous mood. I poured water on the rug to dilute the urine and vigorously scrubbed the soap into the rug. I did all this sans gloves because I'd forgotten to bring them in from the car. Fun. I used more water to rinse and additional paper towels to sop up the gift. Eventually I felt the job was done. Now to let it all dry... I finished off with a fine mist of Eau de Febreze, with just a hint of Lysol, to freshen the air... I then upped the AC to encourage the rug to dry faster.

"I'm really sorry about that, Elena. I didn't mean to get so bloody mad; it's just that I've been walking this dog *every* chance I can, and she's done *noth*ing. When Pete and I had her those first couple of days, we were making such good headway in housetraining her – or hotel-training her, I should say – and walking with her on a leash. She's forgotten it all in these last six weeks. It's just supremely frustrating to me to know that this pup hasn't had any training whatsoever – and that we have it do to over again. Or *re*do it, altogether. She should be a poster child for manners by now."

"I think, under the circumstances, Laura, that I would feel pretty much exactly the same way. Don't worry about it. I think you're being very patient, actually." I shook my head; I didn't know where she had gotten that idea with the anger she'd just witnessed.

I decided to change the subject. "How would you like to go for a swim, Elena? I'm going to vent with some pool exercises and end up in the hot tub. I'll take Pelli back there to give her room to run a bit. She hasn't been able to stretch those puppy legs in Lord only knows when."

"I'd love to, Laura, but I didn't think of bringing a suit with me. I've missed several opportunities to swim."

"That's okay; I have two." And then I thought a moment. I eyed her dubiously. "Tell you what, why don't you take both my suits back to your room and see if you can't make one of them fit you with safety pins and whatnot. I have some of those, too." I sorted through my suitcase, dug out the suits and the pins and handed them to her. She looked doubtful; I was a size 8/10 to her 4, but she ventured back to her own room for the fitting. I settled Pelli's things in the bathroom, while waiting for Elena to take the appropriate nips and tucks.

I heard a soft knock on my door soon after. I opened the door and she peeked in: "I made the black one fit with a few strategic gathers." She pulled back a big overshirt, "See." Elena handed me my lavender and blue swirl suit. I checked the safety pin holds in back of her black suit to make sure they were secure.

"Okay, you're good to go. Let me duck in here and I'll change into this one." I grabbed an old denim over-shirt that I use to double as a pool/ beach wrap and a pair of cover-up shorts and went into the bathroom with my second suit. Elena wandered around the room while waiting. "Pour us a couple of wines in those plastic cups and we'll take 'em to the pool for our swim." I called from inside. "The bottle is on the dresser."

"Laura, you *are* bad!" Elena called from in the room. *Funny, that particular sin wasn't on my list of 'bad'; maybe if we took the wine in glass and not plastic...I thought.*

"Hey, live a little," I called back. "If we're going to live on the edge, we might as well go all the way!"

 The water area was huge, with a fairly good-sized rectangular pool in the center, a swirling hot tub to the side and his and her bathrooms behind it. Sets of chairs and tables sat between large fica trees. "Elena, I'm going to get in the big pool for 20-30 minutes and go through my routine with the kickboard to work through some kinks. Come join me, if you think the suit will hold."

"No, that's too energetic for my tastes. I'm heading straight for the hot tub. Break a leg," she called.

"May I call you 'Pete'?" I kidded her; "You're a woman after my husband's heart."

We had brought Kokopelli with us to give her a run in the huge enclosed room, her first real taste of freedom since Ricardo's imprisonment. She had been tentatively tiptoeing around the perimeter, carefully sniffing the plants, objects on the floor, around the tables and chairs, all the while keeping one watchful eye on me. As I headed down the steps into the water Pelli's head perked up, fully alert, eyeing me and whining. I thought about it from her perspective and laughed. "Look, Elena, watch the puppy – she's watching my body disappear into this thing and she's not liking it at all…"

Pelli was now running beside the pool, head down, sniffing. Her whining intensified. I assured her it was fine, but she wasn't convinced. As the water came up to my shoulders she was now watching a talking head, where just a second ago a whole body had been. With this she didn't know what to do… she snuck to the edge and I reached out and patted the concrete, splashing her a little. She leapt aside, bewilderment on her young face. I could hear Elena laughing from the hot tub. "Come here, Pelli. It's okay, girl. I'm still me. Here, come sniff." She inched over and leaned towards my hand, but I didn't smell like me; the strong odor of chlorine had replaced my scent. She jumped back, totally puzzled, and whined louder to the talking head. "It's okay, little blond mutt – it's still me." I splashed some water at her and she jumped and dodged; I laughed and floated backwards, kickboard under one arm. "I'm going to start my exercises, girl. You'll just have to get used to this new me…"

I started my routine, watching her and trying to settle her with my voice. She would run from one end of the pool to the other, watching my moving head; occasionally she would bark in frustration and I'd call "No, no, Pelli, girl. Let's stay quiet." She'd settle down and resume her puzzled pacing. At least she, too, was getting some exercise.

When I finished I swam around a little and then over to the edge. Pelli would again inch tentatively to me, ready to retreat to safety if the head did anything strange. Her expressions were hysterical, changing from inquisitive to worried to playful, her golden-brown eyes on full alert. Elena and I exchanged comments back and forth, though Elena looked as if she had melted into the suds over there. I climbed out, using the steps, and Pelli watched me, blatantly mollified as my body reappeared. She yelped in relief and came wriggling over, careful of the drips but very happy indeed that I'd gotten my whole self back. I knelt down, laughing, and rumpled her ecstatic little body. "Okay, girl, come watch me disappear in this itty bitty pool with Elena." I went to the hot tub, the puppy carefully trailing behind.

"Did you guard my wine, Elena?"

"*Hmm*?" a lazy response floated up. I had a vision of her disappearing in bliss there in the bubbling suds. Her long auburn hair was plastered to her shoulders and some floated around her; she looked like a mermaid in bubble bath. I walked down into the frothing water; Pelli resumed her nervous pacing, her concentration now focused on the two of us, as if she had to protect us from what*ever* this stuff was. I splashed some suds towards her and she jumped back and then came over to curiously sniff the ethereal object billowing on the concrete. Elena barely opened her eyes; I think she was liquescing from too much of a good thing. I had an image of the wicked witch from *Wizard of Oz* screaming, *"I'm melting! I'm melting!"* but 1) this 'witch' wasn't wicked. And 2) this lady was in absolutely *no* distress at all.

After our evening swim we came back to my room. I turned down the AC, so it wouldn't be so chilly; the rug was drying well. I called Pete and gave him a quick heads up as to location, letting him know that we'd arrived in Grants just fine. He told me all was well on the home front. "Downright boring," he added. "We miss you, 'Kokopelli.' Call tomorrow night from Santa Fe, okay, LauraWop?" I promised I would. We said our goodnights. Elena and I visited a little longer, with my showing her some photos from a small album I'd brought of the family. She showed me snapshots of her family from her purse. Soon she headed off to her room. We planned to meet in the morning for breakfast before we parted ways.

A knock on the door came early. Being my usual night owl self, despite the weariness of earlier, I had stayed up until 1:30ish writing in my travel journal. "*Hmm*?" I called lazily. Maybe the knocking was in a dream. I wanted to call "Go away…" but manners forced me to answer the door. It was 8AM.

"Hi," Elena said brightly, standing there all petite and sprightly and raring to go. There was no sadness in her face this morning.

"My, you're cheerful in the morning. I stayed up late writing last night; it's a bad habit. I had the alarm set for 9:00."

"Well, I'm all ready to leave. Got my car packed up. But I thought we might have that breakfast together before I go. They have a presentable buffet all laid out. So what do you say, Laura?"

"I say give me about ten minutes to get me ready, and how about getting us a couple of coffees — mine a decaf, please — and we'll walk Pelli first. Okay?"

"I'll meet you out front in ten minutes exactly." And off she went, all chipper and awake and chirping like a chickadee. I just shook my head in wonderment and headed to the bathroom to splash some cold water on my face and say good morning to my dog.

Indeed a 'presentable' buffet was laid out on the lengthy countertop behind the lounge-type seating in the lobby area. On the far wall, beneath sunny windows, small tables and chairs enticed guests to savor their morning meal.

Columbian high-test, as well as Columbian decaffeinated, were offered. God bless 'em. This place would see my business again — if I stayed a free woman. This was a treat in itself. A thermos of hot water and a selection of teas lay beside the coffees. All sorts of muffins and pastries were offered, passed up by the both of us. Several types of bread, English muffins and bagels were available, along with spreads, cream cheese, jams and jellies. A large bowl of mixed fruit salad rested on ice and beside it a large wooden bowl of apples, bananas, oranges and ripe pears sat. A variety of cereals were displayed beside a milk dispenser housing whole and 1% milk. Arrangements of fresh flowers adorned both the counter and each of the tables.

Elena had chosen an English muffin, jam and a cup of Orange Spiced tea. She took these to one of the tables and came back for a big bowl of colorful mixed fruit. I made whole-wheat toast and chose both a dollop of raspberry jam and orange marmalade, along with a small self-packed bowl of Kellogg's Raisin Bran. I took these to our table and came back for a steaming cup of the coveted decaf and a bowl of the luscious fruit salad. This, and a last good visit with Elena, was certainly worth leaving the toasty bed.

We sat at the sunny table, taking the time to comment on the saffron carnations and fern sprays on top, greeting a cheery hello. Elena told me how well she had slept after her leisurely lounging in the hot tub. I, too, had slept deeply after the exercise and hot tub time; how nice it was to get some solid rest, even if abbreviated. Pelli had been relatively quiet in the bathroom, there on her trusted Indian blanket. I had stepped in and talked to her, reassuring her twice, and this was the last I had heard until morning.

Elena and I exchanged addresses and phone numbers. She gave me her e-mail address and I explained to her I was one of the five people, or so, in America that did not use e-mail. She goaded me about getting 'into the 21st Century.' I had heard all that before; Cynthia had teased me, as well as many friends back at home. I had just told them all that I didn't slow down enough to keep up with incoming mail and the responses needed. By the time I answered my incoming e-mails, so much spamming and slamming and jamming had occurred that the account had self-destructed. It was blown into bits in cyberspace; fragments of unanswered e-mails were probably still floating around out there, just littering the great invisible vastness of this electronic netherworld.

While we were talking and laughing, I noticed a New Mexican patrol cruiser drive into the lot and park directly in front of the hotel lobby. I was sitting so that I could look out front; I sat in profile to the desk. Elena watched my expression change, saw me swallow and followed my gaze. And she burst out laughing. I whispered to her, "Now I know *exactly* what a wanted criminal feels like." I peeked around and watched the snappily dressed lawman walk inside and stroll over to the desk. He rang the bell and a young attendant greeted him with a big smile. I strained to eavesdrop, trying my best to look nonchalant in doing so. Elena was trying her best to keep her face in neutral.

"Is the manager in? I'd like to speak with him, please." Said the stout deputy.

"No, sir; he won't be in until after lunch. Is there anything that I can help you with?"

"No. No, I need to talk directly with the manager. I'll come back later. Thank you." He turned authoritatively and touched his hat to us. We smiled a good morning to him and I held my breath as I watched him drive back to where Pelli lay on her Indian blanket on the front seat of the Malibu. The license plate was in full sight. *If* an APB *was* out, and he had been paying attention, I was a sitting duck. My goose was cooked; my bacon fried – all of those carnivorous literary colloquiums meaning one was in deep hot water. All I could do was sit quietly and pray quickly, asking God and Mom and the Great Spirits and *all* of my guardian angels to come front and center pronto. It must have worked.

He drove slowly to the back of the lot, right by my getaway car, complete with 'hotdog' in plain sight, and turned around back in the dog-walking area. He then left the lot. I let a long slow breath of relief escape. Elena giggled and laid a hand over mine. "I would have gone down with you to the end. I would have told him you're a good person that did a fine, brave thing in stealing your dog back, and that this puppy is now in *ex*cellent hands."

I patted her hand with my other and gave her a big goofy smile of relief. "Thanks there, Elena. Thanks for your show of solidarity. I like that loyalty in a friend." I looked at her sheepishly. "I guessed I entertained you right well."

"Right well," she agreed, giving me a big smile, then announced, "I'm making more tea."

Elena had her bags all packed and was ready to leave right after breakfast. I still had to gather my things and load them, but that would only take about twenty minutes. I walked out with her, a fresh cup of the rich Columbian decaf in hand, and gave her a big hug goodbye. "I can't tell you how much fun I had meeting you, Elena. I think it was meant to be – part of all the kismet of the trip. I wish you a safe journey home and don't be running off the highway now, rubbernecking at these western wonders."

She laughed; we were peas of the same pod. "You know, we should meet up in Santa Fe sometime and hit the town. We'd have *such* a good visit in that creative city, with all of those art galleries. What do you think?" She looked up at me with a twinkle in her eye.

"I think we ought to plan it!"

"Well, I sure enjoyed our visit and your unbelievable story. You need to write this in a book. Heck, ditch the book, make it a *movie!* Disney would be all over it!" She grinned. "And you've been blessed by angels, Laura – don't you worry; you'll get home just fine. You and your precious little Kokopelli. You, too, have a safe journey."

I hated goodbyes, especially of people I liked so much. "I wished you lived in Virginia."

She squeezed my hand, "That's one of the nicest compliments I've ever had. I do, too. We have *so* much in common. You take care of yourself and Kokopelli, Laura."

"I will, Elena. Vaya con Dios, kiddo." And with that she was in her compact Toyota sedan, backing out and waving, and I was left in the wake of her smile.

THIRTY-TWO

On to Santa Fe with Kokopelli/Calling Home

"Where we love is home, Home that our feet may leave, but not our hearts."
Oliver Wendell Holmes, Sr., "Homesick in Heaven"

Thursday, November 15th

Pelli and I had an easy and uneventful departure from Grants. I had loaded Cisco and walked the pup one last time (with no results, despite my pleading). I topped-off my coffee to enjoy on the road; the flavor was worth an extra pit stop. I'd also snagged a bran muffin as a treat for Pelli and a pear and a banana for me to enjoy later. The day was warm, and although not brilliantly beautiful, it was certainly 'presentable.' I smiled at Elena's term and put on Van Morrison's timeless *Moondance* CD.

Travel from Grants east past small towns with a variety of names like San Fidel, Acomita, Seama, Cubero and Casa Blanca had a distinct Spanish flair to them, belying that early influence on this area. I saw signs for the Laguna Indian Reservation, New Laguna, the Laguna Pueblo and Mesita. By this time I was almost halfway to Albuquerque. I had made one stop already and made another quick one in Mesita. The map showed few opportunities ahead on the lonesome stretch of highway that lay before us.

Kokopelli traveled like a trooper. She was in her harness, with the seat belt run through to protect her and keep the wild pup secure and in one place. She sat proudly on her Indian blanket, watching the scenery flash by her window. Her ears and eyes missed nothing, both constantly on the move. When I had the windows down a bit she would sniff the air, deciphering all those multiple scents that wafted in, lost on my human nose. Pelli looked happy and carefree today; her worries and neurotic behavior had abated. Every now and then she would turn to me to try to snuggle in closer or lick my hand enthusiastically, as if thanking me for the freedom and joy rides. I rubbed her head and ruffed her fur and told her to behave. Her purple bandana, which I had stubbornly taken back to Virginia with me, was now around that golden neck again. I had brought it back out as good luck. Life was fine.

As we neared Albuquerque I could see that the anemic blue sky under which we had been driving turn grayer ahead; it looked like rain was imminent. I switched CD's from *Moondance* to a Knopfler mix. How I loved this man's music, now and in years past, when he'd been lead with *Dire Straits*. I'd never heard a song of his I hadn't liked, some more than others, sure, but by and large, his music was a balm to my soul. Kokopelli also seemed to like it. She was now curled up on the passenger seat, napping.

Approaching Albuquerque I started thinking about locating the airport and switching Cisco for another rental to give the law a fresh target. Of course it would be easy enough, with their resources, to trace the Malibu to National Rental Car, see that I had returned this one and traded it for another. It seemed to me that that would be fairly obvious. While I was weighing these options, I passed the interchange for the airport where I-25 headed north and south. Once I figured that out, I gave a sigh of relief; I *liked* Cisco — I didn't want to trade her in for a newer model. While I second-guessed this decision, I noticed a faint but distinct rainbow arching through the dreary sky directly over the Turquoise Trail. I smiled and turned to my traveling buddy, pointing to the rainbow, "See that, girl — it's a most definite 'sign' from the Great Spirit in the soggy Sky that we don't need a new car. All is well; we're on exactly the right path." She awoke, whining her response and nosed my hand, agreeing with whatever it was I had said. "Golden Heart" played; we were on course.

We found our way to the Turquoise Trail relatively easy this 2nd time through. I stopped at a gas station to heed nature's call, fill the car, and walk Kokopelli. No results at all. *Were we heading for a repeat of last night?* I wondered. *Was she simply waiting for an inside carpet? I wish I had a portable carpet sample to use for her as target practice for housebreaking. Necessity certainly was the mother of invention*, I continued to muse, as she continued to sniff energetically at anything in sight.

The sky, as promised, held rain. I heard it begin on the overhang as I filled the little sedan. I reflected on how much I loved the gas mileage this car was getting; it had been a good pick for this trip for many reasons, but especially with the prices so high now with the war in Afghanistan and the price hikes we'd had throughout the fall. Gas at this station was $1.79 a gallon. Ugh. It varied around the country; back east it had been about 20 cents less per gallon, but that might have changed, one way or another; it was a weekly fluctuation. War definitely seemed to be a boon for gas companies. I paid for the gas with a traveler's check, still refusing to use my credit cards, just to be on the safe side.

As we started the climb up the Turquoise Trail, past Cedar Crest, I noticed a small thrift shop on the right. I decided, since we'd made very good time earlier, maybe we could sit out the worst of the rain in here. I turned Cisco around and pulled into the parking area. This little store was called "The Talking Talon." The lady behind the counter, Antje, a very classy dark-haired woman with a German accent, told me the proceeds from all of their sales went to help educate school children on responsible stewardship of wildlife and environmental concerns. I told her of being from Virginia and of Ed Clark and The Wildlife Center of Virginia's goals being very much the same. That, and rehabilitating injured wild animals to return them to the wild, if at all possible. She had actually heard of this organization; she told me it was an 'industry model.' That pleased me no end; I'd have to share this with Ed.

I decided to look around and spend a little money in the shop, whether I needed to or not. But first I made sure she would accept a personal check if I swore on my life it was good. Antje smiled and said she would. So I looked around, reminding myself to think small since I had to pack it all back home in just a few days. I found some jewelry to share with friends, a turquoise-colored coffee mug to use for the rest of the trip, a simple wine glass, a generic flower vase and a robe with Southwest zigzags on it that Skye would love. I found a tee shirt for Jared and a belt for Natalie. There. By the time I'd added up the haul I could write her a check for $25, some of this as a donation.

I told Antje, and her helper, Kathleen, a little of the 'Kokopelli story' when she asked what brought me this far west, and up the Turquoise Trail, no less. They wanted to see Pelli for themselves, so I brought my rambunctious pup inside on her leash. Still exuberant about jumping and not respecting people's spaces, I had to haul her back and scold her several times for her transgressions. This was *such* a different dog than that we'd found in the desert originally; her behavior had gone to hell in a hand basket, as they say, with her time with Ricardo. I explained to them that I was in the process of training her and that — believe it or not – she had actually improved from a day and a half earlier. She knew no boundaries then; now she was beginning to learn that not everyone wanted her boundless attention and *no* one wanted her jumping all over them. Of course she had been pent-up in the car – with the exception of her run in the pool area last night – or in a hotel, and she was still a young pup. She needed room to romp and expend some of this youthful energy. This was to be a baby step at a time. Antje and Kathleen were very understanding, especially being animal lovers, themselves. They knew the steps in training a pup and they were supportive of my return to free her. The ladies at "The Talking Talon" then wished us a safe trip to Santa Fe, hoping we'd elude the law and reach Virginia together.

When we left the rain had turned to a gentle but dense mist that hung over the road and veiled her sights. Vision was limited to a bubble of subdued silvers and grays around us. We traveled northward, enshrouded and protected by these mists. I turned on my lights and told Pelli we'd make good time on this last leg to Santa Fe, qualifying that to mean enjoy it and not worry about the clock. We'd get there on Navajo Time – when we did. Nobody awaited us. I had not made reservations, as so few travelers were on the road since the terrorist attacks, so I didn't worry about availability. I put the Eric Clapton mix on for old time's sake, listening to "Let it Grow," "Hand Jive" and the like, and drove slowly through the small roadside towns that we could barely make out through the fog. By the time we'd made it to the New Mexico State Penitentiary – and its warning not to pick up hitchhikers that I more remembered than was able to see – I definitely had a different perspective on the inmates. I wondered how each had 'arrived' – and if for any of them a wayward, homeless puppy might have been involved.

Santa Fe, Thursday evening, November 15th

Pelli and I have arrived safely for our four-day stay at the Comfort Inn. I hauled our luggage upstairs and settled in, using one of those awkward luggage carts, with each wheel housing a mind of its own. Now it was time to go forage for food and a few flowers to brighten the room. I was too tired to drive all the way to the Plaza from there, and still needed to get a few things at an area grocer, so decided to keep it simple and eat at a Chinese restaurant that Art had recommended on our anniversary trip. The food was good, and I brought a doggy bag for me and bought a serving of rice to bring back to the hotel, to try to coax Kokopelli to eat. Her appetite had been off these last two days. I didn't know if it was all the change and excitement of travel, if she did not like the dry puppy chow I'd been offering, or just what it was, but she was not eating well. She had cleaned up every crumb of the bran muffin I had brought her from breakfast earlier, but she needed real food.

After my quiet Chinese dinner, missing my animated companion from last night, I stopped at a grocery store and bought a few staples to last for several days. I found a bouquet of mixed flowers to brighten the room, more puppy chews for Pelli, and so forth. We then headed back to the hotel. Kokopelli was curled up on the front seat beside me.

As we pulled up to a red light at the intersection of Cerrillos and Rodeo Roads, I noticed a Santa Fe police cruiser on my right. I stopped beside him nonchalantly, as a second Santa Fe cruiser pulled up to my left. I was beset by lawmen! I sat there listening to Joni Mitchell's "Big Yellow Taxi" (*"Don't it always seem to go that you don't know what you got 'til it's gone… They paved paradise and put up a parking lot…"*) and the total absurdity of the moment struck me. I looked to my right at the officer sitting in his car; I looked to my left at the other and burst out laughing. "Well, Pelli, we're sitting here red-handed; if they want us, they've got us… what can I say?" I smiled wryly and shook my head, not worried at all – as I'd been just this morning in Grants with Elena – just highly amused at the ludicrous moment. This could be a Larson joke. They had Arizona's infamous, felonious puppy-thief surrounded and didn't seem to know it. The light turned green and I intentionally held back, letting the cruisers pull on ahead. It was then I decided to do something about these license plates while in Santa Fe.

Calling Home

At my hotel room in Santa Fe I felt we could re-lax a bit now, being in a state other than Arizona, and whatnot. One of the things so convenient in the Comfort Inn is that one can stay in a suite, at a reasonable price, which includes a small refrig-erator and a microwave. The cooler could remain in the car as a travel 'fridge, and I would be able to refreeze the icepacks at night. So now I could  now buy milk, yogurt, fruit and other perishables, and could keep it all fresh.

Safely back at the hotel, I mixed some of the rice along with a half-cup of milk in with her dry food and put it on the floor of the bathroom, beside her water. Pelli came in, sniffed it a moment, and dove into dinner. *Now* we were talkin'! So each meal thereafter, I mixed a little rice in with it, added a splash of milk and encouraged her to eat. Our problem was solved; we had hit the jackpot! I kept dry food down at all times for her to snack on and we worked out a very satisfactory meals program. Like Lakota, and unlike Trey, Kokopelli had a persnickety little appetite and ate only when she was hungry and the food struck her fancy. Gone were the days of her scoffing down anything in sight, as when we had originally found her, there under her sagebrush in Navajo country.

So here I was, sitting on a queen-sized bed in my room, Kokopelli on the floor beside me, busy with a dog bone and very much respecting her boundaries after some initial scolding. ("*No*, Pelli, no jumping on the bed! Not on the *chair*, either!") She didn't have it down pat yet, but she certainly was beginning to re-understand the concept of manners, housebreaking and of discipline, in general. She wanted to learn; she had just been too long without a 'pack leader' – that alpha presence that molds the youth into the adult. This was now my job.

I reflected on my family at home, thinking of them, each now grow-ing up into young adults and following their own inner compass, each with their very different interests. I thought of our busy nonstop exis-tence, full of activities, school and sports programs, and of keeping up with these chock-full lives. I thought of what I often tell my friends: *"I feel like a Cornucopia – that threw up."* We have so much of a good thing it can often be totally overwhelming.

It was time now to call up friends and family, to reach out and touch these someones. Time to celebrate. So I called Pete and the kids, that first night, to let them know we had arrived safely. So far, so good – no prison stripes yet. I thought of each of the children. Only I can no longer really call them children as they *are* all young adults, each now gravitating towards their own goals, interests, and their niche in this fast-paced world. I wondered what it held for them.

Skye

Pete and I had started our family almost ten years after we were married. We had always had animals, which are a wonderful predecessor to the constant responsibility that is required of parenthood. When Skye was born in March of 1984, we thought we were ready to begin that new chapter, although it had scared the hell out of me, as my own mother and I had been estranged so much of my earlier life. I had *no* idea how to raise a child, but Pete and I managed to wing it well.

Skye grew up an energetic, curious, precocious child. She was always gazelle-like, slim and pretty, with straight light brown hair and 'dark chocolate' eyes. She has her Dad's and my high cheekbones and a precious sweet smile. She reminds me of the old nursery rhyme: *"When she was good, she was very, very good, and when she was bad she was horrid."* So horrid, in fact, that my mother's nickname for her was "Hortense;" it got Skye's goat *every* time. While my mother was living these two had a very special relationship. She would call her grandmother "Polar Bear," for the snowy white hair she had always seen on my mom's head. My nickname for Skye was "Skeekeboo." I don't know why; it simply fit.

Skye's intense energy and high intelligence were ideal for school. She blossomed with the challenge of a full day's activities. She put so much of herself into school, in fact, that from about kindergarten through 3rd or 4th grade I've got photographs of her right after she came home. She'd be coloring or reading, or watching *My Little Pony* or *Rainbow Bright*, two of her very favorite videos, and she'd crash and burn on the floor or the couch. I'd photograph her sprawled out, drawing supplies around her, snoring away, or with her head back on the couch, zonked out cold. I would cover her with a blanket or an afghan and let her rest. After her batteries were recharged with this afternoon nap, she'd be up and raring to go again, somersaulting her way around the house. This was her favorite mode of transportation. Some kids skip; Skye somersaulted. For years. This agility was a conversation piece for quite some time.

And so we watched her grow up, our first-born daughter, the one on which we learned. She often teased us about that – she called herself our 'experiment.' And when she didn't want to claim us as her parents – a stage each and every child goes through at some point – she would call herself 'adopted.' This became a family joke.

This daughter is our dreamer, the one most sensitive to the fragile pulse of life, and attuned to the moment. She has a natural gift in writing. Skye questions everything; she often is the deepest of the three and the most prone to philosophical ponderings. Skye has many friends and an active social life, sometimes to the detriment of her studies, as she loves her parties and bands. And now here I was reminiscing of all the years of her growing up, here in this quiet hotel room in the middle of New Mexico, thinking of each and every one of my children. Skye has become a graceful and delightful young lady, a well-balanced teenager, considering all the pitfalls out there for the young these days. I had worked hard to be able to have open dialogues with her, for her to trust me enough to come talk with me about pretty much anything. I wanted to offer my daughter – for *all* of my children – what my mother and I had not had. That delicate balance of respect and trust and confidence that I had come to find was ultimately important in this tenuous relationship between generations. This beautiful young lady and I were close, for the most part – of course we had our moments, but in any honest relationship those 'moments' exist, and we were tight.

Jared

Jared was born two years and four days after Skye, in March of 1986. When he was three months old we moved from Sunnybrook Farm to our new home, which we called "Edelweiss," after the tiny German flower and the song from *The Sound of Music*. My father died of a heart attack the same weekend that we moved. It was devastating. My friend, Donna, pointed out that we were going through three of the major life events, all at the same time: the birth of a child, a major move, and the loss of a parent. What can you do? You cope. You put one foot in front of the other, you close your eyes and pray to your God, and you take one day at a time. Humans are amazingly resilient beings.

Jared had a curly head of pale brown hair and a cherub's build. He was all sweetness and light, an easy-going, delightful child. He grew up in Skye's dominant shadow, adoring her. Skye, you see, was *not* so thrilled to no longer be the one and only with her parents. She would covet Jared's pacifier, bean him with her toys, and take his blanket. If it weren't so frustrating at the time it would have been funny. But again, you cope. They both survived, indeed thrived, at our new home in the country; Amanda had joined us, as well as all of the cats over these growing up years. We had added Holly to our herd, a quiet large gray pony, a cross between Arabian and quarter horse, for the kids to ride. I'm hoping they're not going to have a lot to say in some distant future, sitting in a shrink's chair, explaining why their parents ruined their lives.

Jared grew into a tall drink of water with not a drop of excess meat on his elongated bones. He has a plethora now of thick wavy chestnut hair crowning his head. I kid him that his eyes are 'milk chocolate brown,' not quite as dark as his sister's. He is a reflective young fellow with an irreverent and zany flair. He reminds me for all the world of a cross between John Lennon and Harry Potter, with his new wire rim spectacles that emphasize the deep, sensitive look of this tall young man. Jared exudes kindness that is overridden with a constant air of mischief, most of which he directs at his sisters that bookend him. Payback time.

:-) To prevent the 'middle child' syndrome — lost in the middle of the shuffle of chaotic family life — we call him our 'Number One Son.'

Jared oozes talent: he grew up drawing prolifically, creating his own cartoon characters over the years. He has sketchbook after sketchbook of doodles and drawings that we have saved. Jared has a natural eye and affinity for photography, and he began piano lessons several years ago, following his Dad's interest in music. He gravitates to music as a main form of relaxation. Jared often composes his own piano solos, playing for hours at a time, working through a piece, and then he keeps it stored somewhere in that busy mind. He and I share an avid ear for the 60s and early 70s music, now dubbed "Classic Rock." We'll ask each other if we've heard some obscure song from the past; if not, we'll share it. He burns CD compilations of tunes he'll think I'd like for my birthday; I'll listen for new songs I think he'd like. Our tastes run a gamut from this rock n' roll from the Vietnam era to classical, to musicals, jazz, the blues and some country favorites. Jared and I communicate through music. I've told him if I'm ever in a coma and he wants to help me out of it, he'll know the music to bring to the hospital. Of course, he might want to keep me there by bringing along acid rock/ heavy metal. (One less parent to bug him, and all…)

Natalie

Natalie is the youngest of our trio, born in November of 1988. We celebrated her 13th birthday with a big bash of her buddies just before I returned west to reclaim Kokopelli.

Like the others, Natalie is headed for tall. Her hair is naturally dark chestnut, like me, but she experimented with a blond hair color with friends last summer and her mane is now blended. Her eye color is a mingling of her dad's dark brown Italian eyes and my hazel green 'Irish Eyes.' I kid her that hers are a beautiful shade of 'muddy pond water,' reflecting all sorts of earthy hues. She just says: *"Maummm!"* I love to play with her and she reciprocates with a healthy sense of humor.

Natalie is the most athletic of our trio, with an intense love of soccer. She has a natural talent for the skills of goalie. I well remember the year she ended up, almost by default, in playing JV goalie in field hockey, a position she ironically hated — because she enjoys the action of the running game — but at which she excelled. She looked like a colorful snowman, dressed in Gap castoffs, in her goalie uniform. And in the playoff of the districts, against the very best team at Western Albemarle, she and her team managed to take the Hornets into double overtime before either side scored. Western Albemarle played a fiercely offensive game; we should have been slammed. But Natalie deflected thirty-some possible goals, with one *fin*ally getting through in the second overtime, for Western to win the game 1-0. Natalie was crushed. Simply crushed. She couldn't believe she'd 'let' one get by her. What we had to convince her of was how many shots *hadn't* gotten past her constant defense. Imagine if she had *liked* what she was doing! And the irony of all ironies is that Pete and I had missed that game. It was supposed to have been played the night before, but had been rained out – one rain in a season of drought – go figure. So they had it the next night, but Jared had a one-act play performance in his school, sixty miles away from the Districts play-offs. In retrospect, we should have divided and conquered, one of us being there for each event. C'est la vie. But we heard about Natalie's tenacity from any number of other parents, and the coach, who were all probably wondering where the devil *we* were in missing our daughter's incredible game!

Natalie loves the outdoors, the horses, and all of our animals. She jumps into life with a full head of steam. But along with this love of sports and her outside interests, she stays focused in school, bringing home honor roll grades consistently. She hopes to one day be a veterinarian, an actress (she's a dead ringer for Mary Kate and Ashley Olson), an architect, or to open her own vegetarian restaurant… She dreams her dreams in technicolor.

I thought of each of the children, how different they were, how they had grown, and I grew tremendously homesick. It was quiet now, about 7 PM Mountain Time. It would be 9 PM at home. This would be an excellent time to call home and 'visit.' Dinner would be over and they'd all be awake, although Jared often went to bed ridiculously early (from my night owl perspective)… I dialed, using the 800# we'd put in for the kids. The phone rang three times when Pete picked up.

PeterWop was his usual dear self, worried, but supportive. He filled me in on all the happenings on the farm, the kids and their schoolwork and after-school activities and sports. How each of the animals were doing, mentioning – again – that we had too many. He told me what he had been doing, how work was going, what he had fixed for dinner that night. (The man *loved* to cook, thanks to Jean's culinary influence.) He was much more relaxed than when I had spoken with him from Gallup yesterday afternoon. We talked a good while, glad to just visit.

Finally he said, "The law has been calling home, Laura. The call comes up anonymously. I haven't talked with them, because I didn't know what to say – so I let the deputy just leave a message."

"Who's been calling, Pete? Deputy Dick or Deputy Isabella?"

"Deputy Isabella."

"I guess he's been the one assigned to the case, then. Great. Listen, Pete, if you talk with him, tell him you don't know *where* I am or *when* I'll be home. Tell him we're estranged, or something – which probably isn't far off." I chuckled. "When I get Pelli back safely, I'll face the music then. But I want to get her to Virginia first."

"Listen to you talk! That's fine by me, Ra. This is your baby – I'm just the messenger. But be careful, okay? Did you switch rental cars in Albuquerque?"

"No. I missed the turn-off from I-40 onto I-25. Forgot you had to go south. There was a rainbow over the Turquoise Trail and I read that as a sign that it was cool to head on to Santa Fe, so I did. No problemos there, friend. So I've still got the Plymouth."

"Plymouth? You said you were driving a Malibu. Chevy makes that, Laura."

"No, it's a *Ply*mouth Malibu, Pete. I call it 'Cisco,' after Costner's wonderful little buckskin in *Dances with Wolves*."

"*No*, Laura," the Wop said, ignoring the name, "*Chevy* makes the Malibu. You're driving a Chevy Malibu."

"Well, the law thinks I'm driving a Plymouth – that's what I put down on my registration in the Grand Canyon."

"Ra, believe me, baby, *you're* the *only* one that thinks you're driving a Plymouth Malibu, don't fool yourself. I always knew that you thought outside the box. Now I'm beginning to believe you *live* outside the box. Or you've gone blond on me."

"Oh yeah. That's what I strive to be: a Barbie blond. Oh well. So far I've eluded the law with my 'hot dog' – but I honestly can't believe they're looking for me real hard."

"Probably not. But you never know… You left some pissed-off cops in your wake. They may be out for vengeance, if nothing else."

"Yeah, a male-pride thing. They'll get over it. In the great scheme of law-breaking, I doubt this in on the Richter charts," and I went on to tell him about the rapist/murderer in the Grand Canyon area.

"Well, lay low and be careful, Ra, you *are* now wanted in Arizona. These

APB's cross state lines. And I can't believe I'm even *saying* these words to you. So far, André is the only one I've told about your 'escapades' out west." André was Pete's assistant at work, his right-hand man.

"Did you tell him why I came out? Why I did what I did? I *certainly* hope you told him the whole story, Pete, and that I don't run around doing this kind of thing every single day."

Pete laughed. "I think that goes without saying, Razza. But I did let him listen to your message about 'being on the lam in Arizona.' He roared with laughter on that one and said: 'Pete, your wife has a lot of spunk.' I told him 'if he only knew'…"

I went into my best Scarlett southern accent and said "Petah-Whaap – do ah detect a hent of male priide in your li'l ole' wife?"

"Ah'll neveh eveh ahdmit it, *hon*ey. But you certainly did cut to the chase, I have to *ahd*mit. Ole' Ricardo likely never knew what hit him. And you saved the state of Arizona a bunch of money in needless court costs over jury time and the ownership of this silly pup. I'm sure they've got more important things to contend with."

"Oh yeah. Like rapists and murderers and drug dealers. Terrorists. Things like that. Oh yeah."

We talked a while longer, catching up on our domestic life at home, how the kids were all doing in school, how they were handling the news of their vigilante mother, and so forth. We missed each other. In some ways I was thrilled to be west with time to spend in Santa Fe and my mission accomplished; in others, I was truly homesick. But all would work itself out, one way or another, in just a few days. The key would be to lay low, as Pete had said, and to enjoy the rest of this time visiting friends and kicking around an area that I was falling in love with, all the while training little Kokopelli to the ways of the world, as I knew them – outside the box.

NON SEQUITUR © 2002 by Wiley Miller. Dist. by UNIVERSAL PRESS SYNDICATE. Reprinted with permission. All rights reserved.

Skye got on the phone first, sounding so grown up and responsible at seventeen, telling me about her studies and curriculum. We chatted awhile and she asked me how I was doing 'out there,' and asked if I'd talked with the law anymore. She then paused, considered what she was going to say, and matter of factly asked me: "Mom, are you *sure* this is the example that you want to be setting for your teenage children?"

I leaned my head back and just laughed at her question, responding: "Skye, sweetie, you will learn in life that sometimes you just have to listen to your heart. My heart has been my compass, and it is telling me that I've really done nothing terribly wrong. Certainly nothing worse than Ricardo has done in lying to us and basically stealing her, in the first place, then imprisoning her like that and not even taking care of her basic needs. I don't know why he ever even wanted a dog."

We talked a little longer and then I asked to speak with Jared. My son came on next, grunting as a fifteen-year-old boy is apt do, a man of few words. He responded to my questions about his life and times with basically single syllables. Suddenly there was a pregnant pause, my sensitive son deep in thought, and then he blurted: "Mom, what *possessed* you to break the law in getting your dog back?! What in the world were you *thinking?!!* I'm sure glad *I* wasn't out there with you!"

My boy could speak in sentences! I just grinned at him over the phone, knowing him as I do, and playing with him from a distance, responded:

"Oh yes, you were, buddy. You were out here with me. You were right there next to my heart that night; I was wearing your jacket." I laughed at his exasperation.

See, Jared has had 'experience' with me, before. Years ago, one summer day when my mother lived in Lexington, Virginia, in the Shenandoah Valley, I had taken the children over to visit her when Pete had been working. Driving through the small town of Fairfield on our return home, we had passed this old antiques shop on the left. There on the porch, propped up beside furniture odds and ends, was a black running horse weather vane – just what I had been looking for, to top-off the new shed Pete and I had built! I turned around, parked directly in front of the little shop and tried the door. Locked. The place was closed. I knocked on the door anyway, hoping someone might be inside. Nada. Nothing. We went to the side of the building, where steps led up to a door above. Thinking someone might be living upstairs and running the downstairs shop, I climbed up and knocked. No one was home.

So I went back downstairs, found the name, address of the shop and phone number, posted on a sign in the window, and copied all the information down. As there was no price on the weather vane, I told the kids I was taking it back with us, so no one would buy it before I could talk with the owner. Skye could have cared less — she was in a hurry to get home and make a phone call. Natalie loved it and was totally behind our bringing it with us — she knew I would pay for it. But Jared was another story. He looked at me, frowned, and said:

"But Mom, you're stealing it."

"Jared, I am *not*. Didn't you see me copy down all the information to call the guy? I just don't want it to be sold before I can get back to the Valley — AND I don't want to have to drive back over the mountain to get the thing, when we're already right here."

"But Mom, you haven't paid for it. You can't just take it with you."

"Yes I can, Bud. I'm going to send the fellow a check, if it's reasonable. If it's not, I will bring it back over. You know that."

"Well, if you put that thing in the car, I'm not getting in."

"Jared, damnit, we've got to go." I put the weather vane in the back of the wagon. "Get in and stop being so stubborn."

"*No*." He folds his arms across his ten-year-old chest, plants his feet firmly on the sidewalk, and pokes out his lip. He totally refuses to leave.

"Jared, you're making a scene. Get in. I *will* get in trouble if you don't cooperate!"

"No. I'm *not* going with you with that thing in there."

"Jared, get *in*! I'll call the fellow tomorrow. And if the store is closed then, because it's Sunday, then I'll call him the first thing on Monday morning. I fully intend to pay for it. You know that. Now *get in!*"

Finally, eventually, he does. And he sits in silence, glaring at me, arms tight across his chest all the way home. As soon as we're in our driveway, Jared *leaps* out of the car as we're greeted by Pete, happy to see his family safely home, and exclaims: "Dad, she *stole* it! *Mom* stole *the weather vane!!*" as he ran behind his dad and pointed at me.

Gulp. "Okay. Okay, Pete. There are two sides to every story — let me explain." I tell my husband the story, show him the shop's name and number, and assure him I'm calling Sunday — or Monday. Pete looks up the driveway, I guess expecting a police car to have followed us home, and stands beside Jared. Both look righteous. Father and son. Pete and rePete. *Come on, guys, cut me a break here.*

On Sunday I called several times. No answer. Monday morning I called the shop again, first thing. A man answered. I asked him if he was missing anything from his front porch and he glibly asked: "Why, what'd you steal?"

I laughed at his easy comeback and replied: "Your weather vane. That black running horse you had out front – it's just what I've been looking for, and I didn't want to have to drive all the way back for it. Is it reasonable?"

"How's $100.00?" he asks, and tells me how he acquired it.

Sam and I ended up talking for over half an hour, comparing notes on who he might know up my way, and I, his. Nice guy. In the course of our conversation I found that he had served in Vietnam, that stinking little war where soldiers didn't want to fight and when they did few supported their efforts, in Vietnam, or when they returned to the States (the ones that did). Damned if they did and damned if they didn't. Vietnam impacted their minds, as well as many of their bodies, for the rest of their lives. Vietnam was a war in which many soldiers returned from fighting only to be spit upon when they reached American soil. This was not a battle in which the young had a choice; it was a battle they had been drafted to fight by men their father and grandfather's ages, all caught in a quagmire of politics from which there seemed no escape. Sam had fought there, losing the use of his legs. From teenage years on he would no longer walk, and all for a war in which he did not believe. Yet somehow he was not bitter. I wrote him a note after our call, sent him $125.00 for the weather vane, and made sure Jared saw me enclose the check. I then asked him to take the letter to our mailbox and put the red flag up, signaling out-going mail. "Next time," I said to him, "believe me when I say I'm going to do it." But I had also gotten a huge satisfaction out of my young son's convictions. They would serve him well for the rest of his life.

(Back to Santa Fe) "Mom," (groan) "it's time you talked with Natalie."

Natalie gets on the phone, having eagerly been waiting her turn. She's my little sidekick, my shadow, a carbon copy of myself with fewer years on her face. She is growing out of her smurf-voice and now sounds more teenybopper or often, when she's playing around, California Valley-girl. She's got that impression nailed. Natalie has obviously been listening-in on her siblings (I'll have to commend her for not interrupting their conversations) about their vigilante mother.

First thing she says after "Hi, Mom" is: "Mom, at dinner we've been having these conversations about your adventures, and just about everyone here says that what you did was wrong. You shouldn't have picked the guys lock to get the puppy back. But *I* think what you did was absolutely right." All of this is basically said in one nonstop breath. "You saved that puppy not *once*, but *twice*, and I'm really proud of you." Then Natalie pauses, thinks about what she's going to say, and hesitatingly adds: "But if you *do* get caught and go to jail, I'll be really mad."

I'm laughing at her conviction, her support, her pure innocence and unconditional love, and tell her "Don't worry, Twerpy Doodle" (my long-standing nickname for her). "I'm trying my best to bring Kokopelli back to the family and stay out of jail. But if I *do* go to jail, will you write to me?" I laugh and wink at her, which she knows I'm doing, even at such a distance.

"*Maummm...!!!,*" she exclaims, exasperated. We then continued our conversation about her schoolwork, how she was helping Dad with the animals and things, and how she and Dad would meet Kokopelli and me in Richmond when we flew in Monday night, if all went well. Then I asked to speak with Pete again and we eventually said our goodnights.

After we had hung up, I thought of a poem I'd jotted down, after one of our late dinners, after one of the crazy Varsity night games. It captured a fragment of our insane lives, a fragment from any busy family, doing their best every day, to be there for their children:

A halo over your head
and circles under your eyes,
my dear husband, how hard we try —
We offer our children riches
of laughter and of love
fill their stockings daily
with humble treasures from our trove.
Believe in their tomorrows,
as we give them our todays,
offer them keys to the kingdom,
in our humble, simple ways.

Laura Cockerille Giannini, © 2000

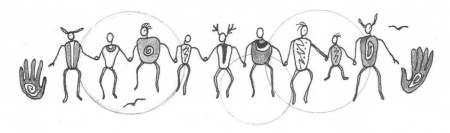

I felt a huge pang of homesickness for this wonderful and crazy family awaiting us with bated breath at home. I got on the floor with Pelli, who had been laying there chewing on the smoked dog bone I had given her before the call, and snuggled into her soft golden fur. I said a little prayer of thanks for our Cornucopia of blessings and asked continued help in getting us home safely, to our own personal family circus. For no matter *how* idiosyncratic the each of us might be, or how dysfunctional the kids all *claimed* us to be, by God we know one another, warts and all, love one another for and despite them, and would go down fighting if it came to that. Kokopelli snuggled in close, eating up the attention, and gave me one of her huge slurpy kisses, with her anteater tongue, all along the side of my face. Love, from whatever source, is sweet.

THIRTY-THREE

On the Lam in Santa Fe/Training Time

"In prosperity our friends know us; in adversity we know our friends."
Churton Collins, Aphorisms

Friday morning, November 16th

An octopus, with a sudsy, warm washcloth in each tentacle, was scrubbing my face thoroughly, one tentacle at a time. Up and down. Up and down. "Okay, okay, it's *clean* already!" I snapped, awaking from my dream with my eyes springing open. There I was, staring into Kokopelli's eager young face, delighted that she had awoken me to greet the day with her. Apparently I had gotten up in the night and left the bathroom door open. I had been sleeping belly down, my head and right arm draped over the edge of the bed, fair game to her busy tongue. I groaned, feeling loved but somewhat violated. Yuck. I know what that mouth tastes and explores and eats. *Yuck!*

No doubt about it, I was awake. Stumbling into the bathroom, I washed my face and rinsed out my mouth, then came out to hug and love this enthusiastic pup as I dressed and found her leash for a morning walk. Having her with me on the trip was very much like having a two-year-old in tow, spontaneous needs to be constantly met, peppered with much love, and love returned, and discipline divvied-out along the way. Just no diapers. Instead, our trusty Marcal/Febreze combo came to the rescue. But this morning Pelli had been excellent. No trace of an accident, anywhere... I congratulated her heartily... maybe *this* would be our "pee outside" adventure, and I could praise her to the high heavens. But it was not to be.

We made it down the long hallway with no problem, and into and down the elevator, no problem. I stopped in the lobby long enough to grab a Styrofoam cup of decaf to go out with us – and we made it as far as the inside doors of the lobby, where a sweet young couple stopped to greet her. And there, in front of them, me, the folks behind the desk – God, and everybody – she peed. She just couldn't hold it any longer. So close, and yet so far... I blanched, just mortified. But Ernesto and the rest of the gang just grinned and came running to help. Pulling the roll of paper towels from under my arm, I immediately started to sop up the liquid. The cleaning fellow said not to worry, as he brought out a pail of soapy water with a ringer-mop, ready to take care of it. I thanked them all profusely, smiled my goodbyes to the laughing couple and led my charge outside to start up our mantra again. But, of course, this got us nowhere, as she no longer had to go. Criminy. Okay, *next* time it's the back way – down those sterile, linoleum steps that terrify her, to the rear of the hotel. I would just have to reassure and coax her on down that slippery, reverberating stairway directly outside. Do not get coffee. Do not pass go.

Afterwards I put her in the car to wait for me, while I went back in to get a little breakfast, myself, and surprise Art with our visit. I winked at Ernesto, who knew what I was doing, and peeked around the corner. There was the dear, kind man, working away diligently at cleaning and refilling the breakfast area. When his back was turned, wiping down a counter, I tiptoed up behind him and goosed him big-time, laughing. He turned in surprise at this behavior from a hotel guest, and looked at me in wonderment. "Laura! What are you doing back so soon?! You and Pete were just here – is Pete with you? Are the kids here, too?"

I shrugged my shoulders no, and laughed, "Art, you won't be*lieve* why I'm back, or what our story is. It's too long to get into right now. Just believe me, my friend, it's a really good one. Peter's back at home, in Virginia, holding down the fort with the kids and the farm. I'm out here on a mission. Let me take you to lunch, when you get off, and I'll tell you the whole thing."

Art smiled, looked a bit confused, but very happy to see me, and asked if he might call Carole to join us for lunch. I had never met her and was soon to have proof that she really existed. I wasn't sure how she might take the story, but why not? I'd been sharing it with everyone else, so far, and been nothing but supported. He called her at home, arranged a time and place to meet, and we had our luncheon date all set up. I had a bowl of cereal and orange juice to tide me over, and then Pelli and I went out to run a few errands and call the veterinarian that Art had recommended to set up an appointment for later.

The four of us met back at the hotel and drove my car to Castro's, finding a space in deep shade to park. They asked me about the puppy in the back seat with Art. I inwardly smiled and remained vague, telling them only that they had almost inherited her. They looked at one another questionably, and I just promised them the story. "Wait until we're settled inside," I said, "I'll tell you from start to finish why I'm back in Santa Fe so soon, and with a wild pup in tow..." Art and Carole accepted that, and into Castro's we went.

I found Carole to be a delight. She was quiet at first, with soft dark, gray-infused hair framing her very kind face. She wore tortoise-frame glasses and her matronly manner housed what I thought to be a rather shy personality. But she missed nothing. As I became animated in retelling and reliving the whole adventure, she, too, came to life. She and Art enjoyed the tale from beginning to end, interjecting with comments or questions. We spent a couple of hours at Castro's, over lunch and drinking coffee, visiting and laughing. They kidded me good-naturedly about the felon in their midst.

Art had told me that since Carole's retirement as a librarian she had loved to stay up late and read. In fact, she and Art were both avid readers, devouring books of all nature. He has suggested all sorts of titles for Pete and me to check out (couldn't resist the pun) over the time we had known him. Carole would stay up into the wee hours of the night, much later than Art, as he had his breakfast shift at the hotel during the weekdays to rouse him out of bed early. It was a schedule that worked well for them. When Art came home mid-day, she would be up, well rested, and they would have the afternoon and evening ahead. The two were dear together – a couple that had been there for one another through thick and thin, knew one another's strengths and weaknesses, and loved each other, anyway. Their devotion was precious. And the sweetest part, to me, is that they had opened a magical door into their lives, into their family, and invited me inside. I felt safe and protected in their presence.

I grinned in sharing the story, especially the part about trucker Gordie, and told them this is what I had meant about them almost inheriting the pup out of the wild blue sky. Art just gave me a wink and said, with that wonderful twinkle in his eyes, "Laura, as cute as that puppy is, if you had shown up at our doorstep and said that you wanted her back, why, you probably would have had to pick our lock. And *then* you'd be wanted in *two* states!"

Some friend, eh? But knowing Art, and now Carole, I'd probably have let Kokopelli stay with them, realizing in my heart that if she died of anything in their care it would be from too much kindness. Between the two of them, and their daughter, Christina, she would be spoiled rotten – a real life rags-to-riches story.

The Vetting Appointment

After our long and sociable lunch at Castro's, Art, Carole and I took the newly notorious pup to her appointment at 1:00 at the Southwest Veterinary Associates, over on Rodeo Road. I had called to make the appointment, explaining that all I needed was a health check and rabies shot for the pup, in order to fly home with her on Monday. We arrived about 12:45 and I stuck my head in the door to let them know the puppy was there; I was going to walk her first before bringing her inside. Art and Carole said they would wait and signal me if the vet was ready before we came in. They sat beside one another in the open waiting area, magazines in hand. They reminded me of Jean and Allan, having lived and loved for so many good years that they almost breathed as one.

Today was as misty as the day before. There was no rain, however a fine vapor hung in the air, moistening the surface of all it touched. A large hemlock stood in the front yard of the clinic; underneath the ground was adorned with tiny, absolutely perfectly shaped cones from this evergreen. "They're beautiful, aren't they, girl? Perfect little specimens of nature, with their very own niche in this world." The yellow pup slowly wagged that curvaceous tail of hers and licked my hand in agreement and then her attention turned to a scent off in the grass. She strained at her leash, her purple bandana beginning to pick up the dampness. I picked up several of the cones and put them in my pocket, after studying their intricate conical overlay pattern. Pelli came back to me to poke around my hand with her curious face, wanting to share in my discovery.

Carole opened the door and called to me, "Laura, the vet lady is ready to see your puppy, dear."

I called back, "Okay, Carole, we'll come right on in!" I turned to Pelli, "Okay, pipsqueak, show her your stuff, kiddo. If she sees a fraction of the energy I've been seeing, there'll be no doubt at all as to your health." She followed me on inside, not old enough or experienced enough yet to know this wasn't the sort of place dogs usually willingly went.

A young woman met us and smiled over her horn-rimmed glasses.

She wore a clinical white coat with a nametag that said 'Marti Merritt, DVM.' Her gingery hair was short and curled; she had a pixie quality about her. "I see you want a health check in order to fly with this puppy on Monday. And let's see," she scanned her notes, "a rabies shot. No fecal exam? No other shots? Anything else?" She glanced over her shoulder for a response, as we followed her into a small room. Art and Carole had chosen to continue to stay in the waiting room, both of them now absorbed in their magazine articles.

We hoisted Kokopelli onto the stainless steel table. I hadn't thought of bringing one of her stool samples in with me. They had been flushed in the hotel toilet. "I think a rabies shot is the only vaccine for now. I'll take her to our vet back at home and get the rest of her shots. I don't want to fill her full of serums just before traveling." I thought of talking with Dr. Merritt about her bladder and our housebreaking dilemma, but decided that there seemed to be nothing wrong with her plumbing but confusion. And I'd have to explain why a six-month-old puppy wasn't housebroken; this could trigger too much of the story — and I was too close to getting home to throw us a curveball now.

"She's a pretty young dog," said the vet. "Where did you get her?" I decided that part of the truth wouldn't be a problem. "I found her out in Monument Valley, Arizona, on the Navajo rez. She was hungry and homeless, so I decided to bring her home to our farm."

"Oh? Where's home?" asked the lady, as she listened to Pelli's heartbeat and checked her gums. She then placed a thermometer up the pup's rectum, which Kokopelli didn't cater to in the least.

"Virginia. I'm from Virginia. Around the Charlottesville area – a place called Somerset."

"I've been to Charlottesville before. It's a beautiful town. Thomas Jefferson's home, if I'm not mistaken." She looked up. "Vitals are all fine."

"You're not. Monticello lies on the outskirts and his University of Virginia lies in the heart of town. It is a very beautiful, and very eclectic, city. But it's growing way too rapidly. It's beginning to suffer from urban sprawl, like so many other places. Shopping malls and fast-food strips have it looking like Everywhere Suburbia USA."

"Yes, we're seeing that around here, too. All the cities are growing. Just too many people. What do you mean by eclectic?" She looked up again from the exam. Pelli took this as a cue that we were finished and attempted to flee her intense scrutiny.

"Oh no you don't, rascal," I told her and tightened her leash. "It's okay, girl. This nice lady won't hurt you at all. Or – as my husband likes to say – 'it won't hurt, did it?'" We laughed. Pelli resignedly stopped her escape attempts, realizing she was surrounded. "We have the 'intelligence community,' I like to joke, with the law school at UVA, as well as the University, in general, with all the professors and students. And there's the University of Virginia and the Martha Jefferson Hospitals, both of them well respected. There are communities on the outskirts of the mountains, and beautiful horse and cattle farms in Albemarle County. There's even Georgetown Farms – a *buffalo* farm – up in Madison County. Go figure. If you eat meat, this is very lean and they don't use hormones or antibiotics in the feed. And if you're worried about 'mad cow disease,' why, this is *buf*falo." I kidded her.

She looked up and smiled while I continued. "There are a lot of retirement-aged folks, and a lot of old hippies, such as myself. The area is a hodge-podge of people from all walks of life. But it's getting more and more a bigger city feeling. Charlottesville's also a kind of a haven for creative types, like writers and artists and poets. Rita Dove lives there. Steven Soderbergh used to. Sam Shepherd and Jessica Lang used to live outside town; Sissy Spacek still does. John Grisham and his wife live somewhere south of town. Howie Long and his wife live in the area. That kind of eclectic. Celebrities like it because they can live their lives in relative obscurity."

"Oh. Quite impressive. I'll have to go back and visit again. I've been to New York and to New England, too. *Very* different than the Southwest. I'm from California. Anything verdantly green out in these parts is artificial."

"Well, yes. At the moment – with our drought – it's the same in Virginia. We'll soon need to install irrigation systems, as well."

"Drought? I was under the impression that Virginia was consistently *green*. Is it bad?"

"When Virginia gets rain, she's like a rainforest in spring and summer – with every nuance of green in an artists' palette. But actually, yes, the drought is very bad. *Very.* The last three of four years have been drought years, which has been a cumulative hell on the water table. They're calling it the worst drought since the dustbowl – since the 30s."

"Oh my, that *is* bad. It's awful here, too. Have you been keeping up with the raging wildfires?"

"How can you not? Yes, they're unbelievably destructive. Yet people just keep building in the wilderness. Like there's a fire station around the corner. That's a leap of faith, isn't it?" I was calming Pelli, who by now was very ready to go.

"Sure is." She changed the subject, "I understand that your governor, somebody-Warner, is an up-&-coming politician. What do you think of him?"

"Oh, we're very well pleased. There's John Warner, who's been a Senator for forever, and is very well respected, and there's Governor Mark Warner. There're not related and the Senator is a Republican and the governor, a Democrat. The governor preceding him left the state damned near bankrupt, and we've always prided ourselves for running in the black. Mark Warner is a businessman, and he's somehow managed to fight tre*men*dous odds to bring Virginia back in the black again. It was uphill all the way, but he did it. He has a sensible approach to just about everything, including the environment. I wish only that Virginia allowed a governor a second term…"

Dr. Merritt smiled at me. "So you decided to name her 'Kokopelli,' I see. Aren't you living dangerously?" This lady lived in the Southwest; *she* knew the reputation of the impish character of mirth and trickery.

"Yeah, well. I've wanted a husky-type for a long time to name Kokopelli, as I love this area, but I've certainly had moments to reconsider the name, believe me."

"Well, your pretty little puppy seems to be perfectly healthy." She took a step back and rubbed her nose under her glasses. "All she needs now is her rabies shot." The young vet turned to prepare the syringe.

I whispered to Pelli, "Brace yourself, girl – this is my least favorite part – the needle… *uh oh*… here she comes!" But I confided this to her softly, in a voice meant to calm her; as for me, I gave a big gulp and turned my head. I vaccinated my horses at home with their annual shots, and was now beginning to do the same with our dogs and cats. But I did *not* like a doctor heading towards me with that acicular instrument, intending to puncture my parts.

The vet squeezed the air from the syringe, ruffed Pelli's coat and found a spot in her haunch, pulling the syringe back to check for blood, and gave the shot. "Okay, all done." Dr. Merritt smiled at Pelli. "You're headed on to Virginia. You're a lucky girl – looks like you'll have a very nice home." She then smiled at me. "What shall we say she is? An Akita mix?"

"She does have an Akita quality, or a Shiba Inu, but the color's all wrong. She also has that Navajo herd-dog look. There's a type out there… But between you and me," I leaned away, as if whispering so that Pelli wouldn't hear me, "I think she's a purebred *mutt*."

The vet laughed. "Can't put that down. I have to put a description. I'm putting 'blond Akita cross,' and your purebred mutt passed this checkpoint. You're all set."

I smiled at her terminology. Very appropriate. "Oh, there is one more thing. May I get a mild tranquilizer for travel Monday, just in case she's nervous in her carrier. It's a long ways home. I don't want her to be overly frightened; she's been through so much already."

"Sure. But I'm going to make it very mild – and don't use it, if you think you won't need it. I know of some animals that have been so doped they drowned in the water bowl that the airlines require you keep in the carrier."

That was grim; I hadn't thought of this possibility. All it would take was enough water to cover a sedated nose. "Thank you. I'll be very careful with it. I don't like to use prescription drugs at all, if I can help it – for our kids, our animals, or myself. But it'll be good to have on hand, just in case."

"Sure thing. I hope you enjoy your stay in Santa Fe, and I hope you two have a safe trip home." She smiled at us over her glasses and left to get the medication. She returned shortly with a vial with two soft yellow tablets marked 'Acepromazine, 25mg., used as directed, Southwest Veterinary Assoc.'s, Rodeo Rd., Santa Fe, NM.'

"Looks good to me. This is like a life insurance policy – good to have – hope you don't need it. I enjoyed our talk, Dr. Merritt."

"Me, too, Ms. Giannini. Take good care of Kokopelli." She gave me a warm smile.

I joined Art and Carole in the waiting area. They sat beside each other contentedly and looked up when we entered. "All set?" Art asked. "She pass the exam with flying colors?"

"Just like a vet," I kidded him, making a pun on his service. He caught it and winked at me. "Let me settle the tab and we can leave."

"$52.00, please." The receptionist looked up. "How would you like to pay for that?"

"Travelers checks okay?" I asked.

"They'll be just fine." I gave her three $20.00 checks and she returned $8.00. This was certainly reasonable for all the time, the shot and the meds. "Thank you all for letting us bring the pup in today, with so little notice."

"You are surely welcome. You caught us on a quiet day. Here, don't let me forget to give you your health and rabies certificates. Remember, she'll need a booster shot on that rabies vaccine in a year."

"I know. Thanks again." With that we gathered our group and left the vet's office. The mist had picked up to a gentle reflective female rain, as the Navajo say. This area needed real rain – a sustained male rain. It had been choked by the need for replenishing fronts that would promise days worth of rains that would aid in refilling water tables in dire need of restoration. We desperately needed these rains all along the east coast, as much of the West and Southwest did here. It seemed that areas of the Midwest and Texas were drowning in an abundance of water. As these areas were flooding, they would gladly love to see the water move on and benefit those that pleaded for this life-blood of the earth to quench wildfires, to water vineyards and orchards and farmland and to refill rivers and streams. Much of the West and the Southwest would sell their sunshine for a share in this rainfall. Crazy. The country lay helpless in a tremendous imbalance of drought and flood. How to strike a happy medium?

As we headed to the Malibu I picked up a last tiny hemlock cone, an absolutely beautiful little work of art, and decided that if I popped it in the pill container with Pelli's tranquillizers then it would surely make it back to Virginia intact. This moment is what our builder, John Bice, used to call a 'brain fart' – a blip in time that one simply forgot to put two and two together to come up with an obvious four. And later you'll find out why, if you haven't already figured it out…

I returned Art and Carole to their home, thanked the two of them sincerely for our wonderful luncheon visit, and their accompanying us to the vetting appointment. I gave Carole a special hug, telling her how much I enjoyed – finally – meeting her.

"Are you going to be around this weekend, Laura?" Carole asked.

"Well, I hope to get together with Cynthia – you remember Cindy, Art; she came down from Maxwell on her motorcycle to meet us for our anniversary stay?"

"Oh yes, of course. Of course. She's a very sweet and pretty girl. She's so tiny on that big motorcycle of hers, but she seems to know what she's doing. I would never have pegged her for a biker…" he mused.

"No," I smiled, "She's not the stereotype, but you're right, she's certainly competent. Anyway, I'm going back to the hotel now and give her a call, and a couple of other people I know that I hope to see. I may end up slipping up to Taos tomorrow to do some visiting with Kokopelli. Depends on who's around. And I want to do some Christmas shopping at the Jackalope, Art – thanks to you."

Art and Carole looked puzzled. "Thanks to Art?" Carole looked at him and asked.

"Yes. He introduced the Jackalope to us on our first trip with our kids, back in June of last year. And Pete and I went back in September this year. Talk about eclectic – I love it. I'm betting I'll find some very imaginative gifts there."

"No doubt about it, Laura. Sounds like you'll have a busy weekend. No need to worry that you'll be sitting in your hotel twiddling your thumbs."

"Not a chance, Art. Are you going to be at the hotel Monday morning? Will I get a chance to say goodbye?"

"Yes, I will. But wait, Laura! I need to find that license plate for you that we talked about at lunch. I'm sure I've got an extra Santa Fe plate in the garage. Let me locate it and I'll bring it to the hotel tomorrow morning. Will this work for you? And we can take your front tag off then – we don't use them here in New Mexico."

"That works for me, Art. I write late and sleep in, usually – you know, those 'artistic types.' You know I rarely get an early start anywhere. Monday will be a killer," I added, referring to my departure for the airport that would be necessary to arrive two hours early for the frisk and search tactics.

"Okay then, I'll see you in the morning. Tell Cindy hello for me when you talk to her."

"I will. Thanks again for lunch, and for your help seeing that Pelli got vetted properly." They had insisted on paying for lunch – wouldn't hear of my offer to treat them. They reminded me, with an amused nudge, that I was living off of traveler's checks and dared not use a credit card. I owed them one.

Training Time

"You can teach a young dog old tricks." (me)

Pelli's transition from trailer park to rental car to hotel, back to rental car, then tractor trailer, rental car, hotel, rental car and then to a four-day destination of more days and nights in a hotel went fairly smoothly, considering. She started out as a neurotic, attention-deprived, totally untrained six-month old pup on Tuesday evening, when I had first snagged her from Ricardo's. I started conditioning her to her new name immediately, repeating it over and over any time I addressed her, and I started her basic commands, such as "sit" or "stay." I feel strongly that any animal that regularly travels by car must know to sit and stay when their door is opened, else they could jump into traffic and risk being hit, or flee into a parking lot, panic, and run away in the strangeness of it all. So this was her first lesson.

When I opened her door, it would be: "Kokopelli, *sit*, girl. **Stay**... *Good girl*..." Smart as a little fox, and so eager to please, she picked this up quickly. What a heartbreak it would be to fly 2,000 miles to retrieve her, become a potential felon through the best of intentions, only to have the object of all of this excitement become road kill.

Secondary on my list of her social skills to have her fit into civilized society was housetraining. I have come find, over the course of many years with animals, that generally those that learned to take care of bodily functions *out*side were usually much more welcomed *in*side, by one and all. And since this poor pup, who had once known to go only outside, had been forced for over five weeks straight, in her waiting for Ricardo's returns, to do her business inside the trailer — and thus had become "reverse housebroken," we would have to start back at square one. *Hmm*... Therein lay the challenge. Armed with our ever-present Cascade or Marcal towels, with the 'frisky cats' motif just for fun, extra-strength Febreze in a convenient spray bottle, and Lysol disinfectant, and now the gloves, I was prepared to clean up any accidents as they happened.

And happen they did. Grants, New Mexico, first night on the road, as soon as she was in the room. Could she have peed outside on any of our gazillion walks when I pleaded and coaxed her to pee? Not on your life. No... she showed-off her incredible bladder control to me (nah nah ne boo boo... in your face...) by holding it for 24 hours, then promptly squatted on the carpet just inside the door and let it flow, as my jaw fell practically in the puddle. Such a Kokopelli thing to do. This one took about 15 paper towels to mop up, as I couldn't get her to stop, she'd been corked up so long. And I confused her totally, "No, Pelli, no!! *Don't* pee - not *now!!*" Outside, on our many, many walks, as I looked over my shoulder for the law to recognize us, I'd plead to her "Now, Pelli, *now*. Please, *now* you can pee." In fact, this became my mantra; "Pee, Pelli, pee!" She would look at me, innocently wanting to please, but just not understanding the words, then hold it until inside — and I'd say "No, Pelli, no! *Not* **in**.*side*!" And then she must think I was scolding her about peeing altogether. Poor kid.

I do have to say, however, that her pooping inside was short-lived.

Once, maybe twice, in the hotel room in Santa Fe when I was still keeping her in the bathroom, I had to clean her contributions up in the morning, flushing them down the toilet. Just call me "Mrs. Suzie Homemaker to go." And then, this glorious Friday afternoon, she did it outside. I actually had the camera and caught her first outdoor poop on film, praising her as if she had just laid a golden egg. She ran to me, practically delirious with relief over her good work, and from then on it was No. 2's outside in the free-range area.

The peeing, however, took another day or two to figure out, although she continually improved in the hotel room. The hotel room, itself, became off-limits to her after the 2nd night. She would wait until we were midway down the hall. Or just inside the elevator. Or free roaming in the pool area. And each time, I pulled out the Marcal and the Febreze from under my armpit and mopped it up, thinking: *"Okay, that's it. They're going to kick us out, here and now. We'll be homeless."* But I had the clean-up routine down, apologizing for my silly pup, red in the face, but surprisingly, those in the hotel that we encountered seemed supportive. Perhaps Art had shared some of the story and they knew a bit of what I was up against. And so my adventures in civilizing this crazy little critter continued throughout our week on the road. She was trying to cooperate – our challenge lay in the communication between us – and we were both learning (and teaching) one another daily.

Room to Run

One of the most wonderful things about this particular hotel was not any of the amenities inside, although it was quite functional and comfortable, and the kitchenette was a real plus. Also, the people were just great – friendly, caring and helpful. No, it was one of the many elements of our travel kismet that we had encountered throughout these two trips: the outside of the hotel, just beyond the parking lot. Here, fenced to the back and a good part of the side area, and far enough away from the main road in front to make it safe for Kokopelli to run free, was a large open sandy area dotted with scrub pines and tall grasses. A young pup's heaven.

I would walk her through the parking lot and then ask her to sit and stay for me. As soon as she obliged, and refrained a moment from her ecstatic anticipatory wiggles, I would unhook her leash and let her rip. And rip she did! Whereas the largest area this puppy had had to run, since her weeks inside the trailer, had been in enclosed pool areas of our hotels, here was true freedom! Wide open spaces, trees to dodge and grasses to jump! She would become a blond blur of joyous fur racing in grand circles around me, drunk on the elixir of a young heart pumping in her pounding chest. And she *was* drunk, absolutely intoxicated, with the rush. I would laugh at her antics at night, and take photos – on the speed setting, of course – in daylight. The simple act of watching this puppy *be* a puppy, stretching her busy legs to their max, put a lump in my throat. Whatever trouble I'd gotten myself into by coming back for this small desert dog was worth it tenfold.

Kokopelli would run mad circles around me, laid-out almost on her side by centrifugal force, and then she would make a mad dash back to me, tag me with her nose, and away she would fly, jumping a grass clump on her way with sheer utter bliss on her face. And I would just stand there, laughing aloud at the happy little mutt, feeling like I had just freed Willy. This was truly a serendipitous moment in time.

Calling Friends

"Lots of people want to ride with you in the limo, but what you want is someone who will take the bus with you when the limo breaks down." Oprah Winfrey

After Kokopelli's spirited freedom run, I decided to go on back into my room to see if I could reach Cynthia and Johnny to arrange a get-together sometime the next day. I was willing to drive up that way to make it happen. I hoped maybe Johnny and the crew might be in the area. Maybe we could visit for a meal. It might work that I'd introduce Cindy to the balloonist's in her neck of the woods. They'd all enjoy one another. But alas, that was not to be. I called "Pueblo Balloons" and an older woman told me that Johnny was in Arizona on a ballooning con-vention. I told her I was a friend of Johnny's from out of town and she gave me his cell number. I dialed. It rang several times before Johnny's familiar drawl picked up, "Hello. Pueblo Balloons." Habit.

"Johnny?" I found myself semi-shouting his name. There was noise behind him, wherever he was.

"Yes? Who's this?" His familiar Texas drawl called to me.

"It's Laura Giannini – my husband and I ballooned with you all back in September. We all went out to dinner – and we watched your cowboy movie making, remember?"

He thought a moment, mentally reviewing two months of busy schedules and people's faces and then the light bulb of memory flashed in his head, "Of course! I'm sorry it took me a minute. I see so damned many people, and I've been so damned busy – but of course I do. How you doing, honey? Where you calling from?"

"I'm calling from Santa Fe, Johnny. That's *why* I'm calling. I was hoping that maybe y'all had an evening to spare and we could meet for dinner, or something."

"Well, hot damn. If I could, I would, but I'm *way* down here next to the Mexican border, in Yuma, Arizona. I'm nowhere *near* Santa Fe. Wished I'd known you'd be in town. Is Pete with you?"

"No, I'm flying solo this time," not realizing the pun until the words had left my mouth. "I'm out here over a stray puppy we found up in Monument Valley, after we went flying with you all."

"A stray puppy?" He called back over the phone, sounding perplexed.

"Oh boy, Johnny – have I got a story for you." And I told him, sitting back against the pillows in my bright sunlit room, my voice raised so that he could hear, recapturing the events that had unfolded as succinctly as I could.

When I had finished he was guffawing in his crackling cowboy voice, "*Oh*, honey – that's a *good* yarn! That's something my wife would do. Hell, that's something *I* would do!" He belly-roared again.

"Well, I'm trying my best to stay out of jail and get home clean."

"Well Laura, honey, if you *do* get caught and they put you behind bars, you just give ole' Johnny a holler. Me and the boys will come get you out." I thought of all the stories of cowboys hooking up ropes and chains and yanking the bars out of old timber jail-houses – or, hells bells, pulling down the whole *walls* even – to free up someone inside. I could easily visualize this crew of cowboys and Indians doing just that; it gave me a great big inner grin. This was the Old West and I was smack in the *middle* of it. I laughed at the idea.

"And just *how* are you planning to do that, Johnny?"

Obviously he didn't have the same vision. "Well, we'll fly over, of course – and we'll drop you a rope. You and the puppy can just climb on up and we'll sail away." He was guffawing again. "Wait'll I tell the boys about *this* one! I'm so sorry we missed you, Laura."

"I'm sorry, too, Johnny. Tell everybody hello from me – from the 'li'l ole' puppy thief from back east' – and y'all have a *great* time in Yuma." Wherever the hell that was; I'd have to look at a map. "Fly safely, okay?" I grinned over the phone, telling him goodbye.

Okay, now to call Ms. Cynthia. See what she was cooking up for her Saturday night...

Cindy was home and happy to hear from me. She was astonished that I was back in New Mexico so soon. I stayed evasive as to why, promising her a rollicking Wild West story if she could clear her schedule and meet me tomorrow for dinner. She said her son, Byron, had a Little League game at 3:00, but she thought she'd be able to meet me in Taos about 6:00. I asked her to suggest a place. She thought a moment and then said, "How about the Out Back Pizza? It's just outside of Taos, proper, and the food is excellent – very Mediterranean – I think you'd like it."

"If you do, then I'm sure I would, Cindy. Mainly, I just want to have a chance for a good, long visit. I should have called you sooner, but I've been on the run, practically since leaving home." This was certainly the truth. Tomorrow I'd tell her why. "Listen, let me give you my hotel number here. I still don't have a cell – not that they really work out here, anyway. But call in the morning if something happens that you can't come. I'm going to do some touristy shopping in the afternoon and take the High Road up to get late-afternoon photos along the way." I gave her my number.

"Okay. I'll call you by 9:00 – how's that? – if anything changes. And it's *great* to hear from you, Laura! I can't *believe* you're back in town!"

"Yeah, well, honestly Cynth, I'm a little disbelieving, myself. But buckle your seatbelt when you hear the why."

"Can't wait. See you tomorrow night – Wild West Woman." She joked, referring to the e-mail name she'd set me up with months ago, before that account had disintegrated with erratic use.

"Goodnight then, Motorcycle Mama." I countered and grinned, as I hung up the hotel phone. I'd used our calling card from home, bracing for the gazillion numbers needed, but I hadn't wanted to cut into the time left on the Lowe's card, if it wasn't necessary.

TV Time

I sat against the fluffed-up pillows on the bed. The curtains were pulled back as far as I could, allowing the late afternoon light from the large window to spill into the room. The Southwest aqua, adobe and persimmon colors of the room shone warmly in the sunlight. The spray of carnations, statice, daisies and Baby's breath in the vase from the thrift shop sat cheerfully beside the TV. I decided to turn it on to get an update on "Operation Enduring Freedom" – I hadn't slowed to listen to the news or even read the *USA Today's*, even though I'd been collecting them daily. Terror alerts set up by the new "Homeland Security" regularly ranged on the warm end of the spectrum, from yellows to orange, keeping Americans jumpy and on edge, wondering what could possibly be next. George W.'s popularity, from lame-duck pre-9/11 had skyrocketed, post-9/11. I had pulled out the articles on the war and our home front battle against terrorism and had saved the rest for potty training. Indeed, I still kept select close-ups of bin Laden for housetraining practice.

As I channel-surfed past the weather station, some cooking program using artichokes and leeks and okra (*yuck!*) – which I quickly changed – I paused on an old Science Fiction movie. My hesitation turned to fascination as I watched a particularly odd show that depicted heavily armored Viking warriors streaming from a huge wooden ship onto a sandy shore of some barren and foreign-looking planet. Racing to meet the incoming combatants were bizarre-looking little green creatures with six legs and three heads, each with several antennae. These alien creatures hoisted shields and spears. I blinked my eyes a couple of times at the clash of cultures before me. Only in Sci-Fi, I wanted to rationalize. But then, okay – albeit, stretched a *little* – wasn't this representative of the culture clashing that had taken place over the centuries in the self-same area over which we had just traversed? Wasn't this what was happening in America now?

I shook my head and looked at the TV again. The screen was thick with angry little green creatures 'dé-ter-minded' to defend their home planet – wher*ever* the hell it was – from these fierce Viking invaders. My friend, Bob, a Viking descendent, would have had a grin over this show. I smiled and shook my head again, finally found CNN, and watched a brief interview of two of the young ladies that had been held hostage in Afghanistan and were soon to return home to greatly relieved parents.

After the calls to my Taos-based friends, and a little TV updating, I took Kokopelli and her blanket back to the car. I needed to cut this thing in half, or something, to have one for the room and one for travel. Like my old denim jacket in the beginning had been, this Indian blanket was now a huge source of comfort for the pup.

We buckled our belts and headed on down Cerrillos Road, past the Villa Linda Shopping Mall and Rodeo Road, past the College of Santa Fe and St. Michael's Drive, on to cross the railroad tracks, pick up the Paseo de Peralta and head on to the Plaza, Santa Fe's jewel in her illustrious crown of history. Pelli and I drove past the State Capital Building on our left, built in the shape of the Zia sun symbol, on the Old Santa Fe Trail. We wrapped around Paseo de Peralta, passed Canyon Road and over the Santa Fe River, where we took a left on Palace Avenue and another left on Cathedral Place and found a prime parking place in front of the St. Francis Cathedral.

Jean Baptiste Lamy, a native of France and Santa Fe's first archbishop, built this Romanesque-style cathedral in 1853. This man founded schools, hospitals, and built new churches, such as this and the Loretto Chapel. Lamy was a controversial figure as he defrocked a number of native priests, bringing the church under more central control. The Saint Frances Cathedral stands tall and regal on Cathedral Place, with an adobe-style side-chapel incorporated into the stone structure that dates from 1718. A 375-year-old statue of the Virgin, who is known as the city's patroness, stands on the front lawn. Across the street from the chapel lies the renowned Institute of American Indian Arts Museum, dedicated solely to contemporary Indian arts. One of Santa Fe's in-season attractions is the legion of Native Americans that sell their pottery, weavings, crafts and artwork under the shadowed overhangs throughout the Palace of the Governors.

I left Pelli in the car and walked alone down San Francisco St. to the maze of streets of the inner Plaza, past brightly colored, beautifully decorated windows, until I found the Santa Fe Tee Shirts store. I made it inside just as they were closing up. The teenage clerk, her wavy red hair pulled back in a series of braids and sporting a nose ring, as well as an eyebrow ring, said she'd finish up what she was doing while I chose a tee shirt for each family member for Christmas. I wanted them to have some sort of Kokopelli figure(s) to celebrate this (mis)adventure in the fall of 2001.While looking, I noticed an assortment of tee shirts sporting the American flag – truly Patriotism's emblem of solidarity.

This mission accomplished, I counted out my traveler's checks, realizing I was getting low and had better cool my purchases, unless I resorted to credit cards. I thanked the gaily-pierced young woman for staying open. As she counted my change back to me she looked up and smiled, "Hey lady, no problem. I get a commission on sales. I was happy to help you." The freckles on her face made her look so young; I thought of my own kids and their employment now in jobs such as this. We had all once been in their places, just starting out, on our way to independence and untying the umbilical cord from home – some of us sooner than others.

Now it was on to Starbucks, with my bag of tees and my journaling supplies, to get a latte and write for a while. I hadn't written in a couple of days and wanted to update my trip. The warm desert-colored brick walls welcomed my return, as did friendly smiles from behind the counter. With my latte and journal in hand, I found the overstuffed chair Pete had sat in two months before, and made myself comfortable so the words might flow, feeling the karma of his presence envelope me, as did the arms on this chair.

I wrote solidly for an hour or better, thoroughly enjoying the expensive warm coffeed-milk beverage and the quiet time to think. But then I started feeling badly that Pelli was waiting for me, so I found a place to close the writing, gathered my bag of tee-shirts and journal, and meandered the back streets until I found Cisco. It was dark by now and the St. Francis Cathedral was aglow in her apricot halo of evening attire, beautifully resplendent. Archbishop Lamy, by now a Catholic angel, would have been proud of the enduring beauty of his Santuario.

I put my journal and bag inside the car and asked Pelli, who was now eager to be out for a stroll, herself, to sit and stay – which she did, wriggling and squirming in a puppy anticipation of a cheap thrill – and invited her out. She leapt down, pulling my arm along, and immediately began her olfactory ground search, as I balanced her leash and pulled on a jacket. I walked her to the park in the center of the Plaza, a beautiful area filled with picnickers, musicians and strollers through the day; it was quiet now on this fall evening. Pelli and I pretty much had the park to ourselves. I ventured to let her off the leash to explore, keeping a close eye on her and allowing her freedom as long as she answered my call. This liberty thrilled her.

I sat back on a bench and watched the little dog, with her crazy cork-screw tail and her curious foxy face, dash around the park, exploring new territory. *Oh, just wait 'til we get home,* I thought; *you'll be overcome with new sights and smells, new people and animals to meet. You won't know where to begin!* I watched the young pup and reminisced of our adventures so far, then packed up to head back to the Comfort Inn for the night.

Tonight we'd keep it simple. I had two laundries to run; we'd "eat in," using up some of the leftovers I'd been refrigerating. I'd call Pete between wash cycles and visit long-distance a while. Maybe after that I'd take Pelli down to the pool area for a romp while I swam. Maybe Ed would be there and I could say hello. Ed was to the pool what Art was to the breakfast bar; both took great pride in their jobs and saw to it that their customers were quite happy with the results. I enjoyed talking with him. He was a tall man with a perpetual smile and soft-spoken manner that I sensed covered a good amount of introspection and intelligence. I'd shared with him a little of the Kokopelli story, which explained my arriving to swim with paper towels and cleaners in tow. He was very patient with my enthusiastic pup and asked me to let him know if we had an 'accident' so he could make sure the area was thoroughly disinfected. It was wonderful to have a comrade-in-training.

I left Pelli in the bathroom, started a laundry downstairs, then came up to feed the pup and heat some dinner, myself. After we ate I went back to begin the drying cycle on that load and start the second. While these ran, I called Pete and we visited long-distance a good while, with Pelli and her bone beside me. I grinned, watching her spy a movement of her tail in the corner of her eye, and begin a mad dash in circles around the room as she chased it, trying to unfurl the curl.

I then went down for the first load to bring up to fold and put the second one in the dryer. While doing this, I turned on the TV and found CNN for an update on the war. Everyone was ebullient about the release of the 8 hostages from the German-based Christian aid group. Along with 4 Germans and 2 Australians, there were 2 American women, Dayna Curry and Heather Mercer. They had all been held since August 30th and charged with trying to convert Muslims to Christianity – an offense under the Taliban that could carry the death penalty. Heroic efforts by U.S. special operations troops had snagged them in a field some 50 miles from Kabul and had airlifted them to safety. I thought back on the time that they had been rescued – sometime Wednesday morning – and thought how ironic it was that Kokopelli had also been freed from her weeks of captivity just the night before. So fitting; all part of the kismet. I then checked the *USA Today* I'd been given by the hotel. Huge headlines read: **Bin Laden hunt escalates as U.S. aid workers freed: Taliban left group in field outside Kabul.** The headlines went on: **Military Tribunals: Swift Judgments in dire times: Civil libertarians are wary of Bush's wartime model for terrorist trials, but the system, last used by FDR, for terrorist tribunal during World War II. Southern tribes help fight Taliban: Pashtun forces join battle and may have taken control of airport at Kandahar. NYPD thanks Britain for its support in war.** And, too, **Antibiotic overuse can silence medicine's big guns.**

After I packed and organized and cleaned away some clutter, I brought up the second laundry and draped it to fold later, after the swim. It was 9:30ish by now and I didn't want to push Ed's closing time of 11:00. Pelli and I left for a walk before our swim time and she thrilled me again with a second bowel movement of the day *out*side. But still she did not pee; she was probably saving up for Ed's and my cleanup brigade.

Saturday morning, November 17th

After my pool exercises and hot tub time last night, and a visit with Ed while he puttered and cleaned the area while I soaked in the suds, I'd come back to my room and written a good long time. In fact, I'd gotten wound up and had written for several hours. When my hand had mutinied, I called it a night.

The phone beside my bed startled me out of a deep sleep even before Pelli had her chance. I rolled over and looked at the clock: 9:07 AM. *Ugh.* I'd written until 2AM. I reached over, tangled in covers, and grabbed the receiver. "Hello?" My voice sounded drugged.

"*Good* morning, sunshine," came Art's cheerful baritone. "I'm in the lobby and I have something special so that our resident puppy-thief won't get caught. Are you still sleeping?"

"I was Art, but that's okay. I stayed up *way* too late last night writing. Hey, give me about ten minutes and Pelli and I'll be right down, okay?"

"Okay, Laura. I'll have some coffee waiting for you. Want any juice?"

"No thanks, Art, I'll only have two hands, and one will be holding a leash. Will you remember to make that decaf?"

"Of *course* I will. Need you ask?" Of course not; Art remembered the details.

I got up and stretched; the sleep I did have had been deep. Pelli romped around me, happy to see me awake. I checked for signs of trouble around the room. It was clean – no wet spots, no piles, nothing chewed. The only sign of her being there at all were a few blond hairs on the green rug and her rumpled-up Indian blanket beside the bed. "Come here, girl." I knelt down. "*Good* girl – you did *really* well! Now let's get you outside and in a hurry. Let me get dressed first, though."

I took her down the back way, but she couldn't quite make it. She peed on one of the steps, triggered more by fright on this noisy reverberating stairwell than lack of bladder control. I wanted to cry – *so* close, like yesterday, and yet so far. *Damn.* And I hadn't brought the paper towels today, fully expecting her to make it; the words of praise were on my lips, perched and ready to verbally stroke her no end. "Oh Pelli," I said instead, "*Oh*, Pelli – we al*most* made it today, girl." She looked up at me, knowing I was disappointed; I was sure then she was understanding what was becoming expected. "Oh well," I said again, "Come on outside. Let's meet Art. I'll come back for the mop-up."

He was out by Cisco, already busily working away. "Hey there, Art, top o' the morning and how are you doing? Careful you don't get yourself in trouble, aiding and abetting a criminal, and all."

"And a top o' the morning to you," he responded. "There's your coffee on top the car," he pointed. Art stood up with the front Nevada tag in his hand and bent his thin shoulders back, stretching the connecting muscles. "My old back doesn't work like it used to," he explained, and added, "Laura, you're worrying about this *way* too much. They've got more important fish to fry than you, hon. But you had better put this plate up in your room, just in case. You don't want to have to explain why you have that plate in your car, should you be pulled over for any reason at all. Especially if they start snooping around and see the back plate is covered with a Santa Fe." He gave me a mischievous wink. I loved this gentle old man and his devilish humor.

"Okay, I'll do that. Thank you for finding – and installing – this, Art." I grinned at him. "After Kokopelli's morning romp, how 'bout joining me for breakfast?"

"How 'bout Castro's? Carole's still sleeping. I'm just beating around. My treat."

"Oh, no sir. If we go to Castro's you've got to *promise* me you'll let me treat today. Or else we eat here."

"Then you treat. I see too much of this place as it is."

And so it was. With the front Nevada plate safely tucked in my hotel room and Kokopelli comfortably on her Indian blanket after her freedom run, I drove Art to Castro's. Inside many greeted him and we were invited to sit with a few folks at a large round table. After we ordered, Art got a twinkle in his merry brown eyes under those thick gray brows and said, "Laura, tell these good people here your story. They would get a very large laugh from it."

I looked at my friend. He was grinning widely and egging me on. There were two men there and one woman, all looking at this stranger (me) curiously. *What kind of story could this be?* "I dunno,' Art – I'm so close to home…" I hesitated.

"Oh, come on – they won't turn you in, Laura. They'll love it! Talk!"

And so I shared with this trio of Art's buddies the Kokopelli story, cutting a few corners as I went along. We talked and laughed through our wonderful brunch. And afterwards, as the dishes were cleared and we sipped the last of our coffees, my good buddy and older friend informed me that the lady used to be the police commissioner of Santa Fe. She was now retired. She sat back in her chair, laughing her head off, telling me how much she had enjoyed the adventure and saying she sure was relieved not to be commissioner any longer.

After lunch I returned Art to the hotel and we said our goodbyes. I thanked him again for the loaner-tags and said we'd see him to say adios Monday morning. I left Pelli in the car, after a quick freedom run, and went back to the room for my cooler, supplies and camera, planning to be out for the rest of the day. Kokopelli and I then headed down Cerrillos Road for a little shopping before heading on to Taos.

THIRTY-FOUR

Dinner with Cynthia in Taos

"This communicating of a man's self to his friend makes two contrary efforts, for it redoubleth joys, and cutteth griefs in half." Francis Bacon, Essays

Saturday afternoon, November 17th

In my attempt to make Christmas easier, since time east would be abbreviated before the big event on return, I continued to shop. It was mid-November and chili ristras were in their prime. I stopped at a little shop, brightly decorated on its patio with arrays of the bright garnet chili peppers, and a goofy-looking, short-legged, big-headed Pepto-Bismol- pink pony statue beside the door. This creature was to the handsome painted ponies we had seen in September what the stepsisters were to Cinderella. But he sure was cute.

Inside Tin-Nee-Ann Trading Company was an array of Southwest jewelry, blankets, belts, Indian items and trinkets. I made a beeline to the ristras, however, intent on making a quick purchase and then heading out of Santa Fe and on to Taos, via the High Road, to meet Cynthia for dinner. Mid- to late afternoon would be perfect for richly colored shots of the backcountry sights on this cloud-studded day.

I bought ten smaller ristras, topped with festive ruffled raffia 'hats,' to bring home to friends. They could add a hot spot of color to their kitchens and include the peppers in chili's and soups and stews all winter, if they were so inclined. It would be a happy memento to share from my trip — a spicy little 'bouquet' of New Mexico straight out of my adventure. A helpful young fellow named Roupert, whom I had spoken with in late September, waited on me again today. Roupert boxed them up ever-so-carefully, protecting them with wads of newspapers, and tightly sealed the box with packing tape. Perfect. All I would need to do would be to label the box and send it home through UPS.

Shopping now done, Kokopelli and I could now strap on our seatbelts and head out of town. The day was absolutely beautiful; it was warm but promised sweater weather by evening. There was no sign of the rain from the prior two days. The azure sky was filled with billowy clouds. We followed the back roads with no problems, carefully referring to the map and road signs as we passed the cheery fruit and vegetable stands and small villages on the winding highway. An abundance of ripe chili ristras, in all shapes and sizes, hung festively against a backdrop of golden trees in the midst of losing their leaves, at one of the roadside stands.

Crosses draped with flowers and photos sprang up beside the roadside at intervals, like daffodils might appear in random groupings alongside the highway in spring. On one, a helium birthday balloon floated like a ghost above the name on that cross, bringing an instant catch to my throat. As I entered one small village close to Chimayó, I watched a young mother in a long dark skirt and white sweater kneeling before another roadside memorial, her young son standing beside her – too young to realize the heartbreak. I thought of photographing the poignancy of this sight and then I thought against it; this was a private family moment and I had best leave it alone. But its bittersweet penumbra etched itself in my memory. Pelli and I turned away from this scene and headed on towards Truchas.

Somewhere on this high isolated road, on the side of mountains that joined small villages, with the Sangre de Cristo mountain chain a constant as a backdrop, we came upon this crazy rise of sandstone appearing out of nowhere. The striated gold rock wall was dotted at the base by counterpoint scrub pines and cedars; this wall seemed intent on dividing one side of the hill from the other. The flat interspersed tops of the sandstone looked as if, indeed, one of the deities had stepped upon it in his trek over the earth. A lone scraggly cedar claimed the top, like a flag proudly identifying its castle. This sight was so lonely and so beautiful I stopped to photograph it from several vantages, as soft wispy half-hearted clouds drifted behind the sandstone structure as an afterthought.

Soon we were at the top of the mountain leading into Truchas. By now it was late afternoon, with golds enriching the bounty of color in our panoramic drive through this historic area. I pulled Cisco over at the graveyard atop the hill, with the distant snowcapped Sangre de Cristos offering their majesty as background against the medley of crosses and head stones. I put a leash on Pelli and asked her to come walk with me through this timeline of the dead. There was no sadness here today, just souls at rest amid clean air and constant wild beauty. I took a few photographs and we were on our way into Truchas.

Truchas welcomed us, as it welcomes all its travelers, with her proud signs and the feeling that you're sitting atop the world, gazing down through your kingdom. We stopped on the quiet back road, drinking in this scenery, then headed on to find our way through and out and on to Las Trampas. I thought I knew my way through this small town of many turns, but I thought wrong. As I took one of the roads out, I began not to recognize the area at all. A group of Hispanic men were gathered by an old dusty red pickup truck, shooting the breeze in this late day. I pulled beside them and rolled down my window, asking how I would get to Taos from here. They good-naturedly kidded me about being a lost tourista, throwing jokes back and forth between themselves, then gave me directions back out. I thanked the lively group and turned the Malibu around to find my way. I past the welcome sign again and headed up another road out of town – that led me to nowhere. Wrong again. I turned around, my bearings now shot, hearing Pete's teasing remarks about "my keen sense of direction at work" in the little voices in my head.

I ended up driving by the group of men again, all now highly amused at this inept gringa who could not find her way out of their tiny town. They laughed and raised their beer cans in a cheery salute hello; I had added a highlight to their afternoon visiting. I sheepishly rolled down my window once more and told them I had taken the road and it had not worked.

"Then it was not *the* road, verdad? You go back again and be sure to look for the high wall with the paintings on it. *This* is where you are to turn." One stout fellow said kindly.

"Oh yes, the gra*ffiti* wall! Why didn't you all say so? I remember it now. If you don't see me again – and hopefully you won't – you'll know that way worked. *Muchas* gracias, amigos!" They laughed and smiled and toasted me with their cervezas and once again I turned around.

This time I found the graffiti wall, so full of paint and color it blended into the backdrop like camouflage, and turned at the tiny road beside it. I vaguely remembered this turn from Pete's and my trip two months prior. *Now* we were cooking with gas and this was good, as the afternoon had ticked away. By now there was no way I would be able to meet Cindy at 6:00, with the rest of the drive still ahead. Since

I didn't have a cell phone, I hoped she'd, too, be late, or at least have the patience to wait.

I found the Out Back Pizza with minimal effort, even though Pelli and I had reached Taos well after dark. Cynthia was not late, but her patience was kind. She sat at a table in a room to the left as I entered the cozy restaurant, close to a wood stove that radiated welcoming warmth. Her sweet gentle face lit up and she gave me a big smile of relief as I peaked around the corner and discovered her. She got up and we hugged, before we each sat. "We said 6:30, didn't we?" I kidded her, "I'm *so* sorry, Cindy. I took the High Road, with plenty of time – I *thought* – for photographs. But still I managed to get lost coming out of Truchas." I shook my head in embarrassment.

"Truchas is tricky, Laura. In fact, the High Road is – you really have to pay attention. That's okay, I brought a book that I've been trying to read at home, but can never quite find the time. This has been wonderfully decadent." She smiled shyly. It had been a while since we'd seen one another; it might take a few minutes for the awkwardness to pass.

"Okay then. I won't feel so badly. What are you reading?" I asked her curiously.

"Oh, this crazy little book a friend sent me. She knows of the tough times I've had with David and the kids in the last few months. It's called *Fly Fishing Through Your Mid-Life Crisis.* Isn't that a *great* name? She knows I love to fly fish. I think it's tongue & cheek."

"That *is* a great name. It reminds me of an old book called *Zen and the Art of Motorcycle Maintenance*, another you'd probably like; I'll have to see if I can find it for you. I hope the book helps you find your way through this crossroad, Cindy. I know it's been tough, from your letters and e-mails. Hey," I changed the subject, " before we get too settled here, I want to introduce you to somebody."

"Oh? Why didn't you bring them in?" It was her turn to be curious.

"This company wouldn't be too welcome inside – not by U.S. health laws, anyhoo. In Europe, maybe. Grab your jacket and come on out a minute, Cynth." She now arched a brow and picked up her jacket as she rose. We told our waiter we'd be back shortly and walked out into the now chilly, starry night. She followed me to Cisco, where Kokopelli was curled up asleep on her Indian blanket in the second seat of the car, where there was more space. Her rawhide chew lay possessively close by.

As I unlocked the car, Pelli raised her head and wagged her tail at me. "Hey girl, I want you to meet a good buddy of mine. Come here," she did and I asked her to sit, snapping her leash to her collar. "Okay, *come on, girl*. You can get out!" She had been the perfect young lady, perched there, waiting for permission to jump down but too sleepy to wiggle and squirm in anticipation, as she usually did.

"*Ohmygosh!*" Cynthia enthused, "She's so *precious!* Where did you get a *puppy* on your trip, Laura?" She looked up at me in wonder.

"Do you remember my telling you 'do I have a story for you,' Cynth? Well, you're looking at her, my friend. Her name is 'Kokopelli'," Pelli looked up at me when I said her name and I smiled, patted her head and she then resumed her sniffing the line of chrysanthemums beside us. "Pete and I found her at the beginning of our 2nd week into our anniversary trip – and I saved the story to tell you. I *pur*posely haven't told you in letters or anything. But I'm getting ahead of myself. Let's walk her and I'll share this adventure I promised you over dinner." We walked the pup around the parking lot for ten minutes, catching up with the last two months, then hightailed it back to the warmth of the woodstove, once we'd settled Pelli back in Cisco.

Cynthia and I ordered a bottle of Merlot, a couple of salads, and a small Mediterranean-style pizza to share. When the waiter had our order, I told Cindy our story, starting with meeting Johnny and the crew in Taos and the hot-air ballooning adventure – some of which she knew about – and then our going on to Bluff. I told her of finding the puppy and how she had changed the entire complexion of our trip, the decisions thereafter, including the highly emotional one of deciding to entrust her to Ricardo. I told her of our trip to Canyon de Chelly, where Cindy had been on several occasions. We talked of the hike down into the White House Ruins. She loved it there, too. She told me about one of her trips down into this magical canyon. We decided we'd like to meet there sometime in the future and hike together.

I told her of our returning for Dingo – who we'd now decided to name Kokopelli – and of the Lakota/reincarnation connection. I explained that Ricardo had totally refused to return her. I shared the story of our return back to Virginia, the airline chaos, the anthrax madness starting and the whooping cough fiasco waiting for us on return, and of Emily Couric's death. How terribly sad this had been. How I had decided to come back west, of my Plans A & B, and the wonderful flight attendants on Delta. Cindy was laughing and animated, imagining all of this and adding multiple witty comments as we talked. Our salads came and went as the story continued. The bottle of wine evaporated as we laughed our way through the evening. The spicy bubbling pizza, loaded with kalamata olives, artichokes, sun dried tomatoes, spinach, portabellas and feta cheese was brought out on a pedestal. The tale continued as I told her of having to resort to Plan B – and I went into detail of my debut at lock picking, after my bungle with the horn. We laughed until tears were in our eyes at my becoming a possible felon over this unwanted pup. At the farcical twists in the whole enterprise. I quoted lines from Cervantes' play, *Don Quixote*:

> … *"What matter, for each time he falls he shall rise again…*
> *and woe to the wicked, Sancho – "*
> *"Yes, your Grace?"*
> *"My armor! My sword!"*
> *"More misadventures!"*
> **"Ad***ventures, my old friend –*
> *the trumpets of glory now call me to ride,*
> *Yes, trumpets are calling to me*
> *And wherever I ride, ever staunch at me side,*
> *My Squire and Lady shall be…*
> *And the wild winds of Fortune shall carry us onward…*
> *Whither so ever they blow… Onward to glory we go…"*

We laughed again, as Cindy caught up with me in the recitation from *Don Quixote*. I told her of how Marcos and Scott had helped us leave the Grand Canyon; our trip to Williams and Winslow the following morning; of my calls to John Slate and the message to Pete. Of meeting Gordie and following the semi over the state line… of our trip on to Grants and meeting Elena and of our dinner and swim. Of the rainbow over the Turquoise Trail and not exchanging the rental, despite Pete's worries. I shared with her my lunch with Art – and that yes, indeed, Carole truly did exist, and how sweet a lady she was, and that Art said to say hello. I told her of our vetting appointment and that Kokopelli had checked out fine, health wise. I shared my call to Pete and the kids, and what they had all said, and of the talk with Johnny, ballooning down in Yuma, Arizona. She was eager and curious, so I shared all of the adventure with her.

The wine was finished and coffees were ordered. We decided to share a slice of cheesecake with blackberries, as well. I looked at my watch when the dessert came out and exclaimed, "Holy Smokes, Cynth, I've got to call Pete! It's 10:15 here – that's 12:15 back home. He's likely worried sick. Do you know where there's a phone?"

"I think there's a payphone in the hallway, down by the restrooms," she told me and pointed to the far corner. I excused myself and made my way around the tables in the rustic little restaurant. I made a stop first in the ladies room, amid roses on the wallpaper and postcards from various worldwide travel spots. I then found the payphone and dialed our 800#, cupping my hand over my other ear against the background bar noise. Pete picked up immediately and I apologized for calling so late. He told me he'd been up reading a Grisham novel. "I'm getting a lot of reading in while you're gone, Ra. And John Grisham's a good choice now. He often writes about the underdog," he kidded me.

"Very funny, PeterWop. Let me know if you learn anything about law elusion." I good-naturedly retorted. "Hey, by the way, Cindy says 'hi.' We've had a wonderful time up here in Taos. We're at a place called 'Taos Out Back Pizza.' It's a cute restaurant – very good food; we'll have to try it together sometime."

"*If* you stay out of jail," he teased. "By the way, I don't think 'elusion' is a word."

"That's ok; I make up my own. Look, Smartass, get back to your book. I just wanted to say hello and let you know all is well. Cindy is talking about following me back to Santa Fe and staying the night. We can get some more visiting time in."

"Then why didn't you just meet in Santa Fe?"

"What?" I strained to hear what he had said. He repeated the question. "Oh. I dunno', ask Cindy. Anyway, I wanted to get the photos on the High Road. I didn't have time to stop off in Chimayó this time. And I got lost in Truchas. Missed the turn at the wall of graffiti. *Never* again will I forget that turn…"

"Yeah, that one can be easy to miss. But you found your way after that?"

"Sure. No more problems, but I was late meeting Cindy. But she brought a book."

"We all know you by now, Laura. You make us all more literate, in your off-hand way…"

"*Very* funny. You're a real comedian tonight, Wop. But you sound much more relaxed; I'm happy to hear that."

"Well, you're *al*most home. Just two more nights and Natalie and I'll be meeting you in Richmond – *if* the law's not waiting as you leave…"

"Pete, cut if out. Oh, but speaking of that, Art gave me a Santa Fe tag to put over my Nevada plate, and he took off the front plate. They only drive with the back around here. So I'm 'incognito' in Santa Fe." I smiled at him over the phone.

"Razza, you're taking this *way* too far," he tried to scold me, but was laughing instead. "Thank Art, but did either of you ever stop to think that if he had an extra tag, then it had probably expired?"

Actually, I hadn't *thought of that. It made perfectly good sense. Oh well. At least the law would practically have to use a magnifying glass at this point. At first glance, my plate would be Santa Fe – and there was only the one of them on the* back *of the car. The chances of connecting the dots in basically one more day were getting slimmer all the time.* All these thoughts flashed through my mind when I condensed them to "Well, Pete, the *good* news is there's basically the one more day of daylight to drive through – that, and heading to the airport Monday morning. We'll be fine. I'll have to take the Santa Fe tag off before returning the car. Otherwise, *they* might have questions…" I giggled at the thought.

A big sigh followed, "Whatever you say, Ra. I've said it before – be careful. And you and Cindy be careful tonight going back to Santa Fe. It's a long drive. You might consider a hotel in Taos tonight."

"Pete, I've rented the room at the Comfort Inn. All my stuff is there, including most of Pelli's dog food. We'll take the River Road back; it should be considerably faster. You just relax, enjoy your book, and rest. We'll drive convoy. We'll be fine, but thanks for your worry. Oh, and heh? Please say hi to the kiddos in the morning, over brunch." We usually had a big family brunch on Sundays with eggs and good breads or muffins, fruit salad… It gave us time to visit before the week took a mind of its own. If we were lucky, and the youngsters weren't working, we'd have a special Sunday dinner, too. But more and more often the older teens would be off on their own schedules in the evening. "Tell them Mom's on her last leg home – soon they'll be meeting little Kokopelli!"

I could hear the smile in his voice." Okay, I'll be sure to tell them. You two be safe tonight, Ra – and hug a pillow. Please give me a one-ringer when you all get in tonight, will you? Just to let me know you got there okay. I'll talk with you tomorrow night?"

"That's a yup on both accounts. I'll call tomorrow evening, as I'm packing up. And I *prom*ise, it won't be as late. I love you, PeterWop. Oh, one last thing. Has Deputy Isabella called again?"

"Only once, and he left another message. Just wanted to know if you had gotten back.

I didn't return his call, as you've said, and I quote, 'this is your baby'."

"That's fine. I'll take care of all this when we get home. I'll talk with you tomorrow, Pete. Goodnight."

"Goodnight, Razza. Be good. And be safe."

I returned to Cindy and apologized for the length of the call. She had been reading her book again, looking very content with the quiet time to herself. This was a mother of young children's dream come true to have uninterrupted time to read. Most of her coffee was gone, but the cheesecake was barely touched.

"I asked our waiter to bring you a hot cup of decaf when you returned," she smiled up at me.

"Thanks, Cynth. Pete says to tell you hello. He and the kiddos are doing well. I hate it that he does 'Mr. Mom' so well. I feel unneeded," and then I smiled impishly, "but then, on the other hand, it frees up some *great* time to travel…" Cindy smiled. She knew about that. David had their trio at home, being 'Mr. Mom,' himself. She excused herself to call him and let him know our plans, and to see if this worked okay. While she was on the phone I slipped out to walk Pelli again, but she was so snuggled up and sleeping I left her alone. I'd walk her again before we returned. I quietly opened the trunk and removed the Indian blanket I'd bought for Cynthia in eastern Arizona, my first full day back.

Cindy came back shortly after I returned. She insisted on paying for dinner, wouldn't hear of anything else, so I left a big tip, as our waiter had done a good job, and we'd 'rented' his table for a while. We finished the cheesecake as she told me it was fine with David that she come down to Santa Fe for the night. I handed her the bag with the blanket – "Here you go there, friend. Something to keep you warm this upcoming winter. I thought you'd like the colors."

She opened the bag and the stripes of warm turquoise and apricots unfolded in her lap. "I *love* it, Laura! I'll wrap it around me when I read this winter and think of you – and this great visit, *and* your incredible story." She smiled warmly, "Thank you."

"You're entirely welcome. It's a little thing, really, but I just love them. I brought one back for Art and Carole, too. And I'm taking one home for Jared to make a poncho."

"That's a good idea. I hadn't thought of that."

"Neither did I. It was Jared's notion."

"Sounds like something that Phillip would cook up." Said Cindy, referring to her younger son.

"Aren't kids great, younger or older, they're always up to something new. You ready to go?"

"You Betcha'. Let me get my book. Maybe I'll get a chance to read a little tonight."

Cynthia and I stopped for a cup of good joe to go at Island Coffees in Taos before hitting the road; I totally forgot to check and see if they carried any Fair Trade beans. Palm trees and exotic island décor made one feel they might be in the Caribbean rather than in high desert country. We ordered our java's and Cindy discovered the worldly array of small cigars the owner carried and spent a little time discussing flavors before deciding on a selection. This was a surprise; I didn't realize she liked to smoke these little rascals. I insisted on treating this purchase and we were on our way back to Santa Fe, via the River Road.

Although we traveled Highway 68 in the dark, it looked as if it would be a stunning panorama of the high backcountry separating these two sister towns. The Rio Grande sparkled afar, a darker value slashed deeply in the landscape of blues and grays, sweeping down below us. We made a pit stop in Española and then continued on 84/285. Cynthia passed me at some point after this and signaled me to follow her on into Santa Fe via the bypass. As she had been to the Comfort Inn before, she knew where we were going.

I followed her through the back areas of Santa Fe, of which I didn't have a clue. We arrived somewhere between 12:30 and 1AM, far too late to take a dip in the hot tub. Ed had long since gone home, which was fine, as we were beat. Kokopelli, however, was not. Like a child who had napped too long, her batteries were totally recharged and she was raring to go.

I decided to show Cynthia what a 'freedom run' was, in person. We led the excited puppy to the side of the parking lot and I asked her squirming little body to sit. She did, but Pelli could barely contain herself; she knew what this meant. I told her, "*Good* girl, Kokopelli. *Stay…*" and then I undid her leash and away she shot. Cindy laughed at her exuberance. "No uncertainty there, no si*rree!*" She exclaimed, and we watched our small yellow streaker race around the back lot, barely discernable under the faint light of a slight quarter moon, and the wash of light remaining from the hotel parking area.

She jumped the sage, dodged the larger junipers and cedars, a pale blur of motion, thrilled to be young and loved and alive. "Go, Pelli, *stretch* those busy legs!" I called to her and nudged Cindy's arm. "Ain't it something? Doesn't it just put a lump in your throat?" I turned to my friend, smiling. She smiled back and about that time I was knocked around, almost off my feet. At first I didn't know what had happened.

"What the…?" I turned to Cynthia and this time we saw her coming. Pelli had raced in a large circle around us to get up a head of steam and then cut an ark in the circle to come barreling down on me to hoist herself in the air and slam me with her body, before she raced gleefully away to circle again and come in for another 'hit,' in this game of Kokopelli mischief she had devised. I had never seen this behavior in a dog. Was she so exuberant and drunk with this elixir of freedom that she just couldn't contain herself? I didn't know, but I wanted to nip this crazy behavior in the bud. Those slam-dunks *hurt*. She was headed my way again and all I could do was react by turning my side to catch the impact. I braced; she hit, causing me to stagger as I called after her: "No, Pelli! *No!* That hurts, you little beast!" She raced off again to begin another large circle.

"Cindy, stand behind me so you won't get hit. I don't know *what* she's doing, but this has got to stop." Cynthia stepped back and behind me, laughing at the nutty behavior. "This *isn't* what I meant by a 'freedom run'." I told her. I braced again, and this time, as Pelli hurled her body in the air to tag me, I raised my knee hard and caught her body in the air, yelling, "NO, Kokopelli. *Stop* that — *no!*" She hit my leg and rolled hard. The motion set me spinning and I caught Cynthia, behind me, somewhere in the body. I was laughing at the insanity of it. Time to stop this game and take her inside. She had stretched those puppy legs enough for one night.

"Okay, cut it out, kiddo. Come here, Pelli — come *here*." She stood away from us now, panting, then trotted on over to me, a wild look still in her eyes. She nudged my hand, as I moved her bandana and clipped the leash to her collar. She then tried to lick my face, as if apologizing for her lapse of control. I ruffed her fur and asked her to sit. Discipline — bringing her back into control — was important now. She came back from whatever wild state she had been claimed and promptly sat, looking up at me with that sweet eager face for the appropriate acclaim. "*Good* girl, Pelli, you did that well. Good girl. Okay, let's go inside now…" She jumped up and immediately started pulling on the leash. I hauled her back in, "Not so fast there, dog. This pulling has also got to stop. You'll have some manners before we're through, you can bet on it." I told the world firmly.

"You're a pillar of patience, Laura." Cynthia commented, as we walked to the car for our things.

"Yeah, you should see me sometimes. You'd take back that 'patience' comment."

"Uh huh." Cindy and I carried an armload of goods from Cisco up the back stairwell with Pelli. I settled the pup on her rug beside my bed.

She had been behaving herself beautifully in the room now, and with that came the privilege of leaving the bathroom tile floors.

It was so late at this point that all we did was brush our teeth and wash our faces. I gave Pete his one ringy-dingy to let him know we'd arrived safely and we hit the sack, both of us exhausted. I don't think Cynthia even brought her book in from the car.

Morning seemed to come in a heartbeat. Pelli was whining beside my face, asking to go out. I slipped out of bed, slipped on jeans, a sweatshirt and sneakers, and – after taking care of my own business – headed down the scary back stairway with Kokopelli. If we took it *very* slowly going down, and I kept my voice soft and encouraging on those 'slippery,' reverberating tiled stairs, she accepted them enough for us to make it out. And this morning I was rewarded by full contributions *out*side. I was thrilled and let Kokopelli know it. She came running to me, bounding around in enthusiasm, delirious by my own excitement. "*Good* girl, Pelli – *that's* what I've been talking about all this time!" She climbed in my lap, as I knelt to praise her, and licked the side of my face with one of those slurpy octopus kisses. She was so happy that I was happy – and I was ecstatic.

"Okay, go run a bit, dog. Enjoy yourself." She trotted off to explore a piece of paper she had noticed and I stood to check out the morning. I yawned and stretched, wishing I had a steaming cup of java in hand, and looked to the sky. The Sangre de Cristos sparkled afar and the day promised to be clear and generally magnificent. Our last full day in Santa Fe ... better maximize on it. "Okay, girl, let's go on in and say good morning to Cynthia. *And* get coffee." Pelli came on over, willing to sacrifice her freedom again for obedience. "Good girl. *Sit.*" She did and I clipped on her leash, praising her again.

Cynthia was up and in the bathroom, dressing and readying for the day, when we came back inside. "Good morning!" I called in to her. "Guess what Kokopelli did! *All* of her business *out*side! We're just thrilled – we're ready to celebrate. You must be a good luck charm, Cindy!"

Laughter came from the bathroom. "Congratulations, Mom – you trained her good."

"When you're ready –" I called to her, but then she came out of the bathroom and I lowered my voice, "let's get breakfast. I need coffee."

"Me, too." She had pulled on old faded jeans and a light brown knitted sweater with moccasins. Cindy looked rested. I was glad to see that, as she had looked so drawn last night.

"Do you want to eat here at the hotel or go up to the Pantry? Castro's? Maybe you have a suggestion? Art's not downstairs – he only works on the weekdays, so we won't be seeing him this morning."

Cindy considered the possibilities and then said, "I don't care. I'm not real hungry after our big meal last night," and then she added, "I *would* like to hit the hot tub before leaving, though. May I borrow that suit you loaned your friend, Elena?"

"Sure. I still have the safety pins. We won't need to take as many tucks, but we'll still need to shore 'er up a little. You itty-bitty people..." I teased her and smiled.

We put Pelli in the Malibu with her Indian blanket and a bone and decided to eat downstairs. Another fellow that I didn't recognize ran the show on the weekends and was doing a 'presentable' job, but out of loyalty to Art I decided it wasn't *as* good. Art took a special pride in his duties that was hard to duplicate.

Cynthia and I had coffees, juice and cereals, and split an English muffin with raspberry jam. I had a glass of milk. Cindy told me that David had been offered a job in Hawaii as a school superintendent and was thinking of accepting it. She was torn, as she was born and raised in Arizona and the kids had grown up in these schools. But she was excited as well, with the thought of such a change. We talked about this over breakfast and decided to go on and swim. We'd had time to digest over our discussion.

We went back to my room and I gave Cindy the black suit and safety pins to do the first fitting in the bathroom. I'd make sure everything would hold when she came out. While she changed I put on my blue and lavender swirl suit, shorts and jean shirt, found my zories and kickboard. She came out and I walked over to her, "Okay, let me doublecheck your key holds there, girlfriend. Make sure you keep your modesty about you – and that one of the pins doesn't pop open and jab you." Cindy held still while I probed and eyed the small devices. "Okay, good to go, kiddo! Let's swim!"

Cynthia, a lady after my own heart, actually joined me in the pool. While I did my exercise routine, she swam laps. We saved our visiting for the hot tub afterwards and, after showers, she was ready to hit the road. Cindy called David to let him know of her departure time and we let Pelli out for a good long freedom run and had a last visit before she left.

Kokopelli wasn't as wild this morning as she had been last night. She'd probably been cooped up too long with the road trip. She threatened a couple of the crazy body-slams, but when I lowered my voice to tell her, "No!" and readied my knee for action, she decided to refrain from the game. She then happily explored the wide-open spaces, as Cindy promised to let me know what would be decided on Hawaii and I promised to update her on my Kokopelli saga. It was sad to say our goodbyes, especially with the prospect of her moving to Hawaii before we might have a chance to visit again, but I wished her the very best that life could offer and we had a last big hug before she climbed in her little Honda, headed for Maxwell and her busy home life. I smiled at Cynthia's bumper sticker: **"IT'S NOT A HOT FLASH – IT'S A POWER SURGE."** And on that note, away she went.

THIRTY-FIVE

Last Day, Santa Fe

"Seize the moment. Remember all those women on the Titanic who waved off the dessert cart." Erma Bombeck

Sunday, late morning, November 18th

Before leaving for Jackalope and the Plaza I decided to bring Pelli down to the pool area to write a while. I had peeked in to say good morning to Ed, who wasn't in sight, but had found the place to be enchanting. Not a soul was around. Sunlight streamed in generously through the large side windows, lapping over the languid blue waters and spilling over onto the tables and chairs. It practically called my name, *"Come, spend time, you know you want to!"* I thought, *Why not, the day is yours. Your last in Santa Fe...*

So here Kokopelli and I visit – she, roaming the spacious pool area, knowing now to be a respectful guest and leave her contributions *out*side – and me, with my journal, ready to put down some thoughts in the full light of day, for once.

I sat at a table under a shade umbrella, a fresh orange juice in hand, ready to let free associations from the trip flow from mind to hand to pen to paper. But my attentions were caught by Pelli, who was busy watching a canary yellow life vest floating free and lonesome on the quiet waters. In her world this strange contraption was out of place, a threat to her, to us. So she intently guarded it, barking wildly when the jacket drifted in closely.

I laughed at the intensity of her focus. When it floated away from us she tiptoed close to the edge, her head down and shoulders hunched, alert, sniffing, her curled tail unfurled and draped low, as she checked out the general area where it had been. When it began to drift back to the edge, she would spring aside, growling low or barking – or run to me, to hide behind my legs and peek around to see if it had followed. Now, *I* was to protect *her*.

I laughed aloud at her antics, "Pelli, girl, it's okay – that horrible thing won't get us – I won't let it, I promise." She looked up at me sheepishly and wagged the tip of her tail, appreciating the bravado, and then immediately her attention reriveted on the 'beast' among us. She couldn't let down her guard, not for a minute. This heeding of danger had saved her in the desert; although the weeks in Ricardo's trailer may have allowed her to relax her diligence, these instincts were still alive and well. We were in imminent danger, and she was not *about* to relax. I chuckled and continued to watch her, writing of these antics instead of whatever else might have been recaptured from the trip. That would come later. At the moment, this was too good to miss.

Sunday afternoon – Jackalope revisited

I returned with Pelli to the Jackalope to spend a little time gift shopping for family here. Once home and settling Kokopelli in with our other creatures and all the kiddos – *and* catching up with my commissions – there would be little time to focus on Christmas, itself. Not to mention what I might have to face with legal ramifications. I left Pelli on her Indian blanket in the car. She had had a good breakfast and a lengthy freedom run, while Cynthia and I had visited; she was now ready to settle in for a nap. I found a place under a large tree with dappled shade thrown down over the car. She'd be just fine here.

As I headed toward the main building of Jackalope, I noticed a large greenhouse to my left that I'd never seen. Enticed, I walked inside and was transported immediately into an exotic rainforest lushness of high humidity and a utopia of color enveloping me. It was gorgeous; my senses were delightfully overwhelmed. Orchids and lush tropical ferns and bromeliads filled the long tubular structure. In the center of this paradise a grand fountain spewed its bounty happily over rounded rocks. I expected wood nymphs and fairies to peek out from behind the water, curious of my visit. I was enchanted. I thought this would be what it'd be like for Cindy to leave the desert and make her move to Hawaii with her family. *Trade the hot barren desert for such a paradise? Not bad at all…*

"Hello." A gentle voice to my left brought me back to the here and now. "Can I help you find something, or are you just looking?" The man behind the voice asked. He was in his early 30s, tall and slim, with wavy sandy brown hair capping a kind and intelligent face. Wire-rimmed glasses framed his hazel eyes. He wore leather sandals and some sort of planting smock over his rolled-sleeved shirt and blue jeans. This man now was what my son might become in another 15 years; I felt like I knew him.

"Oh, hi there. No, I'm just intrigued by your jungle here. I wasn't expecting to find this in the desert. It's *beau*tiful!"

He laughed. "We take a lot of people by surprise. I'm Richard; I run the show in here." He reached out a friendly hand.

I smiled as I shook it, "My name is Laura and I'm visiting from Virginia. I *love* your town – can't get back often enough."

"I hear that a lot, too. What brings you this far west?"

"Oh, that's a really long story –"

"*Squawk!*" To my right a raucous clattering voice startled me to jumping aside. A huge macaw was sidling down from his perch. In the visual plethora of color here I had not seen him; how this neon-colored bird had blended, I would never know. He continued his squawking, *"Look at me! Look at me! Watch this!"* And he dropped off this perch upside down, holding himself to the limb with one huge talon. I laughed at his clowning around.

"Oh boy, he's just begun!" Laughed Richard. "His name is 'Salsa,' and he'll go on like that for hours. He's a real hambone. He wants you to take his picture." The crazy bird had seen the camera hanging around my neck and had gone into 'cheese mode' for me. I laughed again and undraped my camera. These shots would be precious; the kids would adore them. Salsa hung by one foot, then switched to the other. He spread his wings to show off his beauty for me, chattering all the while *"Watch this! Watch me! Salsa good!"*

I laughed and finished the impromptu photo shoot with the pièce de résistance: Salsa's hanging by his beak, his lively peridot eyes never leaving the camera, making sure I missed nothing. I finished off a roll of 24 exposures with his antics.

"Thank you, Salsa. Thank you *very* much for your lively performance there, buddy."

"He lives for those moments," commented Richard, who stood behind his desk, arms folded, an amused and patiently adoring look on his face, as if he had been watching his two-year-old show off a new game he'd learned.

"Well, I certainly appreciated the performance. In fact, he made my day. What a clown!" I noticed a movement behind Richard on the low desk, there beside a bronze paperweight of a roadrunner. A much smaller bird was side-walking the edge of the table, as if eyeing a way down. She was a bedraggled, almost mangy-looking, parrot.

Richard followed my gaze, "Oh, that's 'Shirley.' Be careful around her – I'm socializing her. Shirley has had a rough life. She lived most of it in a cage by herself. When she started self-mutilating the owners didn't want her any longer. She was pulling out all of her feathers and getting vicious with them. So they gave her to me. See, parrots have no business in cages – they're *way* too intelligent. They just go neurotic. Imagine where they come from: the jungles of tropical regions around the world, flying freely amongst the foliage, blending in, living close to the sky."

I was listening to Richard, nodding in agreement, and watching Shirley pacing the table. Richard continued, "They are the most endangered species of bird right now, because they've been imported for pets for so long. Between that and habitat destruction, any number of species are on the verge of disappearing..." I eased closer to Shirley and reached out my hand to her very slowly while listening... "Careful," he said, "She doesn't trust people. Go real easy... She likes the back of her head scratched, if you can get there." Shirley eyed me suspiciously, but I was able to ease my hand back behind her head, and with one finger, rub gently. She stopped pacing and I could almost hear her say *"Ahh..."* I knew that place; my neck and shoulders were often tense and knotted from the old riding injury. I often said *"Ahh..."* when stroked there.

I looked over at Richard and smiled. "Poor kid. So you've saved her and she's got the roam of your orchid house. That's a pretty nice deal. From a cage to all of this... It's almost like going home to those lush jungles."

"Yeah, if she'd stay *put*. I have to watch her like a hawk, though. She's always trying to escape. Her wings are clipped, so she can't fly, but if I turn my back and forget about her she hops down off the table and hightails it away. The crazy little bird sneaks under the edges of the greenhouse and I have to run out and find her before she gets stepped on by a tourist or run over by a car. Her nickname is 'Houdini' around here – she's such an independent little thing. You should have seen her when she first arrived, Laura. She had practically plucked herself bald." Shirley was almost cooing under my finger. I could see soft green feathers coming back in. She looked as if she'd been through a heavy molt.

"Well, you're doing a great job, Richard. She's coming along." Salsa was sitting on his perch, preening his feathers and ignoring us, preparing for his next photo-op. I looked at Salsa and then at Richard and smiled, "This reminds me of some quip that I read off of a calendar in my dentist's office. It goes, **'LIVE SO THAT YOU WOULDN'T BE ASHAMED TO SELL THE FAMILY PARROT TO THE TOWN GOSSIP.'** Will Rogers said that. Isn't it a hoot?"

Richard laughed out loud, "I'll have to remember that one. I really do have to be careful what I say around Salsa. You never know *what*'ll come back through him."

"I know. Kind of like having kids." Since he was obviously such an animal lover, I decided to share my Kokopelli saga with him, not going into minute details, but trying to cover the key highlights and the parallels. Richard laughed aloud when I'd finished and said I'd chosen a good name for her — it sure seemed to fit her personality and the chaos afterwards.

"Yup," I agreed, "I'll never dare to name another dog 'Kokopelli.' Never another pet of *any* kind," I added. "Not even a *gold*fish. I should have kept 'Dingo'— this was just tempting fate. I'm coming to understand that there is some sort of mystical, complicated mischievous connotation with this name." We laughed together and I showed him the sleeping puppy. She was so conked out that we didn't wake her; instead we went back inside the orchid house and I shot a new roll of 36 exposures of Kodak Gold 400 on the amazing array of flora, as Richard pointed out a few rare specimens. I had thoroughly enjoyed this part of the afternoon, in the company of another animal and plant lover, surrounded by an exuberant celebration of life that lay within this biotope alien to desert living. Hawaii wouldn't be such a terrible place to live, especially after so many years in the stark Southwest…

After leaving Richard's orchard house I strolled over to the main building at Jackalope, past wooden supports offering a plethora of bleached animal skulls amid blazing red ristras, baubles and beads. One skull in particular caught my eye. It was a goat's head, described beneath it as a "Spanish goat's skull," whatever this meant. Its sturdy horns swept up and away, forming a large 'V,' like an Aries zodiac symbol. They rose high over the top of the skull, a dull textured gray against the bone white. Delicate nasal bones protruded from the front. I had found the skull for my studio this year. Intending to buy it later, I photographed it hanging from the baling twine there on the barn-sided wall, as the light was perfect.

I went on inside to look around and find a few more things for Christmas. Surrounded by colors and shapes and textures from around the world, my senses overloaded, I found it hard to focus. *Let's see, I want to get gifts for two new babes back at home…* I thought. *One for Nancy, who works with Pete, the other for Pete's dear cousin, Judi's, upcoming new bundle… Hmm.* In hunting for these gifts I found a sky blue cotton necktie tastefully covered in Kokopelli's playing their flute. *Perfect for the Wop for Christmas.* I picked this up. *And here are Southwest napkins and wooden napkin rings – a family gift. Good.* I turned to check out the music and found an Ottmar Liebert, a classical guitar player extraordinaire, born to an Hungarian mother and a Chinese-German father, and ending up with a passionate gypsy heart. This CD, *Nouveau Flamenco,* would be a memento from this trip, while on the lam in Santa Fe… for home, the studio, for the bedroom, heh, heh… Thrilled with this find, I continued to wander Jackalope, having the merchandise call out to me.

I found a brightly colored wooden painted pony, ideal for Natalie and symbolic of all the Painted Pony photos from our anniversary trip. I found a brown suede wallet for Jared, stamped with a running buffalo, and a festive string of delicate musical brass bells for Skye. She would love them.

In another area of the store, I found the perfect baby gifts – mobiles from India of stuffed horses and elephants, gaily adorned with ribbons and zigzags of color, hanging from a braided loop. Small brass bells would ring merrily as it swayed above a basinet, crib or bed. I picked out three of these, an extra for later.

Taking my armload of gifts to the counter, I asked the lady there if she would take a personal check from Virginia, if I showed her plenty of I.D. The Indian woman, her gray hair pulled back in a severe bun and a fringed shawl draped over her long dress, eyed me carefully and then said, "Sure. If you have proper identification and a drivers license." I showed her these things and she meticulously transferred additional information onto my studio check. *Good. I still had not used a credit card. Today was Sunday… I would pay the Comfort Inn tomorrow with my studio card, and the airport for Pelli's transport with our joint account card … And then hopefully we would be on our way out of New Mexico and harm's way…*

I left the building with my bagful of purchases and remembered that I still needed to buy the goat skull. *Damn.* I went to it and carefully pulled it off its hanger, taking it back to the Indian woman, since she had already scrutinized me so thoroughly, and wrote another studio check. She then wrapped it in wads of newsprint, to protect the nasal bones, before placing it in a bag.

As I left, headed now to the car to leave, I noticed a low adobe wall off to the side. Curious, I walked over and laughed. Inside was a colony of prairie dogs, all busy at their various tasks or lazing in the warm fall sun. Holes were dug throughout this enclosure and some of the critters disappeared from view as I watched, while others sat on their fat haunches, their small front legs tucked at their chest, nibbling the grasses thrown into them, their fat full cheeks chewing away. The feisty little rascals had it made in the shade here, protected and fed, their job simply to be viewed by us tourists. They could have cared less, totally unaware of their carefree life.

I set my purchases down and snapped a couple of photos of the colony, thinking about them as I walked back to the car. These creatures willingly traded their freedom for this cushy life, not threatened by coyotes or ranchers' poisons or lack of food. If only the Native Americans out here were so lucky. They were relegated to their reservations; most of the rest of their survival on these bleak lands was up to them. They had very little help from Uncle Sam.

When I returned to Cisco, Pelli was awake and wagging that curly tail, happy to see me. I put my bags in the trunk and went to her door, asking her to sit and stay while I clipped on her leash. She willingly obliged, eager to jump out and check out these new surroundings and take in all the scrumptious new scents. We walked around Jackalope a bit; I introduced Pelli to Richard firsthand, and soon after we were on our way to the Plaza, our last visit, this trip.

We found a place to park in the shade on Water Street, close to the Loretto Chapel. I walked down Don Gaspar Avenue, picking up San Francisco Street to Starbuck's to write over coffee, continuing my journals. I found a small table in the center of the flurry of activity and, a latte in hand, settled down for some serious concentration.

As I wrote I noticed four people enter, get their coffees and seat themselves at the table beside me. A handsome middle-aged couple sat with an equally handsome, but older couple, visiting and laughing. I continued to write, but realized soon after that that nature was calling, and rather urgently, too. I had been so focused and lost in thought that I'd overridden (overwritten?) Mama Nature. Looking at my table, spread with papers, and at my camera bag on the chair, I grimaced. This was too much to take with me in the hurry I was in.

"Excuse me," I called to the table of four. They turned to look. "I've got to slip to the bathroom a moment. Would you mind keeping an eye on my things here – especially my camera bag. I'll be right back."

"Of course we will, young lady. You go right on ahead," said the gracious older woman.

I smiled back to her, "Thank you *so* much!" And off I went to the back of Starbuck's.

On return, I thanked them again. They smiled and nodded friendly faces to me. This was such a kindly foursome, I decided to break the ice. "You know, if you all are traveling, you look like the kind of people that might like to experience something called 'The High Road to Taos.' It's really an intimate slice of life here in New Mexico." They smiled amongst one another. "I bet you would *love* a little church up there called El Santuario de Chimayó, sitting there below this little mountain."

The couples looked at each other and laughed. The older gentleman, with a head full of wavy gray hair and very kind brown eyes, smiled at me from a deeply tanned face. "We know about the High Road, young lady. And we're not traveling, at all. We *live* in Chimayó." His merry eyes twinkled in delight.

"Well now," I smiled back sheepishly, "Isn't this a small world – and don't I feel silly." The group exchanged looks again, suppressing grins.

The older woman, his wife, with a lovely mane of gray-streaked dark hair framing her genial face, said to me, "How would you know we lived in Chimayó? That was very kind of you to make the suggestion, though. I'm glad you think so much of our little town."

"Oh, I do. I love the whole High Road – how it's set back in time, so. The slow and easy living. And the Santuario in Chimayó is rich with history and tradition. My husband and I visited it two months ago, right after the September 11th attacks." I immediately grew somber at the memory; repression during this writing session had been easy. "We said our prayers there." I added, as much to myself as to them, remembering that afternoon and the intensity of my praying to Jesus, with his Rosary beads pooled with the blood at his feet.

"Ah, September 11th…" the younger man's voice trailed. He looked to be the older fellow's son, with thick dark hair and similar facial characteristics: the brown eyes and heavy brows, the moderate nose and square jaw. The tenebrous mood settled over us all, like a gray cloud blown into the coffee house.

The older woman, his mother likely, sat up taller in her chair, squared her delicate shoulders, and changed the subject. "Tell use where you are from, dear. I take it you *are* a tourist. What brings you to Santa Fe?" Her colorful scarf and her cerulean jacket brought out the blue in her sweet aged eyes.

"I'm from Virginia. My husband, Pete, and I came out two months ago for our 25th Anniversary – and the year before that we brought our 3 children to the Four Corners and this area. We love it. I'm back to…" I hesitated. *Hmm… How much did they really want to know…? …* "To complete a mission."

"Oh?" The younger man asked curiously.

"Yes. It's a fairly involved story, which began on our anniversary trip – and is being completed with this trip…"

"Well, do tell!" Encouraged the older woman. "By the way, my name is Martha, and this is my husband, Dell. And this is our son, Lloyd, and his lovely wife, Isabelle." Isabelle hadn't said anything and smiled at me shyly now. She had long sable hair pulled back and tied with a ribbon. She wore a pink cotton top and white slacks, with a cream-colored sweater draped over her shoulders, all very feminine.

"*Okay.* My name is Laura, and I'm very pleased to meet you, but my story is kind of complicated. I'll be happy to share, if you *really* want to hear it…" The four nodded in unison. "I'll see if I can give you the 'abbreviated' version…"

So I told them about the trip and September 11th, of traveling anyway and finding Dingo, losing her to Ricardo's duplicity – and thinking we'd lost her altogether. I told them about coming back to Virginia, and then the new sense of empowerment, and deciding to come *back* to the Southwest again to reclaim her… of Plans A and B… and of how I'd resorted to Plan B, and of how I now had the pup, but was now "wanted" by the law – for my own dog, no less. They laughed aloud now, delighted by this lively Wild West adventure set in their neighboring state.

And I wound up the story telling them I'd been sitting there writing about it all, putting my thoughts to paper while it was all fresh. "Tomorrow Kokopelli and I – the good Lord willing – " I added with a big wink, "fly home to Virginia, to all of our critters and teenagers and busy, crazy lives."

"Well now, Laura, you should certainly write a book about your adventures," Lloyd said. "And be sure to include Chimayó." He smiled.

"Oh, I may just do that. Write the book, I mean. But first, I've got to settle-up with the law. I have a feeling this isn't simply going to be swept under the legal rugs out in the Grand Canyon area. The one deputy was fairly adamant about not liking my method of retrieval of my pup."

"Well, my lands, honey, we wish you the very safest possible trip home, and may little Kokopelli find a happy life with you. You've certainly gone over and above the call of duty for this stray dog." Martha intoned.

"With the Lakota connection, it was worth every second. You do what you have to sometimes." I said simply and sincerely.

"When you get back out this way, Laura, you be sure to look us up. You know where Chimayó is." Martha wrote down their number on a slip of paper. "Come visit us." She handed me the paper.

"Thank you. Thank you very much. I'd like that." I told them, as I gathered up my writing and put it away. Kokopelli, the subject of this conversation, would certainly be needing a walk by now. "Let me give you my name and address, too. If you ever make it to Virginia, please plan to visit. We live very close to the Blue Ridge Mountains, and Montpelier – James Madison's home – and Monticello – Thomas Jefferson's home. It's a very historic area. And," I lifted my eyebrows and smiled, "we have *lots* of wonderful vineyards in our backyard. Wine tastings are *very* popular. One of them, Horton Vineyards on Route 33 outside of Gordonsville, even has a red and a white table wine named "Rt. 33" – a takeoff on Rt. 66 – centered in the State Route emblem. And they ain't half bad, either." I joked, with a big smile and a wink, "But Barboursville Vineyards remains our favorite. Pete and I think they have the very best wines in Virginia."

"Well now, how could we pass *that* up," laughed Lloyd. I was up with my things all gathered, in a hurry now to walk the puppy. So much time had passed with my writing and now this visit. I leaned over to shake everyone's hand and say goodbye.

Isabelle looked up and spoke for the first time, "That's a wonderful story; thank you for sharing it with us." She gave me a shy and sincere smile.

"You're entirely welcome." I smiled back. "Thank *you* for listening."

"Remember to call us when you return to Santa Fe," Martha said, adding, "And good luck with your book!"

The small golden pup was about to pop; she must be feeling by now like I had felt earlier. When I returned to the car, Pelli danced around inside on the backseat, delighted to see me. I put the journal in the trunk and unlocked

Cisco. "Okay, girl – sorry I got longwinded there. I met some very nice people," She listened and squirmed, *hurry up, hurry up. I'm dying here…* "Okay, a*lright*, already, hold still while I clip the leash to you! Okay, *siiit…*" Her bottom touched the seat just long enough to show me she'd obeyed, and then, with an expectant look on her restive face, waited for me, "Okay, let's go!"

She was out like a shot, jerking my arm and body behind her, nose to the ground, anxiously sniffing the grass on the median. Soon after this she squatted and peed, while I praised her to high heavens. She finished and jumped around me, full of exuberant energy, ready for an adventure. We walked the streets of Santa Fe for twenty minutes, down Alameda and over to Canyon Road – my allowing her plenty of doggie sniff and roam time, while I enjoyed the outside of the offbeat galleries – before returning her to the Malibu. The Coyote Café would be opened by now. I'd have a last good dinner there and then return to the hotel for a final swim and a call to Pete before packing up my bags to complete the last leg of this journey home.

The Coyote Café
(written on a napkin)

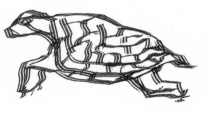

Am sitting here at the Coyote Café; had planned on leaving Santa Fe having feasted on their Calamari Salad and good bread, washed down with a brew. Alas, this is not to be, as they've closed the upper open-air deck and calamari is out of season. Well, damn. I've been hovering in the Plaza, until they opened at 6:00, my mouth watering in anticipation. Oh well... The salad I've ordered now sounds scrumptious, a Mediterranean mix of exotic goodies, and while I waited I reflect on my surroundings. I'm sitting at a wonderful glazed triangular table facing a roaring fire in a true adobe fireplace (took a picture). *Life is good. And this is the calm before the travel storm, so enjoy it, kiddo... Back to reality, mañana. This is great, there are actually round rocks 'holding' the fire and coals inside the domed fire bowl. I'm sure they provide residual heat through the night; this would be a dynamite fireplace to have in one's home... Jean and Al would love it... I'll have to tell them, and share the photo. Southwest rustic – oh, man, I love Santa Fe!!*

If Pelli weren't waiting for me in the car, and if I didn't need to get "home" to pack up, this would be a perfect place to sit back, have a good cup of coffee, maybe even a brandy, and reflect by the light of the primitive fire, like a languishing wolf.

Lakota comes to my mind (he always comes to my mind), as I think of the week's events. What a week! Seems like a blink of an eye in some ways, and as long as forever, in others. Who knew that in my determination to bring Kokopelli to Virginia, into our family: our three busy adolescents, two – now three – happy dogs, two indoor cats and an outdoor cat that thinks he's a dog, our four white love doves, and four horses that think they're dogs... who knew that by this simple determination to bring her 'home' and into our riches, that I would become a fugitive in the state of Arizona. Crazy. Ricardo stole her in the first place. I simply restole her. Deputy Isabella tells me "two wrongs don't make a right." Well, buddy, in this case I feel very much they do, no second thoughts. This feels as natural and meant-to-be as breathing.

Funny, am leaving the Café now, I'm all paid up and ready to go when the lady that has been sitting at the table next to mine, with a bunch of gents that are feeling no pain, stands up. We start up a conversation, somehow, about flying. They ask where I'm from. I ask them. She is a blond woman, tanned and slim, stylish and very friendly. He is a happy-go-lucky-looking, sandy-haired fellow, with a lick of hair falling over his tanned forehead. They're driving from Denver. She asks why I'm in Santa Fe. So I tell them the story. Their names are Annette and Patrick; they listen intently, thoroughly interested, loving it. Patrick tells me not to care what people think – that I listened to my heart and did what needed to be done. He was a regular cheerleader, telling me he was going to write about this story, as well!! And then he told me about how he followed his own heart, concerning a tiny painting his mother had found and fallen in love with when she was pregnant with him. And how his grandfather had invented the viewfinder for Kodak, and how rich their family had become. How, at one point, as the painting had gotten passed down and around, through the family, at one time it had ended up hung in a chicken coop... (!) because, Patrick said, whoever had 'owned' it at that time disliked the painting so. Later he told his father that he loved that little work of art and it became a mission of Patrick's to relocate it within the family and to buy it, so that he could call it his own. He followed his heart, eventually found his small painting, and claimed it to be Van Gogh's *"Windows in the Soul."*

Annette and Patrick walked with me to the Loretto Chapel to see Kokopelli for themselves. Together we walked her up Cathedral Place and around the St. Francis Cathedral, taking pictures of one another in the amber lighting on the stairs, with the beautiful church sitting magnificently behind us. We visited and laughed together, sharing more stories, exchanged names and addresses, and – before parting ways – they invited me to come visit them in Denver.

THIRTY-SIX

Last Leg of our Great Escape

"People who say it cannot be done should not interrupt those who are doing it."
Anonymous

November 19th

Monday morning came in like a ton of bricks. I had stayed up late finalizing all of my packing, including the 2nd box with yesterday's purchases at Jackalope. I had carefully packed around the Spanish goat skull to support the nasal bones, using the bagged tee shirts and mobiles from India, as well as my clothes to be laundered, housed in plastic bags, packing them up under the long horns to support these, too. There wasn't an ounce of space to spare in this meticulously prepared box for UPS. I made up a copy of the contents for inside the box, as well as a duplicate for me and then sealed it up tightly with packaging tape. There. All it needed now was the UPS label.

I had packed my suitcases, except for today's clothes, and slept in the nude so even lingerie wouldn't need to be added. There had been so many loose ends, including the whole satchel of Plan A – all the legal notes and letters and records. There had been refrigerated goods to be sorted through and the cooler to be cleaned; I wanted to give this to Art. By the time I was finished I had two bags of luggage, the Plan A satchel, my camera case, the two UPS boxes, Kokopelli's carrier with her Indian blanket, feed bowls, harness and odds and ends…Plus my safari hat and bone pillow. I still had the cooler and thermos. How the heck *did* people travel lightly?

I found a luggage cart to haul my suitcases and boxes downstairs. In the process, I found Art and gave him the front Nevada plate to reinstall. He replaced it and pulled off the back Santa Fe license. "Thanks, Art. Here, I want you, Carole and Christina to have the cooler and ice packs – if you want them – for picnics or whatever. Can you use it?"

"Sure. We'll keep it for you for your next trip out. Here, take this license plate back with you as a souvenir of your caper, Laura. You'll get a charge out of having it." Art handed the yellow plate with red lettering to me with a grin. The black contact paper in the bottom of my suitcase to change letters would have been useless in New Mexico, too.

"I will treasure this, Art. *And* all the memories it'll conjure up." I smiled at this dear kind old man and gave him a big hug. This was such a fatherly thing to do and I had missed my father for too many years. Art was such an innocent 'accomplice.'

"Well, young lady, the clock is ticking on by. If you're to catch your plane on time you'd better hustle on out of here." Ugh. I would have to climb out of my natural Navajo time and back to the real-world clock to pull off all the schedules this morning. Art was right – I'd better hustle.

"Okay, I'll take this contraption up to my room and bring my luggage down. Don't laugh when you see all the stuff I'm carrying, promise?"

"No. I reserve the right to laugh. But I will help you load your car. Now *go!*" He made shooing motions with his hands. This would be Pete in another twenty years.

"*Alright*, already, I'm gone…"

I went up and checked in on Pelli in the bathroom. She was lying on her blanket, watching expectantly, wondering why this morning was different from the others. "You'll see soon enough, kiddo. Do *you* ever have a surprise in store!" I confided, as I closed the door, thinking of both the plane ride and the homecoming that awaited her.

I clumsily maneuvered the large and lumbering luggage cart and loaded it carefully, putting the larger items on the bottom and balancing the smaller ones in a precarious pyramid atop, wedging the bouquet of flowers, the camera case and my bone pillow in crevices inbetween items. I backed it carefully and opened the hotel door, trying to negotiate the clumsy mobile mountain of movement out the door that continually wanted to close and trap us tightly in its jaws. I was glad no one was videotaping my smooth escape from Santa Fe. I thought of Chuck and John, and the wiseass brotherly comments they'd be making about now, and grinned.

Downstairs, I handed Art the flowers and asked him to please take them to Carole from me with a hug and final thank you for her kindness and support. I gave Art the cooler, complete with refrozen ice packs and a few choice chilled items I hadn't used. He helped me load the suitcases and boxes into the trunk of Cisco, telling me where to find UPS, which was very close by, in the process.

I then went back up for Kokopelli, gathered her blanket and food dishes and came down to check out of the Comfort Inn, thanking Ernesto, Pat, Ed, and the crew for all their help and patience in our stay. Art came out to visit while Pelli had her second freedom run of that morning. We laughed as she raced around the evergreens and jumped the sages. This was her personal obstacle course of merriment. She raced towards me once, considering her body-slam 'game' and I cocked my knee, warning her, "Don't even *think* about it, dog…" She checked and veered her course.

"What was that all about?" Art inquired.

"Oh, some rough game she devised that I didn't think was so funny. We're nipping it in the bud." He raised an inquiring gray-laced eyebrow at me, but didn't say anything else.

I glanced at my watch: 8:23 – time to leave if I was going to make UPS, still get gas and be at the rental car outlet by 10AM. I called Pelli, who responded immediately. "*Good girl!* Now *sit…*" I clipped her leash onto the collar ring. "Oh yeah, pup. The vet said to give you one of the ace tab's before we left Santa Fe. I've got them in my pocket."

I fished down inside my jeans and pulled out the plastic amber vial, pushing and twisting the childproof top, grimacing as I did until I had reached just the right combination to open it. Uh oh. There inside was a pale yellow mishmash of stuff wedged in and around the small pinecone. *Damn.* I knew immediately what had happened. My 'brain-fart.' I had put the damp pinecone in with the two Acepromazine tablets and the moisture had turned the tranquilizers to mush. So much for the forethought to have her relaxed in transit; I took it as a sign that that wasn't meant to be. She'd just have to tough it out. I groaned and showed the vial to Art, who just chuckled at my error. "Oh well, sweetie, that's life. These things happen. She'll be fine."

I smiled and shook my head, then turned to my friend and gave him a last thank you and a great big hug. "I'll miss you and Carole, Art. You're two very sweet people and you've been like family to me out here. Take good care of each other and of Christina."

"Of course we will." He straightened his aged back. "You take care of your*self*, Laura — and that cute puppy. You and Kokopelli go on home now and don't worry about a thing. Nobody is waiting for you at the rental car place *or* at the airport. That's rubbish. You'll be just fine. And that handsome worrywart husband of yours is waiting for you at the end of the line. Don't worry about a *thing*."

I smiled again, thinking of Shakespeare and parting being "such sweet sorrow." I asked Pelli to hop in the car and fastened her to her harness, on the bucket seat beside me. She sat proudly on her blanket, panting and happy from exertion. Her purple bandana lay against her neck, rumpled, ready for another bath, even though I'd washed it and her blanket Friday night. My pup was ready to go on to whatever adventure lay ahead.

I went around to the driver's side of the Malibu, waving and smiling at Art one last time. He stood there, almost shyly, dark pants on those slightly bowed legs of his and his gray hair catching the morning light, his eyes twinkling and his moustache parting with a big smile. I got in, moving aside a bag of breakfast that Art had packed up for me. My thermos with fresh java was perched on the seat; Art had made a pot of Columbian decaf as a special treat, bless him. I poured a cup into Styrofoam, fastened my belt and waved one last time, leaning over the wheel to see him better, as we backed out of the hotel.

I watched Art standing on the sidewalk, becoming smaller as we put on our signal and turned right onto Cerrillos Road to find UPS. The huge American flag over the Horseman's Café next door stood tall and free, waving a proud goodbye to me as well, as she caught the morning sunlight of Santa Fe in her folds of red, white and blue.

I filled up the Malibu and found the UPS that Art had directed me to easily enough. I also found that it didn't open until 10AM — too late to do any good this morning. The boxes would have to go with me on the plane. *Damn. Now what? Maybe I could find a UPS that was opened on the way? Dreamer.* I didn't think until later that I could have taken the boxes back over to Art and left him with a blank check, to send the boxes on at his convenience. *Okay, a quick revamp. Now I drive on down on I-25 to National Rental Car. We didn't have time to fool around, if Pelli and I were going to face the firing squad, so to speak.* I was wired and ready to hit I-25 to get on to the airport. I just could not wait for all the excitement that lay ahead: returning the rental and juggling this mountain of luggage with the puppy and the carrier to the airport by way of the bus shuttle; the bag and body searches; the potential intense scrutiny of every ounce of luggage… Not to mention that the men in blue might be awaiting me with *big* ole' smiles and handcuffs and a warrant for my arrest. No, I was just quivering in anticipation…

With Kokopelli beside me watching the scenery flashing by, we hightailed it down the busy Interstate, heading to our final destination: Sunport. Hopefully we would be met with only minimal inspections – after all, what terrorist suspect would arrive with *3* suitcases, *2* boxes, a camera bag, a fuzzy bone pillow and her *dog*? Soon we would be headed home. Hopefully none of the boys in blue would be waiting to confiscate my cargo. Likely the National Guard would be at the airport as a show of strength, yes. But I was sure even *they* hadn't been informed of this particular heist.

As we drove south I started free-associating thoughts and images of the past two months: of the America before and the America after 9/11. *Two vastly different countries. There had been the America (like my sister, Mary): young and vibrant, living innocently in a country (her home) untouched, unmarred, by the violence that beset so much of the rest of the world.*

On October 1st, 1969, her innocence and trust and the illusion that it was always "someone else, somewhere else" came crashing down around her and her husband, in the nightmare of living hell that irrevocably changed their lives, and Sean's, and ended Galen's life, altogether. And it forever affected the lives of family members and friends left emotionally crippled and helpless to change a thing.

On September 27th, 1997, in George's home and studio, his love of his fellow person, and his trust in humanity as a whole, became his downfall as he allowed Dorian Lester and his "Cruella de Ville" sidekick past his security system. The beginning of his end.

On September 11th, 2001, the world watched, stunned and appalled, as America lost her innocence and sense of isolation that this vicious violence of terrorism only occurred elsewhere; we were immune. Well, we were not. In the course of a morning, we watched in horror as the Twin Towers were impaled by fully fueled jetliners. We watched these mighty, seemingly indestructible, towers slowly cave in upon themselves in a blazing fury and become a massive tomb for those trapped within. We heard that the Pentagon – the fortress of our military might – was also penetrated by a plane, but in the state of chaos we knew so little for a long while. The fourth hijacked jetliner was 'rehijacked' by our own – men who became heroes as they sacrificed their lives for a cause much greater than themselves – as this final plane crashed in a field near Shanksville, Pennsylvania, at over 500 mph, instead of into the White House or into Congress. I have also heard since, from several knowledgeable sources, that there is a distinct possibility that this last plane was shot down by our own government, but this, of course, would be denied. Like the other flights, the impact killed everyone on board. We, the People of the United States of America, witnessed over two centuries of 'innocence' crumble, as our illusion of the USA as a safe haven from such hatred become a sweet memory of our naiveté in our life before this. One apocalyptic morning changed the world. It was no longer "someone else, somewhere else." We were all now mired in the madness that has touched so much of the rest of the world.

I continued driving south, mesmerized by thoughts of the flip sides of so many coins. The faces of Janus. "Gray space" thinking took over. *I thought of Kokopelli's long weeks trapped in Ricardo's trailer, waiting for him to return home to share whatever companionship he might then offer. I thought of the neuroses she had shown after I'd freed her: her clinging and whining behavior, in constant need of comfort and reaffirmation; her lack of boundaries, manners or training of any sort; the wild, unruly and detached look in her eyes as she frantically pulled at the leash, mindless of my asking her to relax and become compliant; the refusal to answer nature's calls outside, at first, as she had forgotten that early 'training' of her first few months on earth. I wondered how much longer she would have 'lasted' in her bondage before her intelligent and sensitive nature would have snapped and she'd turned on herself, as Shirley had done, or had shown some other more subversive and destructive behavior by this endless confinement.*

I thought of Shirley, the intelligent and lonely little parrot who had self-mutilated out of sheer desperation and need of stimulus, some sort of loving contact to occupy her hours. Like any living being, these animals were just two examples of how life needs nourishment, a loving touch, companionship and interaction to flourish and thrive. Humans were no different. Study after study has proven that given all the basic necessities for survival, but withhold the love, the touch and companionship, the subject's — human or animal — capacity for meaningful interaction with another becomes distorted, atrophied, withdrawn. They begin to show exactly these subversive behaviors, as did Pelli and Shirley.

Our prisons are full of inmates whose lives began as by-products and castoffs of families and a society that had neither the time nor inclination to care. Thank God, then, for the insight and foresight to reach out a nurturing helping hand to 'at risk' young children in programs such as Head Start. These proven programs touch the lives of millions of young children that, except for them, might not receive this stimulus, this nurturing, this care — nourishment of mind, body and soul. They offer not just early childhood education, but the tenuous golden gift of hope. That there is something more out there in life worth reaching for than bleakness, isolation, and the cold empty enclosure of poverty. Something more than the dull gray beaten down grind of despair: the antithesis of hope.

As I neared Albuquerque, these thoughts shifted to the dark forces ruling Afghanistan with such an iron fist. Of bin Laden and his death mongers, of the Taliban and their diabolic domain over men, women and children. In concentrating on the

496

dark side of life — like the dark side of the moon upon which I freed Kokopelli from her imprisonment — their archaic brutal beliefs, forced upon those they conquered, buried the country in the dark ages of repression. Like the caves in which they dwelled, these men ran from life, hiding, isolating themselves, threatening their repressive despotic regimes down the throats of those they stifled into submission. The Taliban offered iron rule in a rugged impoverished country that saw little of life's bounty under the best of circumstances.

Albuquerque's horizon was upon us. As we neared this metropolitan Southwest city I passed the I-40 east/west corridor and continued south to find National Rental Car. Loose ends of these thoughts drifted around in my head, as concentration on city driving and signs prevented them from connecting. Gray space thinking quickly evaporated, like the symbolic light bulb of an idea popping only to be replaced by more immediate concerns.

Soon Pelli and I were taking the big loopy off ramp onto Stadium Boulevard to find Cisco's headquarters. As we drove into National we passed a checkpoint and were told to pass on through; I would be helped by porters waiting to aid me in unloading all my earthly belongings. Little did they know what they were biting off…

Two grinning young fellows approached, one of them with a portable luggage carrier. Good. We would need every square inch. I got out and said "Good morning" to the boys and directed them to the trunk, where the suitcases awaited. They opened it with the keys I offered and took a step back, one of them playfully jabbing the other in the arm at the sight of my belongings. "Yep. I've collected quite a bit of 'stuff' in my travels. Think we can carry it all to the shuttle in one trip?"

The optimistic sandy-haired fellow smiled and said, "Sure, I'm an ace at this sort of thing." He carefully pulled the luggage out of the trunk, loading the larger items squarely on the bottom. He had probably started as a grocery bagger, by the careful way in which he worked. The second fellow, a shorter dark-haired young man, quietly assisted him.

"Is Daryl working today?" I asked them.

Sandy-hair, named Chris, according to the badge on his shirt, said, "No, Daryl's off today. He worked the weekend."

"I'm sorry about that. I was hoping to see him. He helped me choose this Malibu and she's worked like a charm. I wanted to thank him." I thought for a moment, as they busily continued stacking loose ends. "Would you please give him this thermos, along with a message?" Chris looked up, curious. "Tell him that Laura — can you remember my name?

— was successful in my mission. I have the puppy and we're returning to Virginia today." He repeated the message, but I remembered how accurate Jared was — and forgetful in details — "Here, I'll write that down for you. If you give him this and the thermos, I would be much obliged."

"I'd be happy to, ma'm. I think he works tomorrow." Chris answered.

The dark-haired fellow, named Jeff, according to his badge, was peering into the Malibu. "What about your dog? I see a carrier in there we forgot to load." *Oops.*

I turned to the fellows. "How far is the shuttle? If I walk the puppy, and we balance the carrier on top of the load, would that work?" They eyed the precarious stack dubiously.

Jeff was the first to respond, "Yes, I think we can do that. I'll hang on to it, so it won't fall off." Chris nodded his head in agreement.

I helped them remove the carrier from the second seat and we balanced it carefully atop my luggage and the two boxes. Then I wedged into nooks and crannies my bone pillow, a small travel bag of snacks and my safari hat. I decided to carry the camera bag over my shoulder to protect it and wedge my backpack/purse on the carrier. The latter could sustain a fall much better than the former.

I checked the glove compartment for loose ends, found an extra pair of sunglasses, checked the CD player again and poked around between and under the seats for anything I might have dropped. I found the AAA Indian Country map and tucked it into the camera bag. As I did this, I silently thanked Cisco for a surefooted journey through Arizona and New Mexico; I would miss my little getaway car, now so full of memories…

"Okay, fellows, we're all set." I left my last minute searching and joined the two young men. Jeff had been holding Pelli and roughhousing with her a little on the end of the leash. She was eating it up. "She's a cute dog." Chris commented. "Where you headed?"

"Back to Virginia; that's where I'm from. I found her in Arizona. She was a stray pup in Monument Valley."

"She don't look like a stray no more," Jeff said. "Lucky dog." *That* had been said before.

Well, here we were full circle — the last leg of this great escape — right back where my New Mexican journey had begun: SunPort. I had my prize in tow and was surrounded by the luggage and boxes and Pelli in her pet carrier, shuffling along in the snaking line until I stood before a dark haired, middle-aged fellow at the Delta ticket counter. He was eyeing my extensive collection, trying his level best to be fair. "Well, I see that you called ahead about your dog and know about the extra $75 fee for travel. But I'm going to *also* have to charge you for the extra boxes. You see, you have so *much*…"

"I know, I know – believe me – I know, sir. Do you see how the boxes are so carefully packed? They were to go out by UPS in Santa Fe this morning – only UPS didn't *open* until 10AM. And, because of the stringency of airport regulations now, of course I couldn't wait. So I have them, too…"

"I guess you didn't notice the UPS center on I-25 shortly before you entered Albuquerque?" he raised a thick dark eyebrow in query. His slick-backed hair looked lacquered.

"No, I didn't. I was thinking of other things and so intent on getting to National on time, so I could get *here* on time, I must have missed it altogether." *Damn. So close.*

"Well, Ms. Giannini, I hate to have to do this, but I have no choice. You're way over total *num*bers of bags – *and* weight. I'll have to charge you an extra $85 to cover the two boxes. Is that okay?"

"No, but do I have a choice?" *Well, hells bells, the cost of these gifts just skyrocketed.* "Go ahead and put it on the same credit card then." *All right, boys – put that trace on me. I'm outta' here.*

He took my card and ran it through, then handed it back with a smile. "Oh, there's one more bit of good news," he shared, as he glanced at his computer screen again. "You've just been flagged to have all your luggage hand-checked." He looked up at me and gave me a genuine smile of empathy. *Damn the frequent-flyer miles,* I groaned. I just squeezed my eyes shut, shook my head and grimaced. *Great. I guess this was to be expected… they're doing it to everybody – little old ladies and mothers with small children, known sports figures – it didn't matter. As long as we didn't 'racially profile.' After all, this IS America… Today, this morning, just this once, I sure wished the airlines would concentrate on swarthy, dark-haired, very serious-looking men of Middle-Eastern descent and leave the rest of us alone. Every man on those hijacked airliners fit that description. So did Richard Reid – and he* looked *crazy, to boot! But God forbid that they would have singled* him *out… Okay, enough… be a good sport. This IS the last leg home…*

"You okay?" Asked the Delta clerk. I looked up and tried to look okay about his good news. I put a lid on my thoughts and signed the receipt. "Yes – I'm fine. I just needed a moment to silently vent." I turned to the older woman behind me. "Sorry about the hold-up, ma'm. I'll be right out of your way – and, good luck." She smiled at me understandingly and said, "No, dear, good luck and God speed to *you*. I'm going to visit my grandchildren; I'm not bothered by any of this."

"Just take your luggage over to the table over there. The baggage inspector will be right with you." The man pointed to my right.

"Sure thing. Thanks for your help." I sincerely tried not to be sarcastic, as the man was just doing his job, and I hauled my luggage, piece by piece, to the right.

A pleasant-faced young lady, with honey blond hair pulled back in a ponytail, met me with a smile. "Hi there," she greeted me, looking up over her wire-rims. "I overheard the conversation." She leaned conspiratorially towards me, "and I *think* I overheard the one in your mind." She laughed. "But this is my job, so let's get started." She pulled on rubber gloves for the search.

"Rubber gloves? That's new."

"You wouldn't be*lieve* what you might find in these here suitcases." She kidded.

She hoisted the first bag onto the table and unzipped it. I noticed the name 'Rita' on her badge. "Now, you just stand back while I work." I watched her adroitly go through every item of clothing, lingerie, and plastic bags with items in them… everything. Rita checked the linings and pockets and places I'd *never* have thought of looking, with a small penlight. "This checks out okay. *Next.*" She said matter-of-factly.

I hoisted suitcase number two onto the table. She did the same thorough check. Satchel number three contained all my legal papers, maps, tourist brochures and loose-end items. Very boring. Again she found nothing.

"Okay, next it's the boxes. Which one you want to go first?"

I groaned again. "*Not* the boxes… I packed them so carefully for UPS. Can't I just tell you what's in them? Can't you *X*-ray them?" She raised a dubious eyebrow and frowned a no, "I wish it were that easy these days. The whole world has changed. It's my job to look through everything that's been flagged."

"Okay, but all you're going to find in this lighter box is chili ristras and wads of newspapers." She opened it anyway, carefully poked through to find ristras and papers. Rita closed and retaped the box.

"In light of that, can I tell you what's in the second box?" I asked her hopefully, but knowing the answer.

"You know better than to even ask. Come on, let's get it over with." We hoisted the heavier box onto the inspections table. She expertly cut through my careful taping job and started through the contents, after moving aside my list of enclosed items. I grimaced again, knowing the TLC I'd used in packing it. Not a square inch was wasted space. I headed towards the box to help her, especially around the goat's skull.

"*Oh no.* I'm sorry, but you can't put your hands in your luggage. For all we know, you might be planting a bomb." Rita rolled her eyes at the regulations.

"Wouldn't that kind of defeat the purpose of my getting home safely? Of bringing these gifts back home to the kids?..." I shook my head at the absurdity of the situation, at this fearful new world of ours, and what it was doing to us as a nation.

"I know. I know. I'm reading your thoughts again." She changed the subject, as she continued her meticulous search through the Santa Fe tee shirts, Skye's robe, my dirty clothes bag, the mobiles from India and the Spanish goat skull. "Where are you from?"

"Virginia. And I'm ready to be going home; I'm kind of homesick."

"That's a long ways aways. I've never been further than Mississippi, myself. How long have you been west? And did you stay in New Mexico?"

"A week. And no, I split my trip between Arizona and New Mexico. But of the two," I confided, "I prefer New Mexico. But there are *some* places in Arizona that are to die for..." I added, thinking of the Grand Canyon and Canyon de Chelly.

"I prefer New Mexico, too. You get your goat's head at Jackalope?"

"Yup. Please be careful with it. As hardheaded as the little critter was, parts are *still* delicate. I'm an artist and I buy a skull of some sort each trip out here. Last time it was a small antelope's skull."

"Well, that's interesting. After Georgia's heart, eh? What kind of art do you do?" She was folding and putting things back into place. It was all I could do to not reach in and help her; I'd had it all positioned just so to pad and pack all the fragile items.

Distractedly I answered her, "I'm an animal portrait artist and a landscape painter. Often the two are combined."

"Well, that's very interesting. I don't think I've ever actually *met* an animal portrait artist, but, of course, I've seen their work. It's beautiful."

I wasn't sure how she could lump all animal portrait artists in one category. Like anything else, each artist had his or her own style and abilities. But I took it as a blanket compliment for the all of us. "Thank you. You all set with that box? Sure I can't just doublecheck the packing – just peek inside a moment? You can inspect my hands, even look up my sleeves, to make sure I'm not armed. I had items arranged just so, and some things are very fragile, like areas on the skull."

"I'm sorry – you can't. Regulations. You know, that bomb and all. But I *promise* I packed it *very* carefully. Let me seal 'er up and then we'll check out your dog."

"My *dog*?" I couldn't mask the surprise in my voice.

"Yes. We have to pull her out of the carrier, check her over, and check out everything inside. You might have put the bomb in there." Again, she rolled her eyes at how ridiculous that had sounded.

"Sure. And if you knew how much trouble I've gone to for this little mutt, that wouldn't even be a joke." Rita just gave me a lopsided smile back and shook her head.

"The world – this industry especially – has gone *nuts* in the last two months. You would not be*lieve* me if I told you some of the new regulations around here."

"No, I probably would." I said, thinking sadly of so many changes and the raw fear behind them all. I went to the carrier and knelt down. Pelli had been lying inside amazingly quietly, her head on her pale paws, just watching the commotion in the airport. She looked very apprehensive, as if expecting anything. The purple bandana looked so dark in the shadows of the cage. "Okay, girl. It's your turn now. Come on out!" I reached in and picked the leash from the carrier floor and hooked it onto her collar. She bent down to make her way out, looking timidly around her. Her tail had lost its curl for the moment. "Come here, Pelli. These are good people. No one wants to hurt you." I said to her brightly. She perked her ears up and looked more alert. Her tail started to curl again.

"Oh, what a cute little dog." Rita knelt down and Pelli came to her to sniff her hand. "What kind is she?"

"A Navajo Reservation mutt. I found her under a sagebrush in Monument Valley. No one wanted her. She was skin and bones."

"No one *wanted* this beautiful little puppy?" she asked incredulously. "She looks a lot like an Akita and my boyfriend just paid $1,200 for a registered Akita puppy!" She shook her head in disbelief, momentarily forgetting her job, which was to inspect this subject of which she was 'oohing' and 'aahing.'

"That's right. No one wanted her. But that's all changed now, hasn't it, Pelli?" I knelt down beside her and rubbed her ears. "Her name is 'Kokopelli,' after your resident mischief-maker. She's well-named, too, be*lieve* me." I added dryly.

"Well, she looks so sweet and innocent and I can see she's carrying no bomb. Now let me check the carrier." Rita remembered her job and turned to the cage, looking inside, pulling out the blanket and feed dishes and running her hand around inside all along the bottom and the top. She leaned in and did a quick scan with her penlight, then stood and said, "Well, lady, I couldn't find a *thing*. You're all set for your trip."

"I told you that… But I know, I know – it's your job – and you do it well," I added.

I smiled at her, "I hope you never actually find anything destructive in anyone's luggage, Rita. Is that naïve of me? And God help us all that we never have a repeat of what caused all this madness."

She sobered, "God help us, no. Have a good trip there, lady – you and your sweet Kokopelli."

I should have been tremendously relieved that we had just passed the final checkpoint out of New Mexico with no major red alerts, but my relief was sobered by this conversation.

Flagging the luggage was now routine and generic, not to be taken personally. However, if the boys in *blue* had been waiting for me, with a warrant for puppy theft in hand, why – *that* would have been personal. And it would have been a whole new chapter to this story. But they weren't.

I said a goodbye to Pelli, as I asked her to return to her blanket in the carrier, wishing that I could explain that these were our last hours of travel and we were now heading home. Home: to our little farm, room to run, kids to play with, fields full of animals – a puppy's paradise. She, of course, didn't know any of this, as much as I wanted her to dream of it in transit. Instead, she looked trapped and resigned. And ready to go into waiting, as she had done so often in her recent past. "Hey, kiddo, practice that art of patience – I'll be waiting for you on the other end. Hang tight. We're almost home free." Or so I hoped and prayed.

Pete and Natalie awaited us at Byrd Airport, in Richmond, Virginia, that Monday night of our safe return. Evidently, there had been no bombs aboard in anyone's luggage. As I strode through the tarmac, balancing my backpack and camera bag, small bag of collected items and snacks for the kids, my bone pillow under my arm and the San Diego safari hat slung over my shoulders atop the backpack, I saw them eagerly watching the faces coming down the pike. I stopped in the crowd for a second to study the two before they saw me. Natalie was standing on her tippytoes, a hand on her dad's arm for balance, scanning the crowd of arrivals. Her precious young face, framed by the long chestnut and blond streaked hair, was full of excitement and anticipation. I expect she thought I might be leading the puppy down the ramp with me. She looked so young, yet so grown, and I swallowed, choking back a tear at my children all now so grown. Here was my *baby* – now a beautiful young *lady*. Yes, time flew by on silver wings.

Pete stood tall beside her, still a full head and a half above her. His salt and pepper hair was neatly combed, longish the way I like it. His goatee and mustache looked newly trimmed. Pete was alert, watching the crowd as intently as Natalie, praying probably that I hadn't been apprehended since the last time we had spoken, after I'd called him from a payphone in Sunport, once my baggage had cleared. He wore one of my favorite shirts, a teal-green chamois, and a pair of faded blue jeans with the silver buckle with Navajo symbols from the White House Ruins, that we had bought together at the bottom of Canyon de Chelly on our trip with the kids. I wondered impishly if he'd remembered the aftershave I liked. His eye caught mine then, as I stood quietly to the side studying them, and he gave me a huge, relieved smile and walked towards me. I picked up my camera bag again and walked over and into his arms. Natalie squeezed up inside our hug, as glad to see her mom as her mom was glad to see her, and the three of us embraced for a silent moment before she squeezed back under and asked me, "So *where's* the puppy, Mom? You *do* have her with you, don't you?"

"No, Twerpy Doodle, after all that I decided she was just too much trouble and I left her with Art." I smiled and rumpled her hair.

"*Maumm!* You did *not!* But where is she? I thought you wouldn't have let her out of your sight!"

"It was hard, sweetie, but I had to. She's in a travel carrier and we'll find her down in luggage, with my bags. Let's go see if she's there, okay?"

She smiled up at me, a part knowing I'd been kidding about leaving the pup in Santa Fe, a part left wondering, and greatly relieved that I'd been teasing. She wrapped a possessive arm around me as we walked to the escalator to find our luggage. Pete had my camera bag in one hand and his other arm around my shoulder. We were a family again.

My luggage came off the conveyor belt, one piece at a time amongst the sea of others, and Pete and I stood by waiting and identifying them and pulling the suitcases and satchel off. "I've got those boxes, too, PeterWop. UPS was closed this morning and I couldn't send them ahead. So I had to pay extra. But the good news is that y'all receive some of your gifts early. Some you'll have to wait for until Christmas, though." I squeezed my arm around his middle and grinned, then reached up to give him a peck on the cheek. *Umm. He* was *wearing that aftershave.* He smiled down at me, but said nothing.

"There she is, Mom!" Screamed Natalie from the side of the room, where we'd been told to watch for incoming carriers. An aged black man carefully came through the door carrying the carrier in his arms. His gray hair was a striking contrast to his very dark skin, reminding me of Uncle Remus. His gentle face split into a big smile as Natalie raced over to see inside the cage. "That your little doggie in there, honey?" He asked her as he set the carrier down.

"No, it's my Mom's dog," she pointed over to me, "But I haven't seen her yet. She found her out west and told me all about her." Pelli was whining inside the cage, watching Nattie and trying to paw her way through the wire mesh door. "Can I let her out, Mom?"

"For a minute, yes, sweetheart; her leash is just inside the door. But be very careful that you hang onto her tightly. I left Pete to join the trio. "Hello." I said to the older gentleman, "Looks like she made it just fine."

"Sure do. She was good as gold back there. We enjoyed talking to her. I saw to it that she had fresh water – she spilled her bowl in there, when she was a wigglin' around in the cage, trying to visit us."

"Thank you, sir. You were very kind." I reached into my zippered vest to pull out my small travel wallet and give him a tip for his help. He saw what I was doing and backed away, putting up the palms of both hands, waving them in the air.

"No, ma'm, now you be putting that away. If'n we can't be offering kindnesses to little puppies like'n this, why then what's the world a comin' to?" He gave me a big sweet grin. His eyes were old and watery but they radiated warmth.

"Well, sir, this puppy and my daughter and I all thank you for your care." He smiled and nodded and turned his tall gaunt frame back towards the door. "You is *wel*come." He laughed and headed back inside.

We had loaded up my luggage in our older Taurus wagon, which I long ago had dubbed *"Jaws"* because of its huge, heavy, trap-like doors that try to snap closed on us every (in)opportune moment they could. You'd think Ford – the original automaker – would know how to build a working hinge by now…

Afterwards we walked Kokopelli in a grassy area outside the parking lot at the airport, and decided to find a place to eat. When in Richmond, on the west end, we usually chose T.G.I.F.'s, and did so tonight. We let Pelli stay out of her carrier now, laying down the Indian blanket on the second seat so that she and Natalie could bond. The two youngsters were magnets to one another.

At dinner I told them about our trip and about dinner the night before with Cynthia, in Taos; about starting the day with Art's help and the breakfast and coffee he had fixed me; … Kokopelli's last freedom run at the hotel; about the flag at the Horseman's Café flying high and proud again; missing UPS;… about the luggage search at the airport… By now it was funny, the deed being done and with time and mileage far behind us. I told them of the blond pilot in Atlanta meeting me as I entered the plane, with a big grin when they handed me the pet claim tag, asking me if that was my puppy and saying, "I was playing with her back there while everyone was boarding. She sure is a cute little thing – cute as a button!" I had left a special message with the flight attendants at Delta to let 'Betty' and 'Page' know that our mission had been successful; the puppy was with me and we were headed home. They would know what that meant.

While we laughed and enjoyed our dinners, Natalie asked me, "Mom, I've never seen a tail like that before. Where did she get that curl?"

I grinned at her again, ready for the answer. "Well, Natalie, I have this theory. You know she was born in the high desert, right? Well, *I* think that when she was just an itty-bitty little puppy, *I* think that she got it caught around one of those cactus' out in the desert and got stuck. You know, like the cactus Snoopy's cousin is always hanging around with? Only they don't have the saguaro that far north, so it must be some other kind. Well, when she was *finally* able to get it loose again, why it had that permanent curl to it. It'll never be the same." I rolled my eyes, scrunched my mouth and shook my head.

"*Maumm!* Like that really happened! Can't you ever just be *straight* with me sometimes?"

"Nope. It's more fun going in circles – like Kokopelli's tail. And I love to hear you say *'Maumm!'* It's good to be home, you guys." I raised my tea in a toast and smiled warmly at my husband and my young daughter.

They raised their glasses back at me and we clinked. Pete said, "To a safe return after a successful – albeit under*cover*," he cleared his throat and gave me a stern look under those wonderful arched eyebrows "– mission. We're glad you and Pelli are safely home, but I really do believe it's *you* that's the Kokopelli here, Razza." He relaxed his expression and smiled at me, relief now all over his face.

Part VI
Long Arm of the Law Comes East

THIRTY-SEVEN

Conversations with the Big Guns

"Always acknowledge a fault frankly. This will throw those in authority off guard and allow you opportunity to commit more." Mark Twain

Tuesday, November 20th

I had tried to sleep in this morning, as we had stayed up so late last night celebrating our return home. Once in bed I had not been able to relax and sleep – my mind was still wired from the trip. The only things that I had unpacked were the gifts for Pete and the kids – the ones that I weren't holding for Christmas, anyway. We had settled little Kokopelli in, introducing her to Heather and Emma, Trey and Amanda. There had been chaos and excitement throughout the evening. We had all fallen into bed at a late hour and left my luggage pretty much where it had landed, except for the gift-searches.

When the phone rang at 9AM, I was very tempted not to answer it. Let it ring – I would catch it later. But something made me want to see who was calling. "Anonymous" sat there staring at me on Caller I.D. **O***kay...Do they have built-in radar? How do they know I'm home? Or are they just being persistent, knowing this usually pays off? Time for a decision here... Should I continue putting off the inevitable and go back to bed, or just go ahead and pick the damned thing up and face the music. I braced myself. If I were to set an example of living up to responsibility for my teenage trio, this would be a good place to start.* With these thoughts in my foggy morning brain, I picked up the receiver: "Hello?"

The no-nonsense voice of Deputy Isabella spoke: "I see that you made it home just fine. Why didn't you call me back?" *And a good morning to you, too…*

"Good morning, Deputy." At least one of us could be polite. "Yes, I made it back. And I didn't call you back because you were going to arrest me for retrieving my dog. And then *you* would take her away, return her to Ricardo while this was all hashed out, and this wouldn't have done, at all." I was waking up fast. While we talked, I pulled my decaf canister down from the cabinet and filled the coffee pot with cold water, bracing the phone to my ear. Guess I was up now. The receiver slipped and banged against the sink, making a racket on the other end of the line. I pulled it up by the dangling cord, juggling that and the coffee pot. "*Sorry!*" I called into the phone. "I'm making coffee – we got in late last night. Things were wild around here."

"I bet. You have the dog there with you?" *Why play footsies with this guy? He/they weren't dumb. Hell, I'd given them notice that I was coming back for her; lined all my ducks up in a row – practically for target practice – and then she disappears out of Ricky's trailer, like magic. Who am I trying to kid?*

So I admitted to Deputy Isabella, there in my own kitchen, as the coffee brewed cheerfully in the background, that, "Yes, I have her with me. She's right here beside me as I speak." And then, in a flush of anger at the imprisonment she'd been in, "And I'm *not* sorry at all for what I did. Ricardo had her locked in that trailer night and day, waiting for him. That puppy didn't know a *name*, she had *no* manners at all, and she was the re*verse* of housebroken!! She didn't pee for 24 hours after I freed her, before she finally let go – and then it was *in*side, on a carpet! This little dog that was born in a desert thought she had to hold her urine until she was *inside!*" And, still angry, I went on to explain that this was no way to raise a pup, trapped in a trailer 24/7, unattended for 10 hours at a time. No company. Nothing."

Well, as John Slate had advised me, as well as my loving husband, "Laura, you talk too much. You are incriminating yourself." And I tried to shut up. But my feelings about this were much too strong and my sense of doing the right thing to free her felt too right to be wrong. Deputy Isabella was loving it. He kept quiet on the other end of the line, listening to me admit to anything and everything, probably with a smirk on his face, while he made notes. Or taped the call. *Was this legal?*

We continued to talk. My coffee was done. I braced the phone under my chin, chose a Lighthouse beach mug and poured a cup of the steaming joe and then, phone still cradled and kind of hoping it would hit the sink again right in the good deputies ear, I poured the rest in a thermos to keep it fresh. He was saying to me, "Well, Ms. Giannini, I've known Ricardo for nine years. There's nothing wrong with living in a trailer, and he's never caused any problems around here. He's never done anything wrong." *This man was not bothered by the situation this puppy had been in; I'd just dug my hole deeper, as far as he was concerned. All this man cared about was that I had broken the law, and now it was payback time. I'd been warned to behave, had taken her anyway, despite everything, under their noses and had not only gotten out of* Arizona *with her, I had gotten back to* Virginia – *and these boys were pissed. They wanted some blood: mine. I also got the distinct feeling that Deputy Isabella wasn't particularly a dog-lover. But he knew and liked Ricardo and didn't especially care that we were the original owners – we had let her go, in his eyes. Tough.*

Coffee poured, I sipped the steaming black liquid and savored the taste. Wonderful stuff. I stood there a moment in silence, thinking, calmer now. "Listen, Deputy, I have absolutely nothing against anyone living in trailers. We knew Ricardo lived in Tinkerville when we entrusted her to him. That's not the point. It's what he did – or *didn't* do – for her, afterwards. Between that, and his lying to us in the first place, is why I did *what* I did and went to the trouble of returning to Arizona for her." I had the strong impression that he thought I was just a bored and rich east-coaster, with time on her hands, that had nothing better to do than fly back and forth between the east and west coast for thrills. Little did he know. This impression was verified when he spoke.

"Well, I see you can afford to fly *out* here for your vacation. And then you can come *back* out for this stray dog. So I guess you can afford to fly back *again* to go to trial."

I responded blondly, "We used our last frequent-flyer mileage for my return for the pup. Sorry." He wasn't impressed, although it was true. *Damn.*

"Well, we have you for Grand Larceny, so we can extradite you." I blew a sip of coffee out. What a *joke!*

"Listen, Deputy Isabella, that's almost funny! This puppy was *starving to death* in the desert. She's a purebred *mon*grel. A *mutt* – she's worth *noth*ing, at least not money-wise! Unless I could tack on all the money I've spent in saving her. 'Grand Larceny' is a *joke!*"

"Well then, we have you for Breaking and Entering. That's still a felony, and that's also extraditable. You're going to face the consequences of your actions, believe me, lady."

"Sir, in all due respect, and if I can remind you – I *broke* nothing and I *entered* nothing. I 'jimmied and opened' – and then relocked his silly little lock so that no-one could take anything that actually belonged to *Ricardo*. All I did was reclaim the puppy that this man stole from us." I again omitted the point of wiping the lock clean. Some things were better left unsaid. "But I could have been real vindictive," I added. "I could have trashed his place, painted graffiti on the side of his trailer… Hell, I could have been *really* vindictive and burned it down! But I didn't do any of that. *All* I did was get my dog back."

Again, he wasn't impressed. I'd broken the law. He liked Ricardo. Black was black and white was white; they were no shades of gray in this man's mind. I bet he'd be hell to live with as a wife. We were going nowhere but in circles, and these were getting tied up in knots, and fast. This call was becoming pointless; I was very much wishing I hadn't answered it; sleep was much more important. But the coffee was good. I took another sip.

"In any case, I need to file my report. I've got your name and telephone number. Please verify your address." I did. "Okay, now I'll need your social security number…"

"No sir, I don't think so. In this electronic day and age, I wouldn't give that out to my grandmother – if she were alive." I paused, "Again, in all due respect."

"Uh huh," the deputy responded, "Then your drivers license number."

"Just a moment, please." I went to my purse and checked for the license in my wallet. My heart skipped a beat; it wasn't there. I closed my eyes and asked myself, *okay, where could it be, if* not *here?* My memory raced back over the last day. *Of course!* It was in one of the zippered pockets of my travel vest, as the airports had clamored for it constantly. I returned to the phone. "Deputy Isabella, hold on for just a moment while I locate it. It's not in my purse, because of the travel yesterday. I have to find my travel fishing vest – it's in one of the pockets in there."

"Your *fish*ing vest?" He inquired dubiously. And then, "Alright, I'll hold."

Okay, where did I take that *off last night?* I looked around the room at the luggage and boxes. There was no sign of it. I went into our bedroom and glanced around. Nothing. I went back to the phone. "Sorry to keep you holding but I can't locate the thing. May I call you back later with that information?"

"Can't find it, huh? Okay. First you won't give me your social security number, and now you won't give me this one. Pretty evasive. Well, we know you're home. We have your address. You'll be hearing from us, Ms.

Giannini, just hang tight." And he hung up.

Great. That went *great*. I hung up the phone from my end and rested my forehead on the wall. *Now what? I'd have to find someone in the Sheriff's office out there that liked dogs, that's what. Someone that might understand why I did what I did. Oh well, time to pull a Scarlett and think about this another time; I had a slew of things to unpack and a life to get on with. Kokopelli needed to be walked and further acclimated to our farm...I had clients to call. There were plenty of things to do to take my mind off this for a while.*

The doorbell rang, starting me from my thoughts. Oh boy... I had a green mask on my face from the night before; my hair hadn't been brushed at all; I probably wore a harried look. If I answered the door I'd be a fright, like something out of *Halloween*. Then I heard a female voice calling me, "Laura! I know you're home – I see your car! Come to the door..." Who could this be? I peeked out the front window and saw a small pickup truck that I didn't recognize. Curiosity overcame vanity and I walked on through the living room in my robe. I opened the front door a bit and peered around it. My friend Sandy stood there, looking all put together and polished for the day, ready for anything. *Okay, I hoped she was...* I opened the door wider, "Good morning, Sandy, I'm sorry I'm such a mess; I've been on a trip and just got in late last night. I've been on the phone and haven't – as you see – even brushed my hair. But come on in. What the heh. I hope you like green."

Sandy was standing there with a big smile on her lively face. In her rich and deep smoker's voice, and with her New Jersey accent, she said, "It's one of my favorite colors. *Good* morning, Laura! I've come to visit for just a little while. I haven't seen you in so long, and since I've got a job just down the road, I thought I'd stop by and see how you were. Everything okay?" She asked pointedly. *Hmm? What did she know that I didn't know she knew...?* Sandy was an area pet-sitter and dog-walker, and a very good one at that. She was energetic and conscientious, loved animals totally, and was as honest as the day was long. I enjoyed her company and loved that voice and her constant chatter.

"Listen, Sandy, let me pour you a fresh cup of coffee, and I'll go and get some clothes on and get fixed up a little. Wash this stuff off my face. I'm feeling self-conscious, here. Is decaf okay? Or I can make you some high-test?"

"Laura, don't go to any trouble for me, hon. You go get dressed. I just wanted to see how you were doing."

"Sure you don't want a cup? How 'bout some hot tea then? We have a ton of different kinds – you name it and I'll bet we have it. We could host the Boston Tea Party."

"No, no – you go on and get dressed. I'll wait for you." Kokopelli had been downstairs checking out the cats. She came charging up the steps, delirious with the sights and scents of our home. There was *so much* to do here! So *much* going on!

"Oh!" Sandy exclaimed, "Who's *this* cute thing? Where'd you get *her*, Laura?"

"Ohhh, Sandy, but *that's* a long story. Her name is 'Kokopelli,' and this lovable little mutt is pure trouble. That's why I was just on the phone. In fact, that's what my trip was all about. Do you have about an hour?" I smiled down at the exuberant puppy, who was squirming in delight under Sandy's playful touch.

"I have lots of time, kiddo. You go get dressed; we'll bond. When you come back, you can pour me that cup of coffee and we'll talk about your story."

I left the two girls romping around in our living room while I slipped into the bedroom to become presentable. I put on a pair of jeans and a Taos tee shirt, as it was late November, but still not cold. Was this global warming in action? I went into the bathroom and washed the mask off my face, brushed my hair and fixed up a little. I then went into the kitchen, while Sandy and Pelli played in the other room, and poured two steaming cups of Fair-Trade Sumatra from Not The Same Old Grind, local and enlightened, in our Lighthouse mugs. It'd be good to share this story with someone here in the east – someone that would understand why I went to these lengths to bring this 'worthless' stray back home. Sandy was a Godsend after that phone call with the by-the-book, tough-guy deputy. She was a breath of fresh air breezing in to soothe my weary soul.

"Sandy, let's take our coffees outside just a minute, so Pelli can do her stuff. You can meet Trey – I don't think you've met him yet. After Lakota died I did a rebound-thing and adopted him from the Orange shelter, back in late July. We haven't been sorry for a minute. He's a big old goof-ball, a sweetheart of a dog – come see; you'll adore him."

Trey didn't let me down. He met us at the back door, wagging his huge body and tail simultaneously, as only he can do, joyfully happy that we'd come down just to see him. Sandy fell for Trey immediately, even for his mug. She thought he was charming. He and Pelli romped around the back yard, after she had done her business. It was exactly as I'd envisioned the two of them playing from the bay window of my studio, back in early November. I stood there with an eerie sense of déjà vu' watching them, barely hearing what Sandy was saying. My visions had completely turned to reality.

After the two romped a bit – Kokopelli totally smitten with her huge and gentle new friend – and she did her business, Sandy and I returned inside with Pelli. I topped off our java and we went into the living room, moving aside some of the luggage, making room to sit. "This is *killer* coffee, Laura. What is it?" Sandy asked me now that we had relaxed, ready to visit.

I told her it was the Sumatra decaf and mentioned that it was Fair Trade stock, organic and shadegrown in Indonesia; Sandy knew about this effort to support the small farmer and was pleased that I did. She said that she'd head on up to Orange to get some later that day.

Dear Sandy, energetic, petite, feisty, opinionated, dark-haired Sandy, sat and listened to me tell her the 'Kokopelli story.' She wanted *all* of the details. After I had finished, she sat back and said, "Wow! But Laura, I've got to tell you something. I have a confession," she said in her throaty Jersey-accented voice. "Pete told Steve a little of the story at work, and Steve told me. So I knew a little something before dropping in. That said, however, I want you to know that Steve and I are behind you 120%. I think what you did for that puppy was above and beyond… And I want you to know that if there is *any*thing I, or we, can do to help you with this mess, you just let me know." She looked at me intensely, as if to drive home the point. "I mean that now. *Any*thing. For example," she continued – it was Sandy's turn to talk – "if you need to have that puppy disappear for a while, we can do that. I'll find a safe place for her, and I'll see that her training is continued. If these lawmen threaten on taking her back, you may just have to 'lose' her…" She gave me a little conspiring smile. How I loved this woman.

"Sandy, you're a true friend and a real sweetheart. I honestly don't know if it'll all go that far – and I *cer*tainly hope it won't – but if it does, I sure will keep that offer in mind." I smiled and took her hand and squeezed. Pelli came to me with her knotted up sock toy and nosed our hands. I smiled down at my pup and Sandy laughed. "Do you know, Sandy, that this little dog knows the difference between *this* sock that I've given her as a toy, and all the dirty, smelly ones the kids leave around their rooms. She leaves them alone and brings this for us to have her play. I think that's phenomenal."

Sandy laughed again. "Yeah. Shows me she's real smart. I wouldn't want to play with the smelly, used socks, either." She took the offered 'play' sock and pulled. Kokopelli immediately rocked back and dug in, tugging with all her weight, quietly, intensely.

"That's another strange thing about her – she doesn't make any noise when she pulls. She just gets this absolutely determined look on her face and lays into it, totally focused. It's no wonder she was able to survive as she did in the wilds. It's that determination."

"She's one smart pup, alright. And she's going to be a beautiful dog, Laura. You're real lucky to have each other." She looked over from the tug of war and smiled again. "Now, I mean what I said. We're ready to help you keep this puppy any way we can, girlfriend."

"Sandy, I have no doubt in the world. And I appreciate it no end. Now let's talk of something else. Here, let me show you some of the gifts I brought back from Santa Fe. *And* I have something for you and Steve."

I warmed up our coffees, showed Sandy the haul and gave her a chili ristra. In opening the larger of the two 'UPS' boxes to show her the tee shirts, mobiles from India and Spanish goat skull, my heart sank. As I unpacked the skull from its surroundings, I found that the nasal bones had not been well supported in Rita's repacking and had snapped off in transit. They lay, broken, in the bottom of the box. *Damnit.* I groaned. "What's wrong, Laura?" Sandy asked me, kneeling beside the box on the floor.

"The goat skull, Sandy – I had originally packed it ever-so-carefully to support its delicate nasal bones, but the airlines insisted on looking through the entire box – and then would not let me touch it to repack. Bombs, and all." I let out a deep breath. "The bones broke off, which distorts the whole balance of this little skull. I know that sounds trivial, but from an artist's perspective…" I let my voice trail.

"You want the balance. I know." She finished. "Steve's forever complaining about baggage checks these days. It's hell on travelers. Makes you want to take a bus or Amtrak. I'm sorry, hon." Sandy told me sincerely.

I shook my head and grimaced. "Oh *well*. What can you do? Use Crazy Glue? I guess I could contact Delta. But they've got so many headaches, themselves, now. And actually, so do I. Oh *well*…" I rolled my eyes and closed the subject.

Sandy stayed a while longer, visiting and laughing, before heading on to find her Sumatra and get on with her mid-day dog walking. I gave her a bear hug for her support and belief in our efforts. She left with a big smile, and called to me, "Remember what I said…" as she climbed into her small pickup to leave.

After Sandy went on her way I continued unpacking, adding my laundry to the inevitable and endless laundries from home. Today was gorgeous – I could run a load or two and hang it/them outside to dry in the breezes, on our clothesline down in the backyard. I much preferred this to the clothes dryer.

For the rest of the afternoon I stayed domestic, playing with Pelli or letting her out to play with Trey, and calling clients in between to let them know I was back from my mission. In the process of organizing from the return, I found my vest under a suitcase from the night before and sure enough, there in one of the lower zippered pockets was my driver's license. Deputy Isabella hadn't believed that I had misplaced it; he had thought 'my story' was just a crock to continue giving him trouble. No matter what my intentions with this man, we never seemed to be able to meet in the middle. Our chemistry simply lacked karma.

Later I decided to try calling the Coconino County Sheriff's Office. Debbie had mentioned a Sergeant Coffey last week. She said that he'd been on vacation, but that if he had been there, he'd have cut to the chase immediately and probably not fooled around with Ricardo and any elusive behavior on his part. I could only hope that this man would be a little more understanding.  Since I had no idea of who else to call, I rang up the Coconino Sheriff's 800# and spoke with dispatch. This person told me that Sergeant Coffey wasn't yet on duty but he'd have him call me when he came in. I had to remember that Arizona was two hours behind us. 4:30 here was 2:30 there.

After leaving this message I tried to get through to John Slate, in Phoenix. Finally the call started through to his office but was cut off in transfer, as it had been twice earlier. Another attempt had it ringing through once more when an incoming call came in from Arizona. I switched over, hoping this would be Sergeant Coffey. It was. He seemed very nice, but only vaguely aware of the case. The man stood up for his deputies, telling me that they were simply doing their duties to the letter of the law, as was and should be expected. I admired that in him. I tried and tried to tell him my end of the story, and *finally*, after much admonishment, he listened.

He said, "So you're out here on your 25th Anniversary and find the pup. Uh huh. And you're torn between keeping her and your vacation – I understand. Go on." He lets me tell him all about it, something I sorely need to do. All the while I'm thinking, *he's the law, he's a good guy, he'll understand that this puppy was stolen from us and why I did what I did.* And *he* was probably taking notes, thinking; *"Geesh, what a sucker she is!"*

I found out that indeed, the good Sergeant was a dog lover, so I even confided to him the Lakota-connection, and the ensuing emotional level of attachment, and he seemed to understand this, eventually comparing it to a child-custody case. Well, damnit, one does *not* leave their child in someone's care, to later come back to claim her and find that the caregiver has "gotten attached." All hell would break loose! Then whose side would the law be on? But this was a puppy, only a silly starving little puppy that no one wanted and now, because of her, the world had gone mad – truly Kokopelli's mischief at work.

And as I'm explaining all of this to the patient lawman out west, Pete walks in the door, in his suit and tie, with his briefcase – my businessman of a husband – and realizes who it is that I'm talking to, and panics. "Laura! Stop *talk*ing to the law! These guys are *not* your friends! You can't be telling them everything you did!"

I covered the mouthpiece and told him, "Hush – this man is *fine*, he's listening, he's being really very understanding. *Hush.* He's going to help us." And Pete just rolled his eyes, saying I was very naïve. They are the law and I'm on their shit list. Be careful…

I don't know how much Sergeant Coffey heard of this conversation, but he was telling me that I needed to send them as much proof as possible that she really was ours. I told him about the photo album that I'd accidentally left in Deputy Dick's office, and how these showed our finding her in Monument Valley. They showed us on the rim of the Grand Canyon, when we had originally been trying to find her a home – before we had gotten so attached. There was a photograph of Lakota in it, which was good, as it could verify my reincarnation-connection. And there were photos of Pete and the kids and me from our trip last year. I don't know what this proved… But they were there. Maybe I truly was a mother of three teenagers and not merely a fugitive in the state of Arizona?

Sergeant Coffey said they would keep this photo album for now as both evidence and a record of ownership of the puppy. He went on to suggest that both Pete and I write down witness statements, telling exactly how we had come about finding this dog and how Ricardo had come to have her in his custody. He said to be detailed and factual. No problems there. He wanted them notarized – again no problems, except that this was so close to Thanksgiving it might be hard to find a notary over the holidays. He told me to just get them written and either mailed or faxed to him as soon as we could. "Oh," he added, "if you can provide us with any telephone records of your conversations with Ricardo from Chinle, that would go a long way to help support your case." I told him of the problems that we'd had with our long distance fiasco, but that I'd double-check the records and see if they would be helpful. It turned out that our long-distance service had kicked in *that* day, the crucial day, and we had a nice itemized record of every call we had made to both Ricardo and to the vet's office in Flagstaff, when we'd made the appointment for her health check, and again, when we had to call to cancel. Sergeant Coffey tried to be very helpful that evening, even with PeterWop breathing down my neck and scowling, after he'd changed into a flannel shirt and blue jeans and grabbed a beer. I kept waving him off, telling him I was handling this just fine. Go away.

So here we end the call, two days before Thanksgiving, a holiday that will *certainly* have a new meaning for us this year, as I am not spending it alone and in jail out west – and I'm feeling all warm and fuzzy inside because I'm thinking I've got an ally in the Coconino Sheriff's Department – someone who has taken the time to listen and is trying to understand. Lord, I *am* naïve. At least it was rose-colored over the holidays... I never did get through to John Slate, who would have reminded me that I had broken the law and pissed these boys off royally, and they truly were *not* my friends – as Pete would later so succinctly drive home. After the holidays I reached Sergeant Coffey to talk with him about a couple of questions concerning the witness statements and he was much chillier on the phone. Apparently he hadn't realized that I had the puppy in Virginia. Now *he* is miffed. What did he think I was *talk*ing about, then?... That I had come all that distance to get her and gotten in trouble with the law – and *not* come home with her? I certainly thought he had known.

Sergeant Coffey tells me that he's turning "the case" over to his deputies, namely Deputy Isbel. *Isbel?* Yes, it's not "Isabella" and never was, he tells me... *Great* – insult to injury here – no wonder the man doesn't like me; he thought I was intentionally feminizing his name. This is not something you want to do to an Hispanic man. This, and not returning the man's call from Winslow, when he thought I was in Williams... *And* now my refusing to give him my social security number and then not being able to find my driver's license number... This relationship was doomed from the get-go. The chain of events made Deputy Dick the 'good cop' and Deputy Isbel the 'bad cop,' if I wanted to make this a black and white dynamic in my mind. But really, all in all, this was the simply the way this man did his job. Sometimes chemistry simply clashed. Case in point.

(Thoughts after this conversation, sometime later.) Okay, it's 4:00 in the afternoon and I'm sitting here in Blackstone's Coffee Shop, in Charlottesville, where at various times I've recapped a good amount of my early homecoming conversations with the law since my return home. I've got to get on with the rest of my life and all my other responsibilities. This little 'predicament' has taken up way too much of my time... But first I want to get something very straight here.

Deputy Isbel has his dander up thinking I'm perhaps looking down on Ricardo because he's Hispanic and lives in a trailer park. Deputy Isbel, perhaps this segment is for you. First of all, I am not a racist and I am not prejudiced; I hold nothing against Hispanics. Many live here in Charlottesville now, and several families have opened fine Mexican Restaurants, where we eat all the time. They are industrious workers and some are friends. When we entrusted Dingo to Ricardo we knew he was Hispanic and that he lived in a trailer. He told us that he had a yard and that the puppy would be in it, and that he knew how to take care of puppies. What I did not know at the time, and only came to find out later, in bits and pieces, was 1) that Ricardo smoked. Then he wouldn't have had the pup at all, because I do have "a thing" about 2nd-hand cigarette smoke. So shoot me. 2) I had no idea that she would be left in this trailer most hours of the day while he worked – and on many of his days off. The magic of having a young pup seemed to have worn off... (I'm speculating here, but he did leave her for 8 hours or more inside on the particular day I retrieved her, and this was his day off. Now I'm thinking that it was overnight, since he didn't even report 'the crime' until the next morning...) 3) That he would not take the time to train her properly, and I realize this statement is, by nature, qualified. But, as mentioned, when I rescued her she was wild, confused, desperately in need of attention and had no manners, whatsoever. Not to mention that she was totally not even housebroken! And 4) Perhaps, most importantly, I did not know that we could not count on Ricardo's word. He lied to us about "babysitting" the puppy (I now believe that he had no intention of returning her from the get-go) and he lied to us about having her spayed. As previously mentioned he said, and I quote: "What pretty puppies she'll make with her golden coat." He probably planned to sell them. This particular character flaw is now why the rest of this story unfolds as it does...

All of this has nothing to do with Ricardo's being Hispanic, Deputy Isbel. He could be Caucasian, an African-American, an American Indian; he could be of Japanese, Australian or of European descent. It is his backing out of his word – and the way he has treated this puppy that he so willfully refused to return to us – that has me up in arms. Let me ask you, should I distrust all African American men because of my sister's attack? Should I distrust all Caucasian men because of George's murder? Of course not. As Dr. Martin Luther King, Jr., said so succinctly, "Let us not judge a man by the color of his skin, but by the content of his character." It is the man, Deputy, not the race or nationality.

So yes, this is complicated. I'm sitting here writing my hand off, trying to relive it as it's happened, trying to make sense of it all. Still, I'm feeling a calm about it, that all will work itself out. Pete thinks that the Prosecuting Attorney in Coconino County will try to "Plea Bargain" the case down to a lesser charge, or drop it altogether, if I only return Kokopelli to Ricardo. Okay then, what's the point of the time, the trouble, my conviction (in potentially more ways than one... Read the definition in the dictionary...) – all of it – if I have to return her to Ricardo's trailer for a sentence of 24/7 inside? I dig in and say, "No way will I do this," to this man I've known for over 25 years telling me, "Laura, you have children and me to put first. You can't let your love of this puppy – no matter how strong – put you in prison. And believe me, you could go there." What a conundrum. But still, God, I hold out hope. All of this can't have happened just to return her to a life of confinement inside Ricardo's trailer, waiting for him to come home from work.

THIRTY-EIGHT

Thanksgiving in the State of Chaos

"For a good cause, wrongdoing may be virtuous."
(Out of five, this was my fortune cookie …)

After the long conversation with Sergeant Coffey, feeling understood and supported by this high-ranking official out west, Pete and I started writing our witness statements. I had heard of them, but had certainly never written one. The Wop and I figured that they simply wanted the entire story, in our own words – not each other's. Because it was a long weekend, we had time to steal away for snatches of time here and there to write.

Also, because it was a holiday weekend heading into winter, I decided it was an ideal time to build our canine's a new doghouse – one that would fit all the dogs snuggled up inside. We had built one years ago, solid and insulated, for Ruffian Tuff Stuff. Although the structure was still around – renailed and repainted several times – it was much too small for Trey, and would certainly never accommodate three.

I had been thinking of working on this new doghouse as Pelli and I flew over all those midwestern states that look like an aerial patchwork quilt. It should be large and roomy, with a raised and insulated floor to keep it dry and watertight. It should also be insulated in the walls and the roof. We could cover the sides with T1-11 and shingle the roof with leftovers from our storage shed. We could stain it the adobe color of our house. It should be built to last and look nice, as well, in our back yard. And its slanted roof should jut out in front enough to provide a protective overhang, in case we ever saw rain again.

I had planned to measure Trey, and eyeball the other two, to make sure it would be sizeable without becoming too massive. Pete had received the news of our Thanksgiving "honey-do" project rather well. Indeed, we love our projects and have built many things together over the years, like Ruffian's doghouse, bookshelves (easy), and all the fencing that enclosed the horses here at Edelweiss. Our projects became larger, as we became more proficient, to include our bookshelf headboard, a TV stand, and a coffee table. We went from furniture to a barn, built around sturdy telephone pole supports, with three inside stalls and a tack room and eventually a front roofline/aisle, with corrals off of this.

I would come up with an idea, sketch out a design, approach Pete and together we would figure out how to get there from here. He'd do the grunt work and I became his lovely assistant and gofer'. We always had projects going... garden gates; a picnic table; porch additions; ... and then in '98 we bought plans at Lowe's for a storage shed on the property. We decided to save about a thousand dollars in labor and build it ourselves – to see if we could. We could, and we did. As we started and because all of our land slopes downhill, I suggested to the Wop that we drop it in the middle, and add that downhill space *in*side the building, instead of having it be lost to airspace beneath. He thought I was nuts (once again), but the more he thought about it, the more he liked the idea. I found him drawing out the plans and refiguring our supplies and, sure enough, we dropped the shed's floor space in the middle. We're the only split-level storage shed in the neighborhood. And to add to that idea, never being able to leave well enough alone, I suggested we continue the roofline to a hip roof pasture side and add extra space, supported by outside 4x4s. This idea he liked immediately, as it gave us protected tractor and lawnmower storage, divided in the middle underneath, as the ground slopes away, to add a loafing shed for the horses in summer and a place to protect a round bale of hay in winter. And so our plans evolved. (This is the shed for which the running horse weather van was destined.)

So, anyhoo. An insulated doghouse, to be built in a 4-day time span, was a piece of cake. We had a project – a goal to work on together. We could have the kiddos help and learn the craft (a nice thought). So we made our plans, figured the supplies and costs, and planned to take our truck to Lowe's the next day to get the goods, as well as groceries for Thanksgiving Day dinner.

Pete and I talked about our Thanksgiving meal. "Shall we go the whole nine yards with a full turkey dinner on Thursday?" He asked, as we made our doghouse list.

"It's just our family this year, Pete. And I'm boycotting factory-farmed turkey. I read a letter-to-the-editor in *The Daily Progress* last year that said these huge poultry farms electrocute the birds, and then – while in shock, while the bird is still alive – chainsaw off their heads. I'm not sure how much of it is exactly true, but I keep reading horror stories about these huge meat and poultry farms and my conscience says 'no way'."

"At least they don't chainsaw off the heads while the bird is alert." Pete responded, trying to make me somehow feel better about the practice. "What about just a turkey breast, then?"

I looked at him closely. "Did you not hear what I just said? Doesn't that make you sick to your stomach? Don't you think the turkey is *still* involved? And as for that part about chainsawing the head off while alert, I can just see these men running around a huge turkey pen, birds running amuck, feathers flying and the chainsaw all fired up – and their adrenaline, too – saying, 'Come here, *gobble, gobble, gobble,* let me decapitate you to feed America…!' Sure, that'd work." I gave him my best disgusted look.

"Laura, it's a Thanksgiving Day tra*dition,* damnit!"

"Traditions are made to be broken – to be changed and customized, family to family. Let's start a new one, Pete. The more I read about beef, poultry and pork production on these factory farms, the less inclined I am to want to partake in their 'product.' These are cruel, and by the nature of the animals, themselves – packed in lots and pens more tightly than nature had ever intended – dirty industries."

"Yeah, yeah, and I know how you feel about the antibiotics they use. 'Antibiotics are used in mass to treat diseased animals – and often as a preemptive, fed to all, to keep disease at bay in these crowded conditions…' " Pete mimicked me almost perfectly. *Damn, we'd been together too long.* But then he surprised me. "But I'm beginning to agree with you, Ra. There are growth hormones and antibiotics in the meat and milk. Salmonella and e-coli are stronger than ever. Now there's Mad Cow Disease… The government claims it's not in the country, but it could happen anytime, with the size of that industry…"

"See. It's pretty disgusting, really. Let's start a new tradition, okay? We have salmon at Christmas, how about salmon at Thanksgiving? I mean, the wonderful ways you cook it, PeterWop… It'd be scrumptious."

Pete rolled his eyes at me, but he happens to also love salmon – and he cooks it like a gourmet chef. He strongly considered the idea. "Okay… I think one of the grocery stores may be having a sale this week. I'll check the papers..." And therein lies the magic of new traditions that will etch the memories that we take from home. For our family, a feast centered around fish may well become what is remembered. And eventually the feast may become centered entirely on vegetables, if this bioengineering – and some of the other horrors I've read now about farm-raised salmon – mucks around too much with the salmon industry...

Thanksgiving morning we finally had time to sit down together, relax, and to catch up on news in papers held from the weekend of my return. We cozied up together on the futon in our Southwest sunroom, pretended it was cold outside and lit a fire in the fireplace, had a thermos of high-test and one of decaf beside us, a pot of hot tea for the kiddos, and the papers spread out around us. Jared sat at the piano, noodling around on some new ideas. The girls were nowhere to be seen. Kokopelli lay at my feet, atypically quiet.

Headlines from *The Albuquerque Journal*, I'd saved from Saturday morning, Nov. 17th, read: **Taliban, al-Qaida reeling:** Reports say leaders are abandoning Kandahar, bin Laden aide *[Mohammed Atef]* killed. **Letter to Senator** [Patrick Leahy] **may contain anthrax. Floods kill at least 6 in Texas; more storms forecast:** *Some areas report over a foot of rain.* **Atlanta Airport evacuated:** *Man running late bolts past security.* **Prehistoric crocodile unearthed:** *University of Chicago paleontologist Paul Sereno discovered the fossil of the 110-million-year-old, 40-foot, bus-size croc last year in Niger, Africa.* **Leno Thanksgiving show for the troops:** *Leno's "Tonight Show" will present a special Thanksgiving Day broadcast for U.S. Servicemen and women around the world via Armed Forces Radio and Television Service.*

From the Sunday, Nov. 18th *Santa Fe New Mexican*: **Diluting New Mexico mining law:** *Critics contend the proposal for shutting down the Chino Mine would let Phelps Dodge avoid millions in remediation expense while defiling pure water.* **Terror Dragnet sweeps up suspects in U.S.**

From *USA Today*, Monday, Nov. 19th: **Afghans look past Taliban:** *New government; War called far from over, but talks are on fast track.* **Some foreign household workers face enslavement:** *There is a new face of slavery in America, one that's often overlooked because victims are hidden in a modern-day version of a sweatshop: the private home.* **Pentagon builds case on Iraq:** *Sept.11 link not vital for action.* **Leahy letter could yield crucial clues:** *Investigators pursue theory sender of anthrax from U.S.* And, in the small print from **Nationline** of this paper: **Palm Beach auctions off voting machines:** *Collectors logged onto an Internet auction to grab 519 of Palm Beach County's voting machines that were at the heart of the 2000 presidential election con-*

troversy in Florida … News from *USA Today* continued: **U.S., U.N. plan reconstruction of Afghanistan:** *Officials estimate cost in billions.* **New U.S. envoy will try to propel Israeli-Palestinian talks. Firms can't build bomb detectors fast enough:** *As many as 2,000 needed for airports by December 2002.* **We're off to see a wizard:** *'Potter'* [Harry Potter and the Sorcerer's Stone] *pulls in a record $93.5M for opening take.*

And a few headlines from Charlottesville's *Daily Progress*: **Poll: Americans would use smallpox vaccine. Bioterrorism expert: Mailer of anthrax 'domestic:'** *The targets of the letters and the American-developed strain of anthrax used in the letters point to someone inside our borders, said Judith Miller, co-author of "Germs: Biological Weapons and America's Secret War."*

From Tuesday's *Daily Progress*: **Alliance looks to overrun last Taliban hold. Holiday travel expected to drop nationwide. Rumsfeld: Money may help to root out bin Laden.** *The Boston Globe* columnist writer, Ellen Goodman, wrote a wonderful article entitled: **Oh, for a Thanksgiving like last year's,** wistfully reminiscing for a return of innocence in America. And so it went. After we caught up with papers through Tuesday, we had had enough news of current events. We put the rest away to read another day and returned to our day of blessings for this year.

The first Thanksgiving of my return from the west, with the wanted puppy in tow, was particularly joyful. With all of us working together in the kitchen, we made a filet of Atlantic salmon with crusted pecans, a sweet potato casserole, asparagus, and a huge salad. We had crusty warm rolls and the typical pumpkin and apple pies on hand for afterwards. We gave the kiddos each a small glass of Barboursville Vineyards Chardonnay, to toast our plethora of blessings, and we had a merry time toasting Pelli's and my return to the farm. Pete's brother, Bob, had called to let us know that he and his girls were in town for the weekend and would spend Thanksgiving Day with Jean and Allan. Bob's wife, Karen, had had to stay in Ohio to work the weekend. But Friday he and the girls would like to come and visit. We told him of our pet project (couldn't resist) and Bob, ever ready to lend a hand, said he'd like to come out and help.

We now had the supplies for the doghouse on the back of the truck. Mid-afternoon on Thursday we began our project. PeterWop and I set up a workspace in the backyard, outside the dogs' fenced-in area, and worked while they watched. Pelli was beside herself, cavorting with Trey one minute and then over by the fence to watch us, the next. I'd talk to her or them and go visit when not needed. As expected, she was blending right in and *very* happy to have companionship. And big ole' Trey-Meister was in love.

By evening we had the basic framework built. We would still need to box it all together, adding the insulation, T1-11, and shingles over the next couple of days – but we had the beginnings of a solid structure that would last for years. I bet when Trey came to us from the shelter, that rainy summer's night back in late July, he never for a minute expected a custom-built – and insulated, no less – doghouse. He was perfectly satisfied to simply have a home and a family to love him, and for him to love and protect, in return.

I think the downpour that evening of Trey's arrival might have been our last serious rainfall; that was four months ago. We had gone back into serious drought again, but as Murphy would have it – the resident mischief-maker of the Universe – it rained. Because we chose an outdoor project over a holiday weekend, he would become playful. And so on Thanksgiving Day's afternoon, a light rain began. Just enough for us to have to refigure our plans and put up a makeshift shelter, to be sure we didn't electrocute ourselves with power tools while working in the damp. We needed rain so desperately we couldn't complain.

Friday entered as a clear and warm Indian summer's day, but as the day progressed the skies began to cloud again. When Bob, 'Becca and Brenda arrived to visit, it had begun to rain again lightly. We joked that they must have brought this with them yesterday from Ohio, as we didn't have any of that wet stuff around here.

Bob came striding down the driveway, his handsome rugged face lit with a big smile. He, like Pete, had once had cinnamon brown hair that somehow had darkened into a dark walnut color with age and was now streaked with plenty of gray highlights. Unlike Pete, he was clean-shaven. Bob was the largest of the five Gianniny boys, the tallest, and most big-boned. And he was a strict meat-and-potatoes kind of guy, which had caught up with him over the years. He had picked up weight that his doctor and his family would rather he lose, as he had had some red-alerts with his heart. Being a year and a half younger than Pete, this did not bode well; the man was only in his mid-forties. Bob, however, oozed goodwill and love of his family – immediate and extended. He radiated warmth and friendliness in his manner, and, when not reflective, was jovial and quick to crack a joke or see the bright side of a situation.

'Becca was tall and big-boned, like her dad. She was a year younger than Skye, with a mane full of long glossy brown hair, rosy cheeks, and the Italian brown eyes. 'Becca was eager to see Skye and so, after a hearty greeting to her aunt and uncle, she was off to inside to locate her cousin and catch up on boys and school gossip.

Little Brenda, six months younger than Natalie, was tiny and energetic, with dark shoulder-length hair, snapping lively dark eyes and a kitten-like-hold-me quality about her. She adored Natalie and, after our perfunctory hugs, ran off to find her young cousin. Soon the two spilled out of the house, gangly young fillies set to explore the farm: see the new puppy and play with the dogs, check out the love doves and Whiskey Cat, and go find Holly to ride for a while. Still tomboys, the outside of our farm proved *so* much more enticing than in, despite the rain.

Pete, Bob, and I grinned and waved them off. They looked like gambling young pups, legs still too long, bodies not quite caught up. It amazed me to see the amount of food they could eat and still remain svelte. Their metabolisms were cranked on high 24/7.

"Well, looks like we'll need to set up some rain protection," said Bob, looking up at the drizzling sky. The foreman of many a fire crew in his younger years, Bob was comfortable with assessing a situation and taking control. "Pete, you gotta' tarp?"

"Yep. I've got a tarp and some bungees. Used them yesterday to set up a shelter. I was thinking of setting it up down under the deck; this seems the most natural place." He pointed.

We left our skeletal doghouse long enough to reset the tarp and bungee cords, and devise a way to hang a more permanent shelter beneath the deck to protect us from the impending rain. The sky looked as if it had no intentions of staying a polite mist. After our makeshift shelter was secure, we dragged the doghouse frame – by now substantial and heavy, built as it was with 2'x 4's – beneath.

Bob grinned when we told him the concept and how soon we'd be adding the insulation. "I don't reckon I've ever seen an insulated doghouse," he drawled, a twinkle in his merry eyes, "much less helped build one. Lucky mutts you have." He looked over at Kokopelli and Trey romping around the yard, my studio visions of a month prior now so real. "I here tell there's quite a story behind that yellow puppy..." he looked at me, the twinkle now making his whole face glow.

"Oh yeah, Bob, where'd you hear that?" I smiled and challenged him. "She's just a little stray pup out of Monument Valley."

"Not from what I here tell," He continued in his soft drawl. "The folks told us all about it yesterday over Thanksgiving dinner. From what I hear, Laura, you've gotten yourself in over your head with the law out west." He laughed. "Is this true?"

Pete and I exchanged a look and the Wop said, "Ra, you go on and explain your way out of this one; I'm just an innocent bystander." He winked at Bob, who was still grinning like an old hound dog in a butcher's shop.

"I'm *not* 'in over my head,' Bob. It's more like a little misunderstanding with the lawmen in Arizona – which I'm working on clearing up. If you heard the story right from the folks, then you *know* why I went back out after Pelli and did what I did – and would do all over again, if necessary." I looked at Pete sternly – the best defense being a good offense, and all.

He laughed, "This is *your* hot water, Razza. You're the one who's got to swim in it. Don't look at *me*." Another wink at Bob.

"Well, from what I hear, you two," Bob's voice grew a little more serious, "is that you might *really* be in trouble, Laura. If I may make a suggestion," he glanced at me, careful to not overstep, "I suggest you be utterly respectful and take this very seriously. You don't want it backfiring on you and your family." He looked at Pete, who met his gaze. Pete nodded a silent thanks to his brother; 'maybe I'd listen better to another's voice,' the look said.

"Guys, guys, *guys*. This will all be just fine. I'll handle it – I *am* handling it. Don't worry. Listen, we're wasting good daylight here over this nonsense; we'd best get back to work. We have a doghouse to finish in just over two days…" They exchanged another meaningful glance, but agreed that we were losing precious daylight, and on a dreary day, no less.

By the end of that afternoon we had the ground floor built, insulated, and boxed in. We then concentrated on the rest of the frame, adding the inner plywood walls and framed the inside roofing. Tomorrow, Saturday, we could add the insulation and cover the roof with the final ply, lay a heavy felt on top and we could then add the shingles at any time, with the leftovers from our shed roof. Once we had added insulation to the walls, and covered them with our T1-11 cutouts – and the weather dried enough – we could prime and paint our creation. And *Voila!* The dogs would then have themselves protection from the winter months ahead.

If the weather grew harsh, we could add a heavy burlap door for wind and element protection, preventing drafts in wind, sleet, and snow. An old rug on the inside – and straw atop this, if needed – would help hold in their body heat. They'd be snug and spoiled in their new canine castle. Trey would want to be writing to all his buddies back at the shelter about this cushy new life he was leading – but I'd nix that in his tracks – that would be *so* unfair to the others.

The next afternoon, we brought Trey out of the back yard to check out what we'd built so far, and see how he fit. If he didn't, we were plum out of luck, as the structure was basically done. Trey did not hesitate for a second. He proudly entered, circled, and then lay his large body down on the unstained flooring, looking like a king on a brand new throne. His pleased expression made the entire project worthwhile. He then crossed his front paws, as he does when he plans to lie there and relax awhile, and started panting happily. He wasn't going *any*where anytime soon. "Natalie," I called, "run in and get my camera, please. It's just inside the door." I had been getting photos of Pete and Bob working under the tarp, in different phases of this project.

Natalie came back and handed me the camera, "Wait a minute, Mom, before you shoot." And she scrambled to the ground and climbed in, saying, "Move over, Trey. If there's room enough for me, then there'll be room enough for the others." She was able to turn around inside, and then she, too, crossed her 'forelegs' – as Trey Meister continued to do, unphased by his new companion – and Natalie started to pant.

"Okay, Twerpy Doodle, hold that pose. Trey, look up at me!" He obliged, and I quickly took the shot. I laughed at the two hambones and took a couple more shots from different angles. Pete and Bob leaned up against the deck posts, there under the tarp, their arms crossed and grinning at the test run. "Okay, everybody – *out!* We've got to get back to work, if we're to finish this weekend."

Natalie gave a mock scowl, but then clamored out, taking Trey by the collar, and saying brightly, "Come on, boy! Let's go see what Kokopelli's doing!" He followed her cheerful voice and she put him back in with his active new friend, who greeted him with leaps and bounces and happy little yelps. The two bounded down through the yard, lost in play.

"Well, boys, that was worth every bit of work involved, wasn't it?" The smiles and satisfied looks on the brothers said yes. We continued on through Saturday, finalizing the structure. Walls and roof were in place, shingles now on. The weather had cleared; we might have gotten ¾'s of an inch of rain, all told, which was a Godsend. Too late to entice anything to grow, the moisture still brightened the world, settled the dust that had lain everywhere, and perhaps backed the forest fire potential down a notch. Tomorrow we would be able to prime the walls, let that dry, and then add the first coat of paint. Once the inside floors and walls were given a coat of waterproofing stain, we'd be pretty much done. Our canine trio would have themselves a fine shelter for all seasons.

THIRTY-NINE

Pelli's Transition to Our Animal Farm

"For the animal shall not be measured by man. In a world older and more complete than ours they moved finished and complete, gifted with extensions of the senses we have lost or never attained, living by voices we shall never hear. They are not brethren; they are not underlings; they are other nations, caught like ourselves in the net of life and time, fellow prisoners of the splendor and travail of the earth." Henry Beston, The Outermost House

Amanda

In the winter of '93, when the children were small, she had come to visit us – repeatedly – as a young pup. She was a beagle or beagle-mix that appeared one day with a tagged collar, from down the gas line that runs by our house. She was precious, her ridiculously long golden-brown ears flopping around her youthful face, as she romped with our children. I'd call the name on her collar and the owner would come and get her, and then there she would be again the next day.

After about the fourth call it was apparent that she enjoyed our home – and all the attention she received from the kids – to her own home. Once again the owner showed up. It was close to Valentine's Day and we were getting attached, so I asked him: "Listen, your dog really likes it here. And we really like her. What do you plan to do with her?"

"Oh, I'll hunt 'er when she's old 'nough, and if'n her nose is good. And then I'll breed 'er later on for more huntin' dawgs." I had a vision of this little dog covered in one litter after another, probably tied to a doghouse, since she tended to be an escape artist.

"Look, will you consider selling her to us? The kids obviously love her. What would you want for the puppy?"

"Well, let'n me think." He thought a moment. "I could take $50 bucks – that would 'bout cover 'er expenses."

What expenses? Did she have any shots? I could go to the shelter and get two *beagles for this,* with *all their shots, and a certificate for reduced spaying,* but I agreed to his $50, and told the kiddos that she was their Valentine's gift from dad and me this year. (Yeah, and I'm a sucker, so there was chocolate, too.) So Amanda, named by Rachel, our young neighbor below us, came into our lives a couple years after Lakota joined the family.

Amanda had the typical black, tan and gold markings of the beagle. And she had the inherent loving personality that rivals a lab for pure trust and loyalty. Her eyes were dark liquid chocolate, large and almond-shaped, and she had the sweetest of faces.

Amanda did indeed have a 'nose' and, once on a scent, didn't know when to let up. She would go deep into the woods, or to the gas-line, and we would hear her wild, excited baying and off she'd go! A few times it would be a day or two before she returned from her jaunt – and then she would sleep for a day, just exhausted. As soon as six months hit, she was into the vet's to be spayed, for the old timer who had owned her before swore that he was not planning "to fix her 'cause it'd ruin 'er nose." We did. It didn't. She lived for the trail. No surprise there – it was what she was born and bred for.

Amanda came to be with our family several years before Trey arrived. As Lakota was no longer a puppy, and seldomly played with her, Amanda took it upon herself to remedy that: she developed an imaginary playmate – the first and only time I have seen a dog do this. I was washing dishes one day, glanced into the back yard, and did a double take. There was our young pup, rearing and dodging and cavorting in the yard, just as if another puppy was there in the game! But there wasn't another pup in sight. I laughed aloud and watched her awhile, calling the kids to see this, all of us delighting in her antics. On several occasions we witnessed Amanda in full puppy-play, romping with her 'friend.' It was hilarious, those huge ears flopping all over the both of them, as 'they' rolled on the ground. These antics of Amanda have kept us in stitches repeatedly.

And then Amanda discovered we had canine neighbors. Her imaginary playmate vanished, as she found the real thing. Amanda began 'hanging' with a few of the local dogs, which proved to be her downfall. For, we found, the local pups had a tendency to chase cars and, although we never saw her do this, she was like a teenager hanging with the wrong crowd. One day a neighboring redneck, who drove his truck up and down the road beside our property with his Labrador in the bed, like bait, stopped his vehicle in the wake of dogs chasing him. The man got out of his truck, with a can of wasp spray that propels 30 feet, and proceeded to spray the group of dogs following him. Apparently Amanda was in the crowd with her buddies that day, looking on, when the bastard shot her full-force with the wasp spray directly into those beautiful, trusting eyes. Neighborhood friends witnessed the 'punishment' he had decided to dish out.

When she came home I saw that her eyes were on fire — red and tearing excessively; I rushed her to our vet's office, having no idea what had happened. And, because I didn't know, I couldn't tell him what we were dealing with. Not that it would have mattered, as the damage was done. Colin flushed her eyes completely and we began antibiotic drops, which helped ease her immediate discomfort, but did not prevent her from gradually becoming blind. Over the years, as I had her vetted or when her eyes became inflamed, we would check and treat them, and Colin would tell me the corneas were scarring. Yes, it was getting worse, but there was nothing any of us could do, except use the antibiotics when they flared up and be sure that her eyes stayed moist.

Frank and Claire, our dear older neighbors who had witnessed this atrocity, hadn't realized Amanda was in the group at the time. But later we put two and two together and realized that she had come home with those burned-up eyes the same day the redneck had 'taught those dogs a lesson.'

Now little Amanda is older — ten or eleven years — and is no longer charmed by the trail. She stays within the perimeters of our farm, finding favorite places to rest in the course of the day. Sometimes she prefers to be inside on hot days, with Trey; other days she snuggles with Whiskey Cat, outside. Her sight is now gone. Those once-beautiful brown eyes are now an opaque milky-blue, but they still 'look' at us adoringly, and she still lives to be loved. And to reciprocate.

Amanda has taken Ruffian's role as the matron of our little homestead, the calming influence over our menagerie. Skye bathes her and gives her extra-special attention. She is especially dear with our disabled older friend. And we have opted to keep them in the backyard, in the fenced-in area we made for Lakota, when his hearing started to go. Trey and Amanda won't have the freedom the others had to roam this countryside, but they will be safe from the few cars around here. They'll also be safe from damned fools who call themselves 'animal lovers,' with dogs in their pick-up beds, and wasp spray in their cabs. Besides, Trey's also an awfully big fellow to be roaming around and showing up uninvited in our neighbor's back yards. It's best he stay at home and romp around in ours, taking care of the place.

Heather and Emma

The agreement had been just the one kitten when Natalie turned 11 years old. Because we had spayed and neutered all of our animals, all of our lives, the children had never experienced the miracle of birth on our little farm. Natalie had been begging for her own kitten, *promising* that she would take on all of its care. So it was decided that we'd allow her one little kitten, the looks didn't matter, but the personality did. Voices for Animals, a local humane group in Charlottesville, had just the cat – fresh out of a dumpster – sweet as can be. The only catch was that this baby kitty had a sister, and I didn't have the heart to break up the two, after the traumas they had faced in their young lives. So for Natalie's 11th birthday she had been given not one, but two, scraggly, nondescript calico kittens, all gray and splotchy in color. She and the kids were thrilled, for what they lacked in looks, they more than compensated for in loving.

These sisters became "Heather," the reserved neatly bibbed and booted shyer little sister, and "Emma," fearless and in the thick of any trouble. Heather was sensitive, tentative and careful. Emma was brazen, bold and adventurous.

Emma's pale green eyes were large and round, with a nutmeg-colored blaze running between them. Half her chin was nutmeg and half was white and no matter what trouble this Kokopelli Kitty mustered up, she would turn that face upon us with this large-eyed and innocent stare and we would have to laugh. She became known as "Owl-Eyed Emma," magnet for mischief. Heather, on the other hand, with her neat white bib, belly and booted feet, remained prim and proper, living by her feline rules of Miss Manners firmly ingrained.

The ducklings turned to swans as they matured. The pair grew into two beautiful calico cats, their coats a palette of oranges and blacks, tans and nutmegs, with Heather's sparkling whites setting hers off. They stayed sweet as can be and became our inside cats, our furry feline companions. Over time, Heather became more Natalie's, and Emma, Skye's. They would sleep with the girl's, or curl on their laps during homework hours, precious feline fixtures now, so much a part of our lives.

Romeo's Whiskey Cat

We had had Heather and Emma a year when Whiskey joined our farm. Whiskey Cat came to us in April of 2000, showing up with Daylight Saving Time, for my birthday. Two gifts from God. We had needed a mouser for the farm and barn but hadn't taken the time to find an outdoor cat, after our last barn cat, Annie, had long ago died.

One morning in the garden I thought I saw an orangeish shape drift under the St. John's Wort bush. That evening, while down at the barn feeding the horses, I saw the shape again. This time I was sure. It looked like a cat — and most definitely meowed like a cat. I left the horses, followed the form and the sound, and found him under the adjoining shed, very timid, but approachable.

He seemed to be a mature cat, an unneutered tom, orange and white, with sweet tangerine eyes. Once I picked him up and assured him it was okay to hang around he was mine for keeps. And Pete's. And each of the kiddos. He had no favorites among us, and no shame, at all. He poured his love into his purrs and followed us everywhere.

In fact at first, when he realized one of 'his humans' was outside, he would start that incessant meowing of his that began to drive me just nuts. If I planned to garden, I'd have to *sneak* outside and try not to make sudden moves, hiding from the damned cat, for if he spotted me, I felt we were in the old game kids play in the pool: "Marco!"...."Polo!"... "Marco!"... "*here* I am, Whiskey – Polo!" and his radar would tune in. He would be all over me, meowing nonstop, driving me bananas. He would stop the birds from singing. We had created a feline monster.

It was Natalie who named him. (I'd wanted to call him 'Loudmouth.') She said, "No, if you can have a horse named 'Tequila Mockingbird',"('Tequila' for short) "we can have a cat named 'Whiskey'." And so our sherbet-colored feline had a name.

Over the next few weeks Whiskey settled into life at the farm, finding his place and his role. The incessantly loud 'radar-meowing' calmed down to a much more acceptable pitch, as he became more secure. But we had other reasons to believe that maybe the poor fellow was inbred – for one, he was dim-witted. Sweet as they come, but plain dumb.

One morning Natalie came inside and told me: "Mom, you won't believe this, but Whiskey *did* it again. He went under the board fence in the horse's paddock, and when his tail hit the board, he thought he was stuck. He wouldn't go any further."

"Nattie, you're kidding, right? He didn't just lower his tail a little and continue on under?"

"Nope, Mom, he didn't. He just stood there, looking at me, like I was supposed to figure it out, and I just laughed. He looked so silly."

But for all the silly and inane things that Whiskey did to convince us of his questionable I.Q. – like walking a fence-line, as any self-respecting cat would do, and then loose his balance and fall off – he managed to worm his way solidly into each of our hearts. The cat oozed love. Like Amanda, he lived for loving. Each of the animals on the farm seemed to sense this. And he trusted each of them implicitly not to hurt him. The horses would mill around in their corrals, Aristo and Tequila, on one side, SunUp and Holly, on the other. And there was Whiskey Cat down amongst them, rubbing up against their fetlocks, oblivious to danger. One or the other would reach down to sniff at him, nuzzling or blowing on him, and he would purr away, totally sure of their love for him. It was uncanny – because he believed it, they did, too. The damned cat was charmed.

Well, with the exception of a neighbor's black tomcat. Whiskey came in one morning, having tangled with the cat the night before, and I said: "*That's* it. We've decided you're part of the farm, which means sacrificing your private parts for that honor. You're going to the vet, little buddy, and you're going to get neutered. No more of these stupid catfights." And so he did – I took him in that day. He got antibiotics for his wounds, his series of feline shots, and his fine line of inbred, Mensa-potential kitties stopped there.

Now Whisky roams the farm, his hormones no longer raging, the black tomcat no longer interested in a challenge, and he can devote all his energy to loving – ironically. He is such a lover to all that Natalie walked in another day and claimed, "Mom, I've decided. 'Whiskey Cat' isn't a good enough name for him. He's such a lover, we should call him '*Romeo's* Whiskey Cat'." And so it came to pass. Our orange and white stray, with no fancy pedigree, was knighted with quite the noble name of 'Romeo's Whiskey Cat,' and it has stuck (though we still just generally call him Whiskey – or Clutz). He and we know what his full name really is...

Trey – who takes it upon himself to protect all the farm-life – thinks old Whisk is the cat's meow. If Whiskey jumps into Trey's pen the dog will follow him around, trying to get him to romp. If Whiskey lies above him on the top of the gate, Trey sits adoringly below. Natalie took a wonderful photograph in the back yard of Trey sitting expectantly under the sugar maple, looking up into the birdfeeder, in which Whiskey lay sprawled. Nattie calls it "The Food-chain."

Whiskey and Amanda have also become good buds, just quietly accepting one another. But then, if they have good manners, Amanda will accept almost anyone. These two are always hanging out together, sunning themselves, and Whiskey makes it a point to give Amanda a daily dose of good loving. Amanda stands 'watching' as Whiskey helps himself to her specialty dog food. I tell you the boy is charmed – Amanda usually protects her meals.

She came to our house and discovered the cats and was thrilled. Like Marcos and his wild animals, I don't think Pelli had ever seen a cat before; they charmed her. For Heather and Emma, however, the pleasure was not returned. Whereupon these two had owned the house, lock, stock, and barrel – allowing us human animals to coexist with them *if* we behaved – in pranced this lively intruder, intent on disturbing their peace.

Kokopelli thoroughly lived up to her Southwest namesake as mischief-maker upon homecoming. The cats intrigued and delighted her; she was quite sure that they had been placed here, in this house, for her entertainment. Here were these furry mobile toys, with the endless straight tails, that would turn and run on cue. She was fascinated at the sounds they would make when she appeared, poking her nose at them like a friendly dolphin, prepared to jump back out of harms reach with the inevitable snarl and hiss and battery of claws and paws, and then she'd be in again, sniffing, curled tail wagging in delight. Fearless of their fuss and furious reprisals, her favorite part, it seemed, was to watch them double in size before her, like feline blowfish. *How* did they *do* that?! Her inquisitive nature and endless puppy energy was determined to figure this one out, so back and back she'd go.

For bold Emma, who quickly came to find that Pelli meant no harm, this became amusement. She would egg Kokopelli on, then run and disappear, a game of hide and seek. Pelli was ecstatic. For shy Heather, however, this bundle of exuberant enthusiasm had best been left out west. To allow the cats a reprieve from Kokopelli's boundless energy, I began closing the child safety gate, that we keep at the top of the stairs, soon after Pelli's arrival. If either of the cats had enough of the 'new kid's' antics, she – or they – could take refuge downstairs.

After a while both cats came to realize that the mutt was harmless. Kokopelli and Emma soon had a new game. Pelli would discover Emma curled up on the chair beside the fireplace in the sunroom and would start nudging her to play. Emma would rise up on her haunches, balanced, and start batting at Kokopelli's head and ears, like a boxer in mid-match. Pelli might back off a minute, panting in enthusiastic play, and then she'd be back in for more punishment, deliriously happy as Emma beaned her repeatedly about the face with her paws. Emma never deliberately hurt the pup, and if she had enough, she'd jump off the chair and find cover, while Pelli, in the meantime – in typical youth's fashion – would be sidetracked by some other amusement that caught her fancy.

Our little desert pup made herself right at home here on the small farm that housed so much life. Gone were her days of scrounging for food or living through long desert nights that made the slow process of starvation just an alternative to a much more violent death.

Gone were drawn out hours cooped in a trailer, awaiting companionship. Kokopelli's days now were filled with fellowship, new discoveries, and puppy play. Her nights were safe and protected where she slept soundly by our bed. Some nights Pelli would be curled on the rug beside my side of the bed, and others on Pete's side. Some nights she couldn't decide, so she slept at the foot of the bed. We never knew where we might find her soft golden body curled and at rest, but we knew she would be close, usually a knotted up sock at her side.

Each morning, after Pete was up and off to work and the kiddos were packed and off to school, I would make my decaf and, while it brewed, take Kokopelli out for her morning jaunt with Trey. After this the two of us would return to the kitchen for our ten minutes of 'training time.' Such a quick study, within a week 'sit,' 'down,' and 'stay' were firmly nailed. Of course we had started all of this while on the lam out west, and she had learned the basics well in that week. But this second week she mastered them, with the allure of Pete's pancakes as her reward.

Now, you have to understand that pancakes have long been a tradition in my husbands' family. Religiously, Tuesday and Thursday mornings were pancake days, and Saturday mornings were waffle days. Pete learned to cook them as a young boy. As a middle-aged man – albeit, with a young boys heart – he still finds comfort in Tuesday and Thursday mornings as pancake days and Saturday mornings for waffles, though oft times the waffles might be passed by with a busy agenda. But this new generation of kiddos had been raised on that culinary premise.

The pancakes, themselves, can vary. We usually start with a whole-wheat, or sometimes buckwheat, batter, made from scratch. Added to that can be any number of ingredients as ripe bananas and pecans, or blueberries, either fresh from our garden in June, or frozen and served year round. With blackberry bushes now on the perimeters of our fields, we might do the same with these. Or add strawberries, or small chunks of fresh peaches and cinnamon… you get the idea. I found a recipe for corncakes, from Betty Crocker's timeless cookbook, given to us by Mary as a Christmas gift. One cuts the whole-wheat flour in half and adds cornmeal. I add a can of creamed corn and then additional solids to compensate for the additional moisture. These make thin, crepe-like melt-in-your-mouth delights that guarantee the kiddos a hearty breakfast to start their days.

I will always remember a comment from Jared when he was a young tyke. He'd seen his father make pancakes from scratch all of his life. Well, Pete was off on one of his many business trips and I made my famous corncakes. Jared, all of maybe eight years old, sat at the breakfast table, chowing down on any number of these thin tasty tidbits. As I gave him more, he looked up at me and gushed, "Mom, these are even better than Dad's!" Then, feeling disloyal to his absent father, quickly added, "But *he* doesn't need to use a cookbook."

Well, it was Kokopelli's luck that the first full day of her arrival was *"Great A, Little a, it's Pancake Day"* (remembered from a Mother Hubbard's nursery rhyme we used to read to the kids). Pete had made whole-wheat batter and, after Sandy left, I cooked the remaining batter into fresh warm golden brown banana nut pancakes. For Pelli I made them plain. She was beside me in the kitchen as the batter hit the griddle in sizzling hisses, her engaged nose in the air and her toenails clicking around the kitchen floor. *Ectasy!*

I had given her puppy chow; it was there on the floor, right beside her water. She didn't *want* her puppy chow — she wanted whatever this incredible scent was, wafting down from above. I put three hotcakes on my plate, putting two aside to cool for Pelli while I ate. I added syrup to my stack, poured a milk and more coffee and carried it all on a tray to the sunroom to eat. Kokopelli followed at my heels, dancing in anticipation.

"*No*, Pelli, thou shalt not beg." I scolded her firmly. She ducked her head from my stern voice and turned away. "Now lie *down*. I'll give you yours in a minute. You have food — I'm famished." It was past noon now and all I'd had were numerous cups of coffee. "Lie *down*, Pelli." She hesitated, circled and finally obliged, lying there watching me hopefully through my entire brunch.

After this meal, as I returned to the kitchen to give her her own pancakes, I decided this would be an excellent time to use for training. I broke off pieces and asked her to sit. After the first bite her little bottom plopped down, as if it had been pulled by an invisible hand under the floor. "Good girl, Kokopelli. I can see this is going to be a piece of cake. Uh, *pan*cake…" I smiled. "Okay, now *down*. I made a lowering hand motion. She studied it, thought, and then lay her front end down. "Good *girl!*" I enthused. "You're just too smart."

For these pancakes, she went nuts. She was shameless. Voice commands, including "*Stay…*", as I held up my hand and backed away from her prone body, were next. She lay there, her excited eyes never leaving the food in my hand, and I'd call, "Okay, *good* girl, come here." And up she would spring, beside me in a flash, "Now *sit –*" (Plop) "Good *girl*, Kokopelli!" I tossed her a morsel and she would catch it mid-air, quick as a flash.

Her lessons were learned so quickly, with either pancakes or dog biscuits as treats, that I decided to teach her sign language. I'd motion 'sit' with my hand, as I asked her with my voice. Down she'd plop. I tapped 'down' with my foot and tell her 'down' and her front end dived to the floor. I'd signal 'stay,' with a raised upright hand while I asked her to do the same, and there she would lie, those intense intelligent eyes studying my face. Soon the hand signals were sufficient, without words at all. *Well, daggone*, I thought, *I'll have to think of something else to teach her. She's learned all this in a heartbeat. Maybe Jared can teach her the scales on the piano.* I didn't fool with shake – that's too easy and a little demeaning. She would learn this in just one pancake session, should I want to teach her. *Maybe I'll teach her to 'wink,' that would be a challenge!* So, after she'd learned 'sit' and 'down,' I started working with her on 'wink' and 'blink.' She has learned these now, but this concept took months. It's much more abstract and involves sharing a silent visionary exchange of energy on some higher multi-species level. But now we do wink at one another – or stare into the other's eyes and give a slow blink of both eyes. It's as physical as a touch.

At times I'll catch Kokopelli watching me, when I'm off and busy with something else, and she'll give me a slow closing of her eyelids. I'll look back into her eyes and slowly blink back, and then she'll lay her sweet head down on her paws, content. I call this our 'Lakota connection,' the part of him that is in her, the part of him that had me return for her, the part of him that has come home.

For Better or For Worse © Lynn Johnston Productions. Dist by Universal Press Syndicate. Reprinted with permission. All rights reserved.

This small golden dog has amazed and impressed me on many levels since our homecoming: her zest in learning, always watching, studying, ever alert to my voice or direction; how quickly she became housebroken, once home; how she would differentiate between socks – which were hers and which were not; how quickly she became part of the plethora of critters on the farm – as if she had been born here. Her transition into our lives went smoothly; soon it was as if she had been with us always.

Heather and Emma quickly accepted her enthusiasm, like it or not. When they did not want a part of the pup's exuberance, they simply slipped through the childproof (Pelli-proof) gate at the top of the stairs and found one of the quiet bedrooms. Trey was glad to have an active companion, one with which he could romp. Amanda had long since become a shadow companion, lost in her world of darkness and age. Kokopelli brought color and energy to young Trey's life. Romeo's Whiskey Cat accepted Pelli as he accepted, and had been accepted by, the others: unconditionally and whole-heartedly – the pup was just another source of love. She was another friend on the farm to sidle up to and rub oneself up against, although he had a much easier time snuggling with Amanda's still, sightless body than with Pelli's overactive constant motion.

The horses were new to this puppy. I'm not sure she had ever seen these creatures before; if she had, she didn't let on. They didn't *look* like dogs to her, didn't *smell* like dogs to her, and they certainly didn't *act* like dogs. What's more, they left this delightful, fragrant mound of banquet behind, hot and steaming, a canine treat. True to what Cindy had told me about the Navajo thinking of dogs as "shit-eaters," Kokopelli lived up to her reputation. Indeed, her most repugnant behavior as a new member of our family was her attraction to the horses' fresh manure and the cats' litter boxes. I caught her soon after her arrival partaking in the litter box in the laundry room and scolded her vigorously. That's all it took.

543

Thereafter, when we walked through this area, Pelli would make a wide berth around the offending box and sidle in as close as she could to the appliances, and then dart on by, looking guilty.

The horses accepted Kokopelli patiently, generally choosing to ignore her presence. She wouldn't allow these huge strange creatures to come close enough to even sniff noses. Instead, when I fed or mucked, she would stand away and warily watch them, or try to sneak off to a safe distance to find a delectable pile. She kept a cautious eye on them, ready to bark if they came too close; I kept an eye on her, ready to fuss if she indulged in manure; the horses stood aside, watching both of us with interest. We all had our roles. And so farm life continued. Throughout the day I had critters to feed or muck, groom or medicate. We had the routine down pat. And soon the pup fit right into these schedules, by my side, eager and interested in all the goings on. Now that we had our new routine down, it was time to center my energies on becoming a free woman, once again.

Peter-Pelli Pancakes:

1 egg
½ cup all-purpose flour* & ½ cup whole-wheat flour
¾ cup of milk, 1% or buttermilk
2 tablespoons vegetable oil
2 tablespoons honey
3 teaspoons baking powder
½ teaspoon salt

(*If using self-rising flour, omit 1½ tsps. baking powder and the salt.)

Beat egg well with milk, oil and honey. Add all dry ingredients and mix well until batter is smooth. Spray flat griddle with nonstick spray & heat until hot. Laddle pancakes onto hot griddle and cook until golden brown. Turn. Makes 9-10 4" pancakes. Double the recipe for more.

Additional Ideas for the Peter-Pelli Pancakes:
Coconut
Bananas (mashed or thinly sliced)
Pecans, walnuts or almond slivers
Blueberries, blackberries or raspberries
Wheat bran or wheat germ (1/4 cup) may be added to the batter

Oatmeal may be added to the batter (increase liquids accordingly)
Sesame or flax seeds sprinkled atop, before turning
Peaches, cut into small chunks, with cinnamon
(Note, peaches are also good with the corncakes, but without the cinnamon)
(Hint: Fruits are best mixed with the batter so they won't stick to the griddle)

LauraWop's Corncakes:

1 egg
½ cup cornmeal & ½ cup whole-wheat flour
¼ to ½ cup milk
1 can cream-style corn, (14 ¾ oz.)
2 tablespoons corn oil
2 tablespoons honey
3 teaspoons baking powder
salt omitted (unless using a low-sodium creamed corn)

Mix as above & then add the creamed corn. If batter is too thin and runny, add more flour &/or cornmeal to thicken. Be sure it doesn't get to be too thick, though, as these corncakes are best with a crepe-like texture. Bacon and maple syrup, and orange juice on the side, with these are mighty fine.

Chapter opening quote by Henry Beston: excerpt from THE OUTERMOST HOUSE by Henry Beston. Copyright 1928, 1949, 1956 by Henry Beston. Copyright 1977 by Elizabeth C. Beston. Reprinted by permission of Henry Holt & Company, LLC.

FORTY

Conversation with Randrue

*"A weed is a plant that has mastered every survival skill
except learning how to grow in rows."* Doug Larson

November 27th

After my conversation with Sergeant Coffey – when he found I had the
dog in question with me in Virginia and became so chilly – I called Pete.
Sergeant Coffey had suggested I call an attorney in Arizona to handle
my case from there, but first, Pete and I agreed, I should talk with our
long-time good friend and attorney, Randy Parker. We had known Randy
for better than a quarter century. Pete had actually gone to high school
with this fellow, and later they became college buddies at UVA. I had
known Randy, whom we affectionately call "Randrue" (Pete is "Pedro"
and I am "Larue" in our friendly banter over the years), as long as I've
known PeterWop.

I buzzed Randy at work, went through all of the switchboard protocol, and was transferred to his office. Randy's familiar soft and articulate
voice came on the line. "La*rue*, how are you? How is Pedro doing? It's
been a long time since I've seen you all."

"Hey there, Randrue. I know – we all get so daggone busy. Pete and
I just went west, back in September/October, to celebrate our 25th. Can
you be*lieve* that? All those years of good loving?" We caught up a little
and then I cut to the chase. "But I've got to bend your ear over something pretty important. Seems I've gotten myself in trouble with the law
out in Arizona. Do you have some time?"

Randy thought for a moment; I heard some papers rustling on his desk and then he answered, "For you, Laura, sure. Tell me what's going on."

I took a deep breath and began, explaining to him the significance of September 11th, our travels, of Pete's folks and Mary taking care of the kids and the farm. I told him all that had transpired as I paced the kitchen floor, cleaning counters vigorously and listening to myself talk. It was so quiet on the other end I had to ask, "Randy, are you still there? Are you listening?"

"Yes, yes, Laura. Go on. Tell me everything. This is un*believ*able." I continued, trying not to omit details I thought would be important to a trained legal mind. And Randy's mind was sharp. He was a topnotch attorney, here in town. Our friend continued to listen quietly until I had told him the complete story.

"Wow. That's *some* vacation — one you can tell your grandkids. *Wow*. But Larue, I've got to say, you could have gotten yourself in some *real* legal trouble out there for doing what you did. You pissed-off those guys *big* time. They may well be out for blood. They'll be aiming for B & E, for sure." His voice was somber.

"But Randy — I didn't *break* anything and I didn't *enter* anything. I did admit that I 'jimmied and opened' — and then relocked the stupid little lock."

He laughed. "But you never went into the man's trailer? Never stepped a foot inside that threshold?"

"Not a foot, Randrue. I have *no* idea what that trailer looked like in-side, except for those kinky lacy curtains. I was focused on Kokopelli."

"Well, this is good. Here in Virginia there is considered the 'invisible threshold' where the door sits. If, when open, one crosses over it into the inside of a building, then that's considered 'entering.' I don't know for sure, but I imagine the law is the same in Arizona."

"I didn't, Randy. And I never damaged his place — no vengeance, at all. I reclaimed my puppy, relocked his lock, wiped off my prints, and left."

He laughed again, "And you successfully picked his lock the first time out? I'm impressed."

"It took me a couple of attempts, but I was determined. My prize was enthusiastically waiting just inside the door. She was as excited as I was, trying to dig her own way out."

His voice grew more somber. "But there *is* the fact that you did all of this after dark. Here in Virginia 'under the cover of darkness' ups the ante. Again, I don't know if it's any different in Arizona, but probably not. You know, you could have put yourself in serious danger out there, Laura – those men all tote shotguns, and use them regularly. You could have been *shot* pulling this escapade." His voice grew stern, a reprimand.

"Right. That occurred to me – especially after that outrageous horn-blowing incident, Randrue – but I wasn't. I went in and accomplished my goal, that's all. And now I'm owning up to it and facing this responsibly. I just need to know my recourse, which is why I called you. So don't fuss at me, okay?"

"Well, don't even pretend you didn't do this. These fellows aren't dumb, and playing dumb on your part would only be an insult." He thought a moment, then chuckled, "Hell, you practically blazed a comet's trail – *first* you call the law and tell them you're coming in, and then you nab your dog right under their noses, when the letter doesn't work out. No, you can't insult them like that." He was talking to himself more than to me at this point, then he brightened, "Of course you could pretend you're just a ditzy housewife who never knew what she was doing."

"Randy Parker, I resent that remark. I am *not* a 'ditzy housewife who didn't know what she was doing'! *That's* playing dumb! I worked hard to get this pup back, and I tried hard to do it legally. When that didn't look like it would be expedient, I resorted to Plan B. But I knew what I was doing every step of the way."

Randy was silent, properly chastised. "I know you did, Laura. I'm sorry. I was just being an attorney and looking at angles. No, what you did was called 'self-help,' where you took the law into your own hands. It's the old vigilante justice – the West, as you know – is well known for this. What are they telling you out there?"

"Well, my friend, they're saying I'm in steaming hot water. They're talking felony and extradition. Deputy Dick has been taken off the case and Sergeant Coffey assigned Deputy Isbel – my old nemesis – to it, instead. The man does *not* like me and he wants to see me hanged for my crime. He *does* like Ricardo, however. I'm between the devil and the deep blue sea here."

"What if you returned the dog to Ricardo? They'd probably let you off the hook – at least they'd drop it all to a misdemeanor."

My jaw dropped. I didn't believe what I'd just heard. *Had he been talking to Pete?* "Re*turn* Kokopelli to this man? After all she's been through be*cause* of him?! After all *I've* been through to get her back! Are you *kidding*, Randy?"

"That might be what it takes to get these people to back down, Laura. No, I'm not kidding. You've got to think of Pete and your family. You're married and you have three children that depend on you. You can't be going to jail over this dog." His voice dropped a notch, dead serious.

"No. I won't do it. I did *not* go to this massive amount of trouble, time, and expense to simply say 'Uncle' and return my dog to this man. No. That's not an option." My jaw set and I stood firmly against the kitchen sink, looking out the window at Tequila and Aristo pretending to graze the withered field grasses. We had recently brought them home. Their bodies glistened in the sun. Pelli came into the kitchen, toes clicking on the floor, and nudged my hand in greeting. I looked down into her precious, trusting face. *No, I was not about to return this little dog to that scum out west. Let them put me in jail, damnit.* "Randy, what happens from here? I'm not sending her back. So now what happens?"

He thought a moment and responded softly. "Well, you could go to jail. I mean they really *could* extradite you over this, Laura, and you could get a Hispanic jury there in Williams – by the way, where the hell *is* Williams, Arizona, *any*way? – and they could decide to use you as an example. Maybe it's an election year and somebody wants the Hispanic vote out there, I don't know – but they could send you to jail. Of course, it could go the other way, too. There's something called 'jury nullification,' where the jury knows the law, but decides to follow their hearts and let you off. With this story, that could happen. But Laura, it's a roll of the dice. No one ever knows how a case might go when it goes in front of a jury. You're really taking your chances by being this stubborn. Again, think of Pete and your kids."

"Randrue, believe me, I *am* thinking of them, but I'm *also* listening to my heart. As crazy as this sounds, I know Lakota is in that pup. Don't ask me how. I also just 'know' all this will work itself out through the legal channels. I am okay with the process. I just need a little guidance as to how to proceed."

He sucked in a deep breath and let it out. "Okay, Larue. I've known you a long long time. I know how strongly you feel about things and how deeply you care – especially when it comes to animals. And I know how stubborn you can be. I can see there is no changing your mind. So here's how it goes. First of all, they'll present this case to the Prosecuting Attorney out there, who will consider the pertinent issues involved and whether or not to prosecute as a 'felony' or reduce it to a 'misdemeanor.' In Virginia the case, if a felony, would first be submitted to a lower court for a preliminary hearing for a determination of probable cause. At that time, the court would have the option of reducing the case to a misde-meanor or disposing of it. If certified as a felony, it goes on to a grand jury that, once again, decides if there is probable cause – if the case will hold up in court. If it continues, a warrant will be issued for you to come to court for the case to be tried." He gave a big sigh, "The problem though, is that no one out there really knows what to do with this case. It falls through the cracks, it's so absurd. Here, they should be disciplining you with a twig over the 'crime' you've committed, but – the way the law is written – all they have are bazookas and scud missiles." He chuckled at the images he'd concocted. I could tell from his analogies that we were a nation at war. "You've got yourself in one neat pickle."

"Oh well. I've been in pickles before, and always found my way clear. Sergeant Coffey is telling me he wants witness statements from Pete and me, as well as phone records, all of which we just faxed him from Kinko's. They're keeping the photo album of puppy shots, as both proof of ownership and evidence. He's suggesting that we prove she is ours any way we can. Though gruff, he's been very helpful. He's just try-ing to clear the case up – and protect his deputies, too. I admire the man. He seems to be a good, solid law official. They could use a man like that in Blue Ridge County," I added, a jab at the shady and borderline corrupt law enforcement in the good ole' boy system in a neighboring county. "He's also saying I should get a good attorney out west to represent me. What do you think about that, Randrue?"

"I think it might not be a bad idea. You'll want someone who knows Arizona law through and through. I don't. Laws vary from state to state. I'll be happy to hold your hand through this and be an advisor. And I can represent you from this end, if necessary. But do be careful, Laura. This all could get very serious. You could end up with a felony record, lose your right to vote, all of that, over this silly dog. Think carefully about what you're doing, okay?"

"I will, Randy, I will. Thank you for listening so long and for caring so much. Thank you for your time. I guess you'll need to be adding up your own attorney fees about now."

"For you and Pete? *Forget about it.* But I do ask that you tread lightly and heed my advice, Laura. Promise? By the way, how is everything else going and how is everyone? How's Pete these days, other than this fi-asco?"

Randy and I talked awhile longer, about our lives in general. His father was sick with cancer. Randy was trying to see him as often as he could. His life was in some turmoil, with his long time marriage dissolving, as it had been for some time. He and his wife, Kathie, had been college sweethearts, had lived through thick and thin, but, for many reasons, it had not been working out. It was my turn to be a shoulder, to listen and be supportive. We actually talked for a good while longer before finally hanging up.

After replacing the phone in its cradle, I knelt down to Kokopelli, who had been lying quietly and respectfully in the corner of the kitchen, her chew-sock at her feet, as if she knew the conversation was about her. She wanted to eavesdrop, to learn her future. I was seriously somber, thinking of both the legal conversation and of the personal turmoil that Randy and Kathie, our two longtime friends, were facing. I buried my head in the ruff of Pelli's neck and stroked her soft back as I said a quiet and sincere prayer for them both to work through this the best way possible, for their needs, and for those of their children. They, like us, had three teenagers.

I fixed a pb&j sandwich and a glass of milk, took this and an apple into our sunroom and sat at the table to eat, continuing to mull through my thoughts. I looked out over the dry fields to the mountains beyond. Even now, in the drought, the view was breathtaking. Late autumn had left a lavender shroud on the deciduous trees and the fields in the foreground lay as golden carpets sweeping ones eyes to the gently rolling mountains. Deep pines rose as dark counterpoint. Pelli had followed me and lay down at my feet, close and protective. *Who was protecting whom here?* I guess I'd better start looking for an attorney out west.

After lunch I fired up the Internet and printed out a list of attorneys in the Phoenix and Flagstaff areas. John Slate could no longer handle this case, as it had gone over to criminal and against me, but he could be an advisor and a friend. Flagstaff was better than Phoenix anyway, as it was much closer to Williams. Shorter driving distances would help keep costs down, and it looked like these costs might become considerable. I looked down at my precious, innocent troublemaker. "We had best change your name, kiddo," I stated firmly. Her head rose and she looked trustingly, adoringly at me. *Yes, I would continue to fight for this little dog — but it looked like I might have to go into hock to do it.*

(Later.) Well, I found a number of attorneys and narrowed the list to those in Flagstaff. I made some cold calls, getting an idea of who they were and what their specialties were. After a number of such calls I rang through to a Sonya Smith and was lucky enough to catch her in. This lady used to be a prosecuting attorney, but now she worked for the defensive side. This was good; she was experienced with both elements of the courtroom. She had time to listen to the story and make suggestions. She said yes, she would take the case for about $1,500 — unless things got complicated. She would need a retainer of $300, along with copies of everything — witness statements and the phone records, the photographs — all that I had just sent to the Coconino County Sheriff's Department. I hung up the phone thinking I'd better have a fine Christmas season painting my commissions this year in the studio. This case, and the trip, was registering "*Ka-ching!*" by the moment.

FORTY-ONE

The Merry Little Month of December

"A woman is like a teabag — only in hot water do you realize how strong she is."
Eleanor Roosevelt

The next morning things were quiet on the home front. Pete was at work, the kiddos were at school, and I had fed and mucked the farm. Soon I should go down and mix up a palette and get back to work on my Christmas portraits, which had been put on hold for far too long. But first I would catch up on some back news. I fixed a late breakfast and a third cup of joe and joined Kokopelli and several days worth of a variety of newspapers in the sunroom.

Saved from Thanksgiving Day, Nov. 22nd, *The Daily Progress*: **Feeling freedom:** *Charlottesville Afghan refugees pleased with Taliban's downfall.* **Grieving firefighters seek reason for thanks. U.S. seals off escape routes for bin Laden.**

From *The Daily Progress*, Sat., Nov. 24th: **Shopping season begins amid tighter security.** Marie Cocco, an editorial writer for *Newsday*, wrote: **Americans still don't get it about oil:** *Back when we were trying to save ourselves from the sheiks, we bought cars that allowed us to brag how far we could go on one tank of gas. Now the driveways boast ever bigger, badder SUVs.* **Death toll reporting changes in N.Y.C.:** *"...the official count stood at 3,646 on Friday, which includes people on the ground and those aboard the two hijacked planes... The number reflects a drop of more than 250 from the beginning of the week — and close to 3,000 from its high in September... The city's new reporting method relies strictly on death certificates and a list of missing persons..."*

From *The Daily Progress*, Sunday, Nov. 25th: **Terrorism may prompt** food safety changes. **Afghanistan farmers replant opium crops. Authorities look for missing virus specialist from Harvard.**

From *The Richmond Times-Dispatch*, Weds., Nov. 28th: **Sprawl takes toll on Virginia forests:** *Recreation spots, habitats threatened.* **'Leadership area' hit near Kandahar:** *U.S. commander: Hunt for bin Laden narrows to two primary areas of focus.* **603 held in terror probe:** *Critics still call for more data.* **Release of sex offenders at issue. Cloning debate goes on:** *Senate unlikely to tackle issue again until next year.* **Ex-FBI officials question new anti-terror tactics.**

From *The Washington Post*, Sat., Dec. 1st: On the front page came the sad news, **Beatles' George Harrison Dies:** *Subdued guitarist pushed Fab Four in new directions.* **George Harrison: 1943-2001: Legions left to mourn as a star fades away:** *Harrison's death defies image of Rock-and-Roll.* The paper continued. **U.S. Wants Custody of Enemy Leaders:** *Interrogation, Trials of al Qaeda, Taliban Eyed.* **Conn. letter has spores of Anthrax:** *Finding boosts theory of cross contamination.* [Energy Secretary Spencer] **Abraham: GAO's Yucca Mountain Report 'Fatally Flawed':** *Energy Secretary Still to recommend Nuclear Waste Plan.* From Tues., Dec. 4th's Daily Progress, **Israeli missiles hit West Bank security posts. Leaders agree on cleanup plan for Chesapeake Bay. Harrison's ashes to be scattered in India:** New Delhi, India… *"George Harrison's intimate relationship with Indian mysticism, music and Hinduism sent his wife, [Olivia] and son, [Dhani] on a pilgrimage to the holy Ganges River, where authorities said the former Beatles' ashes would be scattered before dawn today…"* **Bush puts America on high alert. More mail might be tainted:** *Federal officials believe delivered letters may contain anthrax spores.* (and, same paper, Dec. 6th) **Anthrax won't derail children's letters to Santa.**

I grimly closed up the papers, wondering now why I had really wanted to read the news. So little of it these days was inspirational; conversely, it made one want to crawl under a rock or seek therapy. I saved those papers I wanted and putting the majority of the stack in our recycling box in the closet. I pulled on my old paint-splashed bubblegum pink sweatpants and splattered gray sweatshirt – my usual painting attire, glamorous as it was. After letting Pelli out to romp with Trey, it was time to roll up my sleeves and get to work.

As I sat there facing a canvas of a beautiful black retriever/lab mix named "Julie," lying on an elaborate Oriental carpet, I tried to hush my thoughts and focus. I opened my palette box to mix new paint, as these oils had long since dried. I'd need to concentrate to match my original colors. *Be still – focus*, I told myself. And I tried, but instead a barrage of thoughts were screaming around in my head, struggling to find release. I picked up a pen, instead of a paintbrush, found a sketchpad and wrote down these thoughts:

Written amidst my Christmas commissions, with my own future as a blank canvas... Don't know if what follows will be Abstract Expressionism, a Munch's nightmare vision (i.e. "The Scream")... a Norman Rockwell storybook ending, or a Vincent Van Gogh, in one of his depressed moods. Hells bells, it may be a Cockerille Gianni-ni, in one of her depressed moods... At the moment, in the thick of the adventure, this canvas is more a Bev Doolittle "hide & seek"... Only God knows for sure, and he's keeping his secrets...

However, in all sincerity, I do want to say that everything I have written is (unbelievably) true, except maybe a few name changes here and there to protect my faithful cohorts. I do not condone or encourage anyone else's doing this, however hypocritical that sounds. I have followed my heart throughout this adventure, and, in doing so, have touched a lot of people's lives. Many in a good way - I like to believe - but it has practically given my patient husband, PeterWop, an ulcer with worry. And it is not the best example for a mother to set for her three impressionable teenage children, as my older daughter, Skye, has pointed out to me.

Okay, back to this "jail" thing. What I did, by picking the lock to reclaim Kokopelli, was - technically - wrong. Up until then, the law (apparently) was on my side. I simply ran out of patience and felt the time pressure because I live in Virginia, and all the action was happening in Arizona - including any court procedures. And everyone knows how long a case can drag through the courts, especially one likely not deemed to be too important.....

In the excitement, the adrenalin, my eagerness to reunite with the puppy, my impatient Aries nature, and my feeling that Ricardo would refuse to return the pup, even when confronted with the law, I did what I've now come to realize is "self-help" - I took the law into my own hands. It was the wrong way to go for all the right reasons. I can live with this and face the consequences. But what I must also remember is that Pete and the kiddos are also affected by the consequences. They must live with the worry and all the uncertainty, as well, wondering what the future holds because of my "breaking & entering," which - if the Powers that Be in Arizona decide this is - and I even admitted to the dastardly deed and fully cooperated, once Kokopelli was safe - then it would be considered a felony and I might be looking at extradition. How silly! But the cards - and the canvas - could turn black in the wrong hands: someone in a high position who wants to make an example out of me, for example. The law is politics, and we all know how fairly that game is played... But if this ends up being a felony, and I am convicted, it would mean loss of voting privileges, maybe even some jail time - all over this stray pup no one in the world wanted, until we rescued her. Crazy! How poetic, I sit here thinking: an animal portrait artist, in the business because I love animals so much, turned potential felon because I saved a starving pup, fell head over heels, entrusted her to the wrong person in a state of emotional weakness, and insisted on re-rescuing her. God. How ironic.

After these thoughts were successfully transferred from my overactive mind to the neutrality of white paper, I let out a deep sigh, let Kokopelli inside, and spent the rest of the afternoon continuing details on my portrait of *Julie*. Pelli lay quietly beside me, chewing on a bone, there on Lakota's rug. *Yes,* I thought, *this is meant to be. All will work itself out just fine…* I smiled and went back to work on the minute details of the lush Oriental carpet, thinking now of Betty and John, Julie's owners, and how sweet and supportive Betty had been about this whole fiasco and if I didn't get the portrait finished by Christmas, why, that was okay. It was for an excellent cause and John would certainly be willing to wait until after Christmas. He knew about the painting. I had wonderful clients.

The week passed on by, the dust seeming to have settled on the excitement and hoopla out west. I continued working on *Julie*, and a portrait of *Gavel*, an apricot poodle pup commissioned by a longtime friend and former client, Henry – who happened to *al*so be a judge in Charlottesville. I had spoken with Henry in hypotheticals before leaving for Arizona to reclaim Kokopelli. I told him what had happened, once I returned. And I asked him about his take from a judges' perspective. I found it very ironic, but still part of the entire kismet of this story, that I happened to be working with Henry again, at this particular time, after all of these years. He was amused by the story and was able to help me with questions, but his hands were tied, both with the different laws in another state, and his limits on what he was able to say within his own position, as a sitting Judge in this state.

A third portrait – and final Christmas commission – was of a Jack Russell Terrier puppy named Samantha for a man named Chris, to surprise his wife and children. I normally didn't paint many portraits of young dogs. The animals were usually portrayed in the prime of their lives, or I was commissioned as my clients watched old age loom heavy and foreboding over their beloved friends; together we would peel back the years, through photographs and their memories, to recapture their canines, or felines, or equines – in a younger time and place.

I had kept my painting roster that Christmas to just the three, knowing in advance I was traveling in September/October. I had had no inkling at the time of the way events would unfold to make the task of finishing just these three paintings a challenge. I did not want to sacrifice the quality of any of them for a deadline. Perhaps I *would* take Betty and John up on their offer to finish *Julie* after the holidays. All three paintings would benefit from this pressure-lift. Ultimately, this is just what I did.

I had tried to call Sonya Smith back twice, with questions before I sent her the retainer and the papers that she had required. Each time I left a message; each time there was no response. My third and last call was Friday afternoon, early, to allow her the rest of the afternoon, Arizona-time, to respond. I heard nothing from her. Perhaps she was waiting for the check to arrive before she bothered to respond. *To hell with this,* I thought, *I'd rather go it on my own and take my chances than work with an arrogant and unresponsive attorney, paying her good money when I might be just fine on my own.*

I made a deal with myself that afternoon: if I heard from her, she'd be hired – I'd ask my questions and send her the check and the papers. If not, it was a 'sign' – I'd go solo and ride it out. By 6 PM Friday evening, my time, I'd heard not a word from Sonya Smith. Okay, *that* question was answered.

I did hear, however, from my good buddy Cynthia Elkey. She had heard I was back and wanted to get together for lunch the next week to hear details of this incredible story of which she had gotten wind. We set a date for Wednesday the following week, to meet at a new Shish kabob place on Preston Avenue. And then Beverly called, so I invited her to join us, too. We'd have a grand old time whooping it up, as I related this story to my two good friends, both of them die-hard animal lovers. We were all in a local group called "Piedmont Pet Professionals;" Cynthia and Bev were topnotch dog walkers and I was the token animal artist in the group. There were many others: pet sitters, vet technician's, a trainer, groomers, etc. If one took their job seriously and offered skilled, considerate, professional results – whatever the service – one could be a member. I enjoyed this group of people immensely.

The weekend came and went. Pete and I did some clean-up chores around the farm. We pulled up our spent tomato vines and put them in a pile to burn in the garden. We weeded and tidied up the blueberry and raspberry beds, mulching and tucking them in for the winter. Sunday, so we wouldn't be target practice for local hunters, Natalie and I took Holly and Tequila out for a trail ride. Tequila hadn't been ridden in forever, and acted like it, playing the part of testy, tempestuous thoroughbred throughout our 'leisurely' trail ride. By the time we got home, I was ready to sell her to someone who rode regularly and would appreciate her responsiveness, but wouldn't put up with her nonsense. That, or add her to our frozen section, for winter use; I hear horsemeat continues to be a delicacy in France. All at the farm heard these continual threats and let them roll off, knowing it was just hot air. Besides, Tequila had no extra meat on her bones – she'd be tough as nails. Next time out, however, I'd take Aristo, our adaptable chestnut American Saddlebred gelding; he was so much more pleasant and even to ride. (What I *really* wanted, though, was a trail horse like Costner's buckskin, Cisco – or a clone of him.)

I left Kokopelli inside with Pete, who was happily watching a golf tournament on TV. I didn't trust her yet to follow us on the trail and not be enticed by scents in the woods and disappear in hopes of a chase. Or I worried that she would follow too closely behind the horse's hind feet and be kicked. It was safer all around this way. She and Pete had become good buddies. He was pleased that she went nuts over his cooking and she lay hopefully close, hoping that he might have the urge *to* cook. The two were a pair of Sunday afternoon couch potatoes.

December 5th – Al's Birthday
Dream Conversation with Sergeant Coffey:

Midweek, the morning I was to have lunch with Cynthia and Beverly, I awoke slowly. I had a conversation with Sergeant Coffey this morning, in that fog of sleep one drifts around in before they're consciously awake. It's some sort of in-between world, where the subconscious has taken over the reins and ideas and images float around, as if real, but anything goes. This was a terrifically honest talk, and I need to record the conversation before it fades away into the day.

Okay, I'm frustrated because I am trying to cooperate with the law out west but I can't get the attorney lady, Sonya Smith – who I think I've hired – to return my calls to answer a few questions. So I call my "good buddy" in the sheriff's office, Sergeant Coffey. He was off when I called, so I left him a message, as I've just discovered he has voice mail.

"Hey, Sarge, this is your friendly puppy thief from out east. I am trying to cooperate with y'all out there, but I keep running into brick walls. I need your advice." (Actually, I did call last night and leave that message.) The rest of this is the direction I dreamed our talk would go, once he returns my call. If he does? Maybe "they" have all decided to forget about this case because they're actually working on more important litigation out in Arizona?... Oh, one more quick thought I had last night. A grin. Now, when I tell

THE KOKOPELLI JOURNALS

friends "I may go out and spend time in Arizona" it could be true! Yeah, me. Mid-life mother of three teenagers spending time, as an honest-to-God felon in an Arizona prison (maybe the one I passed on the Turquoise Trail, just before entering Santa Fe? No, that's in New Mexico...) Maybe they'll let me paint in there. I could probably get a whole lot more work done in prison, painting full-time, than I've been able to do at home in years, taking care of everyone else. *Hmmm...* I could paint portraits of our own pets, and my own children, as part of the therapy in missing them all so much.... Here's a thought.... (So, anyway, a little too much free-associating here. Back to our law talks.)

So, in my dream-state, Sergeant Coffey calls me back. First thing he says is: *"Young lady (I love him for that) you and Ricardo are keeping my voice mail tied-up with all your messages. I tell him that's the only one I've left on his — didn't even know he had one until now. Well, he says, Ricardo calls him regularly asking about the status of "his puppy" and "that felon lady out east".... It's driving the good Sergeant nuts. (Way to go, Ricky boy, I'm thinking — you just keep calling — wear out your welcome...)*

I tell Sergeant Coffey that I'm frustrated and need to get his advice because I am trying to cooperate with the law — I really am — have even tried to hire an attorney, and thought I had last week, after looking up "www.azbar.com" on the Internet and coming up with 5 pages — count 'em — of attorney's, about 5 out of Flagstaff. I started calling these names, and the one I wanted was too busy defending drug cases, so his secretary gave me 3 names, 2 women and 1 man. I asked her which one was the animal lover and she said she knew the 1st one had a dog. She then told me the other one, Sonya Smith, used to be a prosecuting attorney, so I chose her. Both sides now, and all that... So I called her, happened to catch her in, and we spoke for about 45 minutes; she told me she would take the case. Only she hasn't returned my phone calls since this initial conversation, and I've called her 3 different times, leaving messages on her voice mail, or with her secretary, just wanting to ask her a couple of simple questions, before I send her my retainer and witness statements and the like. She probably wants the retainer first; I want to see that she will be responsive before I send her money. A Mexican Stand-Off here...

At this point, Sergeant Coffey slips through the phone wires, arriving like a genie in this crazy wee-hour fog, and is sitting there in person with Pete and me. He is tall and languid, with a tanned and weathered face, reminding me very much of Kris Kristofferson, with kind but intense gray eyes, and he is wearing a green uniform shirt and hat, along with faded blue jeans and dusty old cowboy boots. His arms are crossed over his chest, where a shiny star adorns the pocket, his long legs sprawl out in front of him, as he leans back in our chair, listening to us, amused by our marital banter.

I told him that Pete warned me not to speak with him, that he's the law, and I

559

broke the law: "They (you - the law) are not on my side" (Pete's quote). I told them that the law was supposed to be impartial and stand for justice, and this was all I was seeking. Pete said I get wound up and talk too freely. I asked Pete, "What are they going to do, hang me? They stopped doing this years ago in Arizona, I thought – and then it was for horse stealing, not puppies." At this point Pete rolls his eyes, and Sergeant Coffey just groans, and has to cover a smile. God, she's dumb, he's thinking. Good, let him think that... but then, if he had actually witnessed my stealth that infamous night, when I hit the horn gizmo instead of the lock gizmo... Hmm... maybe he has a point. Another grin. Now he's being entertained.

"Okay," I tell Sergeant Coffey, "I've got all these papers together you said I needed for the Prosecuting Attorney. My notarized witness statement, which you'll probably tell me I did wrong, but please forgive me, as I'm new at this. A copy of the phone records and Pete's (unnotarized, but we can resolve that) witness statement that we've already faxed to you. You have my mini-photo album already in evidence. Please don't lose it, as it's very sentimental to me, even more so now that it's become part of the litigation. Who knew... I'll send you – or them, or somebody – a copy of Ricardo's letter that he sent us, in which the claimed that my stealing the puppy was "inexplicable" (!!). Hypocrite. What else? Oh, is there someone else I should send all this to, since apparently my lawyer was/is a figment of my imagination? Or should it all just go to the Prosecuting Attorney? How do I proceed, Sergeant Coffey, I'm trying to make headway here..."

Pete's in the background whispering "Laura, shut up, you're telling him too much."

I'm saying, "Shush, Pete – what's he going to do? Trump up the charges? Get more evidence? Hell, nobody even caught me – I've basically admitted to the 'crime'."

Sergeant Coffey sits there between us and drawls, "Y'all finished yet?"

Good morning, kiddo; your day has started. Take care of things, go feed the farm, then join Cynthia and Beverly for lunch, over a pitcher of beer and some shish kabobs, and share the story with them. I'll take Kokopelli with me and introduce them to my little western canine prankster. Bev knows a good part of the story; Cynthia knows nothing. Both will get a kick out of the escapades to rescue my "Monumental Mutt"... Time to lighten up here! I'll talk with Sergeant Coffey later, when he calls back, now that I've rehearsed the conversation... See if Ricardo really *is* bugging him to death...

I met Cynthia and Bev for our lunch. Kokopelli was with me on this unseasonably beautiful day in early December. It was cool enough for her to go with me in the car, and wait in a shady place while we had our meal, but warm enough for the three of us to eat at a table outside. Go figure. I walked around the corner to find my friends waiting, already laughing at something. I waved and smiled at them.

Cynthia and Beverly are about the same height, both about 5'6", both slim blondes. Bev is several years younger than me, another free spirit, with lively blue eyes and great big dimples that are evident each time her expressive tanned face lights up with a smile. She is also an artist and a teacher and a lover of life, full of spirit and gumption. She was to have been my partner in crime out west, a Thelma to my Louise, but she wasn't able to travel with me, as her dad had been so sick with cancer. I had sent her a letter from Santa Fe, letting her know I had missed her but had been successful picking the lock, even without her. She had known what I meant.

Cynthia is my good buddy; she and I have shared many a lengthy lunch, telling stories of our past and talking endlessly about everything. She is as passionate and aware of environmental and social issues as I am. If Beverly is my old hippie alter-ego free-spirit, Cynthia is my old hippie alter-ego Earth Mother, with her long blond hair, tinged now with threads of silver. She is several years older than me and very matter-of-fact and no nonsense about life, with a wicked sense of humor and a quick true laugh. Cynthia wears little granny glasses and – when not on her face – they hang around her neck with a beaded eyeglass chain, ready and waiting for their next use. I had not seen Cynthia since returning to Arizona for my wayward pup; the only parts of the story she knows were of my plans to return and whatever it is she has heard on the grapevine, since.

We ordered, and with our lunches before us, I shared the happenings in detail with these two laughing ladies. They came to life as the story unfolded, adding rollicking comments and Beverly saying that she wished so much that she could have been there. I told her she was most definitely there in spirit – and Cynthia, too. These ladies stayed in my heart. I finished up the story as we finished our pitcher of beer. By then the comments were flying. I asked them to hang tight for a minute, as I had to get something from the car. I went around the corner, woke my sleeping pup, asked her to sit, and clipped the leash on her collar. They had no idea that I'd brought "Sagebrush Sally" along with me today. Pelli hopped out of the car, stretched leisurely, her curled tail waving, ready for her new adventure. I peeked around the corner and grinned and then stepped out, the object of this rollicking conversation by my side.

Bev exclaimed, "*Oh my gosh!* You've got her *with* you, Laura!"

Cynthia laughed and got up, "Laura, she's *precious*, bring her to us."

Kokopelli trotted beside me, happy to meet new people. Both ladies knelt down and made over her, as she licked their faces in greeting and wagged that famous tail, loving her grand attention. "She's *darling*, Laura," Beverly looked up, "I had *no* idea she would be so beautiful!"

"Actually, Bev, when I first saw her, I hadn't an inkling, either. She was so scrawny and her coat was like straw. But she filled out and softened up. She's had this expressive foxy face all along – and that rolled up, impossible tail."

"She is beautiful, alright," agreed Cynthia, "but have you taught her manners?"

I looked over my sunglasses at my disciplinarian friend. "Of course. Pelli, sit down, girl." She plopped her bottom to the ground, watching me. "Good *girl* – now down…" I tapped my toe on the ground. She immediately dropped her front paws straight out before her enthusiastically, looking up for her kudos. "*Good* girl," I laughed. "Here's your treat." I fished a dog biscuit from my pocket and tossed it to her. With lightning reflexes she snapped it up in mid-air. They both laughed. "Not only pretty, but smart. Sometimes I think she's smarter than I am. It's spooky how quickly she learns. And I know for a fact that Lakota is in there. She has so many of his traits, it's eerie. I can sense his presence. And it's as if she were born into the farm, she's made herself at home, so."

"So how is the legal part of it going?" Cynthia asked. "What are they saying?"

"Well, I haven't heard from the law since last week, when I spoke with Sergeant Coffey. He wanted the witness statements and phone records, which I sent him. I've got a call into him and should be speaking with him later today. I've tried to get an attorney in Flagstaff, but she's not being very responsive. It's all in the works, being reviewed by the Prosecuting Attorney as we speak, to see if it'll be considered a felony or a misdemeanor. I had this crazy, crazy little dream this morning about Sergeant Coffey slipping in over the phone wires, into the kitchen with Pete and me, listening in on our conversations. It was pretty wild! You guess maybe this might be on my subconscious?" I cocked my head and looked at my friends with a wry grin.

They grinned back, "Some dream, eh?" Bev responded. "But naw… they wouldn't *really* be calling this a *fel*ony, would they? Retrieving your *own* dog?" She asked incredulously.

"If Deputy Isbel had his say in it, they would. But there are a lot of people involved. I've talked with a dear attorney friend here, who's helping us with the case. Randy and Sergeant Coffey both suggested I hire that attorney in Arizona. We'll see. Once they get the witness statements and phone records, they'll go a long way in proving everything we've been telling them."

"Well, Laura, we wish you luck, and let us know if we can help. The Humane Society should have been involved, the way that puppy was treated." Cynthia said sternly. "They can't come to the conclusion that you were too far in the wrong."

"Thanks, Cynthia. I've got a good feeling about it all. Don't worry. And if I were caught out there with Pelli red-handed, I was planning to contact the Humane Society or PETA and have them know the way she was treated. Once the 'case' got press, there would be no way they could continue to play hardball with me. The public would be outraged – and that does hold water. But I didn't get caught." I gave them a wink. "Basically, I simply admitted to my crime. And I'm cooperating. But now *I've* got possession – and that *is* 9/10ths of the law." I winked again.

December melted away as it always does, condensing itself into what seems like half a month, what with Christmas shopping and wrapping, decorations and parties. I worked hard to finish *Gavel* and *Samantha* by deadline, so these gifts would be surprises on the big day. *Julie* would be finished after the holiday dust had settled.

Before we knew it, Kendrick's back-to-back parties – one at a home and one at a downtown hotel – were upon us. It was time to get all dolled up in festive attire and go visit Pete's comrades at work, along with their good spouses. Many of these friends we only saw once a year, at these parties.

The first of the two was at Mike and Linda's house. Each year they gallantly opened their beautiful home to a hundred or more employees, many from out of state. This year many had heard of our trip west and the ensuing escapades and wanted to hear the story – over and over. I needed to make a tape. I shared photos of Pelli, from finding her in the desert in her 'Dingo' days, on to present. I felt like a new grandmother. By the end of the evening, Pete and I were drained – we felt like what Mike and Linda must have felt – just simply wrung dry of all energy and emotion.

We left this party, went home, fed the farm the third time that day, and fell into bed to recharge for the next night's party. Pete was up by mid-morning to join some of the guys in the afternoon for what was becoming a tradition of "Christmas Golf" before the main party began. I opted to go to the Omni early, check in and use the quiet time to organize my journals of the trip a bit. Pete joined me later, showered and dressed there. We were planning to stay that night, as we'd likely celebrate heartily. Our teens would take over the farm for a day.

At the party I continued to tell the story to many curious friends who had only heard parts. The tape was becoming more and more a necessity, as my voice gave out. Pete's assistant, André, came to me with his date, and soon to be fiancée, Christine. He had a broad and knowing smile on his handsome face as he introduced us. He was on the inside loop; Pete had filled him in on all the details practically from day one. André had obviously shared the story as he knew it with Christine, as I was pulled aside and congratulated on arriving home safely and with the puppy in tow. I shared the new photo album I'd made of Pelli's baby shots with this young couple, as well. They wanted to know how it was going with the law and I told them the little I knew – that it was, I thought, in the works, but I hadn't heard anything since early December. I guessed "no news was good news." Every time I suggested calling to find out, Pete rose up like one of those lizards with the expanding neckline in *Jurassic Park*, and said "Don't you *dare* stir things up out there. Let sleeping dogs lie."

"PeterWop," I had responded, "It's not just going to go away – *some*-thing is happening behind the scenes and I want to find out what it is." Each time he managed to convince me not to call, but curiosity was nib-bling away at me like a baby piranha.

Later in the evening Steve and Sandy came over. Steve pulled me aside and confided softly, "Sandy told me the whole story. I'm really im-pressed with what you did. I want you to know if this gets out of hand and you need a passport out of the country, I can handle that. And if you need this schmuck 'hurt,' or 'offed,' I can handle that, too. *No*body should treat animals like that. We're behind you all the way."

I grinned at him and said, "I'm glad I'm on your good side there, Steve. Thank you for your generous offers, but I don't think it'll come to either one. The law is working itself out out west and I don't need to see Ricardo 'hurt' – or 'offed.' Whatever *that* means – I'm afraid to ask you to be more specific. But do you realize you're not the first one to offer these special services?" Steve turned and leaned his head back curiously, "Oh?"

"Yeah, a lady at the gym knows the whole story. She was one that encouraged me to go back, in the first place. She's from somewhere in California and she said to me, 'If you need this guy hurt, I can see to that. If you need this guy dead, why, I can see to that, too.' I had been a little shocked, and asked her how that could happen – Ricardo lives in Arizona. She had said, 'Don't you worry about *that*, Sister – these guys will travel.' I had been am*azed* at her offer, saying 'thank you, but no thanks; I have what I had gone out west for, and I wasn't the vindictive type.' But it floors me, Steve, how easy these offers – yours and hers – were made. I've always heard of that, uh… underworld, but I wouldn't have dreamed that I'd ever be privy to these services so freely. Although declined, I think I'm, um… *flattered*?" I laughed. It was actually kind of funny if I chose not to use them. If I chose to say, 'Sure, just tell me how or what to say to make it happen' – or some such – I'd be pretty disappointed in myself for ever allowing this to get so out of hand. *That* crosses a line.

"What's this ladies name at the gym, Laura? I might need her some-time," Steve joked.

"Josephina Jones," I said, "She's a no nonsense, kick-ass type of Af-rican American lady. She's got a heart of pure gold – *a*lso abs and legs of pure steel – and she grew up as a black woman fighting for respect in a white man's world. I love her and respect her, but would *never* want to be on her bad side. Yours, either." I looked at him square in the face and winked.

"I think I'd like this lady," Steve grinned at me and raised his glass. "Anyway, my offer stands, should you change your mind, Laura. And you done good, honey." He added.

I raised my wine glass and toasted him in return, "Thanks again, Steve. You and Sandy, both. If I really get in a pinch, I'll know *just* who to call. Merry Christmas."

Christmas came to our home with much joy this year. During the year, Pete and I are adamant about the kid's setting their own goals if they want something special. This teaches them to budget, teaches responsi-bility, and the joy of anticipating what they are working towards. It pulls the rug from under the all-American attitude of immediate gratification. Put it on a charge card and pay for it later. Have good ole' Mom and Dad buy it for me, and see if I care in a month… Well, no, *this* Mom and Dad are asking that they save and strive and set their goals, and have the inner pride of knowing they made it happen all by themselves. This is our attitude throughout the year, but at Christmas we let up. We get our Santa wish-lists from each of the kiddos, still give them stockings stuffed with treasures, and still stay up until the wee hours of Christmas Eve wrapping the whole shebang. (Lately, the last few years, we've wised-up and have them wrap each others stockings. For this we use the nicer remnants from paper saved in the attic from prior years, as this is part of my unremitting reuse/recycle mentality…)

We went shopping ahead of time to buy books and toys for magnanimous Tom Powell's annual Toy Lift in Charlottesville; we upped the antes in the Salvation Army donation buckets as we shopped; we sent blankets to the Dakota Sioux Indians, as well as cash donations to help them through their wicked winters. As for our crew, each teen had a major gift and a secondary one, and then several smaller surprises. This year the kids had pared down their wish lift, I think realizing the expense of our travels this past summer – and the price on the head of our desert find. I was impressed at their consideration. They, themselves, were beginning to learn the magic of giving.

Each Christmas morning – because we *have* stayed up so impossibly late on the Eve before, finalizing the gifts and wrappings of this day of Jesus' birth – the kids have learned to respect our rest. They, too, have actually become quite good about sleeping in late, beings teens, and all. Gone are the days that Jared would awake before any of the rest of us, wade through the gifts and unwrap the corners of his packages for a preview. For several years we chose reindeer names as code names for the gifts. Thank God this tradition didn't last – the Wop and my brains were already fried by the time Christmas Eve arrived, with*out* needing to constantly remember whether it was Skye or Jared that was Blitzen this particular year.

Now Jared stacks his gifts around him – a squirrel with his winter's stash – ready to gobble them down all at once. My vision of the house richly decorated, calm and soothing strains of Tchaikovsky's *Nutcracker Suite* lulling us in the background, or rousing cords from Handel's *Messiah* causing our spirits to rush, go up in smoke. The vision continues with the house scented naturally by boughs of pine draping our banisters, warm gingerbread and apple pies freshly baked and cooling on the counters… The children all sit with their posture correct, Christmas outfits all perfectly fitting… Sweet, caring smiles on their cherub faces, all straight out of a holiday issue of *Better Homes and Gardens*… No, these visions pop before me like bubblegum in a streetwalker's mouth.

The reality is that the house is decorated in and around the stacks of collected mail we've been unable to read, and junk mail I haven't had time to recycle. Gifts for extended family wait stacked in the corner, in need of wrapping. I'm lucky to have dusted. The scents from the kitchen are a mix of steamed shrimp, fresh-brewed coffee, warm spiced cider, freshly mixed dog food, and fruit salad. The music might be any sort of beautiful Christmas classics that quickly becomes anything anyone got as a new CD, from an old *Miles Davis* remake to *Smashing Pumpkins*, or – if I'm lucky enough – Mark Knopfler's latest. This Christmas we all listened, with somber respect and prayers to the families of September 11th, as *A Tribute to American Heroes* played in the background.

And we were dressed in whatever was comfortable at the time of our awakening. As long as one donned respectable clothing, they were welcomed beside the Yuletide tree, even if their choices clashed. And who cared about posture, *any*way, after three hours of sleep? This was our Christmas reality and, as long as love was in the room, the storybook perception of perfection need not be present to count. It took me a lot of Clairoled grays to come to this acceptance.

And in the thick of our crazy holiday chaos was Kokopelli, alive and delighted to be part of these outrageous goings on. Of course she and the others were included. She had a new pair of knotted up socks. She and Trey and Amanda had favorite dog treats; all the cats had their kitty treats. And for Pelli, other than an interactive loving home, the highlight of her Christmas Day was a braided rag-string toy of a thing, with a crazy green head and squeak-toy middle. When I handed the gift to the little dog, asking her to sit and be polite beforehand, her eyes lit up and she danced around the room, showing if off to anyone who would look. If they were *really* lucky, she'd play tug of war with them, sharing her wonderful new acquisition in her quiet and dé-ter-minded way. The highlight of the day came when Kokopelli parked behind Skye and discovered the squeak-toy inside. As Skye savored her gifts, opening them carefully like the young lady she is, Pelli repeatedly squeaked the toy behind her and Skye piped up, "Excuse me," "Oh, ex*cuse* me," and "Excuse me *again!*" We videotaped this nonsense, laughing at the two of them play this out for ten minutes, or more.

Of course, Heather and Emma were in the thick of the excitement, shy Heather safer on the peripheral, and Emma immersed in the goings on. Each empty box found her sitting in the middle, claiming this as her own. We have never figured out what it is with Emma and her boxes.

Like our Thanksgiving, this Christmas was especially warm and wonderful as we celebrated, grateful to be together. Mary arrived from her coastal home in the evening, having started her morning with friends at Christmas mass. Sean arrived to see his mom and share dinner with us all. Jean and Allan joined the festivities, and we presented them with their brilliantly colored Mexico platter from Santa Fe, which thrilled them. I pulled Mary aside and gave her the delicate guardian angel I'd found for her, and we gave Sean a silver belt buckle we had purchased just for him from the Navajo in the bottom of Canyon de Chelly. It was the bear sign with the lightning bolt, a symbol of strength.

We gave Mary her Navajo necklace and to the girls we gave the matching necklace and bracelets sets. I gave Jared his Indian pottery and suede wallet with the buffalo insignia. Pete got his Kokopelli tie and the Southwest napkins and rings, and a slew of other things special to him. We shared a wonderful time throughout the day and well into the evening, but a good part of the day the thought of the families fragmented by September's hatred haunted me. This would not be a day of joy for these good people; today would simply magnify the absence of the missing loved one that was not part of these festivities. All day long I sent silent prayers adrift, hoping that these many, many individuals left to mourn their loved ones would somehow find some moment of joy and peace.

So Christmas came and Christmas went. We spent the next day, Boxer Day, in Lexington with Jim and Connie, as they generously opened their lives to incoming family, making succulent arrays of homemade pizzas and huge spectacular salads and serving bottomless good wine and fresh coffee. Homemade holiday cookies and favorite stories were passed around with the gifts and, of course, all wanted to hear of my excitement out west, so this was told at the long table over dinner, amidst good-natured ribbing and roars of laughter. Jean and Allan were there, as well as Connie's folks, Ruth and Bill. All three of their grown children had joined the festivities: Laura and her husband, Jamie, and their new young son, Thomas, came from Hawaii; Matthew and his new bride, Amy, glowed. They had surprised the family and had eloped that summer. Rachel was freshly home from James Madison University. Jamie's parents, Jim and Barbara, joined the fun.

By New Year's Eve, Pete and I begged for mercy. Parties and good people had left us pooped. We were thrilled to be home with an array of fresh foods, presentable champagne, exciting videos and each other. Skye celebrated with her friends, but Natalie and Jared were with us – Jared leaving at 9:00 for bed, as he often does. Natalie joined us for a sip of champagne and we lifted our glasses in toast. The Roman God Janus had been kind to us: the past and present looked hopeful, and the New Year had begun. This, too, despite the impending legalities, looked promising. Just please, God, send us snow or rain.

FORTY-TWO

Winter Wonderland at the Farm

"If the Republicans will stop telling lies about the Democrats, we will stop telling the truth about them." Adlai Stevenson

"Democracy means that anyone can grow up to be president, and anyone who doesn't grow up can be vice-president."
Johnny Carson (1925-2005, thanks for the laughs, Johnny…)

January of 2002 was eventful in our lives and throughout America. Warm temperatures continued – so warm we walked around in tee shirts and shorts, pretending it was May and wishing we'd had April showers. Because it *was* so warm there was no chance of snow and, despite our prayers, days went on with no rain in sight. We brought in more hay, shipped in from the Midwest, with the cost to match the distance. But our horses had to eat. I thought often of Benjamin Franklin's statement: *"When the well is dry, we know the worth of water."* I often wondered of the condition – and the depth – of our well. This drought had been going on for several years, with the exception of one wet summer in between. Water tables everywhere in Virginia, and throughout the eastern states, were in trouble.

On these beautiful dry days I would run the family laundries and hang them outside to dry. On some of these days I wore a swimsuit, again pretending – with no trouble at all – that it was late spring or early summer. I watched the crocus, planted at the base of the clothesline posts, bloom. I watched the Bridal Wreath Spirea bush begin to set blossoms. Mother Nature was as confused as we over this balmy January.

I love hanging our clothes out in the wind and warmth to dry in the breezes. I love the connection with nature, watching the sky change above me and the grasses grow below. I watch the horses contentedly (pretend to) graze in the pasture beyond. We have a clothes dryer, but this disconnects that centering, that mindfulness of a simple life that nature so willingly provides. And clothes from the dryer never smell so air fresh – despite the multitude of scented claims – as those brought in fresh from outdoors (unless our neighbor, Rusty, has been burning his trash in a barrel again).

This January was mild enough to do this. Other January's, when the kids were little and my painting creativity was stifled, I would find other ways to be creative – in those far out stretches of the imagination that give artists the reputation for being whacko. I would hang the children's brightly colored clothing on the line, or wash a load of their stuffed animals, and let it/them freeze freeform there in the chilled winter air, gloves on my hands and a warm jacket around me. When the clothes froze in a medley of unnatural shapes, or the animals looked like bright stiff soldiers marching along, I would come out with a camera and have a field day shooting the colors and forms.

This also works for blue jeans, although one needs to use more clothespins to hold the additional weight as they freeze. But it is a *hoot* to watch this heavy denim form a life of its own, as ice crystals cause these pants to look as if they might walk off the line. I've also heard that in trying to fold frozen jeans they will snap in half, instead. This is a great way to make cut-offs. *Not.* The freeze-dried action also creates astounding softness in the material once it dries, although I do have to admit that blue jeans dried on a regular clothesline, without that freezing, are stiff and unforgiving. Here, the dryer works best.

My neighbors have probably long ago written me off as one of "those eccentric artists," which means that now I can pretty much get by with anything. It's my theory that trying to please people in that expected sanity circumference is what actually drives people nuts. There's far too much life "out there" yet to explore to limit oneself to just what's been done. But then again, that's just a theory.

One day, well into the month of January, as Pete and I were driving down our back road at dusk, we spied a funny, shaggy gray and black object trotting down the middle of the road, as if he owned the place. What*ever* it was was too small for a bear – not even a cub – all wrong for a fox, didn't move like a dog, was the wrong color and shape for a deer, and was too big for a cat. We looked at each other, squinted our eyes, and said, "Do you think that's a *goat*? What's a *goat* doing wandering around the neighborhood?!" The little fellow moved off into the woods, still leaving us wondering.

We continued for the next two weeks to have 'goat sightings,' or we'd hear bleating in the woods on our walks. We would look at each other and laugh about the dangerous beast wandering the area. And then one evening a neighbor, Teresa, who lives in a home in the woods below us, knocked on our door. She asked if we owned a goat; this looked like the kind of place that might. I told her no, we didn't, but since our visit at my friend, Kathy's – who has two precious pigmy goats that I'd fallen in love with – I would like to.

"Well," she said, "today might be your lucky day. I have a baby goat we found wandering in the woods trapped under the camper shell of our pickup truck. I've been scouting the neighborhood, but nobody claims it. If I haven't found the owner by 7 PM, he's yours." Theresa gave me her number. I called her at 7:00. There were no takers, so Pete and I drove over, with a collar and a leash in hand, and found a frightened shaggy black, white and gray pygmy goat babe under the shell of Teresa's truck. I crawled under to try to catch it but instead it darted out, right into PeterWop's waiting arms, bleating and crying like a baby in distress. He put the collar and lead on the little fellow and hung on tightly. The tiny goat acted as if he'd never been touched by a human in his short life.

We thanked Teresa for her rescue and I put a blanket on my lap. Pete drove home as I tried to comfort the scared little beast. When we got home we took him into the laundry room to check him out under the light. He was tiny and petrified and shaking with fear. Natalie noticed some minute black bugs crawling throughout his coat, so we peeled off our outer clothes and put them and the blanket into a pre-wash. I put on other grubby clothes and we took the kid goat upstairs to our bathtub, with its independent sprayer nozzle. There, as he bleated and screamed bloody murder as if we were scalping him, we gave him his first bath. The unidentified tiny black bugs floated off into oblivion. That first night, while he dried, was spent in the laundry/utility room with Heather and Emma peering curiously down from their safe heights, trying to fig-ure out what this crazy, noisy creature was. He munched hay and carrots and slept in their litter box, which Natalie had just given a fresh cleaning. And this is how a scrappy stray goat came to be part of our farm. Leave it to us to adopt him.

The following day we introduced the little fellow to the rest of the farm. Dear, patient Trey pretty much took the young goat in stride; he would become the goats' guardian, his bodyguard, a mother replace-ment. Kokopelli, in exuberant puppy fashion, was thrilled and amazed at this bizarre, odorous creature, smaller than she. She would leap about him, barking and inviting him to play. The little fellow, more terrified of humans than the dogs, gamely dropped his head and instinctively butted in her direction, holding her off, though his tiny horns were more a promise than a fact.

We dubbed the newest arrival of our menagerie "Little Baaad Billy Bob." He looked like the youngest and most vulnerable of the "Three Billy Goat's Gruff," all silvery gray and black wiry hairs springing from his newly cleaned body. Billy Bob's eyes were golden, with the vacant, alien look of the goat. His make-believe horns were sprouting, just small gray buds. His cloven feet were tiny, and his legs all tufted with hair going every which way. His belly was rounded, as if he had swallowed a cantaloupe. All in all, the small creature was quite a spectacle, afraid of humans, but spunky and defiant with the dogs, all false bravado, which endeared him to us quickly. *He* thought he was as tough as anybody.

For the first few days we tethered Billy Bob to Amanda's old doghouse outside the dog's pen, so they could all acquaint. He made himself at home, grazing the golden grasses of winter, which were trying their best to green up, or he ate my perennials, or the Asian pear trunks — anything he could reach. We have never had a goat before, and so learned with Billy, but we've come to find that their reputation to eat about anything is pretty much true. All not nailed down, and some that is, is fair game to a goat's unstoppable mouth.

We gave Billy Bob some of the horse's precious hay and a cup of their warm mash each evening. Once he had a taste of this delectable hot grain concoction he momentarily overcame his fear of our large bodies, obnoxiously baahing for more. It was hysterical watching him eat, his long white beard below his mouth going in circles as he chewed. It looked for all the world like his beard clapped to cheer along his ruminations. We'd feed one end and watch the infinite round goat pellets be eliminated from the other in a continual cycle. Another thing we came to learn about goats is that they are en*tire*ly uncouth. If the Navajo have a term especially for dogs as "eater of shit," why they'd have to have an equally descriptive term for goats, as the perpetual supplier of such.

After a few days, when goat and dogs would be found laying side by side with the wire fence between, it became obvious there would be no danger to the little guy to let him have the run of the dog's pen. So we unclipped him from the chain and plopped him over the fence. He went scampering off, with Pelli in happy pursuit nipping at his heels, asking him to play.

Billy Bob more than made himself at home in the dog's large run.

With Trey his massive bodyguard, he was fearless. Kokopelli became a playmate, bounding around him, yelping obnoxiously in his ears as he circled around to butt her with his budding horns. He would eye her and rear, then twist around and lunge towards her, thrusting with his head as she deftly sprang away. The two kept this game alive for many months until Billy's horns grew to be actual weapons and occasionally he'd catch Kokopelli in her side and gore her into submission. She then decided it wasn't *quite* as much fun.

I would look down into our backyard upon this medley of critters, as I leaned over the railing of our upper deck. Billy Bob would be on or around the doghouse, with Trey somewhere close. Kokopelli and the goat would often be at play and Whiskey Cat might be sunning himself atop the doghouse, or elsewhere in the yard. I marveled at how well these creatures had connected and at the bonds of companionship formed between them. Here were three completely different *species* of animals and they had developed this wonderful and compatible friendship. I would stand there, calling down to them and laughing at their crazy antics, wondering why it was that mankind often could not get along with his *own* species – as I thought of wars throughout the world, and now the madness of terrorism striking randomly, with its intent to maim or kill and strike chaos in its victims. Something was terribly wrong with this picture.

Billy Bob had free roam here until he blew it by nature of his nature. He ate *every*thing inside the pen, including the bark on trees, our crocus at the base of the clothesline, and all the Spirea that he could reach. He jumped on top of Treys new doghouse, playing King of the Mountain above Pelli's enthusiastic barking body below, his busy cloven hooves dancing on the shingles. When he started taking over the *in*side of the doghouse, butting away Trey or Kokopelli and leaving behind rolling balls of goat turds in this new shelter, it was the last straw. He had royally blown this free and sheltered life.

Our answer, for a while, was to put Amanda's old doghouse in the dog pen. As Amanda had shelter throughout the farm during these mild winter days, and slept inside at night, this wasn't a problem. We would measure out the chain length attached to his 'goathouse' so that he couldn't reach our coveted plants or the inside of Trey's doghouse. When he grazed down his areas, we'd move him around inside the pen. When he ate what he could there, we'd move him and the house outside the pen. Billy Bob was fine, as long as he could see his good buddy, Trey.

Eventually, as he grew both in size and confidence – that confidence translating to the size of his horns – he became comfortable with being moved to many locations around the farm, as long as he had shelter from any (rare) rain (for which he was a terrible sissy; he *hated* getting wet!). It became okay with him to be tethered around any of the animals, over time, as long as he had companionship and the shelter of his 'goathouse.'

"In our way of life, with every decision we make, we always keep in mind the Seventh Generation of children to come. When we walk upon Mother Earth, we always plant our feet carefully, because we know that the faces of future generations are looking up at us from beneath the ground. We never forget them."
Oren Lyons, Faithkeeper of the Onondaga Nation

January continued, the calm after the chaos of Christmas. I adore the winter months just for this quiet and healing time, after so much celebration and energy gone before. January becomes a month of taking deep cleansing breaths and having the time and eyes to see and feel the world again as she, too, rests and rejuvenates. To center. To simply 'be' for a while. But this quiet month, and our seclusion, was blown out of the water by breaking world news.

The storms of war far from our shores continued taking its toll in Afghanistan, which carried over into Pakistan, as the Taliban tried to flee to safety. The incredibly elaborate caves of Tora Bora had been discovered and, with this discovery, huge caches of weapons and further plans of destruction. Speculation of whether Osama bin Laden was dead or alive continued to fly. It was thought that if he wasn't mortally wounded, that at least he was injured and weakened by months of hiding out in caves in the cruel Afghani winter. Occasionally a tape would appear 'confirming' his existence, but these just added fuel to the fires of speculation. No one knew anything for sure.

It was at this time that America heard of Daniel Pearl's disappearance in Karachi, Pakistan, as he chose to go deep into terrorist territory in promise of a groundbreaking story. Pearl, a talented and well-respected 38-year-old reporter for *The Wall Street Journal,* was kidnapped on January 23rd, 2002. Usually exceptionally careful to cover himself as he researched his stories, Pearl found himself alone in Karachi, which was known as the baddest of the bad in al Qaida/terrorist territory. He was urged not to go, but he was hot on the trail of inside information on Richard Reid – the would-be "shoe bomber" from a month prior. It is thought that Harkat ul-Mujahedeen, a U.S. terrorist with ties to al Qaida, masterminded the kidnapping, claiming Pearl to be a CIA agent.

The Associated Press reported on January 29th that e-mails came over Hotmail to *The New York Times* from a user-name of "kidnapperguy." These phantom, untraceable and ever-changing e-mails made various demands from our government: *"...that Pakistani's detained in Guantanamo Bay, Cuba, be allowed access to their lawyers and families* [a fair and reasonable request], *and that Afghanistan's former ambassador to Pakistan, and the Taliban's most recognized spokesman, Abdul Salam Zaeef, be handed over to Pakistan."* A later e-mail warned, *"Unless demands are met the Amrikans will get what they deserve. Don't think this will be the end. It is the beginning and it is a real war on Amrikans... 'Amrikans will get the taste of death and destructions what we had got in Afghanistan and Pakistan'..."* (*Associated Press*, from Islamabad, Pakistan, © Feb.1st, '02. All rights reserved. Reprinted w/ permission.)

E-mails began to give Pearl only days to live if continued demands were not met. And soon after this news reached America that Daniel Pearl had been gruesomely murdered. Photos were sent as proof. Throughout this ordeal, Marianne Pearl, his pregnant wife – who was also a freelance journalist – pleaded with the captors to release her husband. The story was heartbreaking, an innocent caught in the crossfire of the Islamic jihad against the United States. Even Muhammad Ali, prizefighter turned Muslim devotee, had appealed for Pearl's release.

"Around the world, most journalist's are murdered in reprisal for reporting on official corruption and crime in countries like China, Thailand and Yugoslavia... Pearl's kidnapping suggests that journalists may become political pawns in the terror war..." (*Newsweek*, Feb. 11th, '02, © Newsweek, Inc. All rights reserved. Reprinted by permission.)

The war on terrorism continued, and then attention turned closer to home as the Enron scandal truly hit the fan. Enron – the largest energy-trading company in the world – also happened to become the largest corporate bankruptcy in American history. If the wildfires of 2001 set a precedent for mass scale annihilation of wilderness areas and our National Parks out west, the 'Corporate Scandals of 2002' blazed their own trails through the economic substructure of America. Huge giants of corporations were involved: Enron, Adelphia Cable, WorldCom/MCI. Later even Martha Stewart, herself, got in on the act in an alleged insider trading scandal with her Pharmaceutical friend and confidant, Sam Waksal, over stock in ImClone Systems. The proverbial shit had hit the proverbial fan. So much that a *Wall Street Journal* article from Wednesday, Jan. 30th, read: *"In a warehouse on the Brooklyn waterfront, workers feed a steady stream of documents into shredders the size of a living room. A conveyor belt whisks confidential files of major law and consulting firms, investment banks and other businesses into rows of gnashing blades, which slice them into tangled ribbons. These then get recycled into toilet paper.*

"Arthur Andersen [Enron's notorious accounting firm], *LLP's destruction of papers related to Enron Corp. have given shredding new notoriety…"* The article goes on to describe in detail the increased demand for huge shredders such as these throughout America to protect corporate secrets and prevent identity theft. All I can say is 1) Thank God, all of this is being recycled, 2) this explains why suddenly toilet paper got so cheap, and 3) what a perfect irony that these dirty little corporate secrets evolved into that which America wipes its collective butt.

"Enron was supposed to be the next new thing, a New Economy company with substance to it. Unlike flaky Internet start-ups that substituted ethereal yardsticks like 'eyeballs' and 'stickiness' for revenues and profits, Enron had real businesses, real assets, real revenues and what seemed to be real profits. It owned natural-gas pipelines and electrical-generating plants and water companies. Not only would it do well, it would improve the planet by substituting the efficient hand of the market for the clumsy hand of government regulation… But Enron turned out to be another bubble… [that] exploded like a grenade." (From *Newsweek*, Jan. 21st, '02, © Newsweek, Inc. All rights reserved. Reprinted by permission.)

America came to know Enron chairman Kenneth Lay – or, as the White House knew him, 'Kenny Boy' – as one of the biggest individual contributor's to Bush's presidential and Texas gubernatorial campaigns… His ties to Texas energy were huge; his connections with the current administration ran deep. And then Lay – and his millions – disappeared, as the Enron stocks evaporated in a cloud of corporate smoke. The bread & butter employees of Enron watched their 401k's, tied up in Enron stock – their retirement futures – all disappear as the smoke settled.

I read about this scandal, and the others, shaking my head in disgust, all the while thinking *how low could human nature go?* And then the Catholic Church scandal broke. Was there *no* sanctuary anywhere, any longer?

It is said, "all is fair in love and war." Although Daniel Pearl's death – and the many other journalists killed on the professional frontlines – is horribly tragic, it is a risk they knowingly take. "Corporate Greed" is probably in the dictionary, as the description is so common. Greed, too, is one of the seven deadly sins. I guess, after we stopped reeling from the impact as Enron's demise pointed to such esteemed locales as the White House and Wall Street, Americans should now be immune to such shock.

But the Catholic Church? Is *nothing* sacred and inviolate? Cover-ups of sexual escapades, where a number of trusted priests violated alter boys for decades, (this scandal is being traced back now *sixty* years) – and were protected from this lust, another of the deadly sins, under the omnipotent umbrella of this supposedly holiest of shrines. The world looked to be going to hell in a hand basket. Disgust turned to revulsion and nausea as we read newspapers, *Newsweek,* and watched CNN as the scandal grew. Men and women of all ages were coming out of their shame and hiding, telling torrid stories of these Fathers' 'liberties' with them as children or young teenagers. For heaven's sake, if these priests swear upon celibacy, then have them neutered. If not that, then allow them to marry – women or men, it *is* a brave new world – but for God's sake, leave the children *alone.*

"What shall it profit a man if he shall gain the whole world and lose his own soul?" The Bible, Matthew 16:26

And during all of this good news in our untarnished nation, I continued to read of the continued attacks of the Bush administration on our national environment. As we all looked towards the war on terrorism in the Middle East, "Bush, Inc." looked west towards our National Parks and the Artic National Wildlife Reserve for oil, gas and coal – fossil fuels that line the big boys' pockets while undermining our parks and environmental programs long in place to protect them.

Shortly after his inauguration, the new Bush administration launched the "National Energy Policy Development Group," chaired by Dick Cheney, Vice President. This group became known as the 'energy task force,' and Cheney convened these meetings in utmost secrecy. They were filled with executives and lobbyists from the oil, electric-utility, gas, coal, nuclear, mining and automotive industries. For several months they met in these clandestine groups, blocking those that might have an environmental say until the last few days. The nonpartisan General Accounting Office, for the first time in history, sued the executive branch, demanding access to the records of the energy task force. GAO chief

David Walker asked, *"They just want the basics; who did Mr. Cheney meet with, when, where, and what cost to the tax-payers?"* announcing that his agency will file suit against the White House within three weeks if V.P. Dick Cheney did not turn over information about his meetings with Enron executives. (*Newsweek* quote from its Perspectives page, Feb. 11th, '02)

As Sierra Club president, Carl Pope, said in responding to Cheney's assertion that the group had as much input as Enron did into the Bush energy plan: *"If the Bush administration really thinks their energy plan includes 11 or 12 Sierra Club solutions, then Arthur Andersen must be checking their math."* (*Newsweek,* also from its "Perspectives" page, Feb. 11th, '02).

The Clean Air and Clean Water Acts – protecting our vital resources for over 30 years – were quick to be sacrificed through such underhanded tactics, under the guise of oxymoronic names as "Clear Skies Initiative" and the "Healthy Forest Initiative." Congress has become infamous for pushing through such detrimental legislation on the eve of holidays and on Friday afternoons, when the media are scarce. *What, do they think their children and grandchildren won't be affected by industries given license to lurch and leach even greater amounts of pollutants into our air and water with relaxed standards for older industries?* The situation has become so ludicrous that individual states – with an eye towards their own future – are now suing the federal government to prevent these EPA rollbacks! The Superfund, meant to clean up toxic waste sites, has gone belly-up with lack of funding. Christie Todd Whitman, then president of the Environmental Protection Agency, quit the Bush administration, immensely frustrated by the continuing politics of pollution. History may well score George W. Bush as the Grim Reaper of all presidents for his stealthy (anti)environmental policies of saying one thing and doing entirely another.

The 'Roadless Area Conservation Rule' was finalized in January of 2001, to protect 58.5 million acres from commercial logging and industrial development, just as the Bush administration was moving into office. It was considered to be the most popular undertaking in forest service history, according to EarthJustice, an environmental legal group that defends our lands and water. Since then, the Bush administration has been trying its best to overturn the 'Roadless Rule' and open up our national parks and protected National Forests – including the *Giant Sequoia National Monument* in California – for road building and logging. "The Healthy Forest Initiative" allows timber industries to gain access to old growth forest for board footage and toilet paper, in the guise of clear-cutting the underbrush to prevent forest fires, basing the devastating fires of late as need for these actions. The plans are, however, to

build roads nowhere close to civilization, and to take out mature trees
– not the underbrush. It is, once again, a ploy to circumvent the existing
policy in another underhanded approach, topped with a snazzy name.
Once again the Bush administration has sold America's soul to the company store.

America the Beautiful has been laid out as a bountiful buffet of resources, catered by the White House, expressly for energy corporations
willing to pay lavishly for their seat at the banquet.

I found it extremely ironic that another Republican president, Richard Nixon – who will likely *not* be remembered for these visionary feats
– signed into law The Clean Air Act, the Endangered Species Act and
created The Environmental Protection Agency in the early 70s, working together with a bipartisan Congress. Jim DiPeso, policy director for
Republicans for Environmental Protection (REP), says, "The environment is not, should not, and never should have been made into a polarized, partisan issue. There is no Republican air or Democratic water. We
all benefit from clean air, clean water, and protected public land." The
motto of the REP is "conservation is conservative."

Environmental politics are most certainly not limited to the Democratic Party. The National Park Service and the Forest Service were both
created by Republican president Teddy Roosevelt, who was considered
to be "The godfather of the American conservation movement." The
Artic National Wildlife Refuge (ANWR) – which the Bush administration and his oil cronies so covet – was founded by the vision of a Republican president gone before, Dwight Eisenhower. The Artic National
Wildlife Refuge is considered to be "America's Serengeti," but it won't
be for long if big oil moves in, and builds massive roadways through the
artic wilderness that will remain long after the limited oil is gone.

Bush, Inc. has turned its back entirely on the Kyoto Protocol in 2001,
when, instead, the U.S. should have *lead the way* in global warming reform,
with the knowledge and technology at our fingertips, and the fact that
America creates 25% of carbon dioxide emissions in the world, the main
gas responsible for global warming. This became our first step in isolating and distancing ourselves from the European Union, and the United
Nations – already major grumbles of Imperialism and arrogance have
started.

No, instead, federally mandated tax incentives are given to those
who purchase the monster SUV's and Hummers that gulp down the
gasoline that ultimately line the Bush/Cheney oil pockets and keeps the
umbilical cord tied so securely to the Middle East. American automo-

tive companies are grateful; they want to keep this administration firmly in the White House, as it ignores the fact that although we do have the technology to build vehicles that can get 40-50 mpg, that just wouldn't be as good for an oilmans' business. A bumper sticker I've seen sums it up succinctly: **DRAFT SUV DRIVERS FIRST.**

It is terribly ironic that two respected Congressmen, John McCain (R-AZ) and Joe Lieberman (D-CT), are teaming up to see that the (bipartisan) McCain/Lieberman Climate Stewardship Bill be passed to ensure that America reduces carbon dioxide, and other fossil fuel emissions, drastically. But it's a long, hard road to hoe there in this Congress.

The Bush administration, put simply, is to our environment a massive steamroller, fueled by the energy industries of America, disguised in sugarcoated political rhetoric. Gail Norton – formally an oil and mining *lobbyist* – is now the infamous Secretary of the Interior, whose job it is *to protect our national resources.* She ranks right in there with James Witt in Environmental devastation. She is to our national environment what Cardinal Law was to the Catholic Church in Boston. By both of them standing back and doing nothing, with full knowledge of both the actions and the cover-ups before their eyes, they are tantamount to rapists, plain and simple. One does so on a grand and sweeping scale; the other does so quietly and on the sly. In the end, the results are the same. Something or someone once innocent and pure becomes used and abused, and then tossed aside when deemed no longer of interest. And those of us who love that something or someone are left to pick up the pieces, the fragments of what was once intact and beautiful, and try to figure how to reinstall the soul. It's a long road of many years and many tears, when prevention would have been the simple answer.

No, suddenly the quiet, unsullied month of January, this fresh new beginning of the year 2002, the world – abroad and at home – had turned inside out in greed, twisted ethics, cover-ups, depravity and abuse. Janus had ushered in more than two of the evil faces of mankind, all ugly as sin.

"To announce that there must be no criticism of the President, or that we are to stand by the President, right or wrong, is not only unpatriotic and servile, but is morally treasonable to the American public."
Theodore Roosevelt, The Kansas City Star, May 7th, 1918

I continued to hear nothing from the Powers that Be in the Great American West. I was restless and antsy, wondering just what was transpiring 'out there' and how it was all going to end. Between Thanksgiving and the last time I spoke with Sergeant Coffey right after Thanksgiving, until well after Christmas, there was nothing. Not a word, not a breath from the west – nothing. I felt forgotten and unwanted, after such a ruckus as had gone before. Anytime I made a peep to inquire, Pete would remind me that "No news is good news; count your blessings." But my inquiring mind wanted to know; I did not think, after how irate and perturbed by me these lawmen had been, that they planned to sweep all this under the rug. These fellows planned on teaching me a lesson – they were shooting for a felony charge, trying hard to get B & E to stick. Breaking and entering only *sounded* good to them. Since I hadn't done this at all, I didn't think they could actually claim it, but since this *did* carry the felony charge – and a felony was extraditable – this is what the boys wanted to go for. Think big and all.

But I behaved, and – true to my premise of patience and doing 'something else' in the meantime – kept busy with a myriad of other activities. Natalie and Jared played weekend soccer in the gymnasium at school, through the Department of Recreation. Skye was in her senior year of high school. School activities kept all of us hopping. Pete was again traveling throughout the U.S. I still had a farm full of critters to care for daily; life stayed busy. I finished *Julie*, delivered this portrait, and visited Bette and John at their beautiful home. I started other portraits. Soon I began to think of springtime and, with spring, the promise of a beach vacation in the Outer Banks. Pete and I chose a cottage, made a deposit, and started the fun of anticipating the trip for spring break. And January was soon gone, bringing in February, which continued the mild, dry winter.

There was still no word from the west. Nothing, no word at all, nada. I was beginning to think I was off the hook. The fellows had found better fish to fry than my scrawny carcass. I had had a lot of time to ponder our finding Kokopelli out in open desert country. To me she was the embodiment of all the stray and destitute animals roaming America at any given time: wonderful creatures that have hearts full of love to share, if only given half a chance. In her few short months with us, she had brightened our lives immeasurably; I wanted to give something back. The studio was slow, typical of this time of year, and I needed to stay busy to keep my mind off the doings out west. So I decided to offer my services to organize a fundraiser for our local shelters.

The Humane Society/SPCA of Nelson County was planning to

build a new no-kill pet shelter, to be called "Almost Home Pet Adoption Center," and the Charlottesville-Albemarle SPCA was in the process of building a new and larger facility. Both needed buckets of money to see this happen. I contacted my dear and gracious friend of years, Bette Grahame; she is the mainstay of the Nelson program. Martina Navratilova told the press years ago: *"Think of commitment as this. Think of eggs and ham: the chicken is involved, but the pig is committed. I am committed."* (And she was: a fiery force behind tennis, lobbing the way for female athletes to follow. She and Billie Jean King.) Bette Grahame has that unadulterated commitment to the needy animals in this area south of town. God Bless her. She and her colleagues are the Saint Francis' of Nelson County, much as Sally Meade was to the Charlottesville-Albemarle SPCA years ago. Sally's dedication had put the latter on the map.

So I contacted Bette and suggested a lunch to talk about these ideas, and I contacted the staff at the Charlottesville shelter to arrange a meeting with the board with my ideas. My contact there at the time, Whitney Mason, was a firecracker of an organizer with brilliant ideas; she was excited by my proposal for the fundraiser, the proceeds of which would be divided by both organizations. I envisioned a rock concert at Charlottesville's new amphitheater on the downtown mall. I knew bands that would be very happy to donate their time to perform for such an event. I called City Hall and jumped through their hoops, trying to figure all the permissions and permits that would be necessary to see this happen.

I wanted to organize a huge raffle, with the drawing to be held on the afternoon of the concert. I pictured an array of generous gifts donated from businesses throughout the city and both counties (I would donate a customized portrait). But, because a raffle was considered gambling, and we intended on making a good amount of money, I had to contact the Bureau of Gambling in Richmond. This I did and I received all the specifics of 'hosting' such an event. After I'd done some homework, I called Bette and asked that we have lunch to discuss these ideas – and to tell her the Kokopelli story.

By the time Bette and I met for lunch, I was on fire with ideas and enthusiasm, ready to roll, with volumes of support from friends and businesses ready to see this event become a rollicking reality. We had our buckets ready to fill with some of the mullah these shelters required to build brand new facilities. I told Bette the story over lunch, as we laughed our way through the escapades. She was delighted by the course of events and that Kokopelli was still with us – and that I wasn't in jail. We discussed our plans for the fundraiser, and she shared ideas of her own. And by the end of this delightful lunch I told her that perhaps that was the last we'd hear from the west. *Wrong.* That evening of our wonderful and lengthy lunch, the Long Arm of the Law again reached east.

Late afternoon from town I called Pete about meeting at the gym for our Friday night workout. He told me that we had received a letter from Cynthia, still in New Mexico, a letter from Will (still stationed in the Persian Gulf on the USS Peterson) – and a certified letter from the Williams County Courthouse, in Williams, Arizona, from Judge William Sutton, himself. *Nope, not over at all.* Pete said it was for me and refused to open it, but he said he'd bring it to town. He was still distancing himself, the cad.

We met at ACAC and had our workout. Afterwards we had seafood at the Outback Steakhouse. I had purposefully not opened any of the mail, saving Will's and Cynthia's letters for dessert and the certified letter for heartburn. It burned a hole in my gym bag with anticipation of what might be in there, but I knew that what*ever* it was, it was *not* an invitation to a tea. The good ole' boys out west had not forgotten me at all; they had just silently been doing their homework as to the next step of this whole legal procedure. They were still likely out for blood: *mine.*

Pete and I had a quiet dinner at the Outback with a lively red-haired lady as our waitress; I opened the letter from Will and found a computerized photo of him in a wet suit, looking like he had been swimming in oil. I admired the shot; Brad Pitt has nothing on my dapper nephew… Criminy, what a lady-killer smile… As for the oil, indeed he *had* been swimming in it – they'd been policing the coast of Iran/Iraq for black market oil shipments out of Kuwait. These illegal shipments would be found in old grain-carrying ships carrying oil, instead. Indeed, that fateful night the USS Peterson had located a very ancient single-hulled tanker carrying this contraband and had seized the ship. Eight navy crewmembers were placed on board to guard the ship overnight. But a nor'easter blew in, creating 12-foot swells and capsizing this old ship, which was weighted down by the heavy oil. The sailors aboard were on the verge of drowning. Several of the crew of the Peterson had been trained for this sort of emergency and Will was one of them; he had been thinking of becoming a Navy Seal and had taken appropriate courses. So he donned his wetsuit and diving gear, dove into the high swells of the stormy sea, and was able to save a life or two that night in the oil-slickened waters off of that Middle Eastern coast. He later received the Navy/Marine Life Saving Medal, for heroism in the act of duty, which he proudly tells me is tantamount to the Purple Heart.

But that wicked night this is not what he was thinking, as the waves furiously crashed around them. After the old ship had sunk, and the headcount of the crewmembers was tallied, it was found that two of the USS Peterson crew had died in the sinking of the old Kuwaiti ship.

Will was very proud to have been part of this heroic night, but deeply saddened by the loss of his friend, one of these two men. What I was thinking of was of Marcy's reaction to her son's lifesaving adventure; she would have been blessedly relieved that Will had made it out safely. The idea of his becoming a Navy Seal had terrified her; she just desperately wanted her boy to come home alive and intact. I was as proud of my young nephew as I could be, but continued to say prayers on a regular basis that he would do just that: come home safely. He and all of the others.

Finally I could put off the inevitable no longer. I opened my certified mail. Inside were two pages of official-looking documents, which included a summons from the state of Arizona to me, described as the defendant, to join this merry crew in court on the 20th of February at 10AM, Mountain Time. It continued: If I failed to appear, a warrant would be issued for my arrest. It was signed by Judge William Sutton. I wondered briefly if such a surname was required in order to be a judge in Williams, Arizona.

The second page had my name and address, other pertinent information (sans Social Security Number), and listings for as many violations as five, but only the one filled out: Criminal Trespassing in the 1st Degree, a Class 1 Misdemeanor. *Oh well, this is good, I thought; they did reduce it from a felony to this lesser charge, and a misdemeanor was not extraditable. Although I wasn't entirely off the hook, as least I wouldn't be traveling back to Arizona in handcuffs and leg chains.* My good buddy, Deputy Glenn Isbel, #69, signed this page himself. His lust for my blood had been diluted to something less, over time, probably to his chagrin.

As far as the fundraising event, two things happened. Bette was excited and intrigued with the possibilities and appreciative of the support, but the Charlottesville/Albemarle SPCA thought they had too many irons in the fire to add another. Whitney was let go, under odd circumstances, and new leadership was underway. The shelter was in a flux. As my own life, too, had just re-fluxed, I called Bette and gracefully as I could backed out, telling her of the other shelters' decision and of my news from the west. She, bless her, graciously understood.

I was now free to turn my full attention to the task at hand, which again happened to be untangling myself from my honesty – or stupidity – of admitting to the Arizona law that yeah, it had been me who had reclaimed the lonesome and untrained pup from the four walls of that man's imprisonment on that deep dark Arizona night back in November. Someday, perhaps, I'll learn to keep my mouth shut.

FORTY-THREE

Biting the Bullet Telephonically

"Until you've lost your reputation, you never realized what a burden it was." Margaret Mitchell

Several days after the arrival of the registered letter from the west I called the number provided in the papers, found that the area code had changed, and called again. I spoke with a young woman with the lovely, lyrical singsong voice of the Navajo, which she confirmed. I had questions for Elaine Crane, who clerked in the Williams District Court, and whose name had been on these papers. But Lucy, the Navajo lady, said Elaine was on vacation for the rest of the week. She asked if she could help.

I asked her a few questions about the upcoming trial. Still in search of the illusive answer, I also asked if she might be able to verify that "dog" in Navajo translated to "shit eater," or "eater of shit," – and if she knew how to spell this word "dog."

Lucy gave an embarrassed little laugh and said that she was sadly amiss in her own language. She had been working in Belagaana's world so long that she was afraid she was losing her native tongue. But she would see if she might be able to find this information in a book she thought she had on Navajo oral translations to the written word. I thanked her for her help and told her I looked forward to speaking with her again.

When I called Williams District Court two weeks later, exactly at noon, as appointed, I spoke this time with Elaine Crane, the clerk who had been on vacation. She was young, polite, and in charge. She said

Judge Sutton would be on the phone in just a moment – he was tied up on another call just now – so we talked a bit. She was very friendly. I asked if Lucy had been able to find the Navajo translation for "dog," and I heard her, in a muffled voice, ask Lucy about this. Elaine must have covered the receiver of the phone, but I could still faintly hear Lucy tell her that she had been unable to locate that book and to tell me she was very sorry. Elaine came back with this message and then cleared her throat, "Okay, Ms. Gia-nee-nee," she drew out the syllables, trying to pronounce my name correctly, "Judge Sutton's line just cleared. You can speak with him now." I complimented her on the pronunciation and thanked her; the good judge came on the line.

We exchanged introductions and pleasantries. He was an elderly gentleman, very calm and respectful. I pictured Andy Griffith, right out of *Matlock*, without the accent. I could hear him shuffling through some pages of notes and then a chuckle, "Young lady, I take it you don't do things like this very often."

"No sir," I laughed. "The last time I was in trouble with the law was some twenty years ago, over a speeding ticket."

He chuckled again, "I thought so. You continue to cooperate, and we'll see if we can't go easy on you. Now you just let me do the talking. I'll explain how the process goes." This was fine by me; the redoubtable voice on the line was quiet and grandfatherly, eliciting respect and compliance.

He went on to explain that this case could all likely be handled telephonically, with prearranged dates for a pretrial conference, in which the State's Attorney, or his/her assistant, offers a plea agreement. At that point he/she and I would negotiate and come to an understanding as to the plea. If I were to plead "Guilty," why then we would come to some sort of settlement as to my fine and punishment. If I were to ultimately plead "Innocent," why it would go to court, at which point I would be tried by jury and would probably have to return west.

Judge Sutton told me that setting this in motion would take three weeks time, give or take, and that I should call when the papers arrive, find who the Prosecuting Attorney would be and be sure he/she had copies of the witness statements, phone records and photographs, all proof of ownership detailing the sequence of events. In other words, they needed to be fully informed of the case and prepared to go forward towards closure.

He explained that for a Criminal Misdemeanor, 1st Degree, the maximum sentence for such cases might run $2,500, 180 days in jail, and/or a one-year probation on each charge. I told him that as far as I knew, there was just the one. The judge felt that I would likely be fined much less – in the $200-$500 range, with no jail time. My thoughts raced: *If I cooperated, they would allow me to return to Arizona without the threat of jail looming over me if I so much as jay-walked, or was caught speeding through the Coconino National Park, or took a dog down into the Canyon… any dastardly little thing that would have them checking my I.D., thus realize I was the notorious puppy-thief from out east. Ta Dah! They had me! The fugitive, the vigilante escapee…! And I'd wind up in the slammer, locked away from Pete and the kids, from Kokopelli and all of our other critters, from my friends and my studio and backlog of paintings. All while they were deciding just what to do with such a hardened criminal…*

But alas, all this probably won't be happening as I *am* cooperating; I am polite. And I am smugly aware of the continued absurdities of this whole situation; my curiosity is overcoming any fear of these unknowns and 'what might lurk'… I continue to be amused and inquisitive as to this new direction my life has taken over this crazy little dog. Before we hung up, I pled "Not guilty of any criminal wrongdoing" to Judge Sutton. There. It's now on the record. I continued to stand by my guns.

As promised, within three weeks time a second certified letter arrived from Bill Sutton Jr., Justice of the Peace, Williams, Arizona, postmarked February 26th, 2002. This was to set up and confirm a pretrial conference for the "21st day of March, 2002, at 1:30PM, at the office of the Coconino County Attorney, in Flagstaff, Arizona." Again, I was the defendant, and again this was to be handled telephonically. Below this read, "NO CONTINUANCES WILL BE GRANTED UNLESS RECEIVED IN WRITING AT LEAST 48 HOURS PRIOR TO THE DATE ABOVE. FAILURE TO APPEAR AT YOUR PRE TRIAL CONFERENCE WILL RESULT IN A WARRANT BEING ISSUED FOR YOUR ARREST." Below this, "Copies of the foregoing mailed this 26th day of February, 2002, to the following: County Attorney, Christine Nelson, and Ms. Laura Giannini." Signed was a Rorschach ink squiggle of a signature, and below this, "Bill Sutton, Jr., Justice of the Peace, Williams Precinct, Williams, AZ."

Two pages were attached to this, one of which was an "INITIAL APPEARANCE PROCEEDINGS," with a list of items checked that had already transpired with our first telephonic conference, and a plea of "Not guilty" checked. The third page was written on an "Arizona Traffic Ticket and Complaint" sheet from the Coconino County Sheriff's Department, with the report #, the fact that my SSN was refused, my address, sex, origin (WH) and date of birth were included. No identification of vehicle was described, but time of this Criminal Trespassing was listed as 11/14/01 at 0900 AM. The date exactly of the Missionaries being released in Afghanistan, but not exactly the date of my "crime."

What? Had Ricardo not come home that night at all, or were they setting the date at the time the crime was reported?

This closed with Ricardo — the 'victim's'(*Excuse me, but I just can't seem to comprehend this liar and original thief being the victim here… All along I've thought it was the pup…*) — address and the violation being "Criminal Trespassing, 1st Degree, ARS, Section 13-1504A1 and the docket number. This page was signed more legibly by Glenn Isbell, *(not Isabella at all, see)* Complainant, PSN #69. *Ah, the old 69…*

Okay. Very formal and very final, and I could deal with this. In about a month, just before our family headed off on spring vacation, I would have our telephonic pretrial conference with Judge Sutton. Good enough.

After a few days of thinking of this impending conference looming in the future and clouding our vacation plans like a distant tropical storm building out of Africa, I called the Williams District Court with a few questions on my mind. I was informed that I could no longer talk with Judge Sutton — not until our final telephonic conference, which would be scheduled after the pretrial conference had taken place.

I still had the questions, so I called Randrue and explained to him what had transpired. He asked then if I would like him to be present during this conference, representing me on a 3-way call. A rush of relief washed over me, as this was all old-shoe to him and all a new frontier to me. I could use a hand to hold.

The month of March passed on by. Spring was in glorious bloom around us, early with the mild winter, and intense, despite the drought, almost in defiance of lack of significant rainfall or credible snow over the winter.

Redbuds abounded, their misnamed color far more magenta than red. But what*ever* the color, they sang a bright tune against deep cedars and early blooms of dogwood trees. Dogwoods, Virginia's lovely state flower, bloomed in snowy whites, pale delicate pinks and deeper 'reds' — or more aptly, salmon pinks. Azaleas, in a riot of colors ranging from whites to pinks and reds on to an array of lavender tones, sang counterpoint in the glorious floral concert.

The golden notes of forsythia had truly heralded in an early spring, but had come and gone in late February/early March, in symphony with the daffodils, jonquils and tulips that peeped out to bloom, but only half-heartedly this year. They were tired and thirsty, their throats too dry to sing in tune; they saved their dewy best for a wetter spring.

I finished my commissions to be delivered before leaving for the Outer Banks, and waited for this strange pretrial conference to come and go. It sat heavily in my mind, a fat shadow of questions, never quite fading away.

During this time, Kokopelli continued to grow and thrive on our farm. I hadn't yet had her spayed, as I normally do with all of our dogs at six months of age, regardless. For Kokopelli I was holding out, entertaining the idea of finding a blue-eyed Siberian husky, with the temperament of Lakota, to sire one litter of pups when Pelli turned two years old. This wasn't a given yet in my mind, and the personality of the father would be crucial to my decision, but I wanted to at least have the option.

I had had our pets spayed and neutered all of my life; I'd always been responsible about this. But I realized in doing so, our children had never experienced the wonder of birth, despite living on a farm. If Pelli had one litter with this 'miracle male,' we would keep one or two of these pups ourselves, and would have no problems finding excellent homes for the others, as several friends had already shown a keen interest. And then I would have her spayed. But first let her grow out of puppyhood, herself.

In January, at six months, she had come into her first heat, causing a stir on the farm and our diving into the books to learn how to cope with nature. Neighborhood dogs –males of all types – came out of the woodwork. I had no idea there were so many unneutered fellows running around. A blip seemed to have filtered into all their homes: Bitch in heat, *propagate, propagate!*

Pete, the kids and I were amazed. We duly kept her inside, except for her walks, chased the horny hounds out of our yard, and within a few weeks this heat passed and the farm settled down to whatever 'normal' is in our lives. I was astounded that a pup so young, only six months old, could already begin the cycle all over again. No wonder the world abounded in unwanted strays; this was a cruel joke on Mother Nature's part.

During these winter months melting into spring, Kendrick Plastics was installing a new computer system called SAP. In my opinion, it was the computer straight from hell. German manufactured and the highest of tech, it promised to expedite, accelerate and update all of the systems within the company to one smoothly purring state-of-the-art whole. That was the plan. But as Steinbeck knew, *"the best laid plans of mice and men…"*

This computer system was managing to become the nightmare of every intelligent breathing soul in the company; there was no level that it did not touch. Employees of all status were expected to put in overtime hours, preparing for this monstrosity to go on line. The original start-date was to have been February 1st – but no one was nearly prepared in the computereze required for this to happen, so a new date was arbitrarily set: 2 months later, or the 1st of April. April Fool's Day. Brilliant.

No one happened to think that this *might* not have been the most strategic date to switch all systems to go on a computer that no one yet understood – as all directions were in German. And no one happened to look at the calendar and see that this was also the day after Easter Sunday and the beginning of spring break in our school systems. No, it was written in stone that all key employees would work Good Friday through Easter Sunday, in preparation for **The Transition**, as well as all of the following week, to iron out the inevitable bugs. There went our long-planned vacation.

But even Pete, as loyal to the company as a bloodhound to the trail, mutinied. We had planned our spring break for months around the school schedule for time off and away from this stress. Now they expected him to work these cruel, relentless hours straight through the break – in*clud*ing Easter weekend! Goddamn it, he was going. Many, many people in the company felt exactly the same way. People throughout Kendrick were already strained and stressed by this nightmare technology; overtime and weekend hours had replaced rest. The corporate beast was swallowing its own lifeblood. Tempers were shortened by the oncoming deadline and frenzied hours all had worked in preparation of this beast going on-line continued. This was just asking too much. So we continued to plan our vacation, as the pretrial date loomed closer. The next thing we knew, it was there.

Randy and I arranged to have lunch at Guadalajara, a family-owned Mexican restaurant, before the conference in order to discuss our strategy and to simply catch up with one another's life. He arrived before I did and stood as I joined him. Randy stands about 5'9 or 5'10, not an especially tall man, but an especially bright one. He is quick and clever and a fellow envelope-pusher, but his version of envelope pushing, however — that I was aware of (I also imagined he owned a courtroom version, as well) — came in the great outdoors. He is a fearless kayaker, mountain biker and climber, always pushing himself to the limits of skill and endurance.

Years ago he and Pete had gone hiking in the mountains on a frigid wintery day. When they came home, a degree away from frostbitten extremities and general exposure to the cold, but nonetheless ecstatic, Kathie and I came to find that these two brave and foolish men of ours had been climbing ice falls all afternoon. Had one of them slipped and fallen they might have been impaled by jagged ice daggers below them, or died of hypothermia, in the frigid waters far away from civilization. But this thought hadn't seemed to cross their minds, or if it had, hadn't lingered. I knew that Pete, left to his own devices, would not have tempted this blustery, potentially disastrous, fate. But Randrue's influence brought out the latent adventurous adolescent in him every time.

I also remembered Monroe, another of Pete and Randy's college buddies, and a dear friend. The three of these boys, and one other — Tom — had been very tight in those days, doing everything together. Monroe had married a fine lady named Annie; they had two adorable daughters and lived in New Jersey. Monroe had composed music and taught at Kingsborough Community College, in Brooklyn, New York.

Money lived on the edge, like Randrue, but took one risk too many when he and a friend camped in a cabin midway up Mount Washington, in New Hampshire, in late February of '94. They began the climb early in the day, realized they had left important equipment back at their cabin and returned to get it. This put them off to a late start for their trek up the mountain. Halfway up a storm blew in — Mount Washington is known for its unpredictable weather — and the two became caught on a cliff. They were unable to return to the cabin, or to advance. Monroe and his friend were found frozen to death on the edge of the mountainside, which saw this wicked winter storm plunge to −120° below zero, including the wind chill factor.

Kathie had called us with the unbelievable news of Monroe's death. We were stunned and in shock as all of the college friends, and now their families, gathered to mourn our adventurous friend. Dear sweet Monroe: 6'5, tall and gangly as Abe Lincoln, with a wild shock of gingery hair and his perpetually smiling, long, kindly face…It was crazy; it was surreal. We were living a scene out of *The Big Chill*, as we gathered graveside on the University grounds, with Annie and their girls in attendance. My heart just broke for this nascent family, left with only his colorful memories. *There but for the grace of God go any of us*, I thought, standing there in March, freezing, as Monroe's eulogy was read and I watched Annie standing stoically, their daughters on either side of her, too young to know the magnitude of that moment. Monroe's parents stood quietly and in shock, unbelieving that they were burying their son. God. I kept thinking back to when Money sat at our kitchen table at Highland Avenue, in Charlottesville, earnestly trying to convince me that it had been medically proven that cinnamon was hallucinogenic. Dear nutty, sweet Monroe. He, too, had lived outside the box.

Such were the memories in my mind of our dear friend, Randrue, and those of Monroe, and the history of the circles of friendships that go back so many years, as I gave this man a big hug. Randy's bright blue eyes danced under his graying black brows, the impish little boy still very much alive in the middle-aged man before me.

"Larue!" He greeted me warmly, "So how is our own east-coast puppy-snatcher?" he asked with his laughing articulate voice.

"Fine, fine, Randrue. Looking forward to this day," I told him sarcastically, as we were both seated. "Actually, I *have* been looking forward to our lunch, and a chance for a good visit – but this conference thing has been weighing heavy."

"Don't let it get to you, Laura. It's no big deal, just one step in the process. Really. Don't sweat it. So how is Pete?"

We visited and laughed, partaking in the bountiful Mexican fare. I told Randy of the computer fiasco at Kendrick and how we were trying to get our taxes done in between all the madness, and of our plans for our upcoming family vacation. I told him of 'Little Baaad Billy Bob's' joining the family, how Kokopelli was doing, and of the bonfire we were hosting for Skye and Jared to celebrate their upcoming birthdays in late March. I loved it that they wanted to invite their friends and still celebrate at home in these teenage years. I invited he and Kathie and their trio to join us. He said he might bring his kids out, but wasn't sure about Kathie's plans – they continued to be very distant, and chances for reconciliation weren't very hopeful. He also said his father was not responding especially well to the medication for his cancer, and if it was hard on his dad, it was even harder for his mom. Our conversation turned somber for a while as he talked. Here he needed a friend, so I listened and then the conversation took a turn to the west, but not in legal matters.

Randy told me of excursions he had had in Utah, in Canyonlands National Park, the Arches and Moab, areas I longed very much to see.

He shared tales of wonderful mountain biking and hiking trips of other years. We compared our notes and I shared with him more of our travels, both in 2000, with the kiddos, and of our anniversary trip in the year past. And soon it was time to head back to his office for our 3-way conference with Christine Nelson, the County Attorney assigned this very important case.

We sat in his office mid-afternoon, waiting for the predestined time to call of 1:30 PM, Flagstaff Time, and we talked of music. We reminisced of Monroe, and his avant-garde compositions, and laughed over different memories we had of our friend. Music had been these boys' connection back in those carefree days of college; it connected to this day.

Randrue, like Pete, loved jazz. He, like Pete, played music: Pete, the trumpet and fluegel horn, and Randy the saxophone, flute and piano. The two old friends loved to get together and jam and now Jared, at times, joined them on clarinet or piano. We talked of Mark Knopfler – of whom Randrue is also a fan – and Steely Dan, and he introduced me to Norah Jones, Ravi Shankar's daughter. He put on her new CD, *Come Away with Me.* Her sweet voice was wonderfully soothing, as the minutes before our deadline ticked away. We listened until it was 3:30 EST and it was time to call.

Christine Nelson answered and told us that yes, she had all of our information and just needed to ask me a few questions. She wanted to be sure I understood everything and went on to explain what to expect of the upcoming telephonic trial with Judge Sutton in April; Randy listened to her questions, interjecting with his own now and then.

Eventually it came to her telling me, in order to settle this case, that I would need to change my plea from "Not guilty" – which would mean I needed to go before a jury for sentencing – to "Guilty," and that they would need a fingerprint. It was here I balked.

"Excuse me, Ms. Nelson," I cleared my throat and Randy looked over at me, his hand over the receiver, "It's okay, Laura, all of this is standard," he whispered. "Excuse me, but I have two questions," I continued. "First off, if I change my plea from "Not guilty," don't you have a more neutral plea than the other extreme of admitting guilt? And two, *no* one, not *ever* to this date, has required, or even *men*tioned, a fingerprint. Why is this coming out of the blue now?" I was perturbed by this new bit of information.

"Well, as to your first question, yes, there is a plea of 'No contest,' which, technically, I suppose, is a little more neutral. You could plead that and it would stand."

"Then I will." I said, with no hesitation, my voice firm. Gone was the trepidation over this call.

"As for your second question about the fingerprint, why, that's just standard procedure. You'll need to send that back with the papers I'll be sending you after this call."

"And why is that?" I asked her. It was a simple question. Randy rolled his eyes; they said, 'Laura, don't be difficult.' I rolled mine right back at him. I felt like being difficult just now. And I wanted an answer.

"Well, to prove that it's you. To have your prints on record. They're important in closing this case. Your plea is necessary, as well as your agreement to the fine."

"And what is that?" I asked.

"$300. It's a straight fine of $300 for the Criminal Trespassing charge, with no jail time and no probation. Do you agree to these terms, Ms. Giannini?"

There it was, laid out in black and white in front of me. Randrue was nodding his head, 'Yes, take it! *Take* it!' he seemed to be fervently saying.

"I tell you what, Ms. Nelson. This sounds fair enough – all, except that fingerprint. Why don't you send the papers on out and we'll look them over before I totally agree."

"Good enough." She said, over the lines from her office in Flagstaff, Arizona. "I'll send the papers directly on. Would you like them sent to your home, Ms. Giannini, or to your office, Mr. Parker?"

Randy responded immediately, "Send them to my office; I'll look them over first, before Ms. Giannini signs and we'll discuss it." He gave her the office address.

"Okay then, I think we're done here. Is there anything else?" Christine Nelson asked.

I looked across the desk at Randy and he nodded a 'no.'

"I don't think so, Ms. Nelson. Thank you for your time today. We'll look forward to the papers."

We hung up our phones and I looked over at Randrue. He gave me a big smile, "Take it, Larue. *Take it.* You're getting off with a hand-slap, and then it's settled. They've withdrawn the bazookas."

"I want to see the fine print, Randrue. I'll read the papers first – and I've got to think about that fingerprint thing."

He rolled his eyes again and shook his head. "Don't let that be a show-stopper, Laura. It really is *not* a big deal."

"It is to me, my friend. It is to me. It's the principal of it all."

The papers came a few days before we left. I met Randy in town to look them over; he had scrutinized them and said that everything was in order and again strongly recommended that I sign and be done with this fiasco.

With my mind on ten thousand picayune details to be done before we could leave our farm and our lives for a week, and thinking of a friend's sage comment, "It's not senility, it's saturation," I took the packet with me, intending to be in contact with Ms. Nelson from the beach. I'd deal with sending them back later, after I'd had a chance to read them over carefully, and then respond. At least this set the ball in motion. The next step would be the date for my final telephonic conference with Judge Sutton, to be scheduled for sometime later in April.

Hoping spring grasses might be more inclined to grow with the horses off the fields and not eagerly hunting down every delicate new blade of grass that dared show its hopeful head, we once again trailered them to Barboursville Vineyards' grand pastures. Thankfully late March was bringing enough rains to entice a hopeful carpet of tender greens; *please God, let the rains continue to nourish this bone-dry world*, I silently begged him. He must have been listening, as spring brought rains enough to cajole the fields to grow and bring in one fine crop of first-cutting hay before the spigots above once again turned off, and the awful drought continued.

Pete came home shortly before our leaving for the beach. He looked exhausted and worn down, desperately in need of this vacation. He changed into jeans and a denim shirt, grabbed a Sam Adams and led me to the back deck. "I've got really bad news, Laura. Brace yourself."

I looked at him, thinking a friend at work had died. "André just resigned. He's joining Christine in Australia; this timing has something to do with his visa there." He took a long sip of his ale, as his eyes wandered over the deep shadows of afternoon on our back fields. "His last day is Friday." He looked over at me tiredly. Well, here was the kiss of death on our vacation. Without André there to hold down the fort this upcoming weekend and next week, as the SAP computer system went on-line, there would most certainly be no vacation.

I groaned, for him, for us, for the kids, but mostly for him. We had all looked forward to this trip so much; and Pete, more than any of us, needed it so badly. This man needed rest, some downtime with no one clammering at him constantly to put out fires. As he put it, he yearned for the chance to 'hear his ribs crack,' which was his term for deep relaxation. My heart just bled for my good husband. "Pete, there's no other way for you to take this trip?" I asked.

"Ra, you know the answer to that. I was bucking the system at work in the first place, as unfair as it is right now for them to be asking what they are. But there is just no way that I can leave my employees stranded like that, without André there, at least. I've got to stay, but you all go on. I've got to work through the weekend – and week – now. There's no use for you all to just sit at home, twiddling your thumbs waiting for me, when we have the cottage already rented."

"We have renters insurance just for crisis' like this. We can stay and be your back up system. You *will* be able to come home at night, won't you?" It suddenly occurred to me that he might be held prisoner there, sleeping on a cot with others in that boat, to get this damn job done.

"Yes, I'll be home at night – but I can't say just when. Whenever the work gets done for that day. It'll be a zoo. You all go, Laura. Take the kids. There's no need for all of you to be impacted because of this. *Go*. I'll be fine. I can watch golf on TV in my down time, and not have to hear it from you." He nudged my arm and gave me a weak smile, then finished his beer.

"Is there a chance you might be able to at least come down for my birthday? That's next Thursday. Maybe you could drive down after work Wednesday night? At least be able to take a *couple* of days off for your scheduled vacation?" I asked him hopefully.

He looked over, "Maybe that'll work. But I'll have to pull teeth."

Pete did pull teeth, working it out that he would drive down after work Thursday, the day *of* my birthday, which gave him all of Friday off and Saturday, too, at the beach, before we would have to check out on Sunday. Will, now fresh out of the Navy and back in school, was planning to come and visit the farm at the beginning of the week, his spring break as well, so Skye decided to stay home, see him, and keep her dad company on the trip down.

I left the farm and Kokopelli in Pete and Skye's capable hands, taking Jared and Natalie with me in our Taurus, Jaws. Jared, hot off the press of sweet sixteen, was learning to drive. We were logging in hours behind the wheel for Virginia's new graduated driving program, whereupon the student drives 40 hours – hopefully in an array of road conditions – with their parent or legal guardian, after they had taken their drivers education course through the school. This would be an excellent opportunity for Jared to log in Interstate hours, both day and night, as the roads were not busy Easter Sunday, the day we departed. As a precaution I drove through the Richmond area, but Jared did the Lion's share of driving, adding another five hours to his log and arriving one giant step closer to his transition to 'manhood,' (this definition translated through the independence of wheels). He was pleased as could be, and young Natalie had been a fine backseat cheerleader, reminding him of road conditions and speed limits, in between her chapters of Harry Potter's antics. We arrived in Avon late and in a light rainfall, found the keys at the rental outlet, and settled into our cottage by the sea.

Since Pete had to work, I had packed my journals, a suitcase of reference materials and plenty of paper and pens to start this book — the mind-staggering reliving of this incredible journey. When the kids were diverted, I planned to write.

Mary drove down from her coastal home to visit us Monday. She arrived, stout and sturdy, a big smile on her tanned face and her long and lustrous gray hair pulled back neatly with a spray of flowers tucked in, in celebration of Easter and of spring.

Mary is fourteen years older than me and was a mother figure at times in my turbulent adolescence; we have been close since then. After the knife wounds healed she could no longer have children of her own, and she had never had daughters, so I had shared mine. From the beginning she and Skye have been close, forming a tender bond over the years, as Skye grew up with Mary ever in the wings, loving and supportive. The two have a precious subtle bond, formed as much by unspoken gestures as by words.

When Skye was thirteen and hanging with a neighborhood friend, these two began to do wild, dumb and foolish things — the kind of trusting stupidity that gets young girls raped or killed in this madcap world. We had had several disappearances of young girls precisely this age in Spotsylvania County — close enough to be far too close for comfort. Three teenagers, two of them sisters that had disappeared from their front yard at the same time, had vanished from the safety of their homes, later to be found raped and strangled and tossed aside. It was a tragic heartbreak for the state of Virginia; the unknown killer remained lurking behind every strange man who drove a dark pickup truck. Shadows of doubt swirled in our uneasy minds, as we pulled our children close, wanting only to protect them.

One day at dusk I had found Skye and her friend, Rachel, walking alone — sitting duck's — on our backcountry road. After dropping Rachel by her home I had lit into Skye, who sat pouting and sullen beside me.

"Have you not been paying *any* attention to the news? To these girls disappearing in their own yards? Skye, this sick man *rapes and kills* these girls and then throws them away like garbage. Don't think it can't – or won't – be you. It doesn't always happen 'only to someone/somewhere else.' This brutal kind of attack happened to your own *Aunt Mary*, Skye, *in her own home!* There are madmen that look perfectly normal in this crazy world. People you just can't trust." As we drove home, I found myself telling my shocked young daughter the vivid ghastly details of Mary's attack and Galen's murder, this young cousin that she never knew she had had. She had always thought Sean was Mary's only son.

When I finished, drawing in a deep cleansing breath to refill my lungs with fresh pure air, I stopped the car beside the road and looked over at my precious, precocious, innocent daughter, watching the stubborn belligerence of thirteen slip from her face. Angry tears streamed down my face as I had relived the attack through the retelling; her own eyes flooded in disbelief and she said, "You really do care. You really *do* love me, Mom?"

I had looked at her, stunned by this question and her strange response to what I had just spontaneously shared, in order to save her from herself. "Of course I do. Of course I love you, Skye. Why do you think I worry so?"

"I dunno'." She had responded. "You're always so busy and distracted. Did that really happen to Aunt Mary?" She ventured tentatively, unbelieving.

"Yes it did. All of it. I was waiting to tell you when you were older, and I didn't mean to tell you like this – but your actions forced it out. Jared and Natalie don't know anything about this, Skye, and I'd appreciate it very much if you wait until they're older and I can tell them when the time is right – whenever that is. But you can come to me with any questions at all. And I'll let Mary know, so you can talk with her, too, or with Dad."

We continued to discuss the attack, the car pulled off on the side of the lonesome country road. When we returned home she and I were much closer. Her belligerence disappeared, as did her wanderings with Rachel at dusk.

When Skye later visited Mary, during our next Easter vacation at the beach, Mary had said that Skye had not talked with her directly about the attack, but had been absolutely devoted and attentive, treating her aunt as if she were a rare and delicate flower. Their relationship grew even closer, although I don't think to this day they have been able to broach the subject of that godless fall day in October of 1969.

Mary stayed on a couple of days, as we visited and beach combed and caught up with our lives, exchanging Easter baskets and sisterly goodies. When Mary left for home on Wednesday, Natalie returned to her *Chamber of Secrets*, and Jared left on his bike to explore Avon. I began perusing my journals, trying to figure how to begin such an undertaking as *The Kokopelli Journals*, when I'd never written more than long letters to my friends or chapters in my journals before. But I hunkered down and got started, at least, as I waited for my overwrought husband and older daughter to join our family and make five. It was here that I read the package sent from the west and responded with a letter to Christine Nelson concerning our recent conversation, planning to type it out and send it on, once we returned.

Christine Nelson, Dep. Atty.
Office of the County Attorney
Coconino County, Arizona, etc.   April 3rd

Dear Ms. Nelson:

I am responding to the telephonic conference that you and I had on Thursday, March 21st, along with my friend and attorney here in Virginia, Randy Parker. During the course of that conversation, we were told of my options to the plea bargaining, and that I was to be fined $300, should I choose to pay this, rather than continue the case in court. The three of us agreed to a plea of "No contest," in lieu of my original plea of "Not guilty" – or changing it altogether to "Guilty." We asked that you send the papers to Virginia, for Randy and me to look over, which you promptly did. Thank you.

At no point before this conversation, with my telephonic conversation with Judge Sutton on February 20th – that I recall – with either Deputy Dick or Deputy Isbell, or with any of my talks with Sergeant Coffey, was it ever mentioned that you all would need a fingerprint. Good grief – I was barely given my Miranda Rights by Sergeant Coffey... The way he informed me of them was downright comical; I truly doubt that this would stand up in court. But this is neither here nor there. It's just that this cannot be an exceptionally important case, in the great scheme of law-breaking out there, and we are no longer looking at a felony. We are now in the misdemeanor realm. When I agreed with you of a charge of "No contest," and the $300, fingerprints were added to the fine print.

I think it has been established that I have cooperated with the law in Arizona fully, upon my return to Virginia with my puppy. I fully believe that all I did was retrieve what was rightfully mine, and in doing so harmed no one, nor was any damage done to anyone's property. I also think that Arizona law, and its representatives, have been straightforward and fair. It seems to me, however, that Ricardo Santillan's actions, throughout this ordeal, have been far more criminal than mine ever were. He has managed to steal what was not his, lie to my husband and myself repeatedly – and now to the law – when he insists that I came inside his trailer for her leash. (And as far as this goes, this likely was the leash that Pete and I left with Ricardo in the first place, when we entrusted her into his care. We left it, and dog food, with him on October 2nd, 2001. I brought a leash from home on the second trip. I bought a collar and harness for her, once in Arizona.)

Finally, Ricardo, in his witness statement to the Coconino County law, claimed that this puppy "Was like a child to him: priceless." And then he goes on to say "I could only consider $1,000 for her." Isn't this like a ransom, or extortion? Isn't this illegal? Come on! This puppy was found starving to death only days before this whole mess began.

I am not saying that I am an angel. I am saying that before and after Kokopelli's return, however, I have tried to cooperate with the law in Arizona and have honestly answered the questions put before me. And a funny thing about all this, Ms. Nelson, numerous family and friends had suggested that Ricardo did not originally return the puppy to us, as agreed, when we returned to the Grand Canyon for her on October 4th, 2001, because he expected us to pay him for her. Like a ransom. And I actually tried to think the better of him, saying, "No, the man was probably lonely, and she was a bright spot for him to come home to." I said this to Sergeant Coffey, in fact, early on. Ha!! What does Ricardo do? He locks her in his smoky old trailer for over five weeks, night and day, while he works, waiting for him to come home. In all this time his neighbors did not even know he had a puppy! And this is how "he loves a child." When I retrieved this little dog she no longer knew to go to the bathroom outside! A puppy that had spent her first three-four months in the desert! This, in itself, is criminal; I should have reported him to Arizona's version of the SPCA.

It still makes me seethe, this total lack of response to her needs. She had had no training, whatsoever, was starved for attention, and was borderline neurotic. She had an altogether different personality than when Pete and I left her in Ricardo's "care," though he claimed he knew how to handle a puppy. Pete and I totally misjudged this man. What I did to reclaim Kokopelli pales to his thievery and lies.

Under the circumstances, Ms. Nelson, I will not be treated like a common criminal. Charges have been reduced from a felony to a misdemeanor. I will be sending the $300 to you soon to close this case, once and for all. Good enough. If you all then insist on a fingerprint, I suggest it be found, then, inside Ricardo Santillan's trailer, since he insists I was there. I have explained to you about her leash. Let that settle it.

One last thing. I have been thinking that a truly fitting way to end all of this fiasco would be that the $300 might go to help the homeless animals there. Might you all consider that it be donated to the Grand Canyon Shelter, that serves as the local humane society in that area, for spaying and neutering programs, for example? (You could give it to Karen, say, in Ricardo's name… just kidding.) But it would be a fitting and circular way to close this chapter of our lives. Please talk it over with the Powers that Be…

Respectfully,

I finished the letter draft, tucked it in with the packet from the law, and then went on with my work, occasionally stopping to read a chapter or two in *The Icarus Agenda*, the Ludlum novel I'd brought to the beach with me. It was fascinating and riveting reading, so pertinent now with this novel staged in the Middle East (little has changed).

Long tall Jared returned from his bike outing, insisting that Wednesday was my birthday and he had a gift to share with me. He strode into the room, his shaggy cinnamon hair windswept, and reminding me so much of his father when we had met that it took my breath away. I had journals and loose papers and notes all over the bed. Jared laid out a beautiful green and sand-colored sarong unceremoniously atop it all. "Happy Birthday, Mom," he had mumbled, embarrassed to have remembered, and turned shyly to leave.

I had looked up, distracted and surprised and touched, thinking of the similarities between father and son, "*Thank* you, Jared, it is gorgeous, just beautiful. But today isn't my birthday – tomorrow is."

"No, Mom, it's today," he explained to me like I was an old woman and might not understand.

"No, Jared, it's tomorrow. Today is April the 3rd. Tomorrow is the 4th. My birthday is on the 4th. Look at the calendar." I felt silly arguing over the date when the thought is what clearly mattered. "But never mind, buddy, this is lovely and I will enjoy it always. In fact, I'll wear it right now, while I work." I picked up the length of colorful batiked rayon fabric and wrapped it around my shoulders, over my tee shirt. Yummy.

He had left the room, but later he muttered to me that indeed he had looked at the calendar and realized that Easter Sunday had been the 31st. All along, he had thought it was the 1st. No, I explained, the 1st was April Fool's Monday – the day Kendrick was to start that damned fool computer on line, and the reason that Dad was not with us.

The next day, Thursday, my actual birthday, a dozen red roses in a long white box were delivered at noon. A note inside said, *"I love you, Ra, and wish I was there with you to celebrate. Happy Birthday. We'll see you tonight. Love, Peter Wop."* Because the writer of the words was strictly secretarial on the other end of the phone, 'Peter Wop' was two words. What did she know, anyway? But that was okay; the message was appreciated. And the bonafide Wop and our daughter would be joining us by nightfall.

Jared and Natalie and I took a long beach walk that beautiful spring afternoon. Later, while they watched a movie, I continued my work. While I worked, Natalie baked a German chocolate birthday cake and Jared went on his bike for another outing. Evening came, and I took them both to dinner at a local seaside restaurant. We returned and watched *Rainman*, a video we had brought with us, and an old family favorite, with Dustin Hoffman and Tom Cruise, who, in the course of the movie, found his humanity.

After *Rainman* the kids watched *Southpark* on TV, while I continued with my work, watching the clock tick on by. I thought of Pete and Skye leaving for the long drive down. We had our cell phones out (he had given me one for Christmas) and every hour on the hour he or Skye called, updating us on where they were. I was glad she was with him to help him with the driving and to keep him awake with her music, when it was his turn. I knew Pete would be exhausted by now, consumed as he had been, day and night, by SAP. I had on a long white sleeveless cotton nightgown and kept my beautiful new sarong/shawl around my shoulders, as I plugged away on my writing or read chapters of the Ludlum, sipping Shiraz, waiting for our family to be complete.

My birthday came and my birthday went and I was feeling no pain, as I sipped the good wine. The clock struck midnight and kept on going, with a call letting us know they were just leaving the mainland and crossing the Wright Memorial Bridge. A long and productive hour later, father and daughter found our cottage and the light awaiting them.

I heard their footsteps on the weathered old stairs out front and jumped up to greet them both. Skye was wide-awake and full of talk, her long light brown hair pulled back and her brown eyes shining. Peter, pumped with adrenaline from the lengthy trip and the endless week, was pushed and pulled between the fight or flight hormone and sheer exhaustion. I showed Skye her room and asked her to put her headphones on and be quiet, as everyone else was asleep, knowing she would be ready to party for a while.

I returned to give Pete a second big welcoming hug, snuggling into him, then showed him our room, with the outside sliders open to the sussurant sea and the salty air blowing the sheer curtains around inside. I gathered up all of my work from the bed and put it in one neat stack and poured red wine for Pete and more for me, turning the lights off and the candles on. "How would you like a back rub to ease those tired shoulders, PeterWop?" I turned to him and smiled.

"I won't argue with you at all, if you have the energy, Ra. It would feel *great*." He returned the smile tiredly, unbuttoning his chamois shirt. "It's so good to hear the ocean."

"I've left the doors open a good bit of the time we've been here, and kept the heat off. If we get cold, we just layer up. Look, see what Jared gave me for my birthday?" I lifted the sarong off my shoulders and twirled around in my gown to show him. "He got mixed up and thought it was yesterday – actually now the day be*fore* yesterday – but it's the thought and all. I love it – and have had it on practically since he nonchalantly tossed it on the bed." Pete had taken off his jeans and was lying on the bed in his skivvies and socks, resting on his elbow, watching, in anticipation of the promised rubdown. "Okay, you're here to relax now, Wop, even if it's just for a couple of days. This will help start the process." He rolled to his belly and I smiled at his familiar back, uncapping the massage oil I'd brought down. "*Hmmm…*" was all he could muster.

I hiked the gown up around my legs, poured the scented oil into my hands, rubbing them together to warm the liquid, as the sea sang her constant song outside our cottage. Antonio Carlos Jobim's ultra smooth Brazilian *Jazz Masters 13* played softly from a CD. I massaged his shoulders, upper arms, neck and back until I could feel the tensions loosen, thinking that he'd gone on and surrendered to sleep. But as I put the cap back on the bottle, Pete rolled over and it was clear he wasn't yet dozing. *Hello.* "Come here, you," he mumbled, pulling me down to him for a deep kiss. We fell into one another's arms, hungry from our absence, and made tender sweet love, grateful finally to be together in this seaside cottage, with the cool salty air washing over our intertwined bodies. And this is how we fell asleep. Embraced and entwined, warmed by our passions, blessed to be reunited, the blankets pulled up over us like a cocoon.

Pete slept deeply until noon on Friday. I got up quietly and fixed us all a hearty brunch, trying to keep the newly regathered trio quiet, as they eagerly wanted to share their adventures from the week prior. We spent the next day and a half kicking up our heels, strictly having fun, on no schedule but that which spontaneously evolved. We walked in the afternoon, exploring the open stretches of windswept beach, finding treasures and breathing deeply of the salted air. We fixed a fine dinner of fresh fish and foods from the 'fridge that needed to be finished before we left. The kids watched the wonderful movie, *Renaissance Man,* while Pete and I sat on the deck, under the stars and sliver of watchful moon, listening to the waves lapping the shoreline, as we sipped a bottle of champagne.

Again we made love, with more passion and verve this time, as we both were more rested, listening to a new CD of timeless Santana's "Black Magic Woman," "Oye Como Va," "Gypsy Woman," and "Havana Moon." Again we slept, interlaced, as the ethereal curtains blew around our room, like the ghosts of hundreds of shipwrecked sailors that had once roamed these island shoals, probably wishing they, too, could still partake in such earthly pleasures.

Saturday, our last full day of vacation in the cottage, Pete and I made the family a hearty breakfast before we all went off on another beach walk. In the afternoon we packed up a lunch, still trying to use up refrigerated goods before our departure, and then we headed off to play putt-putt with our trio. We bought a family day pass and played two rounds, took a break for our picnic lunch, played another round together, then Pete and I stole away for a walk on our own, while the three played a version of teenage golf. One more round together, shivering in the chilled spring air, and we were off to dinner, before returning to our cottage to begin the final packing up for our return to Virginia.

I absolutely adore the beach and absolutely hate to leave it. This time was no different – and indeed it was worse, as I felt that Pete had been cheated out of the experience except for just enough to tease. But he was a good sport as we loaded our bags and boxes into two cars, which for once allowed us enough room to breath, on our return to reality. We checked out of our ocean abode, took a last long beach walk and feasted on pb&j's and odds and ends from the 'fridge, on a blanket by the sea, watching the beautiful water stretch for captivating, mysterious miles, before we headed on home.

Jared and Skye did a lot of the driving, trading off between Pete and me, as we played a sort of musical chairs between cars for them to maximize their driving skills. With dueling cell phones we convoyed and relayed stops, making something of a game of it all, until we reached Richmond and T.G.I.F.'s and dinner. After this stop Pete and I chauffeured us on home, the kids finally relinquishing their independent young wings behind the wheel to the older folk. It was time to close this chapter and head on back to the farm, thank our neighbors for their long weekend of animal care, and step back into our responsible lives.

FORTY-FOUR

Judgment Day

"Justice: A decision in your favor."
Harry Kaufman

April 11th

We returned from our beach vacation to pick up where we had left off in our lives. Pete returned to the computerized insanity of Kendrick. The kiddos all returned to school. And I returned to motherhood, our farm/animal care, the studio and the writing of this book, and finalizing my becoming untangled with Arizona law.

Today I called the Williams Justice Court asking to speak with Elaine, who told me the fingerprint was no big deal. They have to do it in all of the state cases, even with vehicle tickets, in case someone doesn't show up in court. It proves identification. She went on to say that many banks were requiring a fingerprint now just to cash a check! I can't imagine that – it seems like a huge infringement of civil rights – another homeland soldier standing for our defense, only to be fallen by a comrade.

I also asked her if I might be able to write out the $300 fine to the Grand Canyon Kennels – as a kind of 'donation' towards their spaying and neutering program – instead of to the Williams District Court. I thought that this would bring poetic closure to this cockamamie case. Elaine left the phone for a few minutes to check with Judge Sutton. She came back to the phone shortly to tell me that although he thought it was a very nice idea, that no, this money was to cover the court costs that I had accrued over the case.

Oh well… What do I know?

So I came into town the next day to go to the bank to retrieve $300 cash from my studio account for a money order, which is the only way they will accept payment. I then went to the post office to purchase this money order, written out to the Williams District Court in Arizona, my fine for re-retrieving this very expensive stray puppy. And then I went to the Charlottesville Police Department, requesting a stupid fingerprint. But no, they only take prints on Monday, Wednesdays and Fridays, between 4 PM and 5 PM. It was the correct hour, but the wrong day; this was Thursday. Please come back. To me it was a 'sign' that a print was not meant to be.

So I brainstormed and asked myself if *all* they wanted to prove was that this was the me I was sup*posed* to be that has signed the papers to plea bargain this case, then would not a notary public's stamp and signature, witnessing my signature and drivers license I.D.#, do just as well? City Hall was opened; they were bound to have a notary. They did and she witnessed and stamped me as me. I added my signature – and she added hers – saying as much. Tomorrow I would call Elaine back and see if this will do. If so, then I could mail the damned thing and say *Voila!*, except for my (hopefully) last telephonic conversation with Judge Sutton on April 19th. I would tell her I'd had the check cut and the papers already notarized, explaining to her about the on and off days of fingerprinting in Charlottesville. As much as I truly enjoyed talking with this kind gentleman of a judge, I was ready for this legal chapter to be *closed*. I called Elaine the next day; she said that this would probably work and that she would ask the judge, herself, and would call me back on it. She did and called me later, saying why yes, that would be fine.

April 19th

Final telephonic conference with Judge Sutton. Question of the day: *Does he – or does he not – want to accept the plea bargain?* Our friend, Matt, had called Thursday before the "big day," to ask if I'd like to join him and a friend he thought I would like to meet for lunch the next day. We'd eat at Christian's Pizza, on Charlottesville's Downtown Mall, and from there walk over to have a personal tour of his photo exhibit at the Downtown Gallery.

I told him I would love to join them. I definitely wanted to see his show, but had been at the beach when it opened. A personal tour would be wonderful. So we agreed to meet at Christian's at 12:30 PM the next day. I shared that I would have to duck out at 1:15 to have my (final?) telephonic conference with Judge Sutton. Hopefully, the good judge would accept my plea agreement, and the "case" would then be closed.

So Friday I got up, fed the farm, made and answered a number of calls, showered and raced to get downtown on time, running my usual 15 minutes late (Navajo time, for me) and praying I'd find a parking spot amidst downtown Charlottesville's creative parking situations. On 2nd Street, close to McGuffy Art Gallery, I found a space waiting. After a successful parallel park, I glanced at the sign above me, making sure it wasn't for handicapped parking, and quickly read "2 hour parking." Good. I was off and running to meet Matt and his mystery guest, for our lunch.

Christian's Pizza, strategically located between the very corporate Regal Cinemas on one side, and the artsy and historic old Jefferson Theatre a little further up the street, was someone's brainstormed culinary goldmine. Not only is the pizza – sold by the slice – scrumptious, it's reasonable. The toppings have a strong Mediterranean influence. Slices are loaded with kalamata olives, feta cheese, basil leaves, artichokes, sun dried tomatoes, mushrooms, spinach, roasted garlic cloves, pine nuts, broccoli, and the like. New 'designs' are always in the works; today I saw circular stuffed pastas shapes on one pizza. Of course, the old tried and trues are all offered, but I go for a Mediterranean mix every time, then spend the next 10 minutes with a toothpick, excavating for Italian spice and red pepper bits from deep within tooth nooks and crannies.

One may eat inside or outside at Christian's, with a fine view of the mall and the Charlottesville trolley bus passing by on a regular basis. But this day there wasn't a chance at the outdoor tables. I found Matt, and his friend (soon to be ours), Janice, seated at a table for two (soon to be three) in the rear corner. Matt got up and grinned, telling me he was glad I'd been able to join them, and gave me a big ole' bear hug. Matt is 6-foot-something, long and lean, with black hair streaked lightly with gray. His clean-shaven face is gaunt and reflective, a man who studies the world and human nature as a hobby, continually washing facts and knowledge through his sieve of a highly educated mind. One learns only later the results of this processing, but can count on it having been reflected upon ever so carefully and one *knows* there will be an opinion of some sort. His voice is soft and deliberate; each word is carefully spoken. I don't know Matthew's birthday, but if I were to guess, the guess would be a June or a December date, making him either a Gemini or a Capricorn. The Gemini would explain the mercurial workings of his mind and the changes in his persona from time to time. The Capricorn would explain the precise and careful deliberations of his actions. I'll have to remember to ask him.

Matt is the man who asked me to dinner shortly after my infamous return from the west, "hot dog" in hand, and wanted to know the whole story. He listened, fascinated, as we ate at Escafé and he concluded, in his slow, enunciated voice (Matt had once been a Criminal Psychologist) that "this normally isn't the behavior of a middle-aged, middle-income, Caucasian mother of three."

Matthew introduced me to Janice, whom he said "also was an artist," but later I found she teaches yoga down in Nellysford, in Nelson County. I asked her if she knew my friend, Evelyn, who teaches yoga in Charlottesville. She did – she'd known her a long time. So we were off to a good start. Janice was a lean and graceful lady about my height with shoulder length sable brown hair. Her face was angular, attractive and animated.

At 1:00 I reminded them that I'd have to duck out at 1:15 with my cell phone and find a quiet place (ha ha) on the mall for this telephonic conference with the Judge. Of course Matt knew about the goings-on, but Janice knew nothing. How does one explain this story in five minutes between pizza bites? So I told her a little while Matt laughed and said we'd fill her in on the way to his show and soon after that I took my manila file, with several months of legalities, off to a row of newspaper boxes across from the Mudhouse Coffee Shop (which offers many types of Fair Trade Certified beans).

Thinking back to the fall, and our travels thereafter – the familiar box stands being the bearer of updated news – I felt at home. Somehow this was appropriate to be standing in front of this lineup of newspapers. Actually, I was a little surprised at how calm I was. In fact, I was looking *forward* to talking with Judge Sutton and hearing his quiet, calm grandfather-like voice, explaining the details of this plea agreement with me. The honest truth of it was, I was leaning towards effervescence; I'd have to bite my tongue and not get glib or push my luck, just from the relief of being on the verge again of freedom.

I dialed the William's Justice Court number, listened to it ring and, at 1:15 precisely, Eastern Standard Time, 11:15 Mountain Time, Elaine picked up. She greeted me in a friendly voice, explaining that the Prosecuting Attorney from Flagstaff was on the line, as well. I was to have a 3-way conversation with he and the Judge. Could I hold for a minute while they lined that up? No problem, I had plenty of phone minutes left on this month – it's ridiculous how many minutes I *don't* use each month on this prepaid technological contraption. She came back on a bit later, asked if I was still there, and then the line went dead. Oh well. Knowing the batteries had just been recharged for this very special occasion, I figured *that* wasn't the problem, so I called back. Elaine apologized profusely, explaining they were having trouble with their old phone lines, but were still trying to line up the 3-way. I had a chance to ask her if they had received the papers and money order that I'd sent to them by Priority Mail that Monday. They had; the Judge had it all before him, ready to go. He came on the line; the image of Andy Griffith again popped into my mind. "I'm sorry it's taken so long to arrange this call, Ms. Giannini. Our phone lines are about thirty years old, and are showing every minute," he explained. "How are you today?"

"I'm fine, thank you, Judge Sutton, and how are you?" Pleasantries done, he asked if I had any questions or concerns about the gist of this call. I told him I didn't, that I was pretty clear now on the nature of the agreement.

"So you've changed your plea to 'Guilty,' I see," said the Judge, as he glanced over the papers in hand. "And I see you did not have a fingerprint taken, but here's the notary's stamp." His voice trailed as he perused the report.

"Yes, sir, I explained all of that to Elaine before sending the papers to Arizona. I really did go to the Charlottesville Police Station last week, after talking with Elaine. I was there on the wrong day, though, for fingerprinting. But since Elaine explained that what you needed to have done was validate that it was indeed *me* signing these papers and sending in the check, I figured notarization would work. And City Hall was open." I paused and then decided to have a *little* fun, added, "Judge Sutton – my friends aren't good enough to put their fingerprint on that paper and send in $300 for me."

He chuckled, "Yes, yes. Elaine explained to me that you had tried to have it done last week. We did need to get the papers back. This should be fine."

"But, Your Honor, there is one more thing. I never pleaded 'Guilty.' My plea bargain was for 'No contest' – which I understood at the time from Christine Nelson, in the Prosecutor's Office – was more of a neutral ground sort of thing. It's not pleading 'Not guilty,' but I'm not comfortable with 'Guilty,' either. Since then, however, I've come to understand that this is basically the same thing."

"Well yes, it pretty much is. In order for this not to go to trial, you had to change your plea to one of them, and agree to pay the fine. Are you comfortable with that now?"

I thought a moment. "I guess so. Honestly, sir, I'm just ready for this to be over and to get on with life. Does this mean, then, that I can come back to Arizona again and not worry about getting arrested?" I had to ask… *But bite your lip, Laura* – behave… *don't blow this now*…(all these thoughts flitted around in my mind in answering).

"Yes, yes – you can come back to Arizona now, young lady." I could hear the smile in his voice. "Now I have to be sure that you understand the charges, and that you realize you have waived your right to a trial-by-jury to be proven innocent, by agreeing to this. And that *you* cannot appeal this decision afterwards. The case will be closed. You do understand all that you read, and the papers you signed, don't you?"

"Yes sir, I do. They were very clear."

"You were not coerced in any way to sign them, were you?" asked the good judge.

"No sir, I was not. I knew what I was doing."

"Good, then. I can fairly say this is pretty well squared away." Said the quiet voice over the many miles between us. The case was closed.

How did I feel? *All of these months of cat and mouse with the deputies, the sergeant, and learning about the Prosecuting Attorney, who he was and how his role in all this would play, had been an eye-opener to the inside trappings of the law. Suddenly* Law & Order, *on TV, held a whole new perspective. I had learned from Sergeant Coffey about Judge Sutton, hearing the respect in his voice for the man and assuring me that he would be fair in his decisions. Yes, I was relieved for it all to be over, but even more than this, I felt good about myself for standing behind my own convictions with all of these lawmen. I'd held my ground, kept Pelli with me and safe, and faced all these fellas not as a 'ditzy housewife who didn't know what she was doing,' as Randy had suggested, but as someone with convictions and strength of character. I still strongly felt that in this particular situation, "two wrongs did make a right," but then I had faced the music afterwards, when the law didn't necessarily agree. I had broken the law and trespassed. I had been fairly warned of the consequences. Pete and I had sent out our witness statements and the phone records supporting our claims to Kokopelli. I had answered a multitude of questions from all the men honestly and upfront – ironically through these same convictions – sometimes volunteering even more than was necessary. But I knew there were consequences, and I was willing to face them. I think these fellas out west appreciated that, perhaps respected it. Most of all, I respected it in myself. Somehow, in all of this hoopla over this starving, unwanted (at the time) puppy, I had come to know myself much better. I felt strongly that she and I had completely won this case, in the end – not lost it, at all.*

I had come to understand, over the course of these months and emotions, that this pup that we had found starving under that sagebrush in high desert country – in the middle of nowhere, USA – was indeed a golden ray of Hope. I may well have saved her, but she had also saved me. From the depths of my emotions over the deaths of autumn, and of the horror and hatred of the September attacks, and of Lakota's sudden death just weeks before this – which pulled the rug from the fall before it even began – I had been submerged in subliminal grief. This puppy brought innocence back to a twisted world. Believing in this starving young dog – and knowing that Lakota's spirit had somehow found its way home to us – and then fighting to the end to bring her into our lives, had me, once again, believing in the importance of life, by being able to make a difference in one simple life. And going for what you believe in with passion and courage, despite the odds. After all, this is America – and this is the American way. Or at least that's the premise upon which this great country was founded.

My "Operation Desert Pup's Enduring Freedom" mission was successful. There were no casualties, no hostages, not a drop of blood was spilled, despite the offers to the contrary. There had been minimal cost, if any, to the state of Arizona over litigation. I can't say the same for us, but Ricardo, at least, didn't come out with a dime for his duplicity. All in all, I'd have to say the experience was priceless.

These thoughts, which had been percolating for some time, flashed through my mind at this time, and I realized I didn't want to stop talking, not quite yet, with the Judge. So I asked him, playfully, "Do you know I bought a tee-shirt especially for this occasion, Judge Sutton? Yup. It says, 'X-Con' on it, and now I can wear it."

I could again hear the smile in his voice when he asked, "And are you wearing it now?"

"No sir. I was waiting for all of this to be done. Finished. Kaput."

"Well, you know, Ms. Giannini, that this is only a misdemeanor – you wouldn't have been a convict."

"Well, in all due respect, sir, that's *not* what they were telling me at first, out west. No, sirree, those boys wanted a felony charge real badly."

"That's all fine and good, but it *is* only a misdemeanor now. You go on and wear your tee shirt, if you want. And come on back to Arizona and visit us again anytime."

"Thank you, Judge Sutton. Thank you for everything. And please thank Elaine for me for all her help, okay?"

"I'll do that. Have a fine day, young lady."

"Thanks, sir. I plan to do *just* that. Same to you. Goodbye." And so, it was a done deed. I was a free woman again. I walked back to Christian's, light as air. Matt was standing outside and asked how it had gone. I gave him a thumbs up and a huge smile as I headed his way and then gave him a quick recap. He gave me a big congratulatory bear hug and we went back in and sat down again. They had long finished, so Matt gave Janice a condensed recap of what happened on our anniversary trip while I ate and interjected here and there with pertinent details. Matt cocked a dark eyebrow at me and said, "Eat."

"Okay, okay, but you get the story straight," I grinned, basil and peppercorns stuck in my teeth. Janice laughed, loving the story. She was an animal lover and knew the Four Corners area. She had been to Taos and Santa Fe. She knew Monument Valley and the Grand Canyon. She became a fine cheerleader of "the event."

We finished, I grabbed toothpicks for all and we left, and the three of us strolled up the mall, through Charlottesville's eclectic downtown, amongst historic buildings that had withstood the Civil War, past tables and sellers of goods from around the world, past a black music man wearing a boa, with springy eye-thingy's bouncy from a headband and wearing fuzzy bear slippers while he strummed his guitar. It felt great to be free, to be American, and to be with friends.

Postscript:

As I walked along E. Jefferson Street I spied the happy pale full moon, drifting amongst the clouds, practicing her opening act for the dark side of day. She tipped her hat and sent down her congratulations on a job now completed. She could go on from here and watch other nighttime antics now, witnessing and willing and smiling them on, spreading her magic throughout the world. She had been as a guardian angel to me throughout this mission and I smiled up my silent thanks. With much yet to do I stepped up the pace, heading for 2nd Street, but by a different route, this time.

There was 2nd Street, up by the library – I glanced down towards the mall. No, I didn't park that close, so I headed north, passing many a car as I went on up, but none that looked like my Taurus wagon. I hadn't been giving this my full attention a minute ago, but now I was focused. *Jaws was gone!*

I walked one block further up, all the while knowing I hadn't parked that far north. So I turned around, scrutinizing each car passed, and then the parking signs. Oh, *great*. These signs all said: "15 minutes parking" in the green letters and underneath, in smaller green: "2 hour parking after 6 PM." Apparently, in my hurry this is what I had seen, and regardless, I was almost 2 hours late, so the point was moot. *Damnit, double damn – I just today got out of trouble with the law in one state, and here I am in trouble with the law in another, my home state, albeit, although not nearly as seriously. Go figure.* I had to grin to myself at the irony of it all. I turned around and headed down to the library, first things first – and I knew where the bathroom was there. Afterwards, I'd call the tow truck number a construction worker was kind enough to point out, and then he had loaned me a pen so I could write it down on my legal binder.

From the library I called, using my trusty little cell phone, freshly fished from deep within my backpack. No, they didn't have a Taurus wagon in custody. Perhaps I should try Charlottesville Wrecker. She gave me the telephone number. I dialed. They didn't. I told them it had been on 2nd Street, but it was gone – where then could it be? Maybe in towing transit? She assured me not. *Should this be a relief? The good news is my car hasn't been towed, but the bad news is that I don't happen to know where it is? Now what? Hmmm... I felt a little stupid standing there, looking at the phone and not knowing what to do with it.* About then a pleasant woman about my age, with short brown hair walked over and said, "Excuse me. I couldn't help overhearing your conversation about your looking for your car. I bet you don't realize there are *four* "2nd Streets" downtown. There is 2nd Street NE, and 2nd Street NW. There is 2nd Street SE and 2nd Street SW. All are divided by 1st Street."

I looked at her like she had to be joking and asked, "Why in the world would they do that, except to be cruel? That's totally nuts in planning."

She smiled and agreed. "The only reason I know this is this is where I was to meet my husband some time ago. We were to meet on 2nd Street and I found all of them, ex*cept* the right one. It was then I eventually realized there are four. I suggest maybe you go one more over. I bet that's where you're parked."

I thanked her sincerely, considering her to be another one of those angels that happen to appear when the time is right. Feeling silly, but hopefully relieved, I crossed 2nd Street NE, walked past the 1st Street division and found 2nd Street NW – and, of course, McGuffy. I turned north, headed up a couple of blocks, hoping to find my car and thinking that just a parking ticket would be a relief, at this point. So what's another little fine, *any*way?

Here I had made it past all those crazy airport checks out west, driven safely through those two huge western states, with my wacko sense of direction and a wild dog in tow, no less, managed to elude the law and return home with my prize, only to lose my own car in a city I supposedly knew. *Tourist.*

And sure enough, there was Jaws, parked *exactly* where I had left it hours ago, on 2nd Street NW. Miraculously, there was not a trace of a ticket in sight. I smiled to myself then, thinking that God has a sense of humor and he had been just pulling my chains big time with this one. He and Mom and all those Great Spirits had rallied and were up there probably holding their stomachs with a *big* ole' belly laugh right about now…

Endnotes

"We make a living with what we get.
We make a life with what we give."
Winston Churchill

List of Organizations that Give a Damn

"Alone we can do so little. Together we can do so much."
Helen Keller

I have compiled lists of organizations that go forth each and every day, intent on helping make our world a better place for its human and animal inhabitants. Please consider becoming a party to any of these very worthwhile charitable groups. Go to their websites and learn about the astounding things they are accomplishing. If I have omitted any, I apologize in advance – there are so many caring organizations. These are the ones that come into my home on a regular basis. Good Luck and – as the old Navajo woman wished me at Antelope Ruins – many blessings to you…

Environmental Groups:

Natural Resources Defense Council (NRDC)
40 W. 20th St., New York, NY 10011
www.nrdc.org/naturesvoice, 212-727-4500

Environmental Defense Action Fund
257 Park Avenue South, New York, NY 10010
www.environmentaldefense.org, 212-505-2100

EarthJustice
426 17th Street, 6th Floor, Oakland, CA 94612
www.earthjustice.org, 515-550-6740

The Sierra Club
85 2nd St., 2nd Floor, San Francisco, CA 94105
www.sierraclub.org, 415-977-5500

The Nature Conservancy
4245 N. Fairfax Drive, Suite 100, Arlington, VA 22203-1606
www.nature.org

The Rainforest Alliance
665 Broadway, Suite 500, New York, NY 10012, USA
www.rainforestalliance.org, 1-212-677-1900 or (888) MY-EARTH

The Trust for Public Land
116 New Montgomery St., 4th Floor, San Francisco, CA 94105
www.tpl.org, 415-495-4014

Republicans for Environmental Protection (REP)
3200 Carlisle Blvd., #228, Albuquerque, NM 887110
e-mail:info@repamerica.org
www.repamerica.org, 505-889-4544

American Rivers
1025 Vermont Ave., N.W., Suite 720, Washington, DC 20005-3516
www.AmericanRivers.org, 202-347-7550

The Chesapeake Bay Foundation
6 Herndon Ave., Annapolis, MD 21403
www.cbf.org, 1-888-SAVEBAY

The Ocean Conservancy
1725 DeSales Street, NW, Washington, DC 20036
www.oceansonservancy.org, 202-429-5609

Southern Utah Wilderness Alliance
1471 South 1100 East, Salt Lake City, Utah 84105
www.suwa.org, 801-486-3161

The Wilderness Society
1615 M St., NW, Washington, D.C. 20036
www.wilderness.org, 202-833-2300 or 1-800-THE-WILD

Earthwatch Institute
1-800-776-0188, www.earthwatch.org

Union for Concerned Scientists
Two Brattle Square, Cambridge, MA 02238-9105
www.ucsusa.org,

The National Audubon Society
700 Broadway, New York, NY 10003
www.AUDUBON.ORG, 212-979-3000

Special Editions:

U.S.News Special Edition: The Future of Earth (summer '04)
Special issues #, 1-800-836-6397

National Geographic, September 2004 issue, *"Global Warming: Bulletins from a Warmer World"* (cover story) 1-800-647-5463 or go to nationalgeographic.com/magazine/0409

Seafood Watch, Monterey Bay Aquarium (to find what fish is safe to eat, and those that aren't on the endangered species list) www.montereybayaquarium.org

Human & Indian Rights Organizations:

Amnesty International
5 Penn Plaza, 14th Floor, New York, NY 10001
www.amnestyusa.org, 1-212-807-8400

TransFair USA
1611 Telegraph Ave., Suite 900, Oakland, CA 94612
www.transfairusa.org, 510-663-5260
e-mail: info@transfairusa.org

Southwest Indian Relief Council
P.O. Box 16777, Mesa AZ 85211-9963
www.swirc.org, 866-228-0124

American Indian Relief Council
P.O. Box 6200, Rapid City, SD 57709-9979
www.airc.org, 1-800-370-0872

Native American Heritage Association
P.O. Box 512, Rapid City, SD 57709
www.naha-inc.org, 605-341-9110

The Southwest Indian Foundation
P.O. Box 86, Gallup, NM 87302-0001
www.southwestindian.com, Exec. Dir. Bill McCarthy, 505-863-9568
(This is a magazine of Southwest-related items & CD's; proceeds benefit the Navajo Nation)

St. Labre Indian School
Ashland, Montana 59004
www.stlabre.org, 1-866-753-5496

Zuni Pueblo Pot

Heifer International
P.O. Box 8058, Little Rock, AR 72203-80458
www.heifer.org, 1-800-422-0755

U.S. Fund for Unicef
333 East 38th St., 6th Floor, New York, NY 10016
www.unicefusa.org, 800-486-4233

"Never doubt that a small group of thoughtful, committed citizens can change the world. Indeed, it is the only thing that ever has." Margaret Mead

Animal Protection Groups:

(Note, many of the environmental groups are also involved in protecting wildlife on our planet)

Best Friends Animal Society
5001 Angel Canyon Road, Kanab, UT 84741
www.bestfriends.org, 435-644-2001

Defenders of Wildlife
P.O. Box 1553, Merrifield, VA 22116-1553
www.defenders.org

World Wildlife Fund
1250 Twenty-Fourth St., N.W., Washington, D.C. 20037
www.worldwildlife.org, 202-293-4800

African Wildlife Foundation
1400 Sixteenth St., N.W., Suite 120, Washington, D.C.20036
www.awf.org, 1-888-4-WILDLIFE

Greenpeace, Inc.
702 H Street NW, Suite 300, Washington, DC 20001
www.greenpeace.org, 1-800-326-0959

National Wildlife Federation
11100 Wildlife Center Drive, Reston, VA 21090-5362
www.nwf.org, 1-800-822-9919

American Society for the Prevention of Cruelty to Animals (ASPCA)
424 92nd St., New York, NY 10128
www.aspca.org, (Brooklyn) 718-272-7200 (Manhattan), 212-876-7700

The Humane Society of the United States
2100 L Street, NW, Washington, DC 20037
www.hsus.org, 1-202-452-1100

The Wildlife Center of Virginia
P.O. Box 1557, Waynesboro, VA 22980
www.wildlifecenter.org, 540-942-WILD

People for the Ethical Treatment of Animals (PETA)
501 Front St., Norfolk, VA 23510
www.PETA.org, 1-757-622-7382

It is my hope and prayer that we as individuals can learn tolerance for one another in this great country and abroad. Immediately post-September 11th Americans united under one flag, in a common love for country. Somehow this solidarity has been torn asunder in a few short years and we are a nation polarized as never before, both with ourselves and with the world. Humans, worldwide, are more alike than different, and our basic needs are the same. One of the most basic of our needs is a healthy planet, the great earth upon which we live, that offers up her sustenance for us all to share. Let us learn to treat these great bounties – clean air & earth & water – as the gifts they are, and to cherish them, as if our lives depended upon them, for they do.

Terrorism does not need to divide us, in fear and distrust. It should bring us together as a nation, standing strong against this enemy – and then, as a nation, based on love of fellow man, go again into the world and spread this light of true democracy.

This is what America is about; let us please find our way home again.

Bibliography & Suggested Reading

"When I despair I remember that all through history the way of truth and love has always won. There have been tyrants and murderers and for a time that can seem invincible. But in the end they always fall. Think of it. Always."
Mohatma Gandhi

Tony Hillerman, series of mysteries, set on the Navajo reservation

www.readsouthwest.com

www.womenwritingthewest.org

The Navajos, from Indians of North America series, Peter Iverson (Frank W. Porter, General Editor), Chelsea House Publishers, New York/Philadelphia © 1990

People of the Desert, Time-Life Books, the American Indian series, © 1993

Indian Country, Peter Matthiessen, The Viking Press, © 1984

The Southwest – A Pictorial History of the Land and Its People, Steven L. Walker, Camelback Design Group, Inc./Canyonlands Publications, © 1993

(Timeline of) Native American History, by Carl Waldman, illustrated by Molly Braun, TD Media, Inc., © 1994

Drawdown: Groundwater Mining on Black Mesa, Natural Resources Defense Council (NRDC), Authors: David Beckman, Michael Jasny, Lissa Wadewitz & Andrew Wetzler, © 2000

Monument Valley – The Story Behind the Scenery, KC Publications, Photographs by Joseph Muench, text by KC DenDooven

Grand Canyon, Stewart Aitchison, Sierra Press, 4988 Gold Leaf Drive, Mariposa, CA 95338, © 1999

New Mexico Magazine, 495 Old Santa Fe Trail, Santa Fe, NM 87501, 1-800-898-6639

Arizona Highways Magazine, 2039 W. Lewis Ave., Phoenix, AZ 85009, 1-800-543-5432

Preservation, The Magazine of the National Trust for Historic Preservation, www.preservationonline.org, 1-800-944-6847

Newsweek, Inc., 251 West 57th St., New York, NY 10019-1894, 1-800-631-1040

AAA TourBooks – Arizona-New Mexico/Colorado-Utah, 2001/2002 Editions and the **AAA Indian Country Map** of Arizona, Colorado, New Mexico, Utah

The Official Santa Fe Visitor's Guide, City of Santa Fe Convention & Visitors Bureau, 201 West Marcy Street, Santa Fe, NM 87504

Historic Bluff City by Bicycle & Foot, the Bluff City Historic Preservation, © 2002

Discover Navajo – The Official Navajo Nation Visitor Guide, a pub. of Navajo Tourism, Office Of Economic Development, Navajo Nation, 2001, PO Box 663, Window Rock, AZ 86515

Williams: Gateway to the Grand Canyon, Fall/Winter 2001, 118 S. 3rd St., PO Box 667, Williams, AZ 86046

Petrified Forest National Park brochure

TransFair USA, 1611 Telegraph Ave., Suite 900, Oakland, CA 94612 www.transfairusa.org., 510-663-5260

More About the Author/Artist:

Laura Cockerille Giannini is a native Virginian with a deep respect for animals, art and the great outdoors. For twenty-five years she combined these loves in her paintings of landscapes and animal portraits in the Central Virginia area. Her customized oils are sensitive, yet energetic and full of life, capturing the personality inherent in each animal.

In the late '70s, Laura had "The Belmont Stretch – 1978" (the stretch run between Affirmed and Alydar in the last Triple Crown win, to date) made into limited edition prints, as well as "Early Morning Hunt," in 1979. In the mid-80s she had a third print, "Winter Warmth," made of The Keeping Hall, at Historic Michie Tavern, below Monticello, painting much of this work on location.

In 1981, when Egyptian president Anwar Sadat was assassinated, Laura painted 'the most passionate portrait of her life,' in a large oil of this man, pouring feelings of grief directly onto the canvas. A second, more sedate, portrait of Sadat followed the first.

For several years Laura also painted involved "family heirloom portraits," or montage paintings (she called them 'the heart & soul of one's life'). Usually these were of large horse farms. She traveled the east coast painting these portraits, before her children were born, capturing for families anything meaningful in their lives – realistic and symbolic – imagination being the limit. Among her clients were Mr. & Mrs. L. Clay Camp, who commissioned Laura's first montage, back in1979, of their stately and historic "Glenmore Farm," in Shadwell, VA. This was followed by a commission of the "Nydrie Stud/Old Woodville" montage for Mr. & Mrs. Daniel G. Van Clief, in Esmont, VA and two montages for Mr. & Mrs. Magruder Dent, of "Polaris Farm," in Earlysville, VA. This was followed by a commission in Cartersville, GA, when Laura painted "Old Mill Farm," in 1983, for Mr. & Mrs. Horatio Luro (who trained Northern Dancer). Her last montage was done of "BR Horse Ranch," for Burt Reynolds, in Jupiter, FL, in 1985. These large and extremely involved montages became too much to juggle, while raising two young children (soon to be three), amidst Pete's constant travels. Laura continued her animal portrait commissions after this, and tended their home and farm.

Laura has contributed over the years to many important Central Virginia fund-raisers, such as the Bayly Museum, The Shelter for Help in Emergency, The Wildlife Center of Virginia, and WVPT Public Television. Her future plans include greater participation with wildlife organizations to protect the rapidly growing list of endangered species, and involvement of spay & neuter awareness through a nationwide "Kokopelli Puppy" fund-raising program.